TEXTBOOKS IN MATHEMATICS

EDITED BY

R. D. CARMICHAEL

PROFESSOR OF MATHEMATICS, UNIVERSITY OF ILLINOIS

INTRODUCTION TO THE THEORY OF

Groups of Finite Order

By ROBERT D. CARMICHAEL

PROFESSOR OF MATHEMATICS
UNIVERSITY OF ILLINOIS

GINN AND COMPANY

BOSTON · NEW YORK · CHICAGO
LONDON · ATLANTA · DALLAS · COLUMBUS · SAN FRANCISCO

437.6

The Athenæum Press
GINN AND COMPANY · PROPRIETORS · BOSTON · U.S.A.

PREFACE

EVERY SERIOUS student of mathematics should early become acquainted with the elements of the theory of groups of finite order, since the concepts employed in this subject will illustrate for him many large domains of mathematics and since these concepts can be acquired more readily and more satisfactorily from a study of group theory than in any other way. What such a student needs for an introduction to this subject is an exposition which first of all prepares him for the development of the theory and then rapidly introduces him to a few fundamental theorems by which the construction of a large part of the theory may be effected. The first reason for the existence of this book lies in these facts and in the frequently expressed desire of students for a clear and direct presentation of the more important ideas and theorems belonging to this subject in the order and with the type of exposition best suited to the needs of the learner.

The second reason for the existence of the book arises from the fact that the author has established important connections of the theory of finite groups with other domains of mathematics and desires an opportunity of adequately relating these matters to the whole theory of finite groups. Since the ideas involved are in the main essentially elementary in character, they are well adapted to the purposes of a systematic exposition. By including them in the book it is possible to take the reader in one direction to the boundary of present knowledge and to give him an outlook on domains yet to be explored. It has been found possible to do this without introducing such complicated details as would render the material unsuited to such an exposition.

In preparing the book, and especially the earlier part of it, I have drawn freely on the existing expositions of the theory as well as on numerous older and newer memoirs in the journals; but references have been supplied only when they seemed useful to a learner. The books which have principally served me in this way are the following: Burnside's *Theory of Groups*, Hilton's *Finite Groups*, Miller, Blichfeldt, and Dickson's *Finite Groups*, and Dickson's *Linear Groups*. When it has been necessary to employ theorems from the theory of numbers, I have assumed familiarity on the part of the reader with such very elementary material as is included in my *Theory of Numbers*. The further knowledge, apart from a certain requisite intellectual maturity, needed for the reading of this exposition of group theory belongs mainly to elementary algebra and (for Chapter VIII) the elements of the theory of matrices.*

The learner can master the theory of groups only by doing much practice work in connection with his reading and frequent re-reading of the text. This will not only familiarize him with the theorems and give him a needed facility in applying them, but it will also render him an especially important service in helping him to understand the relative importance of the principal theorems. Accordingly many exercises are inserted for his use. Not a few of them are taken from the books already mentioned, with the purpose of inducing him to consult those books frequently in the course of his study; this is particularly true in the case of Chapter V. Problems in the miscellaneous exercises may be omitted (if desired) without destroying continuity as regards problems in the other exercises. Of the remaining exercises in Chapter I, and perhaps in other chapters, the more difficult may be left at first, to be taken up again later. Throughout the book a much greater number of problems is given than any one student will wish to solve.

---

* The student is advised to acquaint himself with Chapters I to VI of Bôcher's *Higher Algebra* and to use other parts of this book for reference as occasion may demand.

Chapter I is introductory in character. The learner is led to some of the principal elementary ideas of group theory and is given an opportunity of becoming familiar with them by using them in the analysis of several notions which are important in the later development. In particular, he is introduced to operations with permutations, to the definition of "group" and to certain permutation groups, to the concept of subgroup and of generators of a group, and to the notion of simple isomorphism and of abstract groups. The chapter is intended to prepare him for a systematic exposition of the theory.

The main novelty in the organization of the earlier material consists in bringing together in Chapter II five fundamental theorems of group theory and in giving the proofs of these as rapidly as is possible without sacrificing the comfort of the learner. The reason for this ordering of material lies in the fact that an important part of the remaining theory may then be made to depend on these five fundamental theorems and that much of it may be associated directly with them. Additional properties of groups in general are then developed in Chapter III.

Chapters IV and V contain introductions to the general theory of Abelian groups and of prime-power groups. An elementary account of permutation groups constitutes Chapter VI, while Chapter VII contains a few of the known (fragmentary) results pertaining to defining relations for abstract groups.

In Chapter VIII is given a very brief introduction to some of the main results belonging to the theory of groups of linear transformations, including the theory of group characteristics. Some of the more remarkable applications of these theories are included; but the celebrated theorem of Burnside concerning groups of prime degree (first demonstrated by means of group characteristics) is proved in § 60 by the more elementary method of Schur. The later chapters may be read independently of Chapter VIII.

A general introduction to the theory of Galois fields follows in Chapter IX; and this is employed in Chapter X in investigating the properties of the groups of isomorphisms of Abelian groups of prime-power order p^m and type (1, 1, . . ., 1).

An introduction to the theory of the finite geometries $PG(k, p^n)$ is to be found in Chapter XI. A representation of these geometries is given by means of Abelian groups of prime-power order p^m and type (1, 1, . . ., 1). By means of this representation a very significant part of projective geometry becomes capable of translation into a corresponding part of the theory of these groups (see § **87**). Thus by a single act of thought a significant extension is given to the theory of Abelian groups.

The principal theorems concerning collineation groups in the finite geometries are developed in Chapter XII.

In Chapter XIII, on algebras of doubly transitive groups of degree p^n and order $p^n(p^n - 1)$, is given a development of the theory of certain algebras introduced by Dickson in 1905, together with further results concerning the named doubly transitive groups. There are also some applications to the theory of finite geometries.

The final Chapter XIV contains a brief introduction to tactical configurations and the groups characterized by them.

More than 750 exercises are included. Many of these are easy and are intended for practice work on the part of the reader. Others give important results which might be included in the text of a larger exposition. Interspersed throughout the exercises are many particular results which have never before been published; they consist in the main of special theorems whose demonstration is not difficult.

In a book containing so many propositions, it can hardly be hoped that the author has always escaped error. He will be grateful to any of his readers who will give him notice of necessary corrections. He wishes now to express his cordial appreciation of the valuable assistance rendered him by two younger colleagues, Mr. Paul R. Halmos and Mr. Robert M. Thrall, who have read all the proofsheets and have made numerous helpful suggestions.

R. D. CARMICHAEL

CONTENTS

CHAPTER I · INTRODUCTION

CHAPTER II · FIVE FUNDAMENTAL THEOREMS

CHAPTER III · ADDITIONAL PROPERTIES OF GROUPS IN GENERAL

CHAPTER IV · ABELIAN GROUPS

CHAPTER V · PRIME-POWER GROUPS

CHAPTER VI · PERMUTATION GROUPS

CHAPTER X · GROUPS OF ISOMORPHISMS OF ABELIAN GROUPS OF ORDER p^m AND TYPE $(1, 1, \cdots, 1)$

CHAPTER XI · FINITE GEOMETRIES

CHAPTER XIV · TACTICAL CONFIGURATIONS

INTRODUCTION TO THE THEORY OF

Groups of Finite Order

CHAPTER I

Introduction

---

1. Sets, Systems, and Groups. A mathematical object is an object so clearly conceived or defined or *so fully characterized by relevant properties* as to be subject to the precise treatment required in mathematics. The positive integers 1, 2, 3, 4, $\cdots$ are among the mathematical objects which have been longest in use. The negative integers, zero, the rational fractions, the so-called imaginary number $\sqrt{-1}$ and the complex numbers of algebra defined by means of it, points, lines, triangles, spheres, displacements (rotations, translations, etc.), algebraic roots of unity, arrangements, combinations, matrices, determinants, functions, collineations, transformations in general, undefined elements in systems of postulates — all these furnish examples of mathematical objects. We shall employ the word *element* to denote a mathematical object.

A moment's consideration will convince one that such elements are constantly being presented to our thought in *sets*, or *classes*. Such a set, or class, may contain either a finite or an infinite number of elements. As examples of sets each of which has an infinite number of elements we may mention the following: (1) all positive integers; (2) all prime numbers; (3) all lines in a plane and through a given point in the plane; (4) all lines intersecting each of two given lines; (5) all the rotations of a plane about a line perpendicular to it. As examples of sets each of which has a finite number of elements we may mention the following: (1) all the nth roots of unity for a given value of the positive integer n; (2) all the combinations of a given finite set of n elements taken r at a time when r is less than n; (3) the set of non-negative integers less than a given positive integer n; (4) all the possible linear arrangements of a given finite set of elements.

The conception of a set, or class, is of such generality and is so often met with that it may be said to afford the logical foundation of all mathematics.

In many cases the sets of elements appearing in mathematical investigations are of such sort that every two elements in a given set are subject to one or more *rules of combination* by means of which a new element is obtained from the two elements when they are combined in a given order. The new object, in general, may or may not belong to the set. Thus the numbers of ordinary algebra are subject to the two fundamental rules of addition and multiplication, and in each case the resultant number is a number of ordinary algebra. The process by which two points determine a line in ordinary geometry affords a rule of combination of these objects such as to produce a new object of a different sort. The combination of two displacements produces a third displacement. The product of two nth roots of unity is an nth root of unity.

A set of objects, with the associated rule or rules of combination, is called a *system*, or, more explicitly, a *mathematical system*. More generally, any set of mathematical objects which admit either (one or more) rules of combination of elements or relations among elements may be said to form a mathematical system. Systems, as so defined, underlie nearly the whole of mathematical science. For instance, the positive integers with the relation of greater and less form a system in this extended sense.*

Certain important and frequently occurring mathematical systems are called groups. Before giving the definition by which groups are characterized and isolated within the more general class of mathematical systems, it will be convenient to introduce to the learner and to treat briefly a class of elements which are of great importance in the construction and study of those groups each of which has only a finite number of elements and to afford him an opportunity to become familiar with the rule of combination to which they are subject. These elements are treated in the following section.

---

* The reader will find a useful and interesting treatment of the subject of this section in a paper by Maxime Bôcher in *Bull. Amer. Math. Soc.* (2) **11** (1904), 115–135.

2. Permutations. Let $a_1, a_2, \cdots, a_n$ denote n distinct letters or other objects, finite in number. Let $b_1, b_2, \cdots, b_n$ be any arrangement of the same n objects. The operation of replacing a_1 by b_1, a_2 by b_2, a_3 by b_3, $\cdots$, a_n by b_n is called a *permutation* performed on the n objects.* It is denoted by the symbol

$$\begin{pmatrix} a_1 a_2 \cdots a_n \\ b_1 b_2 \cdots b_n \end{pmatrix}.$$

A permutation involving n distinct letters is said to be of *degree n*. It is obvious that in the symbol for a permutation the order of letters in either line of the symbol is immaterial if only the order in the other line is so taken that the symbol represents that replacement of letters which is required by the given permutation.

If the arrangement in the second line of the symbol is the same as that in the first, so that each letter is replaced by itself, the permutation is called the *identical* permutation. The identical permutation is often denoted by the symbol I.

If $c_1, c_2, \cdots, c_n$ is also an arrangement of the same letters, the operation of replacing b_1 by c_1, b_2 by c_2, $\cdots$, b_n by c_n is a permutation denoted by the symbol

$$\begin{pmatrix} b_1 b_2 \cdots b_n \\ c_1 c_2 \cdots c_n \end{pmatrix}.$$

If we call the first of the two given permutations S and the second T, then the permutation S followed by the permutation T is a permutation U whose symbol is

$$\begin{pmatrix} a_1 a_2 \cdots a_n \\ c_1 c_2 \cdots c_n \end{pmatrix}.$$

We say that U is the *product* of S and T in the order indicated, and we write $ST = U$, or

$$\begin{pmatrix} a_1 a_2 \cdots a_n \\ b_1 b_2 \cdots b_n \end{pmatrix}\begin{pmatrix} b_1 b_2 \cdots b_n \\ c_1 c_2 \cdots c_n \end{pmatrix} = \begin{pmatrix} a_1 a_2 \cdots a_n \\ c_1 c_2 \cdots c_n \end{pmatrix}.$$

* It is often called a *substitution* on the n objects. But we shall always use the term "permutation," since we shall have occasion to employ the term "substitution" in another sense. We shall restrict the term "permutation" to the case of a finite number of objects.

This law, or method, or rule, of combination of permutations is called *multiplication* of permutations.

It is clear that all the permutations which can be formed from a given set of letters, with multiplication as the rule of combination, form a system of mathematical objects, in the sense in which this term is used in § **1**. Moreover, the result of combining two of these objects, according to this rule, is another object in the system. This system and certain subsystems contained in it are of great importance in the theory of those groups each of which has only a finite number of elements.

It is obvious that multiplication of permutations, as we have defined it, obeys the associative law of algebra; that is, if S_1, S_2, S_3 are permutations, then we have $(S_1S_2)S_3 = S_1(S_2S_3)$. Accordingly we may write each of these products in the form $S_1S_2S_3$.

But the multiplication of two permutations is not always commutative; that is, we may have two permutations whose product in one order is different from their product in the other order. Thus we have

$$\downarrow\begin{pmatrix} abc \\ bca \end{pmatrix}\begin{pmatrix} abc \\ bac \end{pmatrix} = \begin{pmatrix} abc \\ bca \end{pmatrix}\begin{pmatrix} bca \\ acb \end{pmatrix} = \begin{pmatrix} abc \\ acb \end{pmatrix},$$

whereas $$\downarrow\begin{pmatrix} abc \\ bac \end{pmatrix}\begin{pmatrix} abc \\ bca \end{pmatrix} = \begin{pmatrix} abc \\ bac \end{pmatrix}\begin{pmatrix} bac \\ cba \end{pmatrix} = \begin{pmatrix} abc \\ cba \end{pmatrix}.$$

If the product of two permutations is the identical permutation, then each of them is said to be the *inverse* of the other. Thus each of the permutations

$$\downarrow\begin{pmatrix} a_1a_2 \cdots a_n \\ b_1b_2 \cdots b_n \end{pmatrix}, \quad \downarrow\begin{pmatrix} b_1b_2 \cdots b_n \\ a_1a_2 \cdots a_n \end{pmatrix}$$

is the inverse of the other, since their product is the identical permutation

$$\begin{pmatrix} a_1a_2 \cdots a_n \\ a_1a_2 \cdots a_n \end{pmatrix}.$$

It is obvious that there is a unique inverse corresponding to any given permutation. Moreover, the product of a permutation and its inverse is independent of the order in which the multiplication is performed.

A permutation such as

$$\begin{pmatrix} a_1a_2 \cdots a_{n-1}a_n \\ a_2a_3 \cdots a_n \quad a_1 \end{pmatrix}$$

is called a *circular* permutation or a *cyclic* permutation. For the sake of brevity it is denoted by the symbol $(a_1a_2 \cdots a_n)$. This represents the operation of replacing each letter in the symbol by the one which follows it, it being understood that the first letter a_1 is the letter which follows the last letter a_n. It is obvious that

$$(a_1a_2 \cdots a_n) = (a_2a_3 \cdots a_na_1) = (a_3a_4 \cdots a_na_1a_2) = \cdots.$$

A circular permutation on two letters, such as (ab), is called a *transposition.* We denote by (a) the operation of replacing a by a. The product of two circular permutations may be found directly, as is illustrated by the example $(abcde)(bced) = (acbe)(d)$.

We shall now prove the following theorem:

I. Any given permutation is a product of circular permutations no two of which have a letter in common.

Let the given permutation be denoted by the two-line symbol already employed. Let a be any letter in the first line and let b be the letter in the lower line standing under a in the upper. Let c be the letter in the lower line under b in the upper, and so on. Continuing this process, we must arrive finally at a letter l in the upper line under which a stands. Then the letters $a, b, c, \cdots, l$ are permuted according to the circular permutation $(abc \cdots l)$. If there is an additional letter a' in the original permutation, we can proceed from it in a similar way and form a cycle which may be denoted by the symbol $(a'b'c' \cdots l')$. It is obvious that we may continue this process until we have broken up the given permutation into a product of cycles of the form

$$(abc \cdots l)(a'b'c' \cdots l')(a''b''c'' \cdots l'') \cdots.$$

Since no two of these cycles have a letter in common, the truth of the theorem is now apparent.

If a cycle consists of a single letter, that letter is often omitted from the symbol for the permutation.

As examples illustrating the foregoing theorem we may give the following:

$$\begin{pmatrix}12345678\\24386571\end{pmatrix} = (1248)(3)(56)(7) = (1248)(56);$$

$$\begin{pmatrix}123456789\\231564897\end{pmatrix} = (123)(456)(789).$$

II. Any given permutation can be expressed as a product of transpositions.

In view of the preceding theorem this theorem may be established by showing that it holds for circular permutations. Now we have

$$(a_1a_2a_3 \cdots a_l) = (a_1a_2)(a_1a_3)(a_1a_4) \cdots (a_1a_l),$$

as one may readily verify by forming the product of the transpositions in the second member of this equation. Then Theorem II follows by aid of Theorem I.

Since $(a_ra_s) = (a_1a_r)(a_1a_s)(a_1a_r)$ when r and s are different from each other and from 1, it follows that we have the corollary:

Cor. Any given permutation on the letters $a_1, a_2, \cdots, a_n$ can be expressed as a product in terms of the transpositions $(a_1a_2), (a_1a_3), \cdots, (a_1a_n)$.

It is easy to see (from the fact that relations of the form $(ab) = (\alpha a)(\alpha b)(\alpha a)$ exist) that the number of ways in which a given permutation may be represented as a product of transpositions may be unlimited. Concerning these ways we may prove the following theorem:

III. In the various expressions of a given permutation as products of transpositions on its letters the number of transpositions is always odd or always even.

Let us consider the determinant

$$D = \begin{vmatrix} 1 & 1 & \cdots & 1 \\ a_1 & a_2 & \cdots & a_n \\ a_1^2 & a_2^2 & \cdots & a_n^2 \\ \cdots & \cdots & \cdots & \cdots \\ a_1^{n-1} & a_2^{n-1} & \cdots & a_n^{n-1} \end{vmatrix}.$$

The effect on D of any transposition of two letters is to change D into $-D$. Hence a permutation expressed as a product of an odd number of transpositions changes D into $-D$, whereas one expressed as a product of an even number of transpositions leaves D unaltered. But a given permutation, however expressed, must always have one and the same effect upon D. Then, since D is obviously not identically equal to zero, it follows that in every expression of a given permutation as a product of transpositions on its letters the number of transpositions appearing must be always odd or always even.

A permutation is said to be *odd* if it is expressible as a product of an odd number of transpositions; otherwise it is said to be *even.*

IV. Any even permutation may be expressed as a product of circular permutations each involving just three symbols.

From Theorem III and the corollary to Theorem II it follows that every even permutation on $a_1, a_2, \cdots, a_n$ can be expressed as a product of an even number of transpositions each of which belongs to the set $(a_1a_2), (a_1a_3), \cdots, (a_1a_n)$. This product itself may evidently be taken as a product of pairs of transpositions, each pair being taken as a product in the form $(a_1a_r)(a_1a_s)$, where r and s are different from each other and from 1. But we have $(a_1a_r)(a_1a_s) = (a_1a_ra_s)$, whence it follows that the given even permutation can be expressed as a product of cyclic permutations of the form $(a_1a_ra_s)$, where r and s are different from each other and from 1. Therefore the theorem is established.

Now if 1, 2, r, s are all different, we have

$$(a_1a_2a_s)(a_1a_2a_r)(a_1a_2a_s)(a_1a_2a_s) = (a_1a_ra_s),$$

as one may readily verify by forming the product of the cyclic permutations in the first member of the equation. Hence

COR. An even permutation on the letters a_1, a_2, $\cdots$, a_n can be expressed as a product of permutations each of which belongs to the set $(a_1a_2a_3)$, $(a_1a_2a_4)$, $\cdots$, $(a_1a_2a_n)$.

The product formed by taking r factors, each of which is a given permutation S, is denoted by S^r and is called the rth *power* of S. From the associative law it follows that $S^\mu S^\nu = S^{\mu+\nu}$.

Now consider the set of permutations

$$S, S^2, S^3, S^4, \cdots.$$

Since there is only a finite number of distinct permutations on a given set of letters, it follows that there must be repetitions in this sequence of powers. Then let S^ρ and S^μ be two of these that are equal, ρ being greater than μ. Then if $S_{-\mu}$ is the inverse of S^μ, we have

$$S^\rho = S^\mu, \ S^{\rho-\mu}S^\mu = S^\mu, \ S^{\rho-\mu}S^\mu S_{-\mu} = S^\mu S_{-\mu};$$

whence it follows that $S^{\rho-\mu} = I$, where I denotes the identical permutation.

In the given sequence of powers of S let S^m be the first one which is equal to I. Then m is called the order of S. It is obvious that S^{m-1} is the inverse of S.

If S is of order m $(m > 2)$, then no two of the permutations $S, S^2, S^3, \cdots, S^{m-1}$ are equal. For, if $S^\lambda = S^\mu$ and $\lambda < \mu < m$, then, if $S_{-\lambda}$ is the inverse of S^λ, we have

$$I = S^\lambda S_{-\lambda} = S^\mu S_{-\lambda} = S^{\mu-\lambda}S^\lambda S_{-\lambda} = S^{\mu-\lambda},$$

contrary to the hypothesis that S is of order m.

If k is a positive integer and $S^k = I$, then it may be shown that k is a multiple of the order m of S. For if k is not a multiple of m it is greater than m (in view of the result in the preceding paragraph), and we have $k = \alpha m + \beta$, where β is a positive integer less than m and α is a positive integer. Hence

$$I = S^k = S^{\alpha m+\beta} = (S^m)^\alpha S^\beta = I^\alpha S^\beta = S^\beta,$$

contrary to the hypothesis that S is of order m.

Now the equation $S^{\mu+\nu} = S^\mu S^\nu$ holds when μ and ν are positive integers. If it be *assumed* to hold when the exponents μ and ν range over all integral values, positive or negative or zero, then it is easy to show that S^0 is the identical permutation and that $S^{-\nu}$ is the inverse of S^ν. For

$$S^0 S^\mu = S^\mu \quad \text{and} \quad S^{-\nu} S^\nu = S^0,$$

whence $S^0 = I$ and $S^{-\nu}$ is the inverse of S^ν. The conception of *powers* of S will be extended to include the cases of zero and negative integral exponents. It is easy to see that the extension introduces no contradictions.

We shall now prove the following theorem:

V. If a given permutation S is written as a product of circular permutations no two of which have a letter in common, then the order of S is the least common multiple of the degrees of the circular permutations which compose it.

It is obvious that the order of a circular permutation is equal to its degree. Then the order of S must be a multiple of the degree of any one of its named components, and hence it must be at least as great as the least common multiple μ of their respective degrees. But it is obvious that $S^\mu = I$. Hence μ is the order of S.

When a given permutation S is written as a product of circular permutations no two of which have a letter in common, these component circular permutations will be called the *cycles* of S, and we shall say that S itself is written in *standard form*. If all the cycles of S are of the same degree, S is said to be *regular*. If two permutations have the same number of cycles and the cycles can be made to correspond uniquely, those of the one permutation to those of the other, so that two corresponding cycles always have the same degree, then these permutations are said to be *similar*. Thus $(abcde)(fg)(hij)$ and (12)(345)(67890) are similar. The third power of the circular permutation (123456789) is the regular permutation (147)(258)(369).

From the representation of a circular permutation as a product of transpositions, as in the proof of Theorem II, it is obvious that a circular permutation is odd or even according as its degree is even or odd. Hence any permutation is even or odd according as the difference between its degree and the number of its cycles is even or odd.

If S and T are two permutations, the permutation $T^{-1}ST$ is called the *transform* of S by T, or the result of transforming S by T; and S is said to be transformed by T when one forms $T^{-1}ST$. Since

$$(TU)^{-1}S(TU) = (U^{-1}T^{-1})S(TU) = U^{-1} \cdot T^{-1}ST \cdot U,$$

it follows that the transform of S by TU is equal to the transform by U of the transform of S by T.

VI. The transform of S by T may be found by performing the permutation T on the cycles of S.

Let S and T be denoted by the symbols

$$S = (abcd \cdots)(lmno \cdots) \cdots,$$

$$T = \begin{pmatrix} abc & \cdots & lmno & \cdots \\ \alpha\beta\gamma & \cdots & \lambda\mu\nu\rho & \cdots \end{pmatrix}.$$

Then

$$T^{-1}ST = \begin{pmatrix} \alpha\beta\gamma \cdots \lambda\mu\nu \cdots \\ abc \cdots lmn \cdots \end{pmatrix} \{(abcd \cdots)(lmno \cdots) \cdots\} \begin{pmatrix} abc \cdots lmno \cdots \\ \alpha\beta\gamma \cdots \lambda\mu\nu\rho \cdots \end{pmatrix}$$

$$= \begin{pmatrix} \alpha\beta\gamma \cdots \lambda\mu\nu \cdots \\ bcd \cdots mno \cdots \end{pmatrix} \begin{pmatrix} abc \cdots lmno \cdots \\ \alpha\beta\gamma \cdots \lambda\mu\nu\rho \cdots \end{pmatrix}$$

$$= \begin{pmatrix} \alpha\beta\gamma \cdots \lambda\mu\nu \cdots \\ \beta\gamma\delta \cdots \mu\nu\rho \cdots \end{pmatrix} = (\alpha\beta\gamma \cdots)(\lambda\mu\nu \cdots) \cdots.$$

The last member gives the value of $T^{-1}ST$ in the form stated in the theorem.

It is obvious that the permutation $T^{-1}ST$ is similar to the permutation S. In particular cases it may happen that $T^{-1}ST = S$. When this is so we have $TT^{-1}ST = TS$, or $ST = TS$.

When $ST = TS$ we say that S and T are *commutative* or *permutable.* It is evident that two circular permutations which have no letter in common are commutative. It is easy to see that a necessary and sufficient condition that S and T shall be commutative is that the transform of S by T shall be equal to S. For we have seen that $T^{-1}ST = S$ implies that $ST = TS$, while it is true that the latter relation implies that $T^{-1}ST = T^{-1}TS = S$. Moreover, if S is permutable with both T and U, it is also permutable with their product TU, since $(TU)S = TUS = TSU = STU = S(TU)$.

When S and T are commutative, we have $ST = TS$, whence $T^{-1}ST = S$ and $S^{-1}T^{-1}ST = I$. In general, if S and T are any two permutations, then $S^{-1}T^{-1}ST$ is called the *commutator* of S and T. The commutator of T and S is $T^{-1}S^{-1}TS$. Since the product of these two commutators is the identity, it follows that each of them is the inverse of the other. A necessary and sufficient condition that two permutations shall be commutative is that their commutator (in either order) shall be the identical permutation.

If S_1 and S_2 are two permutations, we have $S_2S_1 = S_1^{-1} \cdot S_1S_2 \cdot S_1$. Hence S_1S_2 and S_2S_1 are similar permutations, since one of them is a transform of the other. But from Theorem V it follows at once that two similar permutations are of the same order. Hence (Theorem VI) a permutation and its transform are of the same order; in particular, S_1S_2 and S_2S_1 are of the same order.

It is important that the learner shall have a ready facility in handling operations involving permutations. To increase his mastery of the processes we now give a set of exercises for his practice. He is advised to add to this set by constructing other exercises for himself.

EXERCISES

1. Show that the total number of permutations on n letters is $n!$. Write down in standard form the 24 permutations on a, b, c, d. How many of these are of order 2? of order 3? of order 4?

2. Find the product of $(a_1a_2 \cdots a_l)(a_{l+1} \cdots a_n)$ and (a_la_{l+1}).

3. Prove that any power of a circular permutation is either the identical permutation or a circular permutation or some other regular permutation.

4. Prove that the order of a permutation of degree m is a factor of $m!$.

5. Show that the permutations $(ab)(cd)$ and $(ac)(bd)$ are commutative. Show that the permutations

$$I,\ (ab)(cd),\ (ac)(bd),\ (ad)(bc)$$

are all the permutations that can be formed from the two given permutations by multiplication, however many times each of them is used as a factor.

6. Find all the permutations that can be obtained by forming products from the permutations (ab), (cd), $(ac)(bd)$, these being taken as factors. Show that they consist of the following eight permutations: I, (ab), (cd), $(ab)(cd)$, $(ac)(bd)$, $(ad)(bc)$, $(adbc)$, $(acbd)$.

7. Show that the function $ab + cd$ is unaltered when its letters are interchanged in accordance with any one of the permutations in Ex. 6. [Thus the permutation $(ac)(bd)$ replaces $ab + cd$ by $cd + ab$, and this is equal to $ab + cd$.]

8. If S and T are two similar permutations, show that there exists a permutation U such that $U^{-1}SU = T$.

9. If A and B are similar permutations, find two permutations whose commutator is $A^{-1}B$.

10. Find the commutator of $(a_1a_2 \cdots a_l)$ and $(a_la_{l+1} \cdots a_n)$.

11. Show that the commutator of two permutations is an even permutation.

12. If $S = (a_1a_2 \cdots a_n)$, show that

$$S^t = \begin{pmatrix} a_1 & a_2 & \cdots & a_n \\ a_{t+1} & a_{t+2} & \cdots & a_{t+n} \end{pmatrix},$$

where each subscript in the second line is to be replaced by the least positive remainder obtained when that subscript is divided by n.

13. The only permutations on $a_1, a_2, \cdots, a_n$ which are permutable with the circular permutation $(a_1a_2 \cdots a_n)$ are the powers of the latter.

14. Find all the permutations on the ten symbols $a, b, c, d, e, 1, 2, 3, 4, 5$ which are permutable with the permutation $(abcde)(12345)$. Show that their number is 50.

15. In the proof of Theorem II of § **2** we saw that a circular permutation of degree n can be expressed as a product of $n - 1$ transpositions. Show that it cannot be expressed as a product of any smaller number of transpositions.

16. Show that

$$\begin{aligned}(a_1a_2 \cdots a_{2n}) &= (a_1a_{2n-1})(a_2a_{2n-2}) \cdots (a_{n-1}a_{n+1}) \\ &\quad \cdot (a_1a_{2n})(a_2a_{2n-1}) \cdots (a_na_{n+1}), \\ (a_1a_2 \cdots a_{2n+1}) &= (a_1a_{2n})(a_2a_{2n-1}) \cdots (a_na_{n+1}) \\ &\quad \cdot (a_1a_{2n+1})(a_2a_{2n}) \cdots (a_na_{n+2});\end{aligned}$$

and thence show that every permutation can be expressed as a product of two permutations of order 2 on the same letters.

17. Show that every permutation on the letters $a_1, a_2, \cdots, a_n$ can be expressed as a product in terms of the permutations

$$(a_1a_2), \ (a_2a_3 \cdots a_n).$$

18. Show that every even permutation on the letters $a_1, a_2, \cdots, a_n$ can be expressed as a product in terms of the permutations

$$(a_1a_2a_3), \ (a_3a_4 \cdots a_n).$$

19. Show that every even permutation on the letters $a_1, a_2, \cdots, a_{2n+1}$ can be expressed as a product in terms of the permutations

$$(a_1a_2a_3), \ (a_1a_4a_5), \ \cdots, \ (a_1a_{2n}a_{2n+1}).$$

20. Show that every even permutation on the letters $a_1, a_2, \cdots, a_{2n}$ can be expressed as a product in terms of the permutations

$$(a_1a_2a_3), \ (a_1a_4a_5), \ \cdots, \ (a_1a_{2n-2}a_{2n-1}), \ (a_1a_2a_{2n}).$$

3. Definition of Group. Mathematical systems of a certain very important type are known as groups. A group may be defined in the following manner.

Let G be a system consisting of a set of distinct elements and one rule R of combination for uniting any pair of them in a given order, this rule being such that the result is always uniquely determined. If a and b are two elements of G, we shall denote by ab the element resulting from the operation of combining a with b in the order written and in accordance with the rule R. By such a symbol as $(ab)c$ we shall mean the result of combining with c the result obtained when a is combined with b, both combinations being in accordance with the rule R. A similar interpretation will be given to the symbol $a(bc)$. If two symbols or combinations of symbols denote the same element, we shall express this fact by writing one of them equal to the other, using for this purpose the usual sign of equality. The elements in the system G are said to form a *group*, and the system itself is said to be a *group*, if the following conditions * are satisfied:

I. If a and b are elements of G, whether the same or different, ab is also an element of G.

II. If a, b, c are elements of G, then $(ab)c = a(bc)$.

III. The set G contains a single element i, called the *identical element* or the *identity*, such that for every element a of G we have $ai = ia = a$.

IV. If a is an element of G, there is a unique element a' of G, called the *inverse* of a, such that $aa' = a'a = i$.

A system satisfying Postulate I alone is sometimes said to have the group property. This postulate was the only one usually mentioned explicitly by the older writers on the subject, but they generally tacitly assumed the remaining postulates.

It is convenient to use the name *multiplication* for the rule R of combination and to say that ab is the *product* of a and b in the given order and to use for products the customary symbols of algebra. Then Postulate II asserts that the *associative* law holds for the multiplication of the elements of a group G.

---

* See § 100 for the removal of certain redundancies.

Since the identity plays the role of unity in multiplication, it is often denoted by the symbol 1. It is evidently always its own inverse.

A group G is said to be *finite* or *infinite* according as the number of elements in it is finite or infinite. If the number of elements in G is the finite number n, then n is said to be the *order* of the finite group G. An infinite group is sometimes said to be a group of infinite order.

The following afford examples of groups (as one may readily verify):

1. The set of integers, positive and negative and zero, the rule of combination being ordinary addition. (The identity is zero; the inverse of an element is its negative.)
2. The set of all real numbers, the rule of combination being addition.
3. The set of all real numbers except zero, the rule of combination being ordinary multiplication. (Here unity is the identical element, and the inverse of an element is its reciprocal.)
4. The set of numbers $+1, -1, +\sqrt{-1}, -\sqrt{-1}$, the rule of combination being ordinary multiplication.
5. The set of all nth roots of unity, with ordinary multiplication as the rule of combination, n being a fixed positive integer.
6. The set of permutations in Ex. 5 on page 14.
7. The set of permutations in Ex. 6 on page 14. (It may be shown that this group contains within itself five groups of order 2 and three groups of order 4.)
8. The set of all distinct powers of any given permutation.

As another example let us consider certain rotations of a plane about a fixed line l perpendicular to the plane. Let ω be an angle such that $n\omega = 360°$, where n is a given integer greater than unity. Then let the elements of G consist of the rotations about l of angular measures $\omega, 2\,\omega, 3\,\omega, \cdots, n\omega$. We shall call $(n+k)\omega$ the same rotation as $k\omega$, since it leaves the plane in the same final position. Let the rule of combination be that of addition of rotations. The identity is the rotation $n\omega$. The inverse of the rotation $k\omega$, where $0 < k < n$, is the rotation $(n-k)\omega$. It is now easy to see that this set of rotations forms a group of order n.

The set of transformations

$$x' = x,\ x' = \frac{1}{x},\ x' = 1 - x,\ x' = \frac{1}{1-x},\ x' = \frac{x-1}{x},\ x' = \frac{x}{x-1}$$

forms a group of order 6, the rule of combination being that of multiplication of transformations. Thus, the product of the sixth and the third may be obtained in the following manner: From

$$x'' = 1 - x',\ x' = \frac{x}{x-1},$$

we have
$$x'' = 1 - \frac{x}{x-1}, \quad \text{or} \quad x'' = \frac{1}{1-x};$$

and this is the fourth transformation of the set. It is easy to complete the verification of the fact that the set forms a group. It may be observed that all six of these transformations may be obtained by taking products with the second and the third as the factors.

A group of order 6 is formed by the transformations

$$x' = x,\ x' = x + 1,\ x' = x + 2,\ x' = 2x,\ x' = 2x + 1,\ x' = 2x + 2,$$

the rule of combination being that of multiplication of transformations followed by a reduction of coefficients modulo 3 to their least non-negative values. As a part of the verification we note that from $x'' = 2x'$, $x' = x + 2$ we have $x'' = 2x + 4$, or $x'' = 2x + 1$ when reduced modulo 3. It may readily be shown that all six of these transformations may be obtained by taking products with the second and the fourth as the factors.

Consider the transformations S and T, namely,

$$x' = x + 1,\ x' = 2x,$$

respectively, and those which may be obtained from them by multiplication of transformations followed by reduction of coefficients modulo 5 to their least non-negative values. When so treated S is of order 5 and T is of order 4. The products $S^{\alpha}T^{\beta}$ ($\alpha = 0, 1, 2, 3, 4;\ \beta = 0, 1, 2, 3$) are twenty in number and are all distinct, as the reader may readily verify. It may also be shown that these twenty transformations are all that can be obtained by means of products formed from S and T, all transformations being taken modulo 5. These transformations form a group of order 20, as the reader may verify.

Since we are concerned (in this book) only with finite groups, we shall hereafter often use the word "group" to denote a finite group when there is no danger of confusion.

4. Certain Permutation Groups. A group whose elements are permutations on a given (finite) set of symbols is called a *permutation group* on those symbols, the rule of combination being multiplication, as defined in § 2. If the given symbols are n in number, the group is said to be of *degree n*.

It is easy to see that a set of permutations involving only a finite number of symbols and satisfying condition I in the definition of "group" in § 3 also satisfies the remaining conditions. For multiplication of permutations is associative; an appropriate power of any permutation is the identical permutation; and the next lower power is the inverse of the given permutation. This observation will sometimes shorten the labor of determining whether a given set of permutations forms a group.

The total set of permutations on n letters $a_1, a_2, \cdots, a_n$ contains $n!$ permutations. In view of the properties of permutations it is easy to see that this set of permutations constitutes a group. It is called the *symmetric group* on the n given letters. It is of degree n and order $n!$.

Consider the even permutations on $a_1, a_2, \cdots, a_n$ $(n > 1)$. The product of any one of them by the transposition (a_1a_2) is an odd permutation, and no two such products are equal, whence it follows readily that the number of odd permutations on $a_1, a_2, \cdots, a_n$ is at least as great as the number of even permutations. Similarly, from the facts that the product of an odd permutation by (a_1a_2) is an even permutation and that no two such products are equal, it follows that the number of even permutations on $a_1, a_2, \cdots, a_n$ is at least as great as the number of odd permutations on the same letters. Hence *the number of even permutations on $a_1, a_2, \cdots, a_n$ is equal to the number of odd permutations on the same letters.*

Now the inverse of an even permutation is even, and the

product of two even permutations is even. Therefore it follows readily that the even permutations on $a_1, a_2, \cdots, a_n$ form a group. It is called the *alternating group* on these letters. It is of degree n and order $\frac{1}{2} \cdot n!$. When $n = 2$ the alternating group consists of the identical element alone.

The method of proof used in the preceding paragraph may be employed to show that *all the permutations of any given permutation group G are even, or else exactly half of them are even and the even permutations form a group.* In such proof the transposition (a_1a_2), of the former argument, is to be replaced by a fixed odd permutation belonging to the group G, in case G contains odd permutations.

In the case of four letters the symmetric group is of order 24 and the alternating group is of order 12. The permutations in Ex. 6 on page 14 constitute a group of degree 4 and order 8 known as the *octic* group; those in Ex. 5 on page 14 constitute a group of degree 4 and order 4. There are also other groups of degree 4. An important problem in the theory of finite groups is that of constructing all the permutation groups of given degree. This problem has been completely solved only for the lower degrees.

It is easy to verify (see Ex. 7 on page 14) that the function $ab + cd$ is unaltered when its letters are interchanged in accordance with any one of the following permutations:

$$I,\ (ab),\ (cd),\ (ab)(cd),\ (ac)(bd),\ (ad)(bc),\ (adbc),\ (acbd).$$

Thus the fourth permutation in the set leaves the terms of $ab + cd$ unaltered, while the fifth interchanges its terms. In all cases the function itself is left unaltered. The permutation (ac) changes this function into $bc + ad$; the same is true of the product obtained from each of the given eight permutations on multiplying on the right by (ac). Thus $(adbc) \cdot (ac) = (adb)(c)$, and the last permutation changes $ab + cd$ into $ad + bc$. Likewise each of the eight permutations obtained by multiplying the eight given permutations on the right by (ad) changes $ab + cd$ into $bd + ac$. It is easy to verify that the eight original permutations and the two sets of eight each obtained in the way just indicated exhaust the total set of 24 permutations on the letters a, b, c, d. Hence the original eight permutations are all the permutations on a, b, c, d each of which leaves unaltered the function $ab + cd$.

Consider the total set of permutations on $a_1, a_2, \cdots, a_n$ each of which leaves unaltered a given polynomial P in the arguments $a_1, a_2, \cdots, a_n$. This set contains the identical permutation. It also contains the inverse of every permutation in the set. Moreover, the product of any two permutations in the set is itself in the set. Hence such a set of permutations constitutes a permutation group. It is said to be the group under which P is *invariant*, or the group to which P *belongs*.

The group so associated with a symmetric polynomial in $a_1, a_2, \cdots, a_n$ is obviously the symmetric group. It is easy to prove that it is the alternating group which is so associated with the function D employed in the proof of Theorem III of § 2, since an odd permutation changes D into $-D$, whereas D is left unaltered by an even permutation.

Let us consider the seven sets of three letters each contained in the seven columns of the following array:

$$\begin{matrix} A & B & C & D & E & F & G \\ B & C & D & E & F & G & A \\ D & E & F & G & A & B & C \end{matrix}$$

These sets are permuted among themselves by each of the permutations $P = (ABCDEFG)$ and $Q = (BD)(EF)$. The total set of permutations on A, B, C, D, E, F, G, each of which permutes among themselves these seven sets of three letters each, constitutes a group Γ, as one sees from the obvious fact that the product of any two permutations in the set is also in the set. Let us determine the order of this group Γ.

Let S be a permutation in Γ that leaves each of the triples ABD and BCE fixed as a triple. Then S must replace B by B; it must interchange A and D or replace each of them by itself; it must interchange C and E or replace each of them by itself; and it must interchange F and G or replace each of them by itself. Hence S must be one of the following eight permutations: I, (AD), (CE), $(AD)(CE)$, (FG), $(AD)(FG)$, $(CE)(FG)$,

$(AD)(CE)(FG)$. Upon testing these it is found that only four of them afford suitable values of S, namely, the following:

$$I,\ (AD)(CE),\ (AD)(FG),\ (CE)(FG).$$

Hence there are in Γ only these four permutations each of which leaves each of the first two triples fixed. We denote them in order by S_1, S_2, S_3, S_4.

If T is a permutation in Γ which replaces ABD and BCE in order by any other ordered pair α and β of triples in the given set, then each of the elements S_iT $(i=1, 2, 3, 4)$ replaces ABD and BCE by α and β respectively. If U is any permutation in Γ which replaces ABD and BCE by α and β respectively, then UT^{-1} leaves ABD and BCE both fixed, so that $UT^{-1}=S_i$ for some i, and hence $U=S_iT$. From this it follows that there are just four elements in Γ each of which replaces ABD and BCE by α and β respectively. But the totality of ordered pairs α and β from the given set of seven triples is $7\cdot 6$ in number. Hence Γ has at most $7\cdot 6\cdot 4$ $(=168)$ elements.

We shall now prove that Γ has at least 168 elements, by showing that there are 168 permutations which can be expressed as products in terms of the permutations P and Q already introduced. We have

$$P^{-2}QP^3=(BCDG)(EF),$$
$$P^{-2}QP^2QP=(BEG)(CDF).$$

Now the powers of the first of these yield four distinct permutations. On multiplying each of them by Q, we have four more, making eight in all. On multiplying each of these eight by each of the three distinct powers of $(BEG)(CDF)$, we obtain all together 24 distinct permutations. On multiplying each of these 24 by each of the seven distinct powers of P, we have 168 $(=7\cdot 24)$ distinct permutations expressed as products in terms of P and Q.

Therefore Γ has just 168 elements, and all these elements may be expressed as products in terms of P and Q. This group Γ of order 168 is one of the most interesting groups of degree 7.

Two permutation groups are usually said to be identical if there is a permutation T which transforms all the permutations of one of the groups into the permutations of the other group. Thus the group

$$I,\ (ab),\ (cd),\ (ab)(cd)$$

is identical with the group

$$I,\ (ac),\ (bd),\ (ac)(bd),$$

into which it is transformed by the permutation (bc); it is also identical with the group

$$I,\ (\alpha\beta),\ (\gamma\delta),\ (\alpha\beta)(\gamma\delta),$$

into which it is transformed by the permutation

$$(a\alpha)(b\beta)(c\gamma)(d\delta).$$

But if two notationally distinct groups are contained in a given permutation group G, they are reckoned as different groups in regard to their relation to G, even though they may be the same in the sense of the preceding paragraph. Thus the first two groups of that paragraph are considered as different groups contained in the symmetric group on a, b, c, d.

EXERCISES

1. Show that the permutations mentioned in Ex. 14 on page 15 form a group of order 50.

2. Find all the permutations on 1, 2, 3, 4, 5, 6, 7, 8 each of which is commutative with each of the permutations (12345) and (678), and show that they form a group of order 15.

3. Find all the permutations on a, b, c, d, e, f, 1, 2, 3, 4, 5, 6 each of which is commutative with $(abcdef)$(123456), and show that they form a group of order 72.

4. Find all the permutations on 1, 2, 3, 4, 5, 6, 7, 8, 9 each of which is commutative with (123)(456)(789), and show that they form a group of order 162.

5. If ω is a primitive nth root of unity, show that the transformations

$$x' = \omega^k x,\ x' = \frac{\omega^k}{x} \qquad (k = 1, 2, \cdots, n)$$

form a group of order $2n$.

6. Construct all the transformations which can be formed by taking products of the transformations

$$x' = \sqrt{-1}\,x,\quad x' = \frac{1}{x},\quad x' = \frac{x+1}{x-1}$$

and show that they form a group of order 24.

7. Show that the largest permutation group on x_1, x_2, x_3, x_4 which leaves invariant the function $(x_1 + x_2 - x_3 - x_4)^2$ is the octic group.

8. Determine the largest permutation group on x_1, x_2, x_3, x_4 under which the function $(x_1 + x_2)(x_3 + x_4)$ is invariant.

9. Show that the symmetric group of degree m contains the symmetric group of any lower degree. State and prove the corresponding theorem for the alternating group of degree m.

10. Show that the largest permutation group on A, B, C, D, E, F, G, each element of which leaves invariant the function

$$ABD + BCE + CDF + DEG + EFA + FGB + GAC,$$

is a group of order 168. (Compare with the array on page 21.)

11. Consider the 42 transformations

$$x' = ax + b \qquad (a = 1, 2, 3, 4, 5, 6;\ b = 0, 1, 2, 3, 4, 5, 6)$$

and a rule of combination which consists of ordinary multiplication of transformations followed by a reduction of coefficients modulo 7 to their least non-negative values. Show that these transformations so considered form a group G of order 42, and prove that each of the transformations of G can be expressed as a product in terms of the transformations $x' = x + 1$ and $x' = 3\,x$.

12. Similarly, show that the transformations

$$x' = ax + b \qquad (a = 1, 2, 4;\ b = 0, 1, 2, \cdots, 6)$$

give rise to a group of order 21. Show also that the transformations

$$x' = ax + b \qquad (a = 1, 6;\ b = 0, 1, 2, \cdots, 6)$$

similarly give rise to a group of order 14.

13. Show that the eleven sets of five letters each contained in the eleven columns of the array

$$\begin{array}{ccccccccccc}
A & B & C & D & E & F & G & H & I & J & K \\
B & C & D & E & F & G & H & I & J & K & A \\
C & D & E & F & G & H & I & J & K & A & B \\
E & F & G & H & I & J & K & A & B & C & D \\
H & I & J & K & A & B & C & D & E & F & G
\end{array}$$

are permuted among themselves by a permutation group of order 660 on the letters $A, B, C, \cdots, K$ and by no larger group on these letters. [SUGGESTION. Observe that the array is invariant for the permutations $(ABCDEFGHIJK)$ and $(CEH)(DKG)(FIJ)$; prove that it is left invariant by only six permutations each of which leaves two columns unaltered; and thence proceed as on pages 21 and 22.]

14. Find a function of $A, B, C, \cdots, K$ which is left invariant by the permutations of the group in Ex. 13 and by no other permutation of its arguments.

15. Arrange seven letters in seven sets of four each so that every two of these sets shall have just two letters in common while every two letters shall occur together in just two sets. Show that these sets must be (apart from change in notation) the seven sets afforded by the columns of the array

$$\begin{matrix} A & A & B & A & A & B & C \\ B & B & C & C & D & D & D \\ C & E & E & F & E & F & E \\ D & F & G & G & G & G & F \end{matrix}$$

[SUGGESTION. Choose the notation so that three of the sets are those in the first three columns, and show that the remaining sets are then determined successively by means of the first two letters in them.]

16. Show that the seven sets of four letters each afforded by the array in Ex. 15 are interchanged among themselves as sets by each of the permutations $(ABCGFDE)$ and $(BG)(FD)$, and prove that the group obtained by forming all the distinct products with these permutations as factors is of order 168 and that it contains all the permutations on A, B, C, D, E, F, G, each of which merely interchanges the given sets among themselves.

17. Arrange eleven letters in eleven sets of five each so that every two of these sets shall have just two letters in common while every two letters shall occur together in just two sets, and show that these sets must be (apart from change in notation) the eleven sets afforded by the columns of the array in the foregoing Ex. 13.

18. Demonstrate that the distinct powers of the permutation $(ABCDEFGHIJK)$ constitute the largest permutation group on these letters the elements of which merely permute among themselves the eleven sets of five letters each afforded by the columns of the array

$$\begin{array}{ccccccccccc} A & B & C & D & E & F & G & H & I & J & K \\ B & C & D & E & F & G & H & I & J & K & A \\ C & D & E & F & G & H & I & J & K & A & B \\ D & E & F & G & H & I & J & K & A & B & C \\ J & K & A & B & C & D & E & F & G & H & I \end{array}$$

19. Consider the 14 quadruples defined by the columns of the following array:

$$\begin{array}{cccccccccccccc} H & H & H & H & H & H & H & G & A & B & C & D & E & F \\ A & B & C & D & E & F & G & C & D & E & F & G & A & B \\ B & C & D & E & F & G & A & E & F & G & A & B & C & D \\ D & E & F & G & A & B & C & F & G & A & B & C & D & E \end{array}$$

Show that these quadruples are permuted among themselves by a permutation group of order $8 \cdot 7 \cdot 6 \cdot 4$ on these eight letters and by no larger group on these letters.

20. Arrange the eight letters A, B, C, D, E, F, G, H into 14 sets of four each so that each triple of these letters shall occur in one and in just one of the 14 quadruples, and show that (except for a permutation of the letters) these 14 quadruples are those afforded by the columns of the array in Ex. 19.

5. Properties of the Elements of a Group.* If A, B, C are elements of a group and $AB = AC$, we have $A'AB = A'AC$, where A' is the inverse of A, whence it follows that $B = C$. Similarly, if $BA = CA$, we have $B = C$.

If S is an element of a group, then the product of k factors each equal to S is denoted by S^k and is called the kth *power* of S. The infinite sequence of symbols

$$S, S^2, S^3, \cdots$$

obviously represents a finite number of distinct elements if S is an element of a finite group. If $S^\mu = S^\nu$ and $\mu > \nu$, and if $S_{-\nu}$ is the inverse of S^ν, we have, using 1 for the identity,

$$1 = S^\nu S_{-\nu} = S^\mu S_{-\nu} = S^{\mu-\nu} S^\nu S_{-\nu} = S^{\mu-\nu}.$$

* Many of these properties are given in § 2 for the special case of elements which are permutations. They are now treated for the more general abstract situation.

Hence there is some power of S which is equal to the identity. If $S^m = 1$ and $m > 1$, while $S^x \neq 1$ for $x = 1, 2, \cdots, m-1$, then m is said to be the *order* of S. (The identity is said to be of order unity.) It is easy to prove that no two of the elements $1, S, S^2, \cdots, S^{m-1}$ are equal. For, if $S^\nu = S^\mu$ $(0 < \nu < \mu < m)$, then as before we have $1 = S^{\mu-\nu}$; and this is contrary to the hypothesis that S is of order m. If $S^l = 1$ $(l > m)$, and we write $l = mq + r$ $(0 < r \leqq m)$, then

$$1 = S^l = S^{mq+r} = (S^m)^q \cdot S^r = S^r,$$

whence it follows that $r = m$. Therefore l is divisible by m. Hence, *if* $S^l = 1$, *then* l *is a multiple of the order* m *of* S.

The relation $S^\mu S^\nu = S^{\mu+\nu}$ obviously holds if μ and ν are positive integers. If we assume (as we may consistently) that this relation holds when μ and ν are any integers, then it is easy to show that $S^0 = 1$ and that S^{-k} is the inverse of S^k; for

$$S^0 S^\mu = S^\mu \text{ and } S^{-k} S^k = S^0.$$

If $S_1, S_2, \cdots, S_\rho$ are elements of a group, then the inverse of $S_1 S_2 \cdots S_\rho$ is $S_\rho^{-1} S_{\rho-1}^{-1} \cdots S_2^{-1} S_1^{-1}$, since the product of one of these elements by the other is evidently the identity.

We have seen that the elements of a group obey the associative law of multiplication. But multiplication is not always commutative, as we saw in connection with the study of permutations in § 2. That is, if A and B are elements of a group, the product AB may be different from the product BA. In the case when $AB = BA$ we say that A and B are *commutative* or that they are *permutable*. If A is permutable with both B and C, then A is permutable with BC, since

$$(BC)A = BCA = BAC = ABC = A(BC).$$

The element $T^{-1}ST$ is said to be the *transform* of S by T, or the result of transforming S by T. In the special case when $T^{-1}ST = S$ we have $ST = TS$. Conversely, from the relation $ST = TS$ we have $T^{-1}ST = S$. Moreover, if $T^{-1}ST = U$, then $T^{-1}S^kT = U^k$, since

$$U^k = (T^{-1}ST)^k = T^{-1}ST \cdot T^{-1}ST \cdot \cdots \cdot T^{-1}ST = T^{-1}S^kT.$$

The element $S^{-1}T^{-1}ST$ is called the *commutator* of S and T. Its inverse is the commutator $T^{-1}S^{-1}TS$ of T and S. A necessary and sufficient condition that S and T shall be commutative is that their commutator shall be the identity, as the reader will easily verify.

Since

$$U^{-1} \cdot S^{-1}T^{-1}ST \cdot U = U^{-1}S^{-1}U \cdot U^{-1}T^{-1}U \cdot U^{-1}SU \cdot U^{-1}TU$$
$$= (U^{-1}SU)^{-1}(U^{-1}TU)^{-1}(U^{-1}SU)(U^{-1}TU),$$

it follows that *the transform of a commutator by any element is itself a commutator.*

Since

$$(TU)^{-1}S(TU) = (U^{-1}T^{-1})S(TU) = U^{-1} \cdot T^{-1}ST \cdot U,$$

it follows that the transform of S by TU is equal to the transform by U of the transform of S by T.

6. Subgroups. If a group G contains within itself a set of elements H which forms a group with the same law of combination of elements as G itself, then H is said to be a *subgroup* of G. Every group contains a subgroup of order 1 consisting of the identity alone. It is usually convenient to include the group G itself among the subgroups of G. A subgroup of G which is not identical with G is called a *proper subgroup* of G.

In § **10** we shall prove that the order of a subgroup of a finite group G is a factor of the order of G.

If S is an element of order m in a group G, then the elements $1, S, S^2, \cdots, S^{m-1}$ form a group of order m which is a subgroup of G. It is a proper subgroup when the order of G is greater than m.

The eight permutations in Ex. 6 on page 14 form a subgroup of the symmetric group on a, b, c, d; and this subgroup does not consist of the powers of one of its elements. The permutations in Ex. 5 on page 14 form a subgroup of order 4 of this group of order 8.

Every group G of order greater than unity contains a set of elements each of which is permutable with each of the others; for the set of all the distinct powers of a given element (not the identity) has this property. Let

$$1, S_2, S_3, \cdots, S_k$$

be a set of elements of G having this property that each of them is permutable with each of the others and having moreover the property that no other element of G is permutable with each element of the set. This set evidently contains the inverse of every element in it, and the product of every two elements in it. The set therefore constitutes a subgroup of G.

If G is a group of order g ($g > 1$), then commutators in G (that is, commutators each of which is formed from two elements in G, the same or different) may be formed in g^2 ways, since each of the two elements used to form a commutator may be chosen in g ways. Since G has only g elements, these g^2 commutators cannot all be distinct elements. Consider the set of all distinct elements of G each of which is equal to a commutator in G. This set contains the identity, since the commutator of 1 and S is the identity. The set contains the inverse of every element in it, since the commutator of T and S is the inverse of the commutator of S and T. But it does not always contain the product of every two commutators, since (as is shown by Ex. 30 on page 39) the product of two commutators in G is not necessarily a commutator in G. Then form from these commutators all the elements which may be obtained by taking products each factor of which is a commutator. This new set of elements constitutes a subgroup of G. It is called the *commutator subgroup* of G or the *first derived group* of G. If the commutator subgroup of G coincides with G, then G is called a *perfect* group.

7. Some Classes of Groups. If all the elements in a group G may be obtained by taking the powers of some appropriately chosen element in G, then G is said to be a *cyclic* group. A group which is not cyclic is said to be *noncyclic*. Every group G contains one or more cyclic subgroups, since the distinct powers of any element in G form a cyclic subgroup of G. If a group G is noncyclic the distinct powers of any element in it constitute a proper subgroup. If G is a cyclic group of composite order m and if S is an element whose distinct powers constitute the elements of G, then, if d is any proper divisor of m different from unity, the distinct powers of S^d constitute a proper cyclic subgroup of G. Hence every group whose order is a composite number contains a proper subgroup other than that consisting of the identity alone. We shall see later (§ **10**) that a group whose order is a prime number contains no proper subgroup other than that consisting of the identical element alone.

If each element of a group G is permutable with every other element in G, then G is said to be an *Abelian* group or a *commutative* group; otherwise it is said to be *non-Abelian* or *non-commutative.* Since the powers of any element are permutable with each other, it follows that every cyclic group is an Abelian group. The permutations

$$I, (ab), (cd), (ab)(cd)$$

or the permutations

$$I, (ab)(cd), (ac)(bd), (ad)(bc),$$

constitute a noncyclic Abelian group. The octic group, consisting of the eight permutations in Ex. 6 on page 14, is a non-Abelian group.

A group whose order is a prime number or a power of a prime number is called a *prime-power* group. The three permutation groups mentioned in the preceding paragraph are prime-power groups. We shall see later (§ **13**) that a finite group which is not a prime-power group always contains certain important subgroups which are prime-power groups. For this reason the theory of prime-power groups is of great importance in constructing a general theory of finite groups.

8. Generators of Groups. If a set of elements contained in a finite group G has the property that all the elements of G may be obtained by forming products whose factors all occur in the given set, then this set of elements is said to constitute a set of *generating elements* of G or a set of *generators* of G, and G is said to be *generated* by this set of elements. The set of generators is said to be *independent* if no one of them is in the group generated by the remaining ones. (An element which generates a cyclic group is said to be an independent generator of that group.) In the case of independent generators no proper subset of the set of generators will generate the entire group G.

The group consisting of the permutations

$$I, (abc), (acb), (de), (abc)(de), (acb)(de)$$

is generated by the permutation $(abc)(de)$ and also by the permutation $(acb)(de)$. Moreover, it is also generated by the two permutations (abc) and (de); and these form a set of independent generators of the group.

It is evident that every cyclic group contains at least one single element that generates it, and that every noncyclic group requires at least two generators to generate it. The example in the preceding paragraph shows that even a cyclic group may have a set of independent generators consisting of more than one element. In fact, it is not difficult to show that a cyclic group may be constructed of such sort as to possess n independent generators, where n is any given positive integer; for, if P is a permutation which in standard form is composed of n cyclic factors of distinct prime orders, then the cyclic group generated by P can also be generated by the n independent generators each of which is represented by a single cycle of P.

If $g_1, g_2, \cdots, g_k$ constitute a set of generators of a group G the group itself is often represented by the symbol $\{g_1, g_2, \cdots, g_k\}$; that is, this symbol denotes the group generated by $g_1, g_2, \cdots, g_k$.

From the corollary to Theorem II in § **2** it follows readily that the transpositions $(a_1a_2), (a_1a_3), \cdots, (a_1a_n)$ form a set of independent generators of the symmetric group on $a_1, a_2, \cdots, a_n$. Similarly, from the corollary to Theorem IV in § **2** it follows that $(a_1a_2a_3), (a_1a_2a_4), \cdots, (a_1a_2a_n)$ constitute a set of independent generators of the alternating group on $a_1, a_2, \cdots, a_n$. From a result in § **4** it follows that $(ABCDEFG)$ and $(BD)(EF)$ generate a group of degree 7 and order 168. The octic group is generated by (ab) and $(adbc)$.

9. Simple Isomorphism. Abstract Groups. If G_1 is a group of order m and if G_2 is a group of order m, and if each element of G_1 can be made to correspond uniquely to an element of G_2 in such a way that each element of G_2 is the correspondent of an element of G_1 while the product of any two elements in G_1 corresponds to the product of the corresponding two elements in G_2, then G_1 and G_2 are said to be *simply isomorphic* and the relation so established between G_1 and G_2 is said to be a *simple isomorphism* of G_1 and G_2; each of the groups is said to be *simply isomorphic* with the other. In such a correspondence the identity in G_1 must correspond to the identity in G_2; for if S corresponds to the identity, then every power of S corresponds to the identity, whence it follows that S itself must be the identity, since the correspondence of elements is unique.

If G_1 and G_2 are the same group, this correspondence is said to exhibit an isomorphism of the group with itself.

The two permutation groups I, (ab), (cd), $(ab)(cd)$ and I, $(ab)(cd)$, $(ac)(bd)$, $(ad)(bc)$ are exhibited as simply isomorphic by the correspondences

$$I \sim I,\ (ab) \sim (ab)(cd),\ (cd) \sim (ac)(bd),\ (ab)(cd) \sim (ad)(bc).$$

If two groups have the same number of elements of order 2, the same number of order 3, the same number of order 4, and so on, they are said to be *conformal.*

Two simply isomorphic groups are conformal. For if S in one of them corresponds to T in the other, then S^k corresponds to T^k, whence it follows that S and T have the same order, since the identity always corresponds to itself. But groups may be conformal without being simply isomorphic; an example illustrating this fact is given in Ex. 28 on page 38.

If two groups are each simply isomorphic with a third group, then they are simply isomorphic with each other, and the isomorphism may be established as follows: if A in the first group corresponds to C in the third while B in the second corresponds to C in the third, then take A and B as corresponding elements in the isomorphism of the first two groups.

It is evident that two simply isomorphic groups have certain of their more abstract properties in common. Let us render more precise the conception of the common characteristics of two simply isomorphic groups.

For this purpose consider the *multiplication table* of a given group G, that is, a table exhibiting the product (in each order) of every pair of elements in G. As an example of such a table, we have for the group

$$S_1 = I,\ S_2 = (abc),\ S_3 = (acb),\ S_4 = (ab),\ S_5 = (bc),\ S_6 = (ca)$$

the multiplication table given below, where the element opposite S_i in the first column and under S_j in the first row is the product S_iS_j. If from the elements of a group all properties are abstracted except those implied by its multiplication table, then the new abstract elements so formed constitute a group which is known as an *abstract group*. It is simply isomorphic with the given group, the correspondence being established by making each element of the original group correspond to the abstract element formed from it in constructing the abstract group. We may call this abstract group the abstract form of the given group or the abstract group corresponding to the given group.

	S_1	S_2	S_3	S_4	S_5	S_6
S_1	S_1	S_2	S_3	S_4	S_5	S_6
S_2	S_2	S_3	S_1	S_5	S_6	S_4
S_3	S_3	S_1	S_2	S_6	S_4	S_5
S_4	S_4	S_6	S_5	S_1	S_3	S_2
S_5	S_5	S_4	S_6	S_2	S_1	S_3
S_6	S_6	S_5	S_4	S_3	S_2	S_1

If two groups are simply isomorphic, it is evident that they have the same abstract group corresponding to them. We may say, then, that the two groups are *abstractly identical*. It is evident that the abstract properties of a group constitute, in one respect at least, its essential properties as a group.

It is possible to define the multiplication table of a group completely by means of certain relations governing a set of generators of the group. We shall illustrate this matter by considering the group $\{S, T\}$ where S and T are subject only to the conditions

$$S^2 = 1, \quad T^2 = 1, \quad (ST)^3 = 1,$$

and such conditions as may be implied by these. The group contains the following elements:

$$\sigma_1 = 1, \sigma_2 = ST, \sigma_3 = (ST)^2, \sigma_4 = T, \sigma_5 = S, \sigma_6 = STS.$$

In order to make sure that no two of these elements are equal, we observe that if we put $\sigma = (bc)$ and $\tau = (ab)$ we have $\sigma^2 = 1$, $\tau^2 = 1$, $(\sigma\tau)^3 = 1$, while 1, $\sigma\tau$, $(\sigma\tau)^2$, τ, σ, $\sigma\tau\sigma$ are six distinct permutations on the letters a, b, c. But σ and τ satisfy all the relations assigned to S and T; hence those relations are consistent and the corresponding six elements formed from S and T must be all distinct, since otherwise S and T would satisfy at least one relation not implied by the given relations.

It may now be shown that the given relations on S and T imply that the elements σ_i have a multiplication table identical with the foregoing multiplication table except that S_i is replaced by σ_i for $i = 1, 2, 3, 4, 5, 6$. We verify a few of the 36 products: thus $\sigma_2{}^2 = (ST)^2 = \sigma_3$, $\sigma_2\sigma_3 = (ST)^3 = \sigma_1$, $\sigma_2\sigma_4 = ST \cdot T = S = \sigma_5$, $\sigma_2\sigma_5 = ST \cdot S = \sigma_6$, $\sigma_2\sigma_6 = ST \cdot STS = (ST)^2S = (ST)^{-1}S = TS \cdot S = T = \sigma_4$. Since the product $\sigma_i\sigma_j$ is some σ_k, it is evident that the elements $\sigma_1, \sigma_2, \cdots, \sigma_6$ constitute a group of order 6. From this it follows that the group $\{S, T\}$ is completely determined by the sole relations $S^2 = T^2 = (ST)^3 = 1$. Since we know nothing about the elements of $\{S, T\}$ other than what is implied by its multiplication table, it follows that $\{S, T\}$ is an abstract group. Such a set of conditions as those used in defining $\{S, T\}$, namely, the sole conditions

$$S^2 = T^2 = (ST)^3 = 1,$$

is called a set of *defining relations* for the abstract group determined by them.

It is evident (from the existence of the multiplication table) that every abstract finite group may be defined by means of a certain finite number of independent generators and a finite number of independent defining relations connecting them. The conception of an abstract group, to which this fact gives rise, is of such importance that we shall at once illustrate it by another example. In Chapter VII we shall take up a more systematic consideration of the matter.

Let us now determine a set of defining relations for the abstract group which is simply isomorphic with the alternating group of degree 4. As generators of the permutation group we may take

$$\sigma = (abc), \quad \tau = (abd).$$

Then $$\sigma^3 = \tau^3 = (\sigma\tau)^2 = 1.$$

Since the permutations σ and τ satisfy these relations and generate a group of order 12, it follows that any abstract generators S and T which are subject solely to the conditions implied by the (necessarily consistent) relations

$$S^3 = T^3 = (ST)^2 = 1$$

must generate a group whose order is at least as great as 12. We shall next show that the order of this abstract group $\{S, T\}$ cannot be greater than 12. For this purpose we consider the following twelve elements of $\{S, T\}$, namely,

$$\begin{array}{lll} 1 & S & S^2 \\ ST & STS & STS^2 \\ S^2T^2 & S^2T^2S & S^2T^2S^2 \\ T^2ST^2 & T^2ST^2S & T^2ST^2S^2 \end{array}$$

The corresponding elements in $\{\sigma, \tau\}$ are distinct, the correspondence being established by making σ and τ correspond to S and T respectively. Hence these are twelve distinct elements of $\{S, T\}$. If each of these is multiplied on the right by S, then, since $S^3 = 1$, we obtain merely the same elements in another order. If each of them is multiplied on the right by T, then, by a repeated use of the relations $S^3 = T^3 = (ST)^2 = 1$, it may be shown that the same set of elements is again obtained (in a new order). Thus we have

$$1 \cdot T = TS \cdot S^2 = S^{-1}T^{-1}S^2 = S^2T^2S^2,$$
$$ST \cdot T = S \cdot S^2T^2S^2 \cdot S^2T^2S^2 = T^2ST^2S^2,$$
$$S^2T^2 \cdot T = S^2,$$
$$T^2ST^2 \cdot T = T^{-1}S^{-1}S^2 = STS^2,$$
$$S \cdot T = ST,$$
$$STS \cdot T = (ST)^2 = 1,$$
$$S^2T^2S \cdot T = S \cdot ST \cdot TS \cdot T = S \cdot T^{-1}S^{-1} \cdot S^{-1}T^{-1} \cdot T = ST \cdot TS$$
$$= T^{-1}S^{-1} \cdot S^{-1}T^{-1} = T^2ST^2,$$
$$T^2ST^2S \cdot T = T \cdot TS \cdot T^2 \cdot ST = T \cdot S^{-1}T^{-1} \cdot T^2 \cdot T^{-1}S^{-1} = TS$$
$$= S^{-1}T^{-1} = S^2T^2,$$

$S^2 \cdot T = S^2T^2 \cdot T^2 = T^2ST^2ST \cdot T^2 = T^2ST^2S,$
$STS^2 \cdot T = ST \cdot S^2T = ST \cdot T^2ST^2S = S^2T^2S,$
$S^2T^2S^2 \cdot T = S^2 \cdot T^{-1}S^{-1} \cdot T = S^2 \cdot ST \cdot T = T^2 = (ST)^2T^2$
$\quad = STSTT^2 = STS,$
$T^2ST^2S^2 \cdot T = T^2S \cdot T^{-1}S^{-1} \cdot T = T^2S \cdot ST \cdot T = T^2 \cdot S^{-1}T^{-1}$
$\quad = T^2TS = S.$

From these results it follows that the twelve elements in the foregoing table are replaced by themselves (in some order) on multiplication on the right by either S or T, and hence on such multiplication by any element of $\{S, T\}$. Hence $\{S, T\}$ is a group of order 12. The correspondence $S \sim \sigma$, $T \sim \tau$ exhibits it as simply isomorphic with the alternating group $\{\sigma, \tau\}$, as the reader may easily verify. Hence $\{S, T\}$ is the abstract form of the alternating group on four letters. Therefore

> The abstract alternating group of degree four is generated by the abstract elements S and T when they are subject to the sole defining relations
> $$S^3 = T^3 = (ST)^2 = 1.$$

EXERCISES

1. Show that the group generated by the permutations (12345), (*abcd*), $(\alpha\beta\gamma)$ is a cyclic group of order 60, and find an element in it by which it may be generated.

2. Show that there exists a cyclic group of every finite order m.

3. Prove that every subgroup of a cyclic group is cyclic.

4. Show that the two permutations (1234)(5678) and (1638)(5274) are commutative and that they generate a group of order 8.

5. Construct the multiplication table for the octic group.

6. Find the commutator subgroup (1) of the octic group, (2) of the alternating group of degree 4.

7. Show that the commutator subgroup of an Abelian group consists of the identity alone, and that the commutator subgroup of every non-Abelian group is of order greater than unity.

8. Show that an Abelian group cannot be simply isomorphic with a non-Abelian group.

9. If each generator in a set of generating elements of a group is permutable with every other generator in the set, then the group is Abelian.

10. A group each of whose elements other than the identity is of order 2 is an Abelian group.

11. Prove that the product of two commutators is a commutator whenever the last factor of the first is the inverse of the first factor of the second; that is, prove that $(S^{-1}T^{-1}ST)(T^{-1}U^{-1}TU)$ is a commutator.

12. If H is a subgroup of G show that the commutator subgroup of H is a subgroup of the commutator subgroup of G.

13. If a and b are elements of a group G, there exist elements g and h in G such that $ag = b$ and $ha = b$.

14. If S and T are two elements subject to the sole conditions that

$$S^3 = T^2 = (ST)^2 = 1,$$

show that they generate a group $\{S, T\}$ abstractly identical with the group whose multiplication table is given in § **9**.

15. If a, b, c are elements of orders 4, 2, 2 respectively, and are subject to the sole remaining conditions that $ab = ba^3$, $ac = ca$, $bc = cb$, then the group $\{a, b, c\}$ is of order 16, and a, b, c form a set of independent generators of this group.

16. Construct a set of defining relations for the abstract octic group.

17. Construct a set of defining relations for the abstract group which is simply isomorphic with the group generated by (ab), (cd), (ef).

18. Construct a set of defining relations for the abstract group which is simply isomorphic with the group generated by (1234)(5678) and (1638)(5274).

19. If S and T are subject to the sole defining relations

$$S^4 = T^4 = 1,\ S^{-1}TS = T^{-1},\ S^2 = T^2,$$

show that $\{S, T\}$ is a group of order 8.

20. Construct five groups of order 8 no two of which are simply isomorphic. (Compare Exs. 2, 16, 17, 18, 19.) Show that a group of order 8 is necessarily simply isomorphic with one of these five.

21. Construct a permutation group of order and degree 8 which has six elements of order 4. Show that no group of order 8 can have more than six elements of order 4.

22. If a and b are elements which generate a finite group G and if $ab = ba^k$, show that every element in the subgroup generated by a is transformed by b into an element in that subgroup.

23. Show that the commutator subgroup of the symmetric group of degree n is the alternating group of degree n. (Use the corollaries to Theorems II and IV in § 2.)

24. Show that the alternating group of degree n is a perfect group if $n > 4$. (Use the corollary to Theorem IV in § 2.)

25. If a cyclic group G is of order p^m, where p is a prime number, and if $0 < r \leqq m$, then G contains just p^r elements such that the order of each is a factor of p^r; it contains just $p^{r-1}(p-1)$ elements of order p^r.

26. Show that the permutations

$(c_1c_{10}c_{19})(c_2c_{11}c_{20})(c_3c_{12}c_{21})(c_4c_{13}c_{22})(c_5c_{14}c_{23})(c_6c_{15}c_{24})(c_7c_{16}c_{25})(c_8c_{17}c_{26})(c_9c_{18}c_{27})$,

$(c_1c_4c_7)(c_2c_5c_8)(c_3c_6c_9)(c_{10}c_{15}c_{17})(c_{11}c_{13}c_{18})(c_{12}c_{14}c_{16})(c_{19}c_{23}c_{27})(c_{20}c_{24}c_{25})(c_{21}c_{22}c_{26})$

generate a non-Abelian group of order 27 containing as a subgroup an Abelian group of order 9 generated by the first of the given permutations and the following:

$(c_1c_2c_3)(c_4c_5c_6)(c_7c_8c_9)(c_{10}c_{11}c_{12})(c_{13}c_{14}c_{15})(c_{16}c_{17}c_{18})(c_{19}c_{20}c_{21})(c_{22}c_{23}c_{24})(c_{25}c_{26}c_{27})$.

27. Show that the commutator of the first two permutations in Ex. 26 is of order 3 and is permutable with each of them.

28. Show that the group of order 27 defined in Ex. 26 is conformal (but not simply isomorphic) with the Abelian group generated by (123), (456), and (789).

29. Let Q and R be two abstract elements and write $Q^{-1}R^{-1}QR = P$. If Q and R are subject to the sole defining relations

$$P^3 = Q^3 = R^3 = P^{-1}R^{-1}PR = P^{-1}Q^{-1}PQ = 1,$$

show that they generate a group of order 27 simply isomorphic with the group of order 27 defined in Ex. 26.

30. Show that the group generated by the elements

$$(ac)(bd),\ (eg)(fh),\ (ik)(jl),\ (mo)(np),\ (ac)(eg)(ik),\ (ab)(cd)(mo),\ (ef)(gh)(mn)(op),\ (ij)(kl)$$

is of order 256, that its commutator subgroup is of order 16 and is generated by the first four of the given permutations, and that the commutator subgroup contains just one element which is not a commutator, namely, $(ik)(jl)(mo)(np)$.

MISCELLANEOUS EXERCISES

1. Show that a regular permutation is always a power of a circular permutation.

2. Show that the commutator of two permutations having just two letters in common is of order 1 or 2 or 3 or 5.

3. Let S be a permutation having at least one cycle of even order or at least two cycles of equal odd order. Show that S is commutative with some odd permutation on the letters involved in S.

4. Determine what permutations can be expressed in terms of the two permutations

$$(a_1a_2 \cdots a_{n-2}a_{n-1}), \quad (a_1a_2 \cdots a_{n-2}a_n).$$

5. Consider the following permutations on $mn + 1$ letters, where m is an integer greater than unity:

$$(a_1a_2 \cdots a_{n+1}),\ (a_1a_{n+2} \cdots a_{2n+1}),\ \cdots,\ (a_1a_{(m-1)n+2} \cdots a_{mn+1}).$$

Show that every permutation on this set of $mn + 1$ letters can be expressed in terms of the given permutations when n is odd, and that every even permutation on these letters can be expressed in terms of the given permutations when n is even.

6. For what values of k from the set $1, 2, \cdots, n - 1$ is it possible to express every permutation on the letters $a_1, a_2, \cdots, a_n$ in terms of the permutations (a_1a_{k+1}) and $(a_1a_2 \cdots a_n)$?

7. If S and T are commutative regular permutations on the same mn letters, m and n being relatively prime integers greater than unity, and if S is of order m and T is of order n, show that ST is a circular permutation on the mn letters. [SUGGESTION. Show that the n cycles of S are permuted cyclically among themselves when S is transformed by T.]

8. Consider the 13 sets of four letters each afforded by the columns in the array

$$\begin{matrix} A & B & C & D & E & F & G & H & I & J & K & L & M \\ B & C & D & E & F & G & H & I & J & K & L & M & A \\ D & E & F & G & H & I & J & K & L & M & A & B & C \\ J & K & L & M & A & B & C & D & E & F & G & H & I \end{matrix}$$

Show that these sets are permuted among themselves as sets by the permutations $(ABC \cdots M)$ and $(ABCDKLHGMJEFI)$, that the products formed from these permutations lead to a group of order $13 \cdot 12 \cdot 9 \cdot 4$, and that this group contains all the permutations on the given letters each of which merely permutes among themselves the given thirteen sets of four letters each.

9. By omitting the letters A, B, D, J from the array in Ex. 8 form a new array defining 12 sets of three letters each and show that the sets thus defined are permuted among themselves by a group of order $9 \cdot 8 \cdot 6$ on the nine letters involved and by no larger group on these letters.

10. Form a function left invariant by the group in Ex. 8 and by no permutations of its arguments except those in this group.

11. Let p be an odd prime number. Show that the totality of distinct congruences

$$x' \equiv ax + b \bmod p, \qquad (a \not\equiv 0 \bmod p)$$

with multiplication of transformations modulo p as the rule of combination, constitutes a group of order $p(p-1)$. (Compare the special case in Ex. 11 on page 24.)

Similarly show that the totality of distinct congruences

$$x' \equiv a^2x + b \bmod p, \qquad (a \not\equiv 0 \bmod p)$$

constitutes a group of order $\frac{1}{2}\, p(p-1)$.

12. If a and b are elements which generate a finite group G and if $ab = ba^k$, show that every element of G may be written in the form $b^y a^x$.

13. The permutations

$$\sigma = (a_1 a_2 \cdots a_{25}), \quad \tau = (a_{26} a_{27} a_{28} a_{29} a_{30})$$

generate an Abelian group H of order 125. The permutations

$$S = (c_1 c_2 c_3 \cdots c_{25}),$$
$$T = (c_2 c_7 c_{12} c_{17} c_{22})(c_3 c_{13} c_{23} c_8 c_{18})(c_4 c_{19} c_9 c_{24} c_{14})(c_5 c_{25} c_{20} c_{15} c_{10}),$$

generate a non-Abelian group G of order 125. Prove these statements and show that G and H are conformal but are not simply isomorphic. [SUGGESTION. Observe that $ST = TS^6$, apply Ex. 12, and show that $T^x S^y$ and $\tau^x \sigma^y$ are of the same order.]

14. If the commutator $c = a^{-1}b^{-1}ab$ of a and b is permutable with both a and b, show that

$$a^{-\alpha}b^{-\beta}a^{\alpha}b^{\beta} = c^{\alpha\beta}, \quad (b^y a^x)^t = b^{yt}a^{xt}c^{\frac{1}{2}xyt(t-1)},$$
$$(a^x b^y)^t = b^{yt}a^{xt}c^{\frac{1}{2}xyt(t+1)}.$$

15. If $aga^{-1} = g^{\alpha}$ and $bgb^{-1} = g^{\beta}$, then the commutator of a and b is permutable with g.

16. If $TS = S^2T^2$, show that

$$TS^2 = S^{2n}(TS^2)T^{2n}, \quad (TS)^2 = (S^4T)^n(TS)^2(ST^4)^n.$$

17. If S and T are elements of orders m and n respectively and if $TS = S^2T^2$, show that S^2 and T^2 are of the same order and hence that $m = \frac{1}{2}n$, n, or $2n$. Show also that S^4T and ST^4 are of the same order.

18. Let S be an element of order mn contained in a finite group G, m and n being relatively prime. Show that integers α and β exist such that $S = S^{\alpha} \cdot S^{\beta}$ while S^{α} is of order m and S^{β} is of order n. Show furthermore that if $S = P \cdot Q$, where P and Q are permutable elements in G of orders m and n respectively, then $P = S^{\alpha}$ and $Q = S^{\beta}$.

19. If $S^{-1}TS = T^{-1}$ and $T^{-1}ST = S^{-1}$, show that $S^4 = T^4 = 1$.

20. If p is any prime number and k is any primitive root modulo p, show that cyclic permutations S and T exist of orders p and $p-1$ respectively such that $ST = TS^k$.

21. Show by aid of Ex. 20 that a permutation group exists (1) of degree p and order $p(p-1)$, (2) of degree p and order $\frac{1}{2}p(p-1)$, for every odd prime number p.

22. Show that the abstract group whose generators σ and τ are subject to the sole defining relations

$$\sigma^{25} = \tau^5 = \sigma^{-1}\tau^{-1}\sigma\tau = 1$$

is simply isomorphic with the permutation group $\{\sigma, \tau\}$ of Ex. 13.

23. Show that the abstract group whose generators S and T are subject to the sole defining relations

$$S^{25} = T^5 = T^{-1}STS^{-6} = 1$$

is simply isomorphic with the permutation group $\{S, T\}$ of Ex. 13.

24. If p is any prime number and k is any primitive root modulo p, show that the abstract group whose generators S and T are subject to the sole defining relations

$$S^p = T^{p-1} = T^{-1}STS^{-k} = 1$$

is simply isomorphic with the permutation group of order $p(p-1)$ in Exs. 20 and 21.

25. If the elements a and b are of finite order and each of them is permutable with their commutator $c = a^{-1}b^{-1}ab$, then show (by aid of Ex. 14) that each of the elements in the group $\{a, b\}$ is representable in the form $a^x b^y c^z$. Show that the order of c is a common factor of the orders of a and b, and thence that $\{a, b\}$ is a finite group.

26. If a and b are two noncommutative elements of odd prime order p and if each of them is permutable with their commutator, show that $\{a, b\}$ is a group of order p^3. (Use Ex. 25.)

27. Show that the abstract group whose generators S and T are subject to the sole defining relations

$$S^3 = T^3 = 1, \quad TS = S^2T^2$$

is of order 12 and that its distinct elements are

$$1,\ S,\ T,\ S^2,\ ST,\ TS,\ T^2,\ S^2T,\ ST^2,\ TS^2,\ T^2S,\ ST^2S.$$

28. Show that the group $\{S, T\}$ of Ex. 27 is simply isomorphic with the alternating group of degree 4.

29. Show that the abstract groups $\{S, T\}$ and $\{P, Q\}$ whose sole defining relations are

$$S^4 = T^4 = 1,\ TS = S^2T^2 \quad \text{and} \quad P^5 = Q^4 = 1,\ PQ = QP^2,$$

respectively, are identical as abstract groups and that their order is 20.

30. By means of the adjoining scheme form 16 sets of 6 letters each by taking for each letter in the scheme the 6 which are aligned with it (excluding that letter itself). Thus we have the 16 sets afforded by the columns in the following array:

$$\begin{array}{cccc} A & B & C & D \\ E & F & G & H \\ I & J & K & L \\ M & N & O & P \end{array}$$

$$\begin{array}{cccccccccccccccc}
B & A & A & A & F & E & E & E & J & I & I & I & N & M & M & M \\
C & C & B & B & G & G & F & F & K & K & J & J & O & O & N & N \\
D & D & D & C & H & H & H & G & L & L & L & K & P & P & P & O \\
E & F & G & H & A & B & C & D & A & B & C & D & A & B & C & D \\
I & J & K & L & I & J & K & L & E & F & G & H & E & F & G & H \\
M & N & O & P & M & N & O & P & M & N & O & P & I & J & K & L
\end{array}$$

Determine the largest permutation group on the 16 given letters each element of which merely permutes among themselves these 16 sets of 6 letters each, and show that its order is $16 \cdot 15 \cdot 12 \cdot 4$. Show that the largest subgroup which leaves the first column fixed permutes its letters according to the symmetric group of degree 6 and that it permutes the remaining 10 letters according to a simply isomorphic group of degree 10 and order $10 \cdot 9 \cdot 8$.

31. By omitting P from each sextuple in Ex. 30 in which P appears, form the 6 quintuples in the columns of the following array:

$$\begin{array}{cccccc} A & E & I & N & M & M \\ B & F & J & O & O & N \\ C & G & K & A & B & C \\ H & D & D & E & F & G \\ L & L & H & I & J & K \end{array}$$

Determine the largest permutation group on these 15 given letters each element of which merely permutes among themselves these 6 quintuples, and determine the permutation group according to which the quintuples are thus interchanged. What is the relation between the two named permutation groups?

CHAPTER II

Five Fundamental Theorems

10. Orders of Subgroups. The following may be regarded as the most fundamental theorem in the theory of finite groups:

I. FIRST FUNDAMENTAL THEOREM.* The order of a subgroup of a finite group G is a factor of the order of G.

Let G be of order n and let H be a proper subgroup of G of order r. We have to show that r is a factor of n. Let $s_1 = 1$, $s_2, s_3, \cdots, s_r$ be the elements of H. Form the following array containing all the elements of G:

$$\begin{array}{lllll} s_1, & s_2, & s_3, & \cdots, & s_r, \\ t_2s_1, & t_2s_2, & t_2s_3, & \cdots, & t_2s_r, \\ t_3s_1, & t_3s_2, & t_3s_3, & \cdots, & t_3s_r, \\ \cdot & \cdot & \cdot & \cdot & \cdot \\ t_\lambda s_1, & t_\lambda s_2, & t_\lambda s_3, & \cdots, & t_\lambda s_r, \end{array}$$

where t_2 is any element not in the first row and in general t_i is any element not in the first $i-1$ rows. It is evident that the elements of G may be exhausted in a scheme of this sort; it is next to be shown that no element of G occurs twice in this array. Let t_1 be another symbol for the identity. Now t_is_k and t_is_l are elements in the ith row. If $t_is_k = t_is_l$, then $s_k = s_l$ and hence $k = l$. Hence each row of the array consists of r distinct elements. If $j > i$ and if $t_js_m = t_is_l$, we have $t_j = t_is_ls_m{}^{-1} = t_is_\mu$, where s_μ is an element of H. Hence t_j is in the ith row, contrary to hypothesis. Therefore no element in one row is equal to any

* This has sometimes been called the *theorem of Lagrange.*

element in another row. Therefore the elements in the array are all distinct. Hence the array contains all the elements of G and no element of G occurs twice in the array. Now the number of elements in the array is λr, since there are λ rows of elements with r elements in each row. Hence $\lambda r = n$, whence it follows that r is a divisor of n.

The quotient n/r is called the *index* of H in G.

The learner will find it an excellent exercise to construct a similar proof by means of an array of the form

$$\begin{array}{lllll}
s_1, & s_2, & s_3, & \cdots, & s_r, \\
s_1\tau_2, & s_2\tau_2, & s_3\tau_2, & \cdots, & s_r\tau_2, \\
s_1\tau_3, & s_2\tau_3, & s_3\tau_3, & \cdots, & s_r\tau_3, \\
\cdot & \cdot & \cdot & \cdot & \cdot \\
s_1\tau_\mu, & s_2\tau_\mu, & s_3\tau_\mu, & \cdots, & s_r\tau_\mu,
\end{array}$$

where τ_2 is any element not in the first row and in general τ_i is any element not in the first $i-1$ rows. It is convenient to use τ_1 as an additional symbol for the identity; and this we do.

These two arrangements of the elements of G in rectangular arrays are often useful in developing the theory of finite groups. It is convenient to denote the elements in the ith row of the first array by t_iH and those in the ith row of the second array by $H\tau_i$.

An element of G of order m generates a subgroup of G of order m. Hence,

COR. I. The order of an element of G is a factor of the order of G.

If G is a group of prime order p, then every element of G except the identity is of order p. Hence,

COR. II. A group whose order is a prime is a cyclic group. It contains no proper subgroup except that consisting of the identity alone.

11. Miscellaneous Theorems. Conjugate Elements and Subgroups. We shall now give some definitions and theorems which are important in themselves and are essential in the proofs of the remaining four fundamental theorems.

II. The elements * common to two finite groups G_1 and G_2 form a finite group H known as the common subgroup of G_1 and G_2.

Any two groups have the identity in common. If S and T are elements common to G_1 and G_2, then ST is in each group and the inverse of each of them is in each group. Therefore these common elements form a group, and this group is necessarily of finite order.

The elements of G_1 and G_2 generate a group which may be either finite or infinite. It is denoted by the symbol $\{G_1, G_2\}$. If G_1 and G_2 are permutation groups, then it is obvious that $\{G_1, G_2\}$ is a finite group.

More generally the elements $S_1, S_2, \cdots, S_n$ (of finite order) and the elements of the finite groups $G_1, G_2, \cdots, G_m$ generate a group (finite or infinite) which is denoted by the symbol

$$\{S_1, S_2, \cdots, S_n, G_1, G_2, \cdots, G_m\}.$$

In case all the elements involved are permutations this group is necessarily a finite group.

If S and T are elements of a group G, then S and $T^{-1}ST$ are said to be *conjugate elements* of G and $T^{-1}ST$ is said to be a *conjugate* of S or to be *conjugate* to S. Every element S is conjugate to itself, since $S^{-1}SS = S$. If every conjugate of S in G is equal to S, then S is said to be a *self-conjugate*, or *normal*, or *invariant*, element of G.

III. Two elements which are conjugate in a given finite group G have the same order.

For if S is of order m and T is any other element of G, then

$$(T^{-1}ST)^m = T^{-1}ST \cdot T^{-1}ST \cdot \quad \cdots \quad \cdot T^{-1}ST = T^{-1}S^mT = 1;$$

* In such matters as this, where the relations of two or more groups or the relations of an element to a group are considered, it is to be understood that all the elements involved are subject to the same law of combination.

and if $T^{-1}ST$ is of order m we have

$$S^m = T \cdot T^{-1}S^mT \cdot T^{-1} = T(T^{-1}ST)^mT^{-1} = 1.$$

Let H be a group and let S be an element which combines with the elements of H. Then we denote by $S^{-1}HS$ the set of elements obtained on transforming the separate elements of H by S. If h_1 and h_2 are two elements of H, we have

$$S^{-1}h_1S \cdot S^{-1}h_2S = S^{-1} \cdot h_1h_2 \cdot S.$$

Hence,

IV. If H is a finite group and S is an element which combines with the elements of H, then H and $S^{-1}HS$ are simply isomorphic groups.

The isomorphism is established by making each element in H correspond to that element in $S^{-1}HS$ into which it is transformed by S. If S belongs to H, then this process exhibits H as simply isomorphic with itself.

If the groups H and $S^{-1}HS$ are identical, then S is said to be permutable with H. In this case the two sets of elements HS and SH are identical, as may be readily proved; for, if $S^{-1}h_iS = h_j$, then $h_iS = Sh_j$.

If H is a subgroup of G and S is an element of G, then H and $S^{-1}HS$ are called *conjugate* subgroups of G and $S^{-1}HS$ is said to be a *conjugate* of H or to be *conjugate* to H. Furthermore, H is said to be *transformed* by S into $S^{-1}HS$. Every subgroup H of G is conjugate to itself, since it is transformed into itself by each of its own elements. If H and $S^{-1}HS$ are identical for every element S of G, then H is called a *self-conjugate*, or *normal*, or *invariant*, subgroup of G.

It is evident that the total set of self-conjugate elements in a finite group G forms a self-conjugate subgroup of G. This subgroup is called the *central* of G.

If S_1 is a given element of G and if all the conjugates of S_1 in G are $S_1, S_2, \cdots, S_l$, then $S_1, S_2, \cdots, S_l$ are said to form a *complete conjugate set* of elements of G.

If H_1 is a given subgroup of G and if all the conjugates of H_1 in G are the subgroups $H_1, H_2, \cdots, H_k$, then $H_1, H_2, \cdots, H_k$ are said to form a *complete conjugate set* of subgroups of G.

If a group G has no self-conjugate proper subgroup other than that consisting of the identity alone, then G is said to be a *simple* group; otherwise it is said to be a *composite* group.

Let $S_1, S_2, \cdots, S_l$ be the complete set of conjugates of the element S_1 of the group G. Then any S_i of the set obviously has the same complete set of conjugates, since the relations $S_i = T_i^{-1}S_1T_i$ and $S_j = T_j^{-1}S_1T_j$ imply the relation $S_j = (T_i^{-1}T_j)^{-1}S_i(T_i^{-1}T_j)$. Hence *no two complete sets of conjugate elements have an element in common.* Therefore the elements of G may be distributed into a certain number of complete sets of conjugate elements in such a way as to exhaust the elements of G without repetition. Let r be the number of these complete sets of conjugates and let $h_1 = 1, h_2, h_3, \cdots, h_r$ be the numbers of elements in the different sets, h_1 being the number of elements conjugate to the identity. Then if n is the order of G, we have

$$n = 1 + h_2 + h_3 + \cdots + h_r.$$

Let $H_1, H_2, \cdots, H_k$ be the complete set of conjugates of the subgroup H_1 of the group G. Then it is easy to show (compare the previous paragraph) that any H_i of the set has the same complete set of conjugates. Hence *no two complete sets of conjugate subgroups contain one and the same subgroup.* Again, if S_1 is an element occurring in a subgroup H of G, it is obvious that all of its conjugates occur in the complete set of conjugates of H.

V. The elements common to the subgroups of a complete set of conjugate subgroups of a finite group G form a self-conjugate subgroup H of G.

That these elements form a group H follows readily from Theorem II. The named complete set of conjugate subgroups of G is transformed into itself by any element whatever in G. In this process an element of the group H is necessarily transformed into an element of H. Hence the theorem.

This group H often consists of the identical element alone.

VI. The elements of a finite group G which are permutable with a given element S of G form a subgroup H of G. The number of elements conjugate to S in G is equal to the index of H in G.

This group H is called the *normalizer* of S in G.

If T_1 and T_2 are permutable with S, then $T_1T_2S = T_1ST_2 = ST_1T_2$, whence it follows that T_1T_2 is permutable with S. Thence it is easily shown that the elements of G which are permutable with S form a subgroup H of G.

Let r be the order of H and let $U_1 = 1, U_2, U_3, \cdots, U_r$ be the elements of H, and let V be any element of G. Then we have

$$(U_iV)^{-1}S(U_iV) = V^{-1}U_i^{-1}SU_iV = V^{-1}SV,$$

whence it follows that each of the elements U_iV $(i = 1, 2, \cdots, r)$ transforms S into the same element $V^{-1}SV$. Again if W is an element of G which transforms S into the element $V^{-1}SV$, we have $W^{-1}SW = V^{-1}SV$, whence $VW^{-1}SWV^{-1} = VV^{-1}SVV^{-1} = S$; whence it follows that WV^{-1} belongs to H so that WV^{-1} is equal to some U_j. Then $W = U_jV$, so that W belongs to the set U_iV $(i = 1, 2, \cdots, r)$. Therefore this set contains all the elements of G which transform S into $V^{-1}SV$. Hence *the number of elements of G each of which transforms S into a given one of its conjugates is r.* If n is the order of G, it follows then that the number of elements conjugate to S in G (including S itself) is n/r, and this number is the index of H in G.

VII. The elements of a finite group G which are permutable with a given subgroup H of G form a subgroup K of G which is either the same as H or contains H as a self-conjugate subgroup. The number of subgroups conjugate to H in G is equal to the index of K in G.

This group K is called the *normalizer* of H in G.

If T_1 and T_2 are elements of G which are permutable with H so that $T_i^{-1}HT_i = H$ $(i = 1, 2)$, then $(T_1T_2)^{-1}H(T_1T_2) = T_2^{-1}T_1^{-1}HT_1T_2 = T_2^{-1}HT_2 = H$; therefore T_1T_2 is permutable with H. Thence it follows readily that the elements of

G which are permutable with H form a subgroup K of G. This group obviously contains H, since H is permutable with each of its own elements. If S is any element of K, we have $S^{-1}HS = H$, so that H, when not identical with K, is contained in K as a self-conjugate subgroup.

If U is an element of G not contained in K, then the elements KU, and no other elements of G, transform H into $U^{-1}HU$, as may be shown by the method employed in the proof of the corresponding part of the preceding theorem. From this it follows readily that the number of subgroups conjugate to H in G is equal to the index of K in G.

VIII. Let $S_1, S_2, \cdots, S_k$ be a complete set of conjugate elements of a finite group G, and let H denote the group $\{S_1, S_2, \cdots, S_k\}$. Then H is a self-conjugate (proper or improper) subgroup of G; and no self-conjugate subgroup of G of lower order contains the element S_1.

The named generators of H are transformed, by any given element of G, into the same set of elements, either in the same order or in some other order. Hence this given element of G transforms H into itself. Therefore H is contained in G self-conjugately.

If K is any self-conjugate subgroup of G containing the element S_1, then K must contain every element into which S_1 may be transformed by elements of G. Hence K must contain all the elements $S_1, S_2, \cdots, S_k$, and hence it must contain H itself.

An exactly similar argument may be used to prove the following theorem:

IX. If $H_1, H_2, \cdots, H_k$ is a complete set of conjugate subgroups of a finite group G and H is the group $\{H_1, H_2, \cdots, H_k\}$, then H is a self-conjugate (proper or improper) subgroup of G; and it is the smallest self-conjugate subgroup of G that contains H_1.

X. Let S be an element of order n which is permutable with a finite group G of order g and let S^m be the lowest positive power of S in G. Then m is a factor of n and the order of $\{S, G\}$ is gm.

Since S is permutable with G, it follows that every product ST_i, where T_i is an element of G, can be put in the form T_jS where T_j is an element of G. Hence all the elements of $\{S, G\}$ can be obtained by multiplying the elements of G on the right by $1, S, S^2, \cdots, S^{m-1}$, so that the elements of $\{S, G\}$ are all contained in the sets

$$G, GS, GS^2, \cdots, GS^{m-1}.$$

No element of $\{S, G\}$ occurs twice in these sets; for if $T_iS^k = T_jS^l$ where T_i and T_j are in G and k and l are non-negative integers less than m, k being greater than l, we have $S^{k-l} = T_i^{-1}T_j$, so that S^{k-l} is in G, contrary to hypothesis. Hence $\{S, G\}$ is of order gm.

If m is not a factor of n, let μ be the greatest common divisor of m and n. Then integers x and y exist such that $xm + yn = \mu$. But S^m and S^n are in G. Hence $(S^m)^x(S^n)^y$, or S^{xm+yn}, or S^μ, is in G, a result which contradicts the hypothesis that μ is less than m. Hence m is a divisor of n.

XI. If G and H are two finite groups such that every element of G transforms H into itself and every element of H transforms G into itself, and if G and H have no common element except the identity, then every element of G is permutable with every element of H.

Let S be any element of G and let T be any element of H. Then $T^{-1}ST$ is an element of G, since T transforms G into itself; likewise $S^{-1}T^{-1}S$ belongs to H. Therefore $S^{-1}T^{-1}ST$ belongs to both G and H, since it is the product of S^{-1} and $T^{-1}ST$, both belonging to G, and is also the product of $S^{-1}T^{-1}S$ and T, both belonging to H. But G and H have only the identity in common.

Therefore $S^{-1}T^{-1}ST = 1$, or $ST = TS$. Hence every element of G is permutable with every element of H.

If G and H are two groups having no common element except the identity and if every element of G is permutable with every element of H, then $\{G, H\}$ is called the *direct product* of G and H. Similarly, we may speak of the direct product of several groups, the direct product of n groups being the direct product of one of them and the direct product of the other $n - 1$.

The reader will easily prove that *the order of the direct product of two finite groups G and H* (when this direct product exists) *is equal to the product of the orders of G and H.*

EXERCISES

1. If G is a cyclic group of order n and if d is any factor of n, show that G has one and just one subgroup of order d.

2. In the group $\{a, b\}$ the elements ab and ba are conjugates.

3. Every element of an Abelian group is self-conjugate.

4. Every subgroup of an Abelian group is self-conjugate.

5. If $S_1, S_2, \cdots, S_n$ generate a finite group G, show that the elements $S_1S_2 \cdots S_n$ and $S_rS_{r+1} \cdots S_nS_1S_2 \cdots S_{r-1}$ are conjugate in G.

6. If the order of an Abelian group G is a multiple of a prime number p, then G contains an element of order p. (This theorem will later be extended to non-Abelian groups. See Cor. III in §**15**.)

7. An Abelian group whose order is a product of k different prime factors is a cyclic group.

8. The elements of a finite group G which are permutable with each subgroup of a complete set of conjugate subgroups of G form a self-conjugate subgroup of G.

9. If H is a subgroup of G and S is an element combining with the elements of G, then $S^{-1}HS$ is a subgroup of $S^{-1}GS$.

10. Let H be a self-conjugate subgroup of a finite group G. If H contains a subgroup K of G, then it contains every conjugate of K in G.

11. If a finite group G contains a subgroup of index 2, that subgroup is self-conjugate in G.

12. The elements which are common to two or more self-conjugate subgroups of a finite group G form a self-conjugate subgroup of G.

13. If S and T are conjugate elements of a finite group G, then $T = SC$, where C is a commutator of two elements of G.

14. The commutator subgroup of a finite group G is self-conjugate in G.

15. If a finite group contains only one subgroup of a given order, that subgroup is self-conjugate.

16. If two self-conjugate subgroups of a finite group G have only the identity in common, then every element of one of these subgroups is permutable with every element of the other.

17. If G and H are two finite groups such that every element of G transforms H into itself and every element of H transforms G into itself, then a commutator formed with an element of G and an element of H is in the common subgroup of G and H.

18. If G_1 and G_2 are two groups of order p^m, where p is a prime number, and if neither of them contains an element of order p^2, then the two groups are conformal.

19. Construct a group of order 12 which has no subgroup of order 6.

20. Denote in order by a, b, c, d, e, f, g the seven triples of three letters each defined by the array in §4. Show that the permutations $(ABCDEFG)$ and $(BD)(EF)$ permute these triples according to the permutations $(abcdefg)$ and $(bc)(df)$, and prove that the two groups $\{(ABCDEFG), (BD)(EF)\}$ and $\{(abcdefg), (bc)(df)\}$ are identical as permutation groups.

21. Solve the similar problem for the array in Ex. 13 on page 24.

22. Show that the group $\{(ABCDEFG), (BD)(EF)\}$ has a subgroup of order 24 each element of which leaves A fixed, and find the complete set of conjugates of this subgroup.

23. Show that the group $\{(ABCDEFG), (BD)(EF)\}$ has a subgroup of order 4 each element of which leaves both A and B fixed, and find the complete set of conjugates of this subgroup.

24. For the group defined in Ex. 13 on page 24 solve the problems similar to those in Exs. 22 and 23.

12. Representation of an Abstract Finite Group as a Regular Permutation Group. Let G be a permutation group of degree n on the letters $a_1, a_2, \cdots, a_n$. If G contains permutations $S_1, S_2, \cdots, S_n$ replacing a_1 by $a_1, a_2, \cdots, a_n$ respectively, then G contains the permutation $S_i^{-1}S_j$ which replaces a_i by a_j. A permutation group which has this property of containing a permutation which replaces any given one of its letters by any other given one is called a *transitive* group. A permutation group which does not have this property is said to be *intransitive*.

The group $\{(a_1a_2 \cdots a_n)\}$, generated by $(a_1a_2 \cdots a_n)$, is transitive. As another example of a transitive group we have the group consisting of the permutations

$$1,\ (ab)(cd),\ (ac)(bd),\ (ad)(bc).$$

These elements in order replace a by a, b, c, d. The octic group affords another example of a transitive group.

A transitive group whose order is equal to its degree is called a *regular* permutation group.

If the letters involved in a regular permutation group G are $a_1, a_2, \cdots, a_n$, then there are n distinct permutations S_{i1}, S_{i2}, $\cdots$, S_{in} in G which replace a_i respectively by $a_1, a_2, \cdots, a_n$. Since there are only n permutations in G, the named permutations uniquely exhaust the elements of G. Hence the permutation S_{ij} is the only element of G which replaces a_i by a_j. If T is an element of G which leaves any given a_i fixed, then TS_{ij} replaces a_i by a_j, whence it follows that $TS_{ij} = S_{ij}$, so that T is the identity. Therefore *the identity is the only element of a regular permutation group which leaves fixed a letter involved in the group*. From this it follows that *all the permutations of a regular permutation group are regular permutations.*

The cyclic group $\{(abc)(def)\}$ is an example of a group which is not regular though every permutation in it is regular. It is intransitive.

Regular groups are of great importance on account of their applications. In fact, as we shall see in the next theorem, every finite group can be represented as simply isomorphic with a regular permutation group. From this it follows that many of the general properties of finite groups may be developed by aid of their representations as permutation groups. In practice this is often found to be more effective than an investigation of the properties of groups by means of any purely abstract mode of representing them.

We shall now prove the following theorem:

XII. SECOND FUNDAMENTAL THEOREM. Every group G of finite order n can be represented as a regular permutation group on n symbols, the latter being simply isomorphic with G. In fact, such a representation can be set up in two ways (as in the following proof) and the two representations are distinct when G is not an Abelian group. Moreover, every permutation in one of these permutation groups is permutable with every permutation in the other, and the n permutations of one of these permutation groups are the only permutations on its letters permutable with every permutation of the other. Furthermore, these two simply isomorphic regular permutation groups are conjugate under the symmetric group on the letters involved in them.

Let $S_1 = 1, S_2, S_3, \cdots, S_n$ be the n elements of the given group G. Then the n elements $S_1S_i, S_2S_i, \cdots, S_nS_i$ are all distinct and all belong to G, whence it follows that they are the elements of G in some order. Then

$$\begin{pmatrix} S_1, & S_2, & \cdots, & S_n \\ S_1S_i, & S_2S_i, & \cdots, & S_nS_i \end{pmatrix}$$

is a permutation s_i performed on the n symbols representing the elements of G. For brevity we denote s_i by the symbol

$$s_i \equiv \begin{pmatrix} S \\ SS_i \end{pmatrix}.$$

The permutation $s_i^{-1}s_j$ replaces S_i by S_j. Hence the permutation group P, consisting of the permutations $s_1, s_2, \cdots, s_n$, is transitive. Since its order is equal to its degree, it is regular. If S_i is made to correspond with s_i, for every i, then G and P are exhibited as simply isomorphic, since S_iS_j corresponds with s_is_j, as may be seen from the relations

$$s_is_j = \begin{pmatrix} S \\ SS_i \end{pmatrix}\begin{pmatrix} S \\ SS_j \end{pmatrix} = \begin{pmatrix} S \\ SS_i \end{pmatrix}\begin{pmatrix} SS_i \\ SS_iS_j \end{pmatrix} = \begin{pmatrix} S \\ SS_iS_j \end{pmatrix}.$$

The process by which this representation of G has been obtained may be called *post-multiplication*, since in forming s_i we multiplied the elements of G on the right by S_i. If we use *pre-multiplication* and write

$$s'_i = \begin{pmatrix} S_1, & S_2, & \cdots, & S_n \\ S_i^{-1}S_1, & S_i^{-1}S_2, & \cdots, & S_i^{-1}S_n \end{pmatrix} \equiv \begin{pmatrix} S \\ S_i^{-1}S \end{pmatrix},$$

then we have a permutation group P', consisting of the permutations $s'_1, s'_2, \cdots, s'_n$. Since S_i^{-1} is replaced by S_j^{-1} by the permutation $(s'_i)^{-1}s'_j$, it follows that this group P' is transitive and thence that it is regular. Moreover, we have

$$s'_is'_j = \begin{pmatrix} S \\ S_i^{-1}S \end{pmatrix}\begin{pmatrix} S \\ S_j^{-1}S \end{pmatrix} = \begin{pmatrix} S \\ S_i^{-1}S \end{pmatrix}\begin{pmatrix} S_i^{-1}S \\ S_j^{-1}S_i^{-1}S \end{pmatrix}$$

$$= \begin{pmatrix} S \\ S_j^{-1}S_i^{-1}S \end{pmatrix} = \begin{pmatrix} S \\ (S_iS_j)^{-1}S \end{pmatrix}$$

and this is the permutation corresponding to S_iS_j. Hence by making S_i and s'_i correspond for every i the groups G and P' are exhibited as simply isomorphic.

Now if $s_i = s'_j$, we have

$$\begin{pmatrix} S \\ SS_i \end{pmatrix} = \begin{pmatrix} S \\ S_j^{-1}S \end{pmatrix},$$

whence $SS_i = S_j^{-1}S$ for each element S of G. Taking S_1 for S, we have $S_i = S_j^{-1}$. Hence $SS_i = S_iS$, so that S_i is permutable with every element of the group. From this it follows that the two representations of G are distinct except in the case when G is an Abelian group. That is, when G is not Abelian the permutation groups P and P' are distinct as permutation groups in the sense that the set of permutations in one is not the same as the set of permutations in the other. But they are simply isomorphic, since each is simply isomorphic with G.

From the relations

$$s_i s'_j = \begin{pmatrix} S \\ SS_i \end{pmatrix} \begin{pmatrix} S \\ S_j^{-1}S \end{pmatrix} = \begin{pmatrix} S \\ SS_i \end{pmatrix} \begin{pmatrix} SS_i \\ S_j^{-1}SS_i \end{pmatrix} = \begin{pmatrix} S \\ S_j^{-1}SS_i \end{pmatrix} = s'_j s_i$$

we see that every permutation in one of the groups P and P' is permutable with every permutation in the other.

Let s be any permutation on $S_1, S_2, \cdots, S_n$ which is permutable with every permutation in P' and let S_k be the letter by which S_1 is replaced by s. Then $s^{-1}s_k$ leaves S_k unchanged and it is permutable with every permutation in P'. By aid of Theorem VI in § 2 it follows readily that such a permutation leaves fixed each of the letters $S_1, S_2, \cdots, S_n$, since P' is transitive on these letters. Hence $s^{-1}s_k$ is the identity, and therefore $s = s_k$. Hence P contains every permutation (on its letters) which is permutable with every permutation in P'. In a similar way it may be proved that P' contains every permutation (on its letters) which is permutable with every permutation in P.

Let t denote the permutation

$$t = \begin{pmatrix} S_1, & S_2, & \cdots, & S_n \\ S_1^{-1}, & S_2^{-1}, & \cdots, & S_n^{-1} \end{pmatrix} \equiv \begin{pmatrix} S \\ S^{-1} \end{pmatrix}.$$

Then from the relations

$$\begin{pmatrix} S \\ S^{-1} \end{pmatrix}^{-1} \begin{pmatrix} S \\ SS_i \end{pmatrix} \begin{pmatrix} S \\ S^{-1} \end{pmatrix} = \begin{pmatrix} S^{-1} \\ S \end{pmatrix} \begin{pmatrix} S \\ SS_i \end{pmatrix} \begin{pmatrix} SS_i \\ (SS_i)^{-1} \end{pmatrix} = \begin{pmatrix} S^{-1} \\ S_i^{-1}S^{-1} \end{pmatrix} = \begin{pmatrix} S \\ S_i^{-1}S \end{pmatrix}$$

it follows that $t^{-1}s_i t = s_i'$. Hence the group P' is conjugate to the group P under the symmetric group on $S_1, S_2, \cdots, S_n$.

This completes the proof of the theorem.

The groups P and P', occurring in the foregoing proof, are called *conjoint* groups. If P is Abelian, it coincides with its conjoint; otherwise the conjoints (though conjugate) are distinct in the sense that the set of permutations in one of them is not the same as the set in the other.

We shall now prove the following corollary:

COR. Two simply isomorphic regular permutation groups K and K' on the same set of n letters are conjugate subgroups of the symmetric group on those letters.

Let $a_1, a_2, \cdots, a_n$ be the n letters involved, and for each i of the set $1, 2, \cdots, n$ let S_i be that permutation of K which replaces a_1 by a_i. Let S'_i denote the permutation in K' which corresponds to S_i in K in the isomorphism of K and K', and let S'_i replace a_1 by a_{k_i}. Let σ_i be the transform of S'_i by the permutation

$$\begin{pmatrix} a_1, a_{k_2}, \cdots, a_{k_n} \\ a_1, a_2, \cdots, a_n \end{pmatrix}.$$

Then σ_i, as well as S_i, replaces a_1 by a_i. To establish the corollary it is sufficient to show for each i that S_i and σ_i denote the same permutation.

The group composed of the permutations $\sigma_1, \sigma_2, \cdots, \sigma_n$ is simply isomorphic with K, σ_i corresponding to S_i for each i. Then S_i^k corresponds to σ_i^k; hence they both replace a_1 by the same letter. Therefore the cycle in S_i which contains a_1 is the same as the cycle in σ_i which contains a_1, this result holding for each i of the set $1, 2, \cdots, n$.

Let $(a_l b_1 b_2 \cdots b_m)$ be a cycle of S_λ not containing a_1 (in case such a cycle exists) and let $(a_l c_1 c_2 \cdots c_m)$ be a cycle of σ_λ not containing a_1. Then $S_\lambda^{-\rho} S_l^{-1}$ replaces b_ρ by a_1 while $\sigma_\lambda^{-\rho}\sigma_l^{-1}$ replaces c_ρ by a_1. Hence b_ρ and c_ρ denote the same letter, since $S_\lambda^{-\rho} S_l^{-1}$ and $\sigma_\lambda^{-\rho}\sigma_l^{-1}$ have the same cycle containing a_1. Therefore S_λ and σ_λ denote the same permutation. Since this holds for $\lambda = 1, 2, \cdots, n$, the proof of the corollary is complete.

13. Sylow's Theorem. We shall now prove the following theorem, which is known as Sylow's theorem:

XIII. <u>THIRD FUNDAMENTAL THEOREM</u>. Let G be a group of order n and let p^α be the highest power of a prime p contained in n as a factor, α being a positive integer. Then G contains at least one subgroup of order p^α. All its subgroups of order p^α form a single complete conjugate set, and their number is $1 + kp$, where k is an integer (positive or zero).

Such a subgroup of order p^α is called a *Sylow subgroup*. Write $n = p^\alpha m$. Then m is prime to p. If $m = 1$ so that G is of order p^α, then G itself is the only subgroup of G of order p^α; whence it follows that the theorem is true in this case. Henceforth suppose that $m > 1$.

In order to prove the existence of at least one subgroup of order p^α we represent G as a regular permutation group P on $S_1, S_2, \cdots, S_n$, as in the proof of the preceding theorem. Let p^β be the highest power of p which is less than $p^\alpha m$. Let T denote any permutation of order p and degree p^β on part of the letters $S_1, S_2, \cdots, S_n$. Then T cannot be transformed into itself by every permutation of P (since P is a transitive group), as one sees by aid of Theorem VI in § 2. Let $T_1 \equiv T, T_2, \cdots, T_r$, where $r > 1$, be the total set of distinct permutations into which T is transformed by the permutations of P. The totality of permutations in P each of which transforms T into itself evidently forms a group P_T; let h denote the order of this group. Let V_i be a permutation in P which transforms T into T_i. Then if U is any permutation in P_T the permutation UV_i transforms T into T_i, since

$$(UV_i)^{-1}T(UV_i) = V_i^{-1} \cdot U^{-1}TU \cdot V_i = V_i^{-1}TV_i = T_i.$$

Conversely, if W is any permutation in P which transforms T into T_i, then W has the form $\overline{U}V_i$, where $\overline{U}$ belongs to P_T, since from the relation $W^{-1}TW = T_i = V_i^{-1}TV_i$ we have

$$V_iW^{-1}TWV_i^{-1} = T \text{ or } (WV_i^{-1})^{-1}T(WV_i^{-1}) = T,$$

so that WV_i^{-1} is a permutation $\overline{U}$ which transforms T into itself, whence $W = \overline{U}V_i$. Hence the number of permutations in P each of which transforms T into T_i is h, h being the order of P_T. Then, writing r_1 for r and h_1 for h, we have

$$p^\alpha m = r_1h_1. \qquad (r_1 > 1)$$

Now consider the totality M of permutations of order p and degree p^β on the letters $S_1, S_2, \cdots, S_n$. Let their number be s. If $s > r$, let T_{r+1} denote one of these permutations not in the set $T_1, T_2, \cdots, T_r$. Let the number of conjugates into which it is transformed by the permutations in P be r_2, and let h_2 be the order of the subgroup of P each permutation of which transforms T_{r+1} into itself. Then, as in the preceding case, we have

$p^\alpha m = r_2 h_2$ and $r_2 > 1$. If the totality M is not exhausted, continue the process. Since it must finally be exhausted, we shall have sequences of numbers r_i and h_i with i varying from 1 to μ (say) such that

$$s = r_1 + r_2 + \cdots + r_\mu.$$
$$p^\alpha m = r_i h_i. \qquad (r_i > 1;\ i = 1, 2, \cdots, \mu)$$

We shall next show that s is prime to p. For this purpose we observe first that the totality M forms the complete set of conjugates of T under the symmetric group on $S_1, S_2, \cdots, S_n$, since each permutation in M can be transformed into any other by a permutation in this symmetric group, as one sees readily by aid of Theorem VI in § 2. Now consider the following permutation in the set M:

$$D = (S_1 S_2 \cdots S_p)(S_{p+1} \cdots S_{2p}) \cdots (S_{p^\beta - p+1} \cdots S_{p^\beta}).$$

It is transformed into itself by each element of the group

$$\{(S_1 S_2 \cdots S_p),\ (S_{p+1} \cdots S_{2p}),\ \cdots,\ (S_{p^\beta - p+1} \cdots S_{p^\beta})\},$$

a group whose order is $p^{p^{\beta-1}}$. It is also transformed into itself by any permutation on its letters which permutes the cycles of D and retains the letters in each cycle in their given order; and the totality of such permutations obviously forms a group of order $(p^{\beta-1})!$, this being the number of permutations of $p^{\beta-1}$ objects, here taken as the cycles of D. Thus we have two groups such that D is transformed into itself by each element in either of them. These two groups have no element in common except the identity. If α is an element of the first group and β is an element of the second group, then it is easy to show that $\beta^{-1}\alpha\beta$ is an element α' of the first group. From the relation $\beta^{-1}\alpha\beta = \alpha'$ we have $\alpha\beta = \beta\alpha'$. From this it follows that every permutation in the group K generated by the elements of these two groups can be written as a product AB, where A belongs to the first group and B to the second. Hence the order of K is equal to the product of the orders of these two groups and hence is

$$(p^{\beta-1})!\ p^{p^{\beta-1}}.$$

Moreover, D is also transformed into itself by the symmetric group on $S_{p^\beta+1}, \cdots, S_{p^\alpha m}$. The direct product of K and this symmetric group is a group L of order

$$(p^\alpha m - p^\beta)! \cdot (p^{\beta-1})! \cdot p^{p^{\beta-1}}.$$

Since this group L is contained in the largest subgroup of the symmetric group on $S_1, S_2, \cdots, S_n$ under which D is transformed into itself, it follows from Theorem VI of § **11** and Theorem I of § **10** that the number s of conjugates of D under this symmetric group is a factor of the quotient

$$(p^\alpha m)! \div [(p^\alpha m - p^\beta)! \cdot (p^{\beta-1})! \cdot p^{p^{\beta-1}}],$$

which quotient is prime to p, as may be shown * from the fact that p^β is the largest power of p which is less than $p^\alpha m$. Hence s is prime to p, as was to be proved.

Since s is prime to p and we have shown that $s = r_1 + \cdots + r_\mu$ it follows that at least one of the numbers r_i is prime to p. Let r_ν be such a number. Then, from the relation $p^\alpha m = r_\nu h_\nu$ $(r_\nu > 1)$, we see that h_ν is divisible by p^α and is less than $p^\alpha m$.

But h_ν is the order of a proper subgroup of P; whence it follows that G has a proper subgroup of order h_ν. If $h_\nu > p^\alpha$, we may apply to this subgroup of G of order h_ν the same process as that just applied to G itself, and with the conclusion that it contains a proper subgroup whose order is divisible by p^α. It is clear that this process may be continued until we arrive at a subgroup of G of order p^α. This proves the existence of at least one subgroup of order p^α in G.

Let H be a subgroup of G of order p^α and let S be an element of G of order p^γ $(\gamma \geqq 0)$ which is permutable with H. Let p^δ be the order of the greatest subgroup which is common to $\{S\}$ and H. Then from Theorem X in § **11** it follows that the group $\{S, H\}$ is of order $p^{\alpha+\gamma-\delta}$. But G does not contain a subgroup of order p^ρ, where $\rho > \alpha$. Hence $\gamma = \delta$. Therefore the element S is in H.

* To prove this observe first that the named quotient may be written in the form

$$\frac{1 \cdot 2 \cdot 3 \cdot \cdots \cdot p^\beta}{p \cdot 2p \cdot 3p \cdot \cdots \cdot p^{\beta-1}p} \cdot \frac{(p^\beta+1)(p^\beta+2)(p^\beta+3) \cdots (p^\beta+[p^\alpha m - p^\beta])}{1 \cdot 2 \cdot 3 \cdot \cdots \cdot (p^\alpha m - p^\beta)}$$

and then that the denominator in the first fraction contains every multiple of p appearing in its numerator.

If G contains only one subgroup of order p^α, then our theorem is true for G. For the remainder of the proof we may then suppose that G contains more than one subgroup of order p^α.

We shall now prove that the number of conjugates of H in G is equal to a multiple of p increased by unity. If H is self-conjugate, the fact is granted. If H is not self-conjugate, let H' be any subgroup which is conjugate to H in G and is different from H. Let p^η be the order of the greatest subgroup h which is common to H and H'. When H' is transformed by all the elements of H, the only elements which transform H' into itself are those of h, and these are p^η in number. Hence H' is transformed by the elements of H into $p^{\alpha-\eta}$ distinct conjugate groups. If these do not exhaust the conjugates of H in G, let H'' be a new conjugate of H in G. If $p^{\eta'}$ is the order of the greatest subgroup common to H and H'', then the elements of H transform H'' into $p^{\alpha-\eta'}$ distinct conjugates of H different from H. No subgroup of this set is identical with a subgroup of the previous set; for, if

$$P_1^{-1}H''P_1 = P_2^{-1}H'P_2$$

and P_1 and P_2 belong to H, then we have

$$(P_2P_1^{-1})^{-1}H'(P_2P_1^{-1}) = H''$$

so that H'' is in the first set, contrary to hypothesis. If the set of subgroups conjugate to H is not yet exhausted, the process may be continued. Finally, we must exhaust the set of conjugates of H in G. Then their number has the form

$$1 + p^{\alpha-\eta} + p^{\alpha-\eta'} + \cdots,$$

where each of the exponents $\alpha - \eta$, $\alpha - \eta'$, $\cdots$ is greater than zero. Therefore the set of groups conjugate to H in G is in number $1 + kp$, where k is an integer.

We shall now show that there is no subgroup of G of order p^α which is not conjugate to H. For, if H_1 is such a subgroup, the number of its conjugates is $1 + k_1p$, where k_1 is an integer, as one sees from the result in the previous paragraph. But if we transform H_1 by the elements of H, then a set of $p^{\alpha-\sigma}$ $(\alpha > \sigma)$ conjugates of H_1 is obtained, p^σ being the order of the greatest subgroup common to H and H_1. If these are not all the conjugates of H_1 in G, an additional conjugate of H_1 can be transformed similarly into $p^{\alpha-\sigma'}$ conjugates, where $\alpha - \sigma' > 0$. By continuing this process we must finally exhaust the conjugates of H_1 and thus show that the number of them is a multiple of p. This contradicts the conclusion that their number is $1 + k_1 p$. Hence all the subgroups of G of order p^α are contained in the conjugate set treated in the preceding paragraph.

This completes the proof of the theorem.

COR. I. The only elements of G which are permutable with a Sylow subgroup of G of order p^α and whose orders are powers of p are the elements of that Sylow subgroup.

This was proved in the course of the argument.

COR. II. The number $1 + kp$ of Sylow subgroups of G of order p^α is a factor of the order of G.

This follows from the latter part of Theorem VII of § **11** and the fact that the Sylow subgroups of order p^α constitute a complete set of conjugate subgroups of G.

COR. III. The number $1 + kp$ in the theorem may be written in the form

$$1 + kp = 1 + k_1 p + k_2 p^2 + \cdots + k_\alpha p^\alpha$$

where $k_r p^r$ is the number of Sylow subgroups of order p^α each of which has with a given one of these subgroups a greatest common subgroup of order $p^{\alpha-r}$.

This follows readily from the arrangement of the Sylow subgroups of G into the sets given in the proof of the theorem.

COR. IV. If K is a subgroup of G of order p^λ, where $\lambda < \alpha$, then K is contained in a subgroup of G of order p^α.

It is sufficient to prove that K is contained in a subgroup of order $p^{\lambda+1}$, for then the process can be continued until it is shown that K is contained in a subgroup of order p^{α}. If K is not contained in a subgroup of order $p^{\lambda+1}$, then the only elements whose orders are powers of p, such that each of them transforms K into itself, are elements of K, a fact which may be established in the same way as a similar result was derived in the proof of Sylow's theorem. Then the methods used in the proof of the theorem may be employed to show that the number of conjugates of K in G must be $1+k_2p$, where k_2 is an integer, and also that this number must be divisible by p. Since this contradiction arises under the hypotheses employed, we see that K must be contained in a subgroup of order $p^{\lambda+1}$.

The three fundamental theorems already given have been called by G. A. Miller * the three most important theorems about finite groups.

EXERCISES

1. Show that the symmetric group of degree 4 has just three Sylow subgroups of order 8 and just four Sylow subgroups of order 3.

2. The greatest common subgroup of the Sylow subgroups of order p^{α} of a finite group G is a self-conjugate subgroup of G.

3. Find the self-conjugate subgroup of the symmetric group of degree 4 which is common to its Sylow subgroups of order 8.

4. If two Sylow subgroups of G of the same order are in a subgroup K of G, then they are conjugate in K.

5. Show that a group of order 200 contains a Sylow subgroup which is self-conjugate, and hence show that no group of order 200 can be simple.

6. Show that there is no simple group having its order equal to one of the following numbers: 204, 260, 2540, 9075.

7. Show that there is no simple group of order 12 or 30 or 56 or 520.

8. Find the Sylow subgroups of the alternating group of degree 4.

9. A group of order pq, where p and q are primes and $p > q$, contains only one subgroup of order p and is therefore a composite group.

* Miller, Blichfeldt, and Dickson, *Finite Groups*, pp. 23, 30, 64.

10. Show that every group of order 15 is cyclic.

11. Show that the number of cyclic permutations of order p that can be formed from p letters is $(p-1)!$. If p is a prime number, show that the number of Sylow subgroups of order p in the symmetric group of degree p is $(p-2)!$, and thence prove that $(p-1)!+1$ is divisible by p.

12. If a prime number p is a factor of the order of a finite group G, then G contains an element of order p.

13. Show that a group of order p^2, where p is a prime number, is either a cyclic group or an Abelian group generated by two elements each of order p. Represent the latter as a regular permutation group.

14. Represent the alternating and the symmetric group of degree 4 each as a regular group.

15. Determine the Sylow subgroups of order 7 in the group Γ, $\Gamma \equiv \{(ABCDEFG), (BD)(EF)\}$, of order 168, first showing that their number is 8.

16. Show that the group of order 660 in Ex. 13 on page 24 has just twelve Sylow subgroups of order 11, and find them.

17. Denote by $a_1, a_2, \cdots, a_8$ (in some convenient order) the eight Sylow subgroups of order 7 in the group Γ of Ex. 15, and construct the permutations on $a_1, a_2, \cdots, a_8$ according to which these Sylow subgroups are permuted when they are transformed by $(ABCDEFG)$ and $(BD)(EF)$, and show that these permutations generate a transitive group of degree 8 which is simply isomorphic with Γ.

18. Construct a transitive group of degree 12 which is simply isomorphic with the group of degree 11 mentioned in Ex. 16. (Compare Ex. 17.)

19. If p^β $(\beta > 0)$ is the highest power of a prime p which does not exceed an integer n, show that the number of permutations of degree p^β and order p in the symmetric group of degree n is prime to p.

20. Show that the number of permutations on nk letters each of which is permutable with a given regular permutation of order n and of degree nk on these letters is $n^k \cdot k!$.

21. If a group G has only one Sylow subgroup of order p^α, then G contains just p^α elements whose orders are factors of p^α.

22. If n is an integer greater than 3 and p is a prime not greater than n, then the symmetric group of degree n contains more than one Sylow subgroup of order p^α.

23. Let H be a self-conjugate subgroup of order p^β contained in a group G. Then H is contained in every Sylow subgroup of G of order p^α.

24. The greatest common subgroup of the groups P and P' introduced in the proof of Theorem XII of § **12** is simply isomorphic with the central of the group G of that theorem.

14. Generators of Abelian Groups. Since all the Sylow subgroups of a given order in a finite group G form a single complete conjugate set, it follows that a given Abelian group can have only one Sylow subgroup of a given order. Hence, since two of these subgroups have no element in common except the identity, we have the following theorem:

> XIV. An Abelian group whose order is not a power of a prime number is the direct product of all its Sylow subgroups.

From this it follows that two Abelian groups which have their Sylow subgroups simply isomorphic are themselves simply isomorphic. Therefore the problem of determining all possible abstract Abelian groups is reduced to the case of prime-power Abelian groups.

We shall now prove the following theorem, called by G. A. Miller * the most important theorem relating to Abelian groups:

> XV. FOURTH FUNDAMENTAL THEOREM. A non-cyclic Abelian group G whose order is a prime-power p^m is the direct product of cyclic groups no two of which have any element in common except the identity.

Let S_1 be an element of G whose order p^{m_1} is not less than that of any other element in G. We take $\{S_1\}$ to be one of the cyclic groups named in the theorem. If any element of G is raised to the power whose exponent is p^{m_1}, the result is the iden-

* Miller, Blichfeldt, and Dickson, *Finite Groups*, p. 89.

tity and hence is in $\{S_1\}$. Let m_2 be such that the (p^{m_2})th power of every element of G is in $\{S_1\}$, while G contains an element T_2 whose (p^{m_2-1})th power is not in $\{S_1\}$. Since $\{S_1\}$ is cyclic and since G contains no element of order greater than p^{m_1}, it follows that every element which is in $\{S_1\}$ and is the (p^{m_2})th power of an element of G is a (p^{m_2})th power of an element of $\{S_1\}$. Let T_2' be an element in $\{S_1\}$ whose (p^{m_2})th power is the inverse of the (p^{m_2})th power of T_2. Then the (p^{m_2})th power of $T_2'T_2$ is the identity. Moreover, no lower power of $T_2'T_2$ is in $\{S_1\}$, since such a power is the product of two factors one of which is in $\{S_1\}$ while the other is not. Put $T_2'T_2 = S_2$. Then $\{S_2\}$ is the second one of the cyclic groups named in the theorem.

If $\{S_1, S_2\}$ is not identical with G, let m_3 be such that the (p^{m_3})th power of every element of G is in $\{S_1, S_2\}$, while G contains an element T_3 whose (p^{m_3-1})th power is not in $\{S_1, S_2\}$. Then there is an element T_3' in $\{S_1, S_2\}$ whose (p^{m_3})th power is the inverse of the (p^{m_3})th power of T_3. Then, if we put $T_3'T_3 = S_3$, the element S_3 is of order p^{m_3}, while no power of S_3 lower than the (p^{m_3})th is in $\{S_1, S_2\}$. We take $\{S_3\}$ to be the third one of the cyclic groups named in the theorem. If $\{S_1, S_2, S_3\}$ is not the same as G, we may continue the process. Finally we have G expressed as a direct product $\{S_1, S_2, \cdots, S_k\}$ of cyclic groups, as demanded in the theorem.

If the orders of $S_1, S_2, \cdots, S_k$ are $p^{m_1}, p^{m_2}, \cdots, p^{m_k}$ respectively, then we say that G is of *type* $(m_1, m_2, \cdots, m_k)$. Obviously we have $m = m_1 + m_2 + \cdots + m_k$.

That an Abelian group of order p^m and type $(m_1, m_2, \cdots, m_k)$ exists for every possible separation of m into the sum $m = m_1 + m_2 + \cdots + m_k$, where $m_1, m_2, \cdots, m_k$ are positive integers, is readily seen. For, if the α_{ij} form a set of distinct letters, such a group is generated by the permutations

$$S_i = (\alpha_{i1}\alpha_{i2} \cdots \alpha_{i\mu_i}). \qquad (\mu_i = p^{m_i};\ i = 1, 2, \cdots, k)$$

By means of Theorems XIV and XV and the examples of permutation groups just indicated, all possible abstract Abelian groups may be determined (see § **23**).

15. Prime-Power Groups. From Sylow's theorem it follows that every group whose order is not a power of a prime contains two or more prime-power subgroups. Moreover, from the first fundamental theorem it follows that a given group may be generated by the elements in a set of Sylow subgroups if this set contains one Sylow subgroup of each possible order; for these subgroups generate a group whose order is at least as great as that of the given group, and hence the group so generated coincides with the given group. This fact shows the great importance of prime-power groups in the development of the general theory of finite groups.

We shall now prove the following theorem, called by G. A. Miller * the most important theorem relating to prime-power groups:

> XVI. Fifth Fundamental Theorem. A prime-power group G of order p^m contains a self-conjugate element of order p.

When G is an Abelian group the theorem is obvious. Then suppose that G is non-Abelian. Let S be an element of G which is not self-conjugate, and consider the complete set of conjugates to which S belongs. From Theorem VI of § **11** it follows that the number of conjugates of S is a factor of p^m, and hence the number is p^α, where α is some positive integer. Therefore the elements of G which are not self-conjugate fall into sets, each set containing a number of elements which is divisible by p. Since no two of these sets have an element in common (§ **11**), it follows that the number of elements in G each of which is non-self-conjugate is a multiple of p, say that it is lp. But the number of elements in G besides the identity is $p^m - 1$. Let k be the number of self-conjugate elements in G besides the identity. Then $k + lp = p^m - 1$, whence it follows that $k + 1$ is divisible by p. This conclusion is not valid if k is zero. Hence G has a self-conjugate element besides the identity; and the order of such an element is necessarily a power of p. An appropriate power of such an element is of order p and is self-conjugate in G. Hence the theorem follows.

* Miller, Blichfeldt, and Dickson, *Finite Groups*, p. 119.

COR. I. The number of self-conjugate elements in G is a power of p.

For the self-conjugate elements in G obviously form a group (which is Abelian), and this is a subgroup of G.

COR. II. A group H of order p^2 is Abelian.

If H contains an element of order p^2, it is cyclic and hence Abelian. If H is not cyclic, let S be a self-conjugate element of order p and let T be an element of H which is not in $\{S\}$. Then $T^{-1}ST = S$, so that S and T are permutable. It is obvious that they generate the group H.

COR. III. Every group whose order is a multiple of a prime p contains an element of order p.

This is an immediate consequence of Sylow's theorem and Theorem XVI.

EXERCISES

1. A prime-power group of order p^m is composite if $m > 1$.

2. If a group G of order p^3 contains more than one self-conjugate subgroup of order p, then G is Abelian and noncyclic.

3. If every Sylow subgroup of G is self-conjugate, then G is the direct product of its Sylow subgroups. (Use Theorem XI of § **11**.)

4. If G is a cyclic group of prime-power order p^m, then every element of G of order p^α, where $0 < \alpha < m$, is the pth power of just p distinct elements of order $p^{\alpha+1}$.

5. If G is a cyclic group of prime-power order p^m, then a single generating element of G may be chosen in just $p^m - p^{m-1}$ ways.

6. If G is an Abelian group of order p^2 and type (1, 1), then two elements to generate G may be chosen in just $\frac{1}{2}(p^2 - 1)(p^2 - p)$ different ways.

7. Determine all abstract groups of order less than 16 and thus verify that the number of each order is that given in the following scheme:

ORDER	1	2	3	4	5	6	7	8	9	10	11	12	13	14	15
NUMBER	1	1	1	2	1	2	1	5	2	2	1	5	1	2	1

8. If G is an Abelian group, the totality of elements of G whose orders are factors of a given integer k form a subgroup of G.

9. If G is an Abelian group, the totality of elements of G which are kth powers of elements of G form a subgroup of G.

10. An Abelian group of prime-power order p^m contains a subgroup of order p^{m-1} and hence of every order k where k is a factor of p^m.

11. An Abelian group of order n contains a subgroup of order k where k is any factor of n.

12. Let n be a number such that a group G of order n and a factor d of n exist of such sort that G has no subgroup of order d. Prove that n is the product of three or more (equal or distinct) prime factors. Thence show that 12 is the least possible value of n.

13. How many elements of each order are there in each of the four Abelian groups of order 36?

14. Let G be a group of order p^2q, where p and q are primes such that q is less than p and is not a factor of $p^2 - 1$. Show that G is an Abelian group.

15. Show that the elements of highest order in a prime-power Abelian group G generate G.

16. If a group G of order 56 contains eight subgroups of order 7, then every proper subgroup of G is an Abelian group.

17. If a group G is the direct product of its Sylow subgroups, so is every subgroup of G the direct product of its Sylow subgroups.

18. If the commutator of every pair of elements in a finite group G is permutable with each element in the pair, then G is the direct product of its Sylow subgroups.

19. Two conformal Abelian groups are simply isomorphic.

20. Let G be a finite group half of whose elements are of order 2 while the remaining elements form a subgroup H of order n. Show that H is Abelian and that n is odd, first proving that an element of order 2 transforms an element not of order 2 into its inverse and hence that H is self-conjugate in G.

21. Construct a group G of order $2n$ having the properties assigned to G in the preceding exercise.

MISCELLANEOUS EXERCISES

1. If each element of a finite group H transforms a finite group G into itself, then $\{G, H\}$ is a finite group whose order is the order of G multiplied by the index in H of the greatest common subgroup of G and H.

2. Show by an example that when G and H are given, H being a subgroup of the finite group G, it is not always possible to choose $t_1, t_2, \cdots, t_\lambda$ in the first rectangular array in § **10** so that they form a group. Give an example in which they do form a group.

3. If H is a proper subgroup of G, then the complete set of conjugates of H cannot contain all the elements of G.

4. If H is a proper subgroup of G, then H cannot contain elements from every complete set of conjugate elements in G.

5. If p is an odd prime, show that a non-Abelian group of order p^3 exists which is conformal with the Abelian group of order p^3 and type (1, 1, 1). (Use Ex. 18 on page 53 and Ex. 26 on page 42.)

6. Show that a necessary and sufficient condition that the two sets $t_1H, t_2H, \cdots, t_\lambda H$ and $H\tau_1, H\tau_2, \cdots, H\tau_\lambda$ of elements of G, employed in § **10**, shall be identical as sets (except possibly for order) is that H shall be a self-conjugate subgroup of G.

7. The elements which are permutable with each element in a complete set of conjugate subgroups of a finite group G themselves form a self-conjugate subgroup of G.

8. If for every complete set $S_1, S_2, \cdots, S_k$ of conjugate elements of a finite group G, other than that consisting of the identity alone, the group $\{S_1, S_2, \cdots, S_k\}$ coincides with G, then G is simple; otherwise G is composite.

9. For a given group G of order n, define numbers $h_1, h_2, \cdots, h_r$ as in the second paragraph preceding Theorem V in § **11**. If no sum $s = h_1 + h_a + \cdots$ formed with a proper subset of two or more of these h's, which set includes h_1, is a factor of n, show that G is simple.

10. Let S be an element of the finite group G and let H be a subgroup of G. Then the group generated by the complete set of conjugates of S and the complete set of conjugates of H is self-conjugate in G.

11. The tth powers of the elements of a finite group G generate a self-conjugate (proper or improper) subgroup of G.

12. Let G and H be two groups of orders m and n respectively, and suppose that every element of G transforms H into itself and that every element of H transforms G into itself. Let λ be the order of $\{G, H\}$, and let δ be the order of the greatest common subgroup D of G and H. Then prove that $mn = \lambda\delta$.

13. Determine the permutation group according to which the 13 quadruples defined by the array in Ex. 8 on page 40 are permuted by the permutation group defined in that exercise, and investigate the relation between this new group and that defined in the named exercise. (Compare Ex. 20 on page 53.)

14. Show that the group defined in Ex. 8 on page 40 contains a subgroup of order $12 \cdot 9 \cdot 4$ each element of which leaves A fixed, and find the complete set of conjugates of this subgroup.

15. Show that the group defined in Ex. 8 on page 40 contains a subgroup of order $9 \cdot 4$ each element of which leaves both A and B fixed, and find the complete set of conjugates of this subgroup.

16. By means of the preceding Ex. 13 and Ex. 9 on page 40, construct two simply isomorphic groups of degrees 12 and 9 respectively, the order of each being $9 \cdot 8 \cdot 6$.

17. Show that the group of order $13 \cdot 12 \cdot 9 \cdot 4$, defined in Ex. 8 on page 40, has 144 Sylow subgroups of order 13, and show how to find these subgroups.

18. If a group of order 60 has no self-conjugate subgroup of order 5, then it must have just 6 subgroups of order 5. Show that there is one and only one abstract group of order 60 which has 6 subgroups of order 5, and prove that it is simply isomorphic with the alternating group of degree 5.

19. Show that there exists a single abstract group of order 84 containing just 28 subgroups of order 3.

20. If p is a prime of the form $6k + 1$, show that there are just 6 abstract groups of order $6p$.

21. If p is a prime of the form $6k + 5$, show that there are just 4 abstract groups of order $6p$.

22. Show that there are just 15 abstract groups of order 24.

23. Determine all the abstract groups whose orders do not exceed 26. (Compare Ex. 7 on page 69 and Ex. 22 on this page.) Show that the number of each order from 16 to 26 is that given in the following scheme:

ORDER	16	17	18	19	20	21	22	23	24	25	26
NUMBER	14	1	5	1	5	2	2	1	15	2	2

24. If G is a prime-power group of order p^m in which no conjugate set contains more than p^s elements, show that the (p^s)th power of every element is self-conjugate.

25. Let G be a prime-power group of order p^m in which any (whatever) element is either self-conjugate or belongs to a complete set of p conjugates. Show that an element of G is either self-conjugate in G or self-conjugate in a subgroup of G of index p.

26. Show that every commutator in the group G of Ex. 25 is a self-conjugate element.

27. Show that an Abelian group of order 3^3 and type (1, 1, 1) has 13 subgroups of order 3 and also 13 subgroups of order 9 and that the subgroups of order 3 are distributed into 13 sets of four each, the four in each set belonging to a subgroup of order 9. By means of this result construct an array like that in Ex. 8 on page 40.

28. Show that a prime-power Abelian group of order p^3 and type (1, 1, 1) has $p^2 + p + 1$ subgroups of order p and the same number of order p^2 and that a subgroup of order p^2 contains just $p + 1$ of these subgroups of order p.

29. By aid of the result in Ex. 28 arrange 31 $(= 5^2 + 5 + 1)$ letters into 31 sets of six each so that any given pair of the letters occurs in one and just one set of six and so that any two sets of six have one and just one letter in common. (Compare Ex. 27.)

30. Determine the number of subgroups of each of the orders p, p^2, p^3 in a prime-power Abelian group of order p^4 and type (1, 1, 1, 1).

31. Show that a prime-power Abelian group of order p^m and type $(1, 1, \cdots, 1)$ has just $p^{m-1} + p^{m-2} + \cdots + p + 1$ subgroups of order p and the same number of subgroups of index p.

32. Let G be an Abelian group of order 16 and type (1, 1, 1, 1). Show that its 15 elements of order 2 may be separated into five sets of three each so that each set of three with the identity forms a group of order 4, and prove that this separation into sets may be carried out in just 56 distinct ways.

CHAPTER III

Additional Properties of Groups in General

---

16. Isomorphism. Let G and Γ be two groups among whose elements a correspondence of the following sort may be established: To each element γ of Γ there corresponds one or more elements $g, g', g'', \cdots$ of G; to each element g of G there corresponds one or more elements $\gamma, \gamma', \gamma'', \cdots$ of Γ; if g_i and g_j are any elements of G, and γ_i and γ_j are any elements of Γ corresponding, respectively, to g_i and g_j, then the element $g_i g_j$ of G corresponds to the element $\gamma_i \gamma_j$ of Γ. Two groups G and Γ so related are said to be *isomorphic*, and the named relation is said to constitute an *isomorphism*, or a *general isomorphism*, between G and Γ.

In order to have an example of the general isomorphism of two groups, consider the groups G and Γ, namely,

$$G: \begin{array}{c|c|c} 1 & (abc) & (acb) \\ (ab)(cd) & (acd) & (bcd) \\ (ac)(bd) & (bdc) & (abd) \\ (ad)(bc) & (adb) & (adc) \end{array} \quad \text{and } \Gamma: \begin{array}{c|c|c} 1 & (\alpha\beta\gamma) & (\alpha\gamma\beta) \\ (ab) & (\alpha\beta\gamma)(ab) & (\alpha\gamma\beta)(ab) \end{array}$$

The required isomorphism is established by making each element in the ith column of elements of G correspond to each element in the ith column of elements of Γ for $i = 1, 2, 3$. That this exhibits an isomorphism the reader may readily verify.

We shall now prove the following theorem:

I. Let G and Γ be isomorphic groups. Then the elements of G which correspond to the identity in Γ constitute a self-conjugate subgroup H of G. If h is the order of H, then h elements of G correspond to each element of Γ.

If both g_1 and g_2 in G correspond to 1 in Γ, then g_1g_2 corresponds to $1 \cdot 1$, or 1, in Γ. Hence the elements named in the second sentence of the theorem constitute a subgroup H of G. If g is any element of G and γ is one of its correspondents in Γ, and if g_1 is any element in G which corresponds to 1 in Γ, then $g^{-1} \cdot g_1 \cdot g$ corresponds to $\gamma^{-1} \cdot 1 \cdot \gamma$, or 1. Hence H is self-conjugate in G.

If g_i and g_j in G correspond to γ in Γ, then $g_i^{-1}g_j$ corresponds to $\gamma^{-1}\gamma$, or 1, in Γ. Hence $g_i^{-1}g_j$ is in H. From this it follows readily that each element g_j in G which corresponds to γ in Γ belongs to the set g_iH, where g_i is a particular one of them. But if h_k is in H, then g_ih_k corresponds to $\gamma \cdot 1$, or γ. Hence the elements g_iH, and these alone, are elements in G which correspond to γ. Since their number is h, the last part of the theorem is established.

From the foregoing theorem we see that if G and Γ are isomorphic groups, and if the largest group in G whose elements correspond to 1 in Γ is of order h, while the largest group in Γ whose elements correspond to 1 in G is of order η, then to each element in Γ there correspond h elements in G while to each element in G there correspond η elements in Γ. The group G is then said to have *an* (h, η) *isomorphism* with the group Γ. When $h = \eta = 1$ the two groups are said to be *simply isomorphic*. The notion of simple isomorphism we have already met in § 9 and have used it on several occasions. The case which is next in importance is that in which $h > 1$ and $\eta = 1$ (or $h = 1$ and $\eta > 1$). When $h > 1$ and $\eta = 1$, then G is said to be *multiply isomorphic* with Γ. In this case only one element in Γ corresponds to each element in G, while to each element in Γ there correspond h elements in G.

II. When G has an $(h, 1)$ isomorphism with Γ, the order of each element in Γ is a factor of the order of each corresponding element in G.

For if S in G corresponds to T in Γ and T is of order r, then S^r corresponds to T^r and hence to 1. Then S^r is the lowest positive power of S in the subgroup of G consisting of those elements of G each of which corresponds to 1 in Γ. Hence the order of S is a multiple of r.

III. If G and Γ, of orders n and ν respectively, have an (h, η) isomorphism, then $n\eta = \nu h$.

Suppose that all correspondences of elements of G with elements of Γ are written down, each correspondence appearing just once. Then each element of G occurs just η times and each element of Γ occurs just h times. Hence the number of correspondences is $n\eta$. It is also νh. Hence $n\eta = \nu h$, as was to be proved.

17. Isomorphisms of a Group with Itself. If g is an element of a group G and if each element of G is made to correspond to its transform by g, then G is exhibited as simply isomorphic with itself, since the product g_1g_2 corresponds to $g^{-1}g_1g_2g = g^{-1}g_1g \cdot g^{-1}g_2g$. In this isomorphism not every element will correspond to itself unless g is permutable with every element of G. In the case of an Abelian group the only correspondence which can be established in this way is that in which each element corresponds to itself. But if G is Abelian and μ is prime to the order of G, then an isomorphism of G with itself can be established by making each element correspond to its own μth power. For then g_1g_2 will correspond to $(g_1g_2)^\mu = g_1^\mu g_2^\mu$. Thus we have two special ways of establishing an isomorphism of a group with itself.

In general, if a correspondence is established among the elements of a group G such that to every element there corresponds a unique element and such that when S and T are any two elements of G and their correspondents are the elements S' and T' of G it is true that $S'T'$ is the correspondent of ST, then the group G is said to be exhibited as *simply isomorphic with itself.* If each element corresponds to itself, the isomorphism is called the *identical isomorphism.*

IV. In every isomorphism of a group with itself two corresponding elements have the same order; in particular, the identity always corresponds to itself.

If 1 corresponds to S and S is of order n $(n>1)$, then 1^n corresponds to S^n, or 1, so that the identity has two correspondents; and this is impossible. Hence the identity always corresponds to itself. If S corresponds to σ, then S^k corresponds to σ^k. Hence, unless S and σ have the same order, we should have the identity corresponding to another element if we take k to be the order of S and S is of lower order than σ.

Let the elements of a finite group G be denoted by $S_1 = 1$, $S_2, S_3, \cdots, S_n$. In an isomorphism of G with itself let S_i correspond to S'_i. This isomorphism we may use to define a permutation on the elements of G, namely, the permutation

$$\begin{pmatrix} S_1, & S_2, & \cdots, & S_n \\ S'_1, & S'_2, & \cdots, & S'_n \end{pmatrix}, \text{ or } \begin{pmatrix} S \\ S' \end{pmatrix}.$$

We shall say that this is the permutation corresponding to the given isomorphism. It is obvious that the permutations thus corresponding to two distinct isomorphisms are themselves distinct.

To the totality of isomorphisms of G with itself there corresponds in this way a certain totality of permutations. This totality of permutations constitutes a group, as we shall now show. If two isomorphisms of G with itself lead to the two permutations

$$\begin{pmatrix} S \\ S' \end{pmatrix} \text{ and } \begin{pmatrix} S' \\ S'' \end{pmatrix},$$

then we have to show that the product permutation

$$\begin{pmatrix} S \\ S' \end{pmatrix}\begin{pmatrix} S' \\ S'' \end{pmatrix}, \text{ or } \begin{pmatrix} S \\ S'' \end{pmatrix},$$

corresponds to an isomorphism of G with itself. From the first isomorphism it follows that if $S_pS_q = S_r$, then $S'_pS'_q = S'_r$; and then, from the second, that $S''_pS''_q = S''_r$. Hence if $S_pS_q = S_r$, we have $S''_pS''_q = S''_r$. Therefore the named product permutation corresponds to an isomorphism of G with itself.

Hence the totality of permutations corresponding to the totality of isomorphisms constitutes a permutation group P.

The abstract group which is simply isomorphic with this

permutation group P is called *the group of isomorphisms* of the given group G.

An isomorphism which can be obtained by making each element of G correspond to the transform of that element by a single appropriately chosen element of G (the same for every correspondence in a given isomorphism) is called an *inner* isomorphism; an *outer* isomorphism is one which does not have this property.

V. The inner isomorphisms of a finite group G constitute a group to which G itself is isomorphic of type $(k, 1)$, where k is the number of self-conjugate elements in G. This group of inner isomorphisms is a self-conjugate subgroup of the group of isomorphisms of G.

Represent the group of isomorphisms as a permutation group as in the preceding treatment. Forming the product of two inner isomorphisms, we have

$$\begin{pmatrix} S \\ g_1^{-1}Sg_1 \end{pmatrix}\begin{pmatrix} S \\ g_2^{-1}Sg_2 \end{pmatrix} = \begin{pmatrix} S \\ g_1^{-1}Sg_1 \end{pmatrix}\begin{pmatrix} g_1^{-1}Sg_1 \\ g_2^{-1} \cdot g_1^{-1}Sg_1 \cdot g_2 \end{pmatrix}$$
$$= \begin{pmatrix} S \\ g_3^{-1}Sg_3 \end{pmatrix},$$

where $g_3 = g_1g_2$. Hence the product of two inner isomorphisms is an inner isomorphism. Therefore the inner isomorphisms form a group.

Let us take the inner isomorphism

$$\begin{pmatrix} S \\ g^{-1}Sg \end{pmatrix}$$

(that is, the inner isomorphism corresponding to the given permutation) formed by means of any given element g of G as corresponding to g itself. Then to every element of G there corresponds a definite and unique inner isomorphism of G. Moreover, to the product of two elements corresponds the product of the two corresponding isomorphisms. Hence G and its group of inner isomorphisms are isomorphic. It is evident that the isomorphism is of the general type $(k, 1)$. If G contains no self-conjugate element besides the identity, then the isomorphism is necessarily $(1, 1)$; that is, the two groups are simply isomorphic. If G contains just k self-conjugate elements, then k elements in G correspond to the identity in the group of inner isomorphisms; and the isomorphism of the two groups is $(k, 1)$.

Let us now transform an inner isomorphism of G by any isomorphism of G with itself. Thus we have

$$\begin{pmatrix} S \\ S' \end{pmatrix}^{-1} \begin{pmatrix} S \\ g^{-1}Sg \end{pmatrix} \begin{pmatrix} S \\ S' \end{pmatrix} = \begin{pmatrix} S' \\ S \end{pmatrix} \begin{pmatrix} S \\ g^{-1}Sg \end{pmatrix} \begin{pmatrix} g^{-1}Sg \\ (g')^{-1}S'g' \end{pmatrix} = \begin{pmatrix} S' \\ (g')^{-1}S'g' \end{pmatrix}.$$

Hence an isomorphism of G with itself transforms every inner isomorphism of G into an inner isomorphism of G. The group of inner isomorphisms is therefore self-conjugate in the entire group of isomorphisms.

18. The Holomorph of a Group. Let $S_1 = 1, S_2, S_3, \cdots, S_n$ be the elements of a group G of order n, and let L of order m be the group of isomorphisms of G. Represent G as a regular permutation group by the first method of § **12**, and let G' be this permutation group. Corresponding to S_i in G we have in G' the permutation

$$\begin{pmatrix} S \\ SS_i \end{pmatrix}.$$

Represent L as a permutation group L' in accordance with the method of § **17**. The two permutation groups G' and L' have no permutation in common except the identity, since every element in L' replaces S_1 by itself while an element in G' other than the identity replaces S_1 by another symbol. Now on transforming an element of G' by an element of L', we have

$$\begin{pmatrix} S \\ S' \end{pmatrix}^{-1} \begin{pmatrix} S \\ SS_i \end{pmatrix} \begin{pmatrix} S \\ S' \end{pmatrix} = \begin{pmatrix} S' \\ S \end{pmatrix} \begin{pmatrix} S \\ SS_i \end{pmatrix} \begin{pmatrix} SS_i \\ S'S'_i \end{pmatrix} = \begin{pmatrix} S' \\ S'S'_i \end{pmatrix}.$$

Hence every element of L' transforms each element of G' into an element of G', so that every element of L' is permutable with G'. Therefore every element of $\{G', L'\}$ may be written in the form $l'g'$, where l' and g' belong, respectively, to L' and G'.

Hence the group $\{G', L'\}$ is of order mn. We shall denote it by K'. It is clear that G' is a self-conjugate subgroup of K'.

The abstract group which is simply isomorphic with the permutation group K' is called the *holomorph* of G.

Now the transform of $\begin{pmatrix} S \\ SS_i \end{pmatrix}$ by $\begin{pmatrix} S \\ S' \end{pmatrix}$ is $\begin{pmatrix} S \\ SS'_i \end{pmatrix}$, and these two permutations of G' correspond to S_i and S'_i, respectively, in G. Hence, if the permutations in G' are transformed by any permutation $\begin{pmatrix} S \\ S' \end{pmatrix}$ of L', an isomorphism of G is set up which is represented by the permutation $\begin{pmatrix} S \\ S' \end{pmatrix}$.

Now we have

$$\begin{pmatrix} S \\ S_iSS_i^{-1} \end{pmatrix}\begin{pmatrix} S \\ SS_i \end{pmatrix} = \begin{pmatrix} S \\ S_iSS_i^{-1} \end{pmatrix}\begin{pmatrix} S_iSS_i^{-1} \\ S_iSS_i^{-1}S_i \end{pmatrix} = \begin{pmatrix} S \\ S_iS \end{pmatrix}.$$

The first factor is in L' and the second is in G'; hence the product is in K'. Hence K' contains the set of permutations

$$\begin{pmatrix} S \\ S_iS \end{pmatrix}. \quad (i = 1, 2, \cdots, n)$$

But these (see § **12**) form a permutation group G'' which is simply isomorphic with G. Moreover, G'' contains the totality of permutations (on the symbols involved) each of which is permutable with every permutation in G', while G' has the same property with relation to G''.

That G'' is a self-conjugate subgroup of K' may now be proved in a way similar to that by which the corresponding property was established for G'.

It will now be shown that K' contains those permutations on the symbols $S_1, S_2, \cdots, S_n$ each of which is permutable with G'. For this purpose let σ be any permutation on the named symbols which is permutable with G'. On transforming G' by σ and making each element correspond to its transform we set up some isomorphism of G with itself. This may be represented by some permutation, say $\begin{pmatrix} S \\ S' \end{pmatrix}$, of L'. Then $\sigma \begin{pmatrix} S \\ S' \end{pmatrix}^{-1}$ is a permutation on $S_1, S_2, \cdots, S_n$ which is permutable with every permutation in G'; therefore it belongs to G'', and hence is in K'. Therefore σ is in K', as was to be proved.

In a similar way it may be shown that K' contains those permutations on $S_1, S_2, \cdots, S_n$ each of which is permutable with G''.

Now G' and G'' are both contained self-conjugately in K', while G' is transformed into G'' and G'' is transformed into G' by the permutation τ,

$$\tau = \begin{pmatrix} S \\ S^{-1} \end{pmatrix},$$

as we saw in § 12. Hence τ transforms the permutations that are permutable with G' into those that are permutable with G''; it also transforms those that are permutable with G'' into those that are permutable with G'. But K' is composed of all the permutations each of which is permutable with both G' and G''. Hence τ transforms K' into itself. When G is not Abelian, in which case (see § 12) the groups G' and G'' are distinct, the permutation τ does not belong to K'. Hence when G is not Abelian the order of the group $\{K', \tau\}$ is twice the order of K'; moreover $\{K', \tau\}$ contains K' self-conjugately.

When G is not an Abelian group, the abstract group which is simply isomorphic with $\{K', \tau\}$ is called the *double holomorph* of G.

If a group G admits no outer isomorphism and if it contains no self-conjugate element besides the identity, it is said to be a *complete* group. If G is a complete group, then (Theorem V of § 17) it is simply isomorphic with its group of isomorphisms. Therefore if the order of the complete group G is n, its holomorph is of order n^2.

19. On Certain Subgroups of a Group G. A subgroup of G all of whose elements correspond to elements in that subgroup in every isomorphism of G with itself is called a *characteristic* subgroup of G. It is necessarily a self-conjugate subgroup of G since it is transformed into itself by every element of G; but G may contain self-conjugate subgroups which are not characteristic. It is obvious that a characteristic subgroup of G is a self-conjugate subgroup of the holomorph K of G, and, conversely, that every self-conjugate subgroup of K which is contained in G is a characteristic subgroup of G.

That the commutator subgroup of a given finite group G (when it does not coincide with G) is a characteristic (proper) subgroup is readily proved. For, if S and T correspond to σ and τ, respectively, in an isomorphism of G with itself, then $S^{-1}T^{-1}ST$ corresponds to $\sigma^{-1}\tau^{-1}\sigma\tau$, so that every commutator in G corresponds to a commutator; whence the theorem follows at once.

Another important characteristic subgroup of G may be defined as follows. We have seen (§ **8**) that a set of independent generators of G is any set of generators such that no one of them is contained in the group generated by the remaining ones. Now the elements of G may be separated into two mutually exclusive classes, the one class containing all those elements of G each of which occurs in at least one set of independent generators of G while the other contains the remaining elements of G. The elements of the second class generate a proper subgroup of G known as the *ϕ-subgroup* of G. It is evidently a characteristic subgroup, since in any isomorphism of G with itself the elements of the first class must correspond only to elements of the first class, leaving the elements of the second class to correspond among themselves only.

If H is a proper subgroup of G such that $\{H, S\}$ coincides with G for every S in G and not in H, then H is called a *maximum* or a *maximal* subgroup of G. A given subgroup may have several maximal subgroups of the same or of different orders.

If G_1 is a self-conjugate subgroup of a finite group G not contained in any other self-conjugate subgroup of G except G itself, then G_1 is called a *maximum* or a *maximal* self-conjugate subgroup of G. A given group may have several maximal self-conjugate subgroups, and these may be of different orders.

Let H be any maximal subgroup of G. Then there is at least one set of independent generators of G that includes any given one of the elements in G and not in H, the remaining elements in the set being taken from H. Furthermore, if S is any element in a particular set of independent generators of G, there is at least one maximal subgroup of G which does not contain S. Hence *the ϕ-subgroup of G is the largest common subgroup of the maximal subgroups of G* — a property of the ϕ-subgroup which might be taken as its defining property. From these considerations it follows also that *the ϕ-subgroup contains no element which can appear in a set of independent generators of G,* so that it consists of the elements of the second class of elements in the classification made earlier in this section.

EXERCISES

1. If two simple groups are isomorphic, they are simply isomorphic.

2. An isomorphism of an Abelian group with itself may be set up by making each element correspond to its inverse. In what case is this isomorphism the identical isomorphism?

3. The totality of elements of a finite group G each of which corresponds to itself in a given isomorphism of G with itself constitutes a subgroup of G.

4. If p is an odd prime, the group of isomorphisms of a cyclic group of order p^α is a cyclic group of order $p^{\alpha-1}(p-1)$.

5. The group of isomorphisms of a cyclic group of order 2^α $(\alpha > 2)$ is an Abelian group of order $2^{\alpha-1}$ and type $(\alpha-2, 1)$.

6. A simple group cannot have a characteristic proper subgroup besides the identity.

7. The central of a group is a characteristic subgroup.

8. Any subgroup of a cyclic group is a characteristic subgroup.

9. The Sylow subgroups of an Abelian group are characteristic subgroups.

10. The kth powers of the elements of an Abelian group constitute a characteristic subgroup.

11. Let G be the noncyclic group of order 4. Show that the group of isomorphisms of G is simply isomorphic with the symmetric group of degree 3, and that its holomorph is simply isomorphic with the symmetric group of degree 4.

12. Show that the symmetric groups of degrees 3 and 4 are complete groups. Construct their holomorphs.

13. Let G be a cyclic group of order n. Prove that a necessary and sufficient condition that the ϕ-subgroup of G is of order 1 is that n shall be divisible by no square greater than unity.

14. Let G be a group containing elements of order greater than 2. Then the elements of order greater than 2 in G are even in number, and they generate a characteristic (proper or improper) subgroup of G.

15. Let G be a group of order n and let m be a number prime to n. Show that every element in G is the mth power of one and just one element in G.

16. Find the holomorph of the group $\{(a_0a_1a_2 \cdots a_{p-1})\}$, where p is an odd prime number, showing that the order of this holomorph is $p(p-1)$.

17. Let H be the subgroup of a group G which is generated by all the elements of G whose orders are factors of a given number r. Prove that H is a characteristic subgroup of G.

18. Prove that a characteristic proper subgroup of an Abelian group G cannot contain an element of maximum order in G.

19. Find the group of isomorphisms of a cyclic group of order n and show that its order is $\phi(n)$, where $\phi(n)$ denotes Euler's ϕ-function of n.

20. Show that $n\phi(n)$ is the order of the holomorph of a cyclic group of order n.

21. Let U be a noninvariant element or a noninvariant subgroup of a group G, and suppose that it is in the ϕ-subgroup of G. Show that the number of conjugates of U under G is greater than the number of its conjugates under the ϕ-subgroup of G.

22. Show that the group of degree 7 and order 168 which leaves invariant the configuration on seven letters in § **4** is simply isomorphic with the group of isomorphisms of the Abelian group of order 2^3 and type (1, 1, 1).

23. Show that the group of isomorphisms of the Abelian group of order 3^3 and type (1, 1, 1) is of order $26 \cdot 24 \cdot 18$.

24. Show that the group of isomorphisms of the Abelian group of order 5^3 and type (1, 1, 1) is of order $124 \cdot 120 \cdot 100$.

20. Factor-Groups. Let H be a self-conjugate subgroup of order r in a finite group G of order $n = \lambda r$. By means of multipliers $t_1 = 1, t_2, t_3, \cdots, t_\lambda$ write G as λ sets of r elements each as in the first rectangular array in § **10**, denoting these components, or *partitions* of G as to H, by the usual symbols t_1H, $t_2H, \cdots, t_\lambda H$. Let the elements of H, as in § **10**, be denoted by

$s_1, s_2, \cdots, s_r$. Then $t_is_x \cdot t_js_y$ is an element of the same partition as t_it_j, say the partition t_kH; for, since H is self-conjugate in G, the element $t_j^{-1}s_xt_j$ is an element s_z (say) of H, whence it follows that $t_is_x \cdot t_js_y = t_it_j \cdot t_j^{-1}s_xt_j \cdot s_y = t_it_js_zs_y$, an element which is in $(t_it_j)H$, and hence in t_kH. Hence if t_it_j is in t_kH, so is every element of the form $t_is_x \cdot t_js_y$; that is, every product of an element t_is_x in t_iH by an element t_js_y in t_jH is an element in t_kH.

Now write γ_l for t_lH $(l = 1, 2, \cdots, \lambda)$. Then the symbols $\gamma_1, \gamma_2, \cdots, \gamma_\lambda$ obey a unique law of combination defined for each i and j by the relation $\gamma_i\gamma_j = \gamma_k$. The symbols therefore satisfy Condition I in the definition of a group in § **3**.

That they obey the associative law, in accordance with Condition II in this definition of a group, may be shown as follows: If every element of the set $t_iH \cdot t_jH$ (that is, the set of elements formed by taking the product of each element in t_iH by each element in t_jH) is in t_kH and every element of $t_jH \cdot t_fH$ is in t_gH, the elements $t_kH \cdot t_fH$ and $t_iH \cdot t_gH$ are in the same partition of G, since the elements of G obey the associative law. Hence $(\gamma_i\gamma_j)\gamma_f = \gamma_i(\gamma_j\gamma_f)$, as was to be shown.

If $t_1 = 1$, as we have supposed, then γ_1 has the property of the identity, since $\gamma_1\gamma_i = \gamma_i\gamma_1 = \gamma_i$, as is obvious from the discussion in the first paragraph of this section.

Again, each element γ_i is of finite order, whence it follows that its inverse is in the set $\gamma_1, \gamma_2, \cdots, \gamma_\lambda$.

From these considerations it follows that the elements $\gamma_1, \gamma_2, \cdots, \gamma_\lambda$, with the named rule of combination, form a group G_1 of order λ. It is completely determined by the given group G and its given self-conjugate subgroup H. It is called the *quotient* of G by H; it is also called a *factor-group* of G or a *quotient* group of G. It is denoted by the symbol G/H. *Its order is equal to the index of H in G.*

From the way in which G/H is formed it is evident that G is *multiply isomorphic with G/H, the subgroup H in G corresponding to the identity in G/H.* The elements t_iH correspond to γ_i.

Factor-groups afford a means of illuminating the concept of the general isomorphism of two groups. Let H be a self-conjugate subgroup of G of order h, and let H' be a self-conjugate subgroup of G' of order h'; and suppose that these several groups are so related that G/H is simply isomorphic with G'/H'. Separate G as to H into the partitions t_1H, t_2H, $\cdots$, $t_\lambda H$ in the usual way; similarly, separate G' as to H' into the partitions t'_1H', t'_2H', $\cdots$, $t'_\lambda H'$: let the notation be so chosen that in the simple isomorphism of G/H with G'/H' the partitions t_iH and t'_iH' are corresponding partitions for each i of the set 1, 2, $\cdots$, λ. Then take the set t'_iH' of elements in G' as the elements corresponding to each element in t_iH, and take the set t_iH of elements in G as the elements corresponding to each element in t'_iH'. This correspondence exhibits G and G' as having a general (h, h') isomorphism, as we shall now show. Denote the elements of H by the symbols h_x and those of H' by the symbols h'_μ. Let t_ih_x and t_jh_y in G correspond, respectively, to $t'_ih'_\xi$ and $t'_jh'_\eta$ in G'. Then if $t_ih_x \cdot t_jh_y$ is in the partition t_kH, the element $t'_ih'_\xi \cdot t'_jh'_\eta$ is in the partition t'_kH', so that the product $t_ih_x \cdot t_jh_y$ corresponds to the product $t'_ih'_\xi \cdot t'_jh'_\eta$. Hence the groups G and G' have the named isomorphism.

We shall now prove the following theorem:

> VI. If H is a self-conjugate subgroup of a finite group G, and if G_1 denotes the factor-group G/H, then to each subgroup L_1 of G_1 corresponds a subgroup L of G, containing H, such that L_1 is simply isomorphic with L/H. If L_1 is self-conjugate in G_1, then L is self-conjugate in G and G/L is simply isomorphic with G_1/L_1.

We retain the earlier notation of the section. In the isomorphism already established between G and G_1 every element γ_α in L_1 corresponds to the elements $t_\alpha H$ in G. If for γ_α is taken in turn every element in L_1, then the corresponding elements $t_\alpha H$ form a set of elements L of G. Since to $\gamma_\alpha\gamma_\beta$, where γ_α and γ_β are in G_1, corresponds every product of an element in $t_\alpha H$ by an element in $t_\beta H$, it follows that the set L constitutes a group containing H and that L_1 is simply isomorphic with L/H.

If L_1 is self-conjugate in G_1, then for every element γ_α of L_1 and every element γ of G_1 we have in $\gamma^{-1}\gamma_\alpha\gamma$ an element which is in L_1. Then if g is any element of G, we have in $g^{-1} \cdot t_a H \cdot g$ a set of elements of L, whence it follows that L is self-conjugate in G. If we separate G_1 as to L_1 into the partitions $\delta_1 L_1$, $\delta_2 L_1$, $\delta_3 L_1, \cdots$, and if every element formed by taking the product of an element in $\delta_i L_1$ by an element in $\delta_j L_1$ is in the set $\delta_l L_1$, then every element formed by taking the product of an element in $\delta_i L$ by an element in $\delta_j L$ is in $\delta_l L$. Hence G/L and G_1/L_1 are simply isomorphic.

VII. If C is the central of a finite group G, then G/C is simply isomorphic with the group A of inner isomorphisms of G.

Let $c_1 = 1, c_2, \cdots, c_r$ be the elements of C, and arrange the elements of G into the partitions $\gamma_i = t_i C (i = 1, 2, \cdots, \lambda)$. Then, since $(t_i c_\rho)^{-1} G (t_i c_\rho) = c_\rho^{-1} t_i^{-1} G t_i c_\rho = t_i^{-1} G t_i$, it follows that the group of inner isomorphisms of G, when represented as a permutation group by the method of § 17, consists of the following permutations:

$$\begin{pmatrix} S \\ t_i^{-1} S t_i \end{pmatrix}. \quad (i = 1, 2, \cdots, \lambda)$$

Letting these permutations correspond in order to the elements $\gamma_1, \gamma_2, \cdots, \gamma_\lambda$, we have the isomorphism whose existence is asserted in the theorem. For if $t_i t_j$ is in the partition $t_k C$, we have

$$\begin{pmatrix} S \\ t_i^{-1} S t_i \end{pmatrix} \begin{pmatrix} S \\ t_j^{-1} S t_j \end{pmatrix} = \begin{pmatrix} S \\ t_i^{-1} S t_i \end{pmatrix} \begin{pmatrix} t_i^{-1} S t_i \\ t_j^{-1} t_i^{-1} S t_i t_j \end{pmatrix} = \begin{pmatrix} S \\ t_k^{-1} S t_k \end{pmatrix}$$

and also $\gamma_i \gamma_j = \gamma_k$, the latter in accordance with the first paragraph of the section.

VIII. When G is non-Abelian, the group A of inner isomorphisms is noncyclic.

If A is cyclic, let a be an element which generates A; and let g be an element of G which corresponds to a in the usual multiple isomorphism of G with A. Then the elements of G fall into the sets $C, gC, g^2C, \cdots, g^{r-1}C$. Now $g^i c_x \cdot g^j c_y = g^i g^j c_x c_y = g^j g^i c_y c_x = g^j c_y \cdot g^i c_x$, so that any two elements of G are permutable, contrary to the hypothesis.

IX. Let Δ be the commutator subgroup of a given finite group G, and let H be any self-conjugate subgroup of G. Then $\{H, \Delta\}/H$ is simply isomorphic with the commutator subgroup of G/H.

Let a, b be any two elements of G, and let α, β be the corresponding elements of G/H in the usual isomorphism of G with G/H. Then the elements $a^{-1}b^{-1}abH$ of G correspond to the element $\alpha^{-1}\beta^{-1}\alpha\beta$ of G/H. Hence any commutator in G corresponds to a commutator in G/H. To a product of commutators of G/H correspond products of commutators of G by elements of H, and conversely. Hence the commutator subgroup of G/H corresponds to the subgroup $\{H, \Delta\}$ of G, and therefore this commutator subgroup is abstractly the same as the group $\{H, \Delta\}/H$, in accordance with Theorem VI of this section.

COR. I. If the self-conjugate subgroup H of G contains the commutator subgroup Δ of G, then G/H is Abelian.

For in this case $\{H, \Delta\}/H$ consists of the identity alone. Hence the commutator subgroup of G/H consists of the identity alone. Hence G/H is Abelian.

COR. II. Conversely, if G/H is Abelian, then H contains Δ.

For the commutator subgroup of G/H then consists of the identity alone, so that $\{H, \Delta\}/H$ consists of the identity alone.

These two corollaries imply the following:

COR. III. The commutator subgroup of G is the smallest self-conjugate subgroup of G such that the quotient group of G with respect to it is Abelian.

21. The Composition-Series of a Group. Let G_1 be a maximal self-conjugate proper subgroup of a given finite group G_0, let G_2 be a maximal self-conjugate proper subgroup of G_1, G_3 of G_2, G_4

of G_3, and so on, till the series terminates with the identity. Then the series $G_0, G_1, G_2, \cdots$ is called a *composition-series* of G_0. A given group may have more than one composition-series. Every composition-series of G_0 terminates with the group which consists of the identity alone. Although G_i is self-conjugate in G_{i-1}, it is not necessarily true that G_i is self-conjugate in G_{i-2}.

The groups $G_0/G_1, G_1/G_2, G_2/G_3, \cdots$ are known as *composition-factor-groups* of G_0, and their orders are known as *composition-factors* of G_0. From Theorem VI of § **20** it follows that these composition-factor-groups are simple. From the same theorem the converse also readily follows; it may be stated thus: if G_1 is self-conjugate in G_0, G_2 in G_1, G_3 in G_2, and so on, and if $G_0/G_1, G_1/G_2, \cdots$ are all simple, then $G_0, G_1, G_2, \cdots$ constitute a composition-series of G.

Concerning the composition-series of a group G_0 we shall now prove the following theorem:

X. Two composition-series of a finite group G_0 lead to two sets of composition-factor-groups of G_0 which are abstractly identical except for the sequence in which they occur.

Let any two composition-series of G_0 be denoted by the symbols

(1) $$G_0, G_1, G_2, \cdots, G_i, G_{i+1}, G_{i+2}, \cdots,$$

(2) $$G_0, G_1, G_2, \cdots, G_i, F_{i+1}, F_{i+2}, \cdots,$$

where $i \geqq 0$ and where G_{i+1} is different from F_{i+1}.

Let D be the greatest common subgroup of G_{i+1} and F_{i+1}. Then D is self-conjugate in G_i, since both G_{i+1} and F_{i+1} are self-conjugate in G_i. Hence D is a self-conjugate subgroup of both G_{i+1} and F_{i+1}.

Let K denote the group $\{G_{i+1}, F_{i+1}\}$. Then K is self-conjugate in G_i, since both G_{i+1} and F_{i+1} are self-conjugate in G_i. Then from the maximal character of G_{i+1} and F_{i+1} in G_i it follows that K is identical with G_i. With respect to the subgroup D the elements of the group G_{i+1} fall into sets of the form $g_1D, g_2D, g_3D, \cdots$, each element appearing just once. Now every element of G_i is a product of an element in G_{i+1} by an element in F_{i+1}, since $G_i \equiv \{G_{i+1}, F_{i+1}\}$ and G_{i+1} is self-conjugate in G_i. Hence any element in G_i may be written as a product $g_\alpha d_\beta f_\gamma$ where f_γ is in F_{i+1} and d_β is in D. Now the products $d_\beta f_\gamma$ are the elements in F_{i+1}. Hence every element in G_i is contained in the sets $g_1 F_{i+1}, g_2 F_{i+1}, \cdots$. If $g_s F_{i+1}$ and $g_t F_{i+1}$ have an element in common, then $g_t^{-1} g_s$ is in F_{i+1} as well as in G_{i+1}, and hence it is in D, whence it follows that $t = s$. Therefore the elements in G_i are contained without repetition in the sets $g_1 F_{i+1}, g_2 F_{i+1}, \cdots$.

From these partitions of G_i and G_{i+1} by means of their respective subgroups F_{i+1} and D it follows that G_i/F_{i+1} is simply isomorphic with G_{i+1}/D. Similarly the simple isomorphism of G_i/G_{i+1} and F_{i+1}/D may be established. Now G_i/F_{i+1} is a simple group, since F_{i+1} is maximal in G_i. Hence G_{i+1}/D is a simple group, whence it follows that D is a maximal self-conjugate subgroup of G_{i+1}. Similarly it may be shown to be a maximal self-conjugate subgroup of F_{i+1}.

Now let $D, D_1, D_2, \cdots$ be a composition-series of D. Then G_0 has the following two composition-series in addition to (1) and (2), namely:

(3) $$G_0, G_1, G_2, \cdots, G_i, G_{i+1}, D, D_1, D_2, \cdots,$$

(4) $$G_0, G_1, G_2, \cdots, G_i, F_{i+1}, D, D_1, D_2, \cdots.$$

Since G_i/G_{i+1} is simply isomorphic with F_{i+1}/D, and G_i/F_{i+1} is simply isomorphic with G_{i+1}/D, it follows that the composition-factor-groups obtained from the series (3) and (4) are abstractly identical except for a single transposition in their order.

The group of order 2 has only one composition-series. Let n be a number such that every group L of order n or less has the following property: either it has only one composition-series, or, if it has more than one, any two composition-series give rise to simply isomorphic composition-factor-groups, except for possible difference in sequence. We shall now complete the proof of the theorem by mathematical induction.

Suppose that G_0 is of order $n + 1$. Then, whatever value i in (1) and (2) may have, the group G_{i+1} is of order less than n. Hence the two composition-series (1) and (3) give rise to simply isomorphic composition-factor-groups of G_0. Likewise the series (2) and (4) give rise to simply isomorphic composition-factor-groups of G_0. But we have already seen that (3) and (4) give rise to simply isomorphic composition-factor-groups. Hence (1) and (2) have this property. The theorem as stated then follows by mathematical induction.

COR. I. The composition-factors arising from any two composition-series of a group are identical except for the sequence in which they occur.

COR. II. The product of the composition-factors of a group is equal to the order of the group.

XI. Let H be a given self-conjugate subgroup of a given finite group G. Then there is a composition-series of G one group of which is H. The composition-factor-groups of G are simply isomorphic with those of G/H and H taken together.

Denote G/H by L, and let $L, L_1, L_2, \cdots$ be a composition-series of L. In the usual multiple isomorphism of G with L let $G_1, G_2, G_3, \cdots$ be the subgroups of G corresponding to $L_1, L_2, L_3, \cdots$ in L. Then from Theorem VI of § **20** it is seen that we have the following pairs of simply isomorphic groups:

$$G/G_1,\ L/L_1\ ;\ G_1/G_2,\ L_1/L_2\ ;\ G_2/G_3,\ L_2/L_3\ ;\ \cdots.$$

The second group in each pair is simple. Hence the first is also. Therefore $G, G_1, G_2, \cdots$ is a part of a composition-series of G, this part terminating with H. Then continue this composition-series by means of a composition-series of H; in this way we obtain a composition-series of G which includes H as one of the groups in the series. Then it is clear that the composition-factor-groups of G have the properties of isomorphism stated in the theorem.

A *soluble* (or *solvable*) group is a group all of whose composition-factors are primes. The composition-factor-groups of a soluble group are cyclic.

Every Abelian group is soluble. For it contains a self-conjugate subgroup of order p, where p is any prime factor of the order of the group, and the quotient group corresponding to this subgroup is itself an Abelian group. The proof may then be completed by mathematical induction with the aid of the preceding Theorem XI.

Every prime-power group is soluble. If p^α is the order of such a group, the group contains a self-conjugate subgroup of order p (Theorem XVI of § **15**). The corresponding quotient group is of order $p^{\alpha-1}$. Then complete the proof by mathematical induction as in the previous paragraph.

22. The Theorem of Frobenius. We shall now prove the following important theorem due to Frobenius:

> XII. Let G be a group of order g and let n be any factor of g. Then the number of elements in G, including the identity, whose orders are factors of n, is a multiple of n.

The theorem is obviously true when $n = 1$ and when $n = g$. It is true also for a group whose order is a prime, for then n has one of the values just named.

Now let h be a number such that the theorem is true for all groups of order less than h. We shall then prove that it is true for groups of order h, whence the theorem as stated will follow by mathematical induction.

Now the theorem holds for $g = h$ provided that $n = h$. Then let m be a factor of h such that the theorem holds for all larger factors n of h in every group of order h, and suppose that $m > 1$. We shall prove that the theorem also holds for the factor m of h, whence it will follow by induction that it holds for all factors of h; and therefore that the theorem holds in general as stated.

Let H be the group of order h now to be considered. Let N_x be the number of elements in H whose orders are factors of x. Let p be a prime factor of h/m. Now

$$N_{mp} = N_m + \overline{N}_m,$$

where $\overline{N}_m$ denotes the number of elements in H whose orders are factors of mp but not of m. Now N_{mp} is divisible by mp according to hypothesis, and hence it is divisible by m. Then if we prove that $\overline{N}_m$ is divisible by m, it will follow that N_m is divisible by m.

Let U be the set of elements in H each of which has for its order a number which is a factor of mp but not of m. Write $m = p^\mu s$, where s is an integer which is not divisible by p. The order of every element in U is divisible by $p^{\mu+1}$. If u_1 is an element in U, then $u_1{}^\alpha$ is an element in U if α is prime to p. Since we may therefore associate with each element u_1 of U those powers of u_1 each of whose orders is divisible by $p^{\mu+1}$, it follows that the number $\overline{N}_m$ of elements in the set U is a multiple of $\phi(p^{\mu+1}) = p^\mu(p-1)$, and hence of p^μ. It remains only to prove that $\overline{N}_m$ is divisible by s.

If H contains no element whose order is a multiple of $p^{\mu+1}$, then $N_{mp} = N_m$; in this case $\overline{N}_m = 0$ and hence $\overline{N}_m$ is divisible by s. In what follows we may therefore confine ourselves to the case in which the set U contains an element of order $p^{\mu+1}$, since such an element exists in H if H contains an element whose order is a multiple of $p^{\mu+1}$.

Then let P be an element in U of order $p^{\mu+1}$. Let K be the subgroup of H which is formed of all those elements in H each of which is permutable with P, and let the order of K be denoted by $p^{\mu+1}\rho$. The quotient group $K/\{P\}$ is of order ρ, and $\rho < h$. Let τ be the greatest common divisor of s and ρ. From the hypothesis formed for the induction argument it follows that the number of elements in $K/\{P\}$ whose orders are factors of τ is a multiple $c\tau$ of τ. If the order of an element in $K/\{P\}$ is a factor of s, it is also a factor of τ. Hence $c\tau$ is the number of elements in $K/\{P\}$ whose orders are factors of s. Therefore there are $c\tau$ elements common to the set U and the group K.

The number of conjugates of P under H is $g/(p^{\mu+1}\rho)$. With each of these is associated $c\tau$ elements of U. With all of them there are then associated $gc\tau/(p^{\mu+1}\rho)$ elements of U. Now g is divisible by s and by ρ, whence it follows that $g\tau$ is divisible by ρs. Hence s is a factor of $g\tau/\rho$ and therefore of $gc\tau/(p^{\mu+1}\rho)$, since s is prime to $p^{\mu+1}$. Therefore the number of elements in U thus associated with P and its conjugates is a multiple of s. The same will be true for any element Q of order $p^{\mu+1}$ which is not conjugate to P in H. When all such subsets of U are considered, it is obvious that the set U is exhausted and that no element in U is taken twice. Hence $\overline{N}_m$ is divisible by s.

We have already seen that this result is sufficient to complete the proof of the theorem.

EXERCISES

1. If H is a self-conjugate subgroup of G of prime index, then G/H is a cyclic group.

2. If H is a self-conjugate subgroup of G such that the partitions of G as to H may be written in the form $H, gH, g^2H, g^3H, \cdots$, then G/H is a cyclic group.

3. Every factor-group of an Abelian group is an Abelian group.

4. A prime-power cyclic group has only one composition-series.

5. If a prime-power group has only one composition-series it is a cyclic group.

6. Construct all possible composition-series for each abstract group of order 8 (see Ex. 20 on page 37).

7. A soluble noncyclic group is composite.

8. There is no perfect group which is soluble.

9. A direct product of two soluble groups is a soluble group.

10. A group whose order is the product of two primes is a soluble group.

11. A factor-group of a soluble group is itself a soluble group.

12. The order of an element of a quotient group G/H is a factor of the order of each element in G which corresponds to it in the isomorphism described in § **20**.

13. If G has a subgroup of index 2, that subgroup contains all the elements of odd order in G.

14. A group of order $4n + 2$ has just $2n + 1$ elements of odd order.

15. If a group G has just $1 + p$ Sylow subgroups of order p^{α}, these subgroups have just $p^{\alpha-1}$ elements in common.

16. If a group G has just $1 + p$ Sylow subgroups of order p^a, then G contains just p^{a+1} elements whose orders are factors of p^a.

17. If a group G has more than $1 + p$ Sylow subgroups of order p^a, then G contains more than p^{a+1} elements whose orders are factors of p^a.

18. If G is a group of order pq, where p and q are primes and $p > q$, then G contains just $p - 1$ elements of order p. Show that G is cyclic unless $p - 1$ is divisible by q. If $p - 1$ is divisible by q, show that there is just one abstract group of order pq and noncyclic.

19. If n is an integer which is divisible by a square greater than unity, then there are at least two abstract Abelian groups of order n.

20. If n is a product $pqr \cdots$ of distinct primes and if $p - 1$ is divisible by q, then there are at least two abstract groups of order n.

21. Let n be a product of distinct prime factors no one of which is a divisor of any number obtained by diminishing another prime factor by unity. Show that there is but one abstract group of order n, namely, the cyclic group. (Compare Exs. 19 and 20.)

MISCELLANEOUS EXERCISES

1. Let $G_1, G_2, G_3, \cdots$ be a finite set of finite groups such that the orders of any two of them are relatively prime and such that $\{G_1, G_2, G_3, \cdots\}$ is their direct product. Let their groups of isomorphisms be $L_1, L_2, L_3, \cdots$ respectively. Then the group of isomorphisms of $\{G_1, G_2, G_3, \cdots\}$ is the direct product of groups which are simply isomorphic with $L_1, L_2, L_3, \cdots$ respectively.

2. If there is an isomorphism of a group G with itself in which more than three fourths of its elements correspond each to its inverse, then G is an Abelian group.

3. Let A and B be two complete groups having a direct product G, and let L be the group of isomorphisms of G. If A is simply isomorphic with B, then G is simply isomorphic with a self-conjugate subgroup of index 2 in L; otherwise G is simply isomorphic with L.

4. The holomorph of a complete group G is the direct product of two groups each of which is simply isomorphic with G.

5. If A and B are simply isomorphic complete groups of order n such that A and B have a direct product G, then the holomorph of G is of order $2\,n^2$.

6. If G is a complete group of order n, then the holomorph of the holomorph of G is of order $2n^4$.

7. That totality of isomorphisms of a group G with itself, each isomorphism of which changes every conjugate set of elements of G into itself, forms a self-conjugate subgroup of the group of isomorphisms of G. This subgroup contains the group of inner isomorphisms of G.

8. An isomorphism of a group G with itself, the order of which contains a prime factor not occurring in the order of G, interchanges some of the conjugate sets of G.

9. A group which has no characteristic subgroup other than that consisting of the identity alone is either a simple group or the direct product of simply isomorphic simple groups.

10. If a group G contains a complete group H as a self-conjugate subgroup, then G is the direct product of H and some other group.

11. No group of composite order exists having the property that every cyclic proper subgroup in it besides the identity is transformed into itself only by its own elements.

12. If the order of a group G is $p_1p_2 \cdots p_t$, where $p_1, p_2, \cdots, p_t$ are distinct primes in ascending order of magnitude, show that G contains a self-conjugate subgroup of order $p_rp_{r+1} \cdots p_t$ for each r of the set $1, 2, \cdots, t$. Thence show that G is a soluble group.

13. An Abelian group of order p^m and type $(1, 1, \cdots, 1)$ has

$$\frac{(p^m - 1)(p^{m-1} - 1)(p^{m-2} - 1) \cdots (p - 1)}{(p - 1)^m}$$

composition-series.

14. If $G, G_1, G_2, \cdots$ is a composition-series of a group G, and if the order of G_i is prime to its index in G, then show that G_i is a self-conjugate subgroup of G by first establishing the following theorem: If A is a self-conjugate subgroup of H whose order α is prime to its index in H, then every subgroup of H whose order divides α is contained in A.

15. A subgroup of a soluble group is itself a soluble group.

16. Let u_i be the number of cyclic subgroups of order p^i in a group G whose order is divisible by p^k, p being a prime number. Then

$$(u_1 - 1) + (u_2 - 1)p + (u_3 - 1)p^2 + \cdots + (u_k - 1)p^{k-1} \equiv 0 \bmod p^k.$$

17. If for each divisor d of the order n of a group G the number of elements whose orders are factors of d is equal to d, then G is a cyclic group.

18. If the group of inner isomorphisms of a group G is of order 4, then G has just three Abelian subgroups of index 2.

19. If G is a non-Abelian group which has more than one Abelian subgroup of index 2, then the group of inner isomorphisms of G is of order 4.

20. Let G_1 be the commutator subgroup of G_0, G_2 of G_1, G_3 of G_2, and so on. We may call $G_0, G_1, G_2, \cdots$ the *commutator-series* of G_0. In order that G_0 shall be a soluble group it is necessary and sufficient that the commutator-series $G_0, G_1, G_2, \cdots$ shall contain a group consisting of the identity alone.

21. Let I_1 be the group of inner isomorphisms of a given group I_0, let I_2 be the group of inner isomorphisms of I_1, I_3 of I_2, and so on. If in the sequence $I_0, I_1, I_2, \cdots$ there is a group of order unity, show that I_0 is a soluble group.

22. In the case of the commutator-series of a group (see Ex. 20) show that each group after the first is a characteristic self-conjugate subgroup of each group which precedes it.

23. Show that a composition-series of G_0 exists containing among its groups the groups of the commutator-series of G_0. (Use Theorem XI in § **21.**)

24. Let G_1 be a maximal self-conjugate proper subgroup of G_0 and let $G_1, G_2, G_3, \cdots$ be a series of self-conjugate subgroups of G_0 such that G_i contains the proper subgroup G_{i+1} but contains no larger self-conjugate subgroup of G which contains G_{i+1} and is a proper subgroup of G_i. Then $G_0, G_1, G_2, \cdots$ is called a *chief-series* of G_0. Show that a composition-series of G_0 exists containing among its groups any given chief-series of G_0. (Use Theorem XI of § **21.**)

CHAPTER IV

Abelian Groups

23. Classification of Abelian Groups. Several theorems concerning Abelian groups have appeared in the earlier chapters. We have shown (§ **14**) that an Abelian group whose order is not a power of a prime number is the direct product of all its Sylow subgroups. From this it follows that two Abelian groups are simply isomorphic when and only when their Sylow subgroups are simply isomorphic. Therefore the problem of determining all possible abstract Abelian groups is readily reduced to that of determining all prime-power Abelian groups. This latter problem may be solved by aid of the fourth fundamental theorem (given in § **14**), namely, the following: A noncyclic Abelian group G whose order is a prime-power p^m is the direct product of cyclic groups no two of which have any element in common except the identity. If the orders of these cyclic subgroups are, respectively,

$$p^{m_1}, p^{m_2}, \cdots, p^{m_k}, \qquad (m = m_1 + m_2 + \cdots + m_k)$$

then the group G is said to be of type $(m_1, m_2, \cdots, m_k)$. It is convenient to choose the notation so that

$$m_1 \geqq m_2 \geqq \cdots \geqq m_k;$$

and we shall suppose that it is so chosen.

Let $P_1, P_2, \cdots, P_k$, respectively, be generators of the cyclic subgroups of orders $p^{m_1}, p^{m_2}, \cdots, p^{m_k}$ named in the preceding paragraph. Then it is obvious that the elements of G may be written in the form

$$P_1{}^{\alpha_1} P_2{}^{\alpha_2} \cdots P_k{}^{\alpha_k},$$

where

$$\alpha_s = 0, 1, 2, \cdots, p^{m_s} - 1, \qquad (s = 1, 2, \cdots, k)$$

each element having a unique representation in this form. From this it follows that $P_1, P_2, \cdots, P_k$ are independent generators of G.

If the orders of two elements A and B of G are factors of p^μ $(\mu > 0)$, then the order of AB is a factor of p^μ. Hence the totality of elements of G, each of which has for its order a factor of p^μ constitutes a subgroup G_μ of G. If the element

$$P_1^{\beta_1}P_2^{\beta_2}\cdots P_k^{\beta_k}$$

belongs to G_μ, then

$$P_1^{\beta_1 p^\mu}\, P_2^{\beta_2 p^\mu}\,\cdots\, P_k^{\beta_k p^\mu} = 1.$$

Let m_{i+1} be the first number less than μ in the sequence $m_1, m_2, \cdots, m_k, m_{k+1}$, where $m_{k+1} = 0$. Let P_{k+1} be a symbol denoting the identity. Adjoin β_{k+1} to the sequence $\beta_1, \beta_2, \cdots, \beta_k$. Then $\beta_{i+1}, \cdots, \beta_{k+1}$ may have any values whatever, whereas any remaining β_t must be a multiple of $p^{m_t-\mu}$. From this it follows that G_μ is generated by the elements

$$P_1^{p^{m_1-\mu}},\ P_2^{p^{m_2-\mu}},\ \cdots,\ P_i^{p^{m_i-\mu}},\ P_{i+1},\ \cdots,\ P_k,\ P_{k+1}.$$

Hence the order of G_μ is p^ν, where

$$\nu = \mu i + (m_{i+1} + \cdots + m_{k+1}).$$

In particular, the identity and the totality of elements of G each of which is of order p constitute a group G_1 of order p^k.

Let us now suppose that the same group G is generated by the set

$$Q_1,\ Q_2,\ \cdots,\ Q_t$$

of independent generators of orders $p^{\mu_1}, p^{\mu_2}, \cdots, p^{\mu_t}$, respectively, where $m = \mu_1 + \mu_2 + \cdots + \mu_t$ and $\mu_1 \geqq \mu_2 \geqq \cdots \geqq \mu_t > 0$, these generators being such that every element of G may be written uniquely in the form

$$Q_1^{\gamma_1}Q_2^{\gamma_2}\cdots Q_t^{\gamma_t},$$

where

$$\gamma_s = 0, 1, 2, \cdots, p^{\mu_s} - 1. \qquad (s = 1, 2, \cdots, t)$$

We shall then show that $t = k$ and that $\mu_i = m_i$ for each i of the set $1, 2, \cdots, k$.

By considering the group G_μ of order p^ν with reference to this new set of generators it may now be shown that

$$\nu = \mu j + (\mu_{j+1} + \cdots + \mu_{t+1}),$$

where j is defined by the fact that μ_{j+1} is the first number less than μ in the sequence $\mu_1, \mu_2, \cdots, \mu_t, \mu_{t+1}$ ($\mu_{t+1} = 0$). A comparison of the two forms of the value of ν will enable us to establish the proposition stated at the end of the preceding paragraph.

Thus if we take $\mu = 1$ we have $\nu = k$ and $\nu = t$, whence it follows that $t = k$.

Suppose that $m_s = \mu_s$ for $s = i + 1, i + 2, \cdots, k + 1$. If $m_i > \mu_i$ we choose μ so as to satisfy the condition $m_i \geqq \mu > \mu_i$. Then we have

$$\nu = \mu i + (m_{i+1} + \cdots + m_{k+1}),$$
$$\nu = \mu(i-1) + \mu_i + (m_{i+1} + \cdots + m_{k+1}).$$

Hence $\mu_i = \mu$, contrary to hypothesis. Similarly we can prove the untenability of the hypothesis that $\mu_i > m_i$. Hence $\mu_i = m_i$. But $m_{k+1} = \mu_{k+1}$. Hence by an induction argument we may show that $\mu_i = m_i$ for $i = 1, 2, \cdots, k$.

Let G' be a second Abelian group of the same order and type as G. Then there exist independent generators $R_1, R_2, \cdots, R_k$ of G' whose orders are $p^{m_1}, p^{m_2}, \cdots, p^{m_k}$ respectively. Then the correspondence $P_i \sim R_i$, for $i = 1, 2, \cdots, k$, exhibits the fact that G and G' are simply isomorphic. It is obvious from the way in which the generators are determined in § **14** that two prime-power Abelian groups cannot be simply isomorphic unless they are of the same order and type.

These conclusions justify our use of the symbol $(m_1, m_2, \cdots, m_k)$ as a representation of the Abelian group G of order p^m and given type. For every partition of m into a sum $m_1 + m_2 + \cdots + m_k$ of positive summands a corresponding abstract Abelian group G of order p^m exists (see § **14**, near end) and (when p is given) there is just one such group for each partition of m.

This affords a complete determination of all abstract prime-power Abelian groups.

Now let $g_1, g_2, \cdots, g_k$ be any set of elements such that

$$g_i^{p^{m_i}} = 1, \qquad (i = 1, 2, \cdots, k)$$
$$g_i g_j = g_j g_i, \qquad (i, j = 1, 2, \cdots, k)$$

and let it be supposed that there are no additional conditions satisfied by the elements g_i except those which are implied by the given conditions. Then we shall show that the group G, $G \equiv \{g_1, g_2, \cdots, g_k\}$, is an Abelian group of order p^m and type $(m_1, m_2, \cdots, m_k)$, where $m = m_1 + m_2 + \cdots + m_k$, so that the given relations afford a set of abstract defining relations for G.

It is evident that G is Abelian and that its order is a power of p. Moreover, its order cannot be greater than p^m, since every element in G is certainly contained in the set

$$g_1^{\alpha_1} g_2^{\alpha_2} \cdots g_k^{\alpha_k},$$

where $\quad \alpha_i = 0, 1, 2, \cdots, p^{m_i} - 1. \qquad (i = 1, 2, \cdots, k)$

But its order is at least as great as p^m, since the elements

$$\gamma_i = (\alpha_{i1} \alpha_{i2} \cdots \alpha_{i\rho_i}) \qquad (\rho_i = p^{m_i};\ i = 1, 2, \cdots, k)$$

satisfy the conditions imposed on the corresponding g's and at the same time generate a group of order p^m. Hence the group G is of order p^m. It is obvious that its type is $(m_1, m_2, \cdots, m_k)$.

24. Abelian Groups of a Given Order. We shall now determine all possible abstract Abelian groups G of order g, $g = p_1^{\alpha_1} p_2^{\alpha_2} \cdots p_s^{\alpha_s}$, where $p_1, p_2, \cdots, p_s$ are distinct primes and $\alpha_1, \alpha_2, \cdots, \alpha_s$ are positive integers. Every such group G, as we have seen (§ **14**), is the direct product of its Sylow subgroups of orders $p_1^{\alpha_1}, p_2^{\alpha_2}, \cdots, p_s^{\alpha_s}$. The Sylow subgroup of order $p_i^{\alpha_i}$ may be of any type $(\alpha_{i1}, \alpha_{i2}, \cdots, \alpha_{ik_i})$, where the α_{ij} are positive integers such that $\alpha_i = \alpha_{i1} + \alpha_{i2} + \cdots + \alpha_{ik_i}$. By taking every possible such partition of each α_i we get every possible set of Sylow subgroups of groups of order g; the direct products obtained from them give every possible Abelian group G of the named order g.

From this it follows that the number of abstract Abelian groups G of the named order g is equal to the product obtained by multiplying together the numbers which separately represent the numbers of partitions of the α_i into positive summands.

Thus the number of abstract Abelian groups of order $p_1^2p_2^3p_3^3$ is 18; the number of those of order $p_1^5p_2^2p_3^4$ is 70.

We have thus reduced the problem of determining the number of abstract Abelian groups of given order n (where the factorization of n is known) to a problem in the theory of numbers, namely, the problem of determining the number of partitions of a positive integer into positive summands. This problem in the theory of numbers has received considerable attention, but it is yet far from being completely solved.

25. Subgroups of a Prime-Power Abelian Group. Let us now consider the possible types of subgroups of an Abelian group G of order p^m and type $(m_1, m_2, \cdots, m_k)$, where $m_1 \geqq m_2 \geqq \cdots \geqq m_k > 0$. Such a subgroup H is Abelian and of order p^n, where $n \leqq m$. Let $(n_1, n_2, \cdots, n_t)$ denote the type of H, the notation being so chosen that $n_1 \geqq n_2 \geqq \cdots \geqq n_t > 0$. We shall prove that $t \leqq k$ and that $n_i \leqq m_i$ for $i = 1, 2, \cdots, t$.

For this purpose it is convenient to consider the subgroup $G^{(\mu)}$ which consists of the totality of distinct elements of G obtained by raising each element of G to the (p^μ)th power. If $m_i > \mu \geqq m_{i+1}$, then the (p^μ)th power of the element

$$P_1^{\alpha_1}P_2^{\alpha_2} \cdots P_k^{\alpha_k},$$

where $P_1, P_2, \cdots, P_k$ have the same meaning as in § **23**, is

$$P_1^{\alpha_1 p^\mu}P_2^{\alpha_2 p^\mu} \cdots P_k^{\alpha_k p^\mu}.$$

Hence $G^{(\mu)}$ is generated by the i elements

$$P_1^{p^\mu}, P_2^{p^\mu}, \cdots, P_i^{p^\mu}.$$

Therefore the order of $G^{(\mu)}$ is p^λ, where

$$\lambda = (m_1 + m_2 + \cdots + m_i) - \mu i.$$

Consider the subgroup H of G already mentioned. Form its subgroup H_1 consisting of the identity and the elements of order p. This is a subgroup of order p^t of the group G_1 of order p^k considered in § **23**. Hence $t \leqq k$, one of the propositions which we were to prove.

Now the subgroup $H^{(\mu)}$ of H is a subgroup of the subgroup $G^{(\mu)}$ of G, so that the number of generating elements of $H^{(\mu)}$ is equal to or less than the number of generating elements of $G^{(\mu)}$, in accordance with the result in the preceding paragraph. If $n_j > \mu \geqq n_{j+1}$, then the number of generators of $H^{(\mu)}$ is j. But the number of generators of $G^{(\mu)}$ is i. Hence $j \leqq i$.

Now it is obvious that $n_1 \leqq m_1$, since p^{m_1} is the greatest possible order of an element of G. Suppose that $n_\rho \leqq m_\rho$ for $\rho = 1, 2, \cdots, \alpha$, but $n_{\alpha+1} > m_{\alpha+1}$. Then let $\mu = n_{\alpha+1}$. Then we have $i = \alpha$ and $j \geqq \alpha + 1$, contrary to the conclusion that $j \leqq i$. Hence $n_i \leqq m_i$ for $i = 1, 2, \cdots, t$, as was to be shown.

From these results we see that the subgroup H of G exists only when $t \leqq k$ and $n_i \leqq m_i$ for $i = 1, 2, \cdots, t$.

Now it is obvious that G has a subgroup of type $(n_1, n_2, \cdots, n_t)$ in all cases in which $t \leqq k$ and $n_i \leqq m_i$ for $i = 1, 2, \cdots, t$.

A part of the results obtained in this section and § **23** may now be summarized into the following theorem:

I. The number of distinct types of abstract Abelian groups of order p^m, where p is a prime number and m is a positive integer, is equal to the number of partitions of m into positive summands. If one such partition is $m = m_1 + m_2 + \cdots + m_k$, then there is one and just one abstract Abelian group of order p^m and type $(m_1, m_2, \cdots, m_k)$. If the notation is so chosen that $m_1 \geqq m_2 \geqq \cdots \geqq m_k$, then the group of type $(m_1, m_2, \cdots, m_k)$ has a subgroup of type $(n_1, n_2, \cdots, n_t)$ with $n_1 \geqq n_2 \geqq \cdots \geqq n_t$ when and only when $t \leqq k$ and $n_i \leqq m_i$ for $i = 1, 2, \cdots, t$.

26. Number of Elements of a Given Order. Let G be an Abelian group of order p^m and type $(m_1, m_2, \cdots, m_k)$ with $m_1 \geqq m_2 \geqq \cdots \geqq m_k > 0$. We saw in § **23** that the subgroup G_μ, which consists of those elements of G whose orders divide p^μ, is itself of order p^ν, where

$$\nu = \mu i + (m_{i+1} + \cdots + m_{k+1}),$$

m_{i+1} being the first number less than μ in the sequence $m_1, m_2, \cdots, m_k, m_{k+1}$ $(m_{k+1} = 0)$. Now let λ be any positive integer not greater than m_1. Then G contains elements of order p^λ; moreover any given element of G (other than the identity) has for its order a number of the form p^ρ, where ρ is a positive integer not greater than m_1. The number of elements of G of order p^λ is obviously equal to the number obtained by subtracting from the order of G_λ the order of $G_{\lambda-1}$, since every element whose order is a factor of p^λ is contained in G_λ, while $G_{\lambda-1}$ contains every element whose order is a factor of $p^{\lambda-1}$. Now let α and β be such that *

$$m_\alpha \geqq \lambda > m_{\alpha+1}, \quad m_\beta \geqq \lambda - 1 > m_{\beta+1}.$$

Then the orders of G_λ and $G_{\lambda-1}$ are, respectively, p^γ and p^δ, where

$$\gamma = \lambda\alpha + (m_{\alpha+1} + \cdots + m_{k+1}),$$
$$\delta = (\lambda - 1)\beta + (m_{\beta+1} + \cdots + m_{k+1}).$$

The difference $p^\gamma - p^\delta$ gives the number of elements of G each of which is of order p^λ, where λ is a positive integer not greater than m_1.

27. Groups of Isomorphisms of Cyclic Groups. Let G be a cyclic group of order g. We shall now determine the group I of isomorphisms of G with itself and shall show that it is an Abelian group.

Let S be a generator of the group G. Then every possible single generator of G is included in the set S^λ, where λ ranges over the set of integers not greater than g and prime to g; and every such element is a generator of G. In any isomorphism of G with itself a generator of G must correspond to a generator of G. From this it follows readily that the group I of isomorphisms of G with itself may be obtained by taking all correspondences of the form $S \sim S^\lambda$, where λ is a positive integer not greater than g and prime to g. Hence the order of I is $\phi(g)$, where ϕ denotes Euler's ϕ-function of g.

Let $S \sim S^{\lambda_1}$ and $S \sim S^{\lambda_2}$ define two elements of I. The first may equally well be defined by the relation $S^{\lambda_2} \sim S^{\lambda_3}$, where $0 < \lambda_3 \leqq g$ and $\lambda_1\lambda_2 \equiv \lambda_3$ modulo g. Likewise the second may equally well be defined by the relation $S^{\lambda_1} \sim S^{\lambda_3}$. Hence their

* An obvious modification is needed when $\lambda = 1$.

product in either order may be defined by the relation $S \sim S^{\lambda_3}$. From this it follows that the group I is Abelian. Groups formed in this way constitute an important special class of Abelian groups.

Once the generator S of G is given, the element of I defined by the relation $S \sim S^{\lambda_1}$ may be uniquely represented by the number λ_1. If two elements $S \sim S^{\lambda_1}$ and $S \sim S^{\lambda_2}$ of I are given, their product is $S \sim S^{\lambda_3}$, where λ_3 is the least positive residue of $\lambda_1\lambda_2$ modulo g. Hence the isomorphisms which we represent by λ_1 and λ_2, respectively, have as their product the isomorphism represented by λ_3, where λ_3 is the least positive residue of $\lambda_1\lambda_2$ modulo g. The group I is thus represented as simply isomorphic with the group I' whose elements are the positive integers not greater than g and prime to g, the rule of combination being ordinary multiplication together with a reduction modulo g.

EXERCISES

1. If G is an Abelian group and H is any subgroup of G, then the factor-group G/H exists and is Abelian.

2. Construct a non-Abelian group G having an Abelian self-conjugate subgroup H such that G/H is Abelian.

3. Let G be an Abelian group of order p^m. Let G_μ and $G^{(\nu)}$ be its subgroups denoted by these symbols in §§ **23** and **25** respectively. Prove that G_μ and $G^{(\nu)}$ are characteristic subgroups of G. Prove also that the greatest common subgroup $K_{\mu,\nu}$ of G_μ and $G^{(\nu)}$ is a characteristic subgroup of G.

4. Determine the group I of isomorphisms of the group whose elements are the eight eighth roots of unity, the law of combination being ordinary multiplication.

5. Show that no group I of the class discussed in § **27** can be of order 14 or 26; show that these numbers are the smallest even numbers that cannot be obtained as the orders of groups of isomorphisms of cyclic groups.

6. The elements of highest order in an Abelian group G generate G.

7. Construct a non-Abelian group which is not generated by its elements of highest order.

8. In order that a given group G shall be Abelian it is necessary and sufficient that G may be exhibited as simply isomorphic with itself by making each element in G correspond to its inverse.

9. Show that the only Abelian groups each of which has no characteristic proper subgroup (other than that consisting of the identity alone) are those of prime-power order p^m and type $(1, 1, \cdots, 1)$.

10. If S and P are elements satisfying the relations

$$P^p = S^{p-1} = 1 \quad \text{and} \quad S^{-1}PS = P^\alpha,$$

where p is an odd prime and α is a primitive root modulo p, and if S and P satisfy no conditions except those implied by the relations already given, show that $\{S, P\}$ is simply isomorphic with the holomorph of the cyclic group of order p. (See Ex. 16 on page 84.)

11. Represent the group $\{S, P\}$ of Ex. 10 as a permutation group of degree p.

12. Let G be a cyclic group of order p^n, where p is an odd prime. Show that the holomorph of G is of order $p^{2n-1}(p-1)$ and that it has the abstract defining relations

$$P^{p^n} = S^{p^{n-1}(p-1)} = 1, \quad S^{-1}PS = P^\alpha$$

where α is a primitive root of the congruence

$$\alpha^{p^{n-1}(p-1)} \equiv 1 \bmod p^n.$$

13. Obtain for cyclic groups of order 2^n the results corresponding to those given in Ex. 12 for the group G there defined.

14. Show that the holomorph of a cyclic group of odd order is a complete group.

15. Determine the cases in which the group I of isomorphisms of a cyclic group G of order g is itself a cyclic group. In particular, show that no such cyclic group I can be of order 8 or 14.

16. Show that any given Abelian group G is simply isomorphic with a subgroup of some group I' of the class discussed at the end of § **27**.

17. If H is any subgroup of an Abelian group G, show that G contains a subgroup simply isomorphic with G/H.

18. Construct a non-Abelian group G having a self-conjugate subgroup H such that the factor-group G/H is simply isomorphic with no subgroup of G.

19. Show that for every Abelian group G a set of independent generating elements $S_1, S_2, \cdots, S_\rho$ exists such that the order of each element in the set (after the first) is a (proper or improper) factor of the order of each element which precedes it.

20. Show that the number of ways in which a set of independent generating elements of an Abelian group of order $p^{\frac{1}{2}n(n+1)}$ and type $(n, n-1, \cdots, 2, 1)$ may be selected is $p^\nu(p-1)^n$, where ν is such that $6\nu = n(n+1)(2n+1) - 6n$.

28. Properties of an Abelian Group G of Order p^m and Type $(1, 1, \cdots, 1)$. The elements of G (other than the identity) are all of order p. Hence a subgroup of G of order p^α is of type $(1, 1, \cdots, 1)$.

Let us consider the number of ways in which an ordered set $S_1, S_2, \cdots, S_m$ of generators of G may be chosen. Since G contains $p^m - 1$ elements of order p, the first generator S_1 may be chosen in $p^m - 1$ ways. The group $\{S_1\}$ contains $p - 1$ elements of order p. The remaining elements of order p in G are $p^m - p$ in number. Hence the second generator S_2 of G may be chosen in any one of $p^m - p$ ways. The group $\{S_1, S_2\}$ contains $p^2 - 1$ elements of order p, so that the remaining elements of order p are $p^m - p^2$ in number. Since any one of these may be taken for S_3, it follows that S_3 may be chosen in any one of $p^m - p^2$ ways. By continuing this process one finds that the ordered set $S_1, S_2, \cdots, S_m$ of generators of G may be chosen in

$$(p^m - 1)(p^m - p)(p^m - p^2) \cdots (p^m - p^{m-1})$$

ways. A given set of m generators may be arranged in $m!$ different orders. Hence the number of distinct sets of generators of G, considered apart from their order, is

$$\frac{(p^m - 1)(p^m - p)(p^m - p^2) \cdots (p^m - p^{m-1})}{m!}.$$

By a similar argument the number of subgroups of G of order p^α is readily determined. Such a subgroup has α generators of order p. The first may be chosen from G in $p^m - 1$ ways; the second, in $p^m - p$ ways; the third, in $p^m - p^2$ ways; and so on till finally the αth may be chosen in $p^m - p^{\alpha-1}$ ways.

Hence the ordered set of α generators to give rise to a subgroup of G of order p^α may be chosen in

$$(p^m - 1)(p^m - p)(p^m - p^2) \cdots (p^m - p^{\alpha-1})$$

ways. But an ordered set of generators of a given group of order p^α and type $(1, 1, \cdots, 1)$ may be selected in

$$(p^\alpha - 1)(p^\alpha - p)(p^\alpha - p^2) \cdots (p^\alpha - p^{\alpha-1})$$

ways. The number of subgroups of order p^α in G is evidently the quotient of these two numbers and hence is equal to

$$\frac{(p^m - 1)(p^m - p)(p^m - p^2) \cdots (p^m - p^{\alpha-1})}{(p^\alpha - 1)(p^\alpha - p)(p^\alpha - p^2) \cdots (p^\alpha - p^{\alpha-1})}.$$

From this it follows readily that the number of subgroups of order p^k in G is the same as the number of subgroups of order p^{m-k}.

Now let $P_1, P_2, \cdots, P_m$ be any fixed set of generators of G. Then an isomorphism of G with itself may be set up by means of the symbol

$$\begin{bmatrix} P_1, P_2, \cdots, P_m \\ S_1, S_2, \cdots, S_m \end{bmatrix},$$

where $S_1, S_2, \cdots, S_m$ is any ordered set of generators of G, this symbol implying that P_i corresponds to S_i for $i = 1, 2, \cdots, m$. The totality of isomorphisms of G with itself is obtained by varying the ordered set $S_1, S_2, \cdots, S_m$ in every possible way. Hence the order of the group I of isomorphisms of G with itself is equal to the number of ways in which the ordered set of generators $S_1, S_2, \cdots, S_m$ may be chosen and hence is equal to

$$(p^m - 1)(p^m - p)(p^m - p^2) \cdots (p^m - p^{m-1}).$$

From § **18** it follows that the order of the holomorph K of G is p^m times the preceding number.

29. Analytical Representations of G, I, and K. Employing the symbols G, I, and K with the same meanings as in the preceding section, we shall now obtain certain useful analytical representations of the groups G, I, and K.

As before, we let $P_1, P_2, \cdots, P_m$ denote a fixed set of generators of the Abelian group G of order p^m and type $(1, 1, \cdots, 1)$.

Then the elements of G are all uniquely represented by the symbols

$$P_1^{\mu_1}P_2^{\mu_2}\cdots P_m^{\mu_m},$$

where $\mu_1, \mu_2, \cdots, \mu_m$ run independently over the set 0, 1, 2, $\cdots, p-1$ of p numbers. An element of G may therefore be represented uniquely by the symbol

$$\{\mu_1, \mu_2, \cdots, \mu_m\},$$

where each μ is a number of the set $0, 1, 2, \cdots, p-1$, provided it is understood that the symbol represents the product $P_1^{\mu_1}P_2^{\mu_2}\cdots P_m^{\mu_m}$. We shall employ the more general symbol $\{\nu_1, \nu_2, \cdots, \nu_m\}$, where the ν's belong to the class of all integers, with the understanding that two symbols of this form are to be considered equivalent if their corresponding elements are congruent modulo p. Thus $\{\mu_1, \mu_2, \cdots, \mu_m\}$ and $\{\nu_1, \nu_2, \cdots, \nu_m\}$ are equivalent if $\mu_i \equiv \nu_i \bmod p$ for $i = 1, 2, \cdots, m$. For the multiplication of these symbols (corresponding to the multiplication of elements in G) we obviously have the formula

$$\{\mu_1, \mu_2, \cdots, \mu_m\}\cdot\{\nu_1, \nu_2, \cdots, \nu_m\} = \{\mu_1 + \nu_1, \cdots, \mu_m + \nu_m\}.$$

Now consider the set of elements

$$\{\mu\mu_1, \mu\mu_2, \cdots, \mu\mu_m\},$$

where $\mu_1, \mu_2, \cdots, \mu_m$ constitute a fixed set of m numbers taken modulo p and not all of them congruent to zero modulo p, μ being a variable integer taken modulo p. This set of elements forms a group of order p having $\{\mu_1, \mu_2, \cdots, \mu_m\}$ for a generator. This group of order p may be denoted by the symbol

$$(\mu_1, \mu_2, \cdots, \mu_m).$$

The same group is also represented by the symbol

$$(\nu\mu_1, \nu\mu_2, \cdots, \nu\mu_m),$$

provided only that ν is a fixed integer incongruent to zero modulo p. The symbol $(\mu_1, \mu_2, \cdots, \mu_m)$ may therefore be treated as exhibiting a set of homogeneous co-ordinates for the given subgroup, analogous to the homogeneous co-ordinates of a point in a space of $m-1$ dimensions. (The geometrical interpretation thus suggested will be generalized and developed in Chapter XI.) In a similar way the symbol $\{\mu_1, \mu_2, \cdots, \mu_m\}$ denotes the nonhomogeneous co-ordinates of an element of G, analogous to the nonhomogeneous co-ordinates of a point in a space of m dimensions.

Let us now consider the conditions under which the symbols

$$\begin{pmatrix} P_i \\ P_1^{\alpha_{1i}} P_2^{\alpha_{2i}} \cdots P_m^{\alpha_{mi}} \end{pmatrix}, \qquad (i = 1, 2, \cdots, m)$$

define an isomorphism of G with itself. In accordance with these symbols an element $P_1^{x_1} P_2^{x_2} \cdots P_m^{x_m}$ is replaced by the element $P_1^{y_1} P_2^{y_2} \cdots P_m^{y_m}$, where

$$y_i \equiv \alpha_{i1} x_1 + \alpha_{i2} x_2 + \cdots + \alpha_{im} x_m \bmod p. \qquad (i = 1, 2, \cdots, m)$$

This represents a transformation of the element $\{x_1, x_2, \cdots, x_m\}$ of G into the element $\{y_1, y_2, \cdots, y_m\}$ of G. In order that this may represent an isomorphism of G with itself, it is necessary and sufficient that $\{y_1, y_2, \cdots, y_m\}$ shall run over all the elements of G when $\{x_1, x_2, \cdots, x_m\}$ runs over all the elements of G. Hence for a given set $\{y_1, y_2, \cdots, y_m\}$ there must be a single set $\{x_1, x_2, \cdots, x_m\}$. Therefore the foregoing set of m simultaneous congruences must have a unique solution $\{x_1, x_2, \cdots, x_m\}$ when the set $\{y_1, y_2, \cdots, y_m\}$ is given. A necessary and sufficient condition for this is that the determinant D,

$$D = \begin{vmatrix} \alpha_{11} & \alpha_{12} & \cdots & \alpha_{1m} \\ \alpha_{21} & \alpha_{22} & \cdots & \alpha_{2m} \\ \cdot & \cdot & \cdot & \cdot \\ \alpha_{m1} & \alpha_{m2} & \cdots & \alpha_{mm} \end{vmatrix},$$

shall be incongruent to zero modulo p.

From these considerations it follows that the symbols at the beginning of the preceding paragraph define an isomorphism of G with itself when and only when the foregoing determinant D is incongruent to zero modulo p. When this condition is satisfied, every set of simultaneous congruences of the foregoing form represents an isomorphism of G with itself, and two distinct sets of congruences represent two distinct isomorphisms of G with itself. Moreover, every isomorphism of G with itself may be represented in such a form. Furthermore, to the product of two isomorphisms of G with itself will correspond the product of the two corresponding transformations of x's into y's.

From these results it follows that the group I of isomorphisms of G with itself is simply isomorphic with the group of elements defined by all congruences of the form

$$y_i \equiv \alpha_{i1}x_1 + \alpha_{i2}x_2 + \cdots + \alpha_{im}x_m \bmod p \quad (i = 1, 2, \cdots, m)$$

when the coefficients α_{ij} are subject to the condition that the determinant D, or $|\alpha_{ij}|$, shall be incongruent to zero modulo p.

The group last mentioned is known as the *linear homogeneous group* modulo p. Its order is found from § **28** and the fact that it is simply isomorphic with I; this order is

$$(p^m - 1)(p^m - p)(p^m - p^2) \cdots (p^m - p^{m-1}).$$

This group and its generalizations (see Chapters X and XI) are of importance in several branches of mathematics.

The corresponding *linear nonhomogeneous group* modulo p consists of the transformations

$$y_i \equiv \alpha_{i1}x_1 + \alpha_{i2}x_2 + \cdots + \alpha_{im}x_m + \beta_i \bmod p, \quad (i = 1, 2, \cdots, m)$$

where again the determinant D is restricted to be incongruent to zero modulo p. It will now be shown that this group $\overline{K}$ is simply isomorphic with the holomorph K of G. Since each of the integers β_i may be selected in p ways which are distinct modulo p, it follows that the set $\beta_1, \beta_2, \cdots, \beta_m$ may be selected in p^m ways. Hence the order of the group $\overline{K}$ is p^m times the order of I, since the β's may be assigned values quite independently of the α's. Therefore the order of $\overline{K}$ is

$$(p^m - 1)(p^m - p)(p^m - p^2) \cdots (p^m - p^{m-1})p^m,$$

and this is the same as the order of K. The transformations

$$y_i \equiv x_i + \beta_i \bmod p \quad (i = 1, 2, \cdots, m)$$

form an Abelian group of order p^m and type $(1, 1, \cdots, 1)$, as one may easily verify. Hence it is simply isomorphic with G. Moreover, this subgroup is self-conjugate in $\overline{K}$. Furthermore, it is not difficult to show that the only elements of $\overline{K}$ which are permutable with every element in this subgroup are the elements of this subgroup. From these facts, and the isomorphism of the linear homogeneous group modulo p with I and the known order of $\overline{K}$, it follows readily that $\overline{K}$ and K are simply isomorphic, as was to be proved.

30. Groups of Isomorphisms of Abelian Groups in General. Let G be an Abelian group of order $p_1^{\alpha_1}p_2^{\alpha_2}\cdots p_n^{\alpha_n}$ where $p_1, p_2, \cdots, p_n$ are distinct primes and $\alpha_1, \alpha_2, \cdots, \alpha_n$ are positive integers. Then G, as we have seen, is the direct product of its Sylow subgroups $G_1, G_2, \cdots, G_n$ of orders $p_1^{\alpha_1}, p_2^{\alpha_2}, \cdots, p_n^{\alpha_n}$, respectively. In any isomorphism of G with itself the elements of the subgroup G_i must correspond to elements of G_i. If I_i is any isomorphism of G_i with itself, then G admits an isomorphism in which the elements of G_i correspond in accordance with the isomorphism I_i while the elements of the remaining subgroups in the set $G_1, G_2, \cdots, G_n$ correspond each to itself. This isomorphism of G with itself is permutable with any isomorphism of G with itself in which the elements of G_i correspond each to itself. From these facts it follows that the group of isomorphisms of G with itself is the direct product of the groups $L_1, L_2, \cdots, L_n$ of isomorphisms of $G_1, G_2, \cdots, G_n$, respectively, each with itself.

In a similar way it may be shown that the holomorph of G is the direct product of the holomorphs of $G_1, G_2, \cdots, G_n$.

Now let m be the least common multiple of the orders of the elements of G. Then G has elements of order m and no element of order greater than m. Let μ be any number not greater than m and prime to m. Then the symbol

$$\begin{pmatrix} S \\ S^{\mu} \end{pmatrix}$$

denotes an isomorphism of G with itself, as one may easily verify. It is obvious (compare § 27) that the product of any two such isomorphisms is an isomorphism of the same sort; for we have

$$\begin{pmatrix} S \\ S^{\mu_1} \end{pmatrix}\begin{pmatrix} S \\ S^{\mu_2} \end{pmatrix} = \begin{pmatrix} S \\ S^{\mu_1} \end{pmatrix}\begin{pmatrix} S^{\mu_1} \\ S^{\mu_1\mu_2} \end{pmatrix} = \begin{pmatrix} S \\ S^{\mu_3} \end{pmatrix}$$

where μ_3 is the least positive residue of $\mu_1\mu_2$ modulo m. Giving to μ in turn all its possible values, $\phi(m)$ in number, we have $\phi(m)$ distinct isomorphisms of G with itself; and these constitute a subgroup of the group of isomorphisms of G with itself. When G is a cyclic group this group of $\phi(m)$ isomorphisms is the entire group of isomorphisms of G with itself, as we have seen in § 27. When G is noncyclic, it is clear that this group is a proper subgroup of the group of isomorphisms of G with itself; we shall now show that it is a self-conjugate subgroup.

For this purpose let the symbol

$$\begin{pmatrix} S \\ S' \end{pmatrix}$$

denote any isomorphism of G with itself. Then we have

$$\begin{pmatrix} S \\ S' \end{pmatrix}^{-1}\begin{pmatrix} S \\ S^\mu \end{pmatrix}\begin{pmatrix} S \\ S' \end{pmatrix}=\begin{pmatrix} S' \\ S \end{pmatrix}\begin{pmatrix} S \\ S^\mu \end{pmatrix}\begin{pmatrix} S^\mu \\ S'^\mu \end{pmatrix}=\begin{pmatrix} S' \\ S'^\mu \end{pmatrix}=\begin{pmatrix} S \\ S^\mu \end{pmatrix}.$$

This shows that the elements of the named subgroup are self-conjugate in the group of isomorphisms of G with itself.

31. Hamiltonian Groups. A *Hamiltonian group* is a non-Abelian group all of whose subgroups are self-conjugate. Since every subgroup of such a group is self-conjugate, it follows that there is only one Sylow subgroup of each order. Now let g and h be elements from two Sylow subgroups. If c is the element $c = g^{-1} \cdot h^{-1}gh = g^{-1}h^{-1}g \cdot h$, then c is in each of these subgroups and therefore is the identity. Hence g and h are permutable. Hence it follows that a Hamiltonian group is the direct product of its Sylow subgroups.

Two elements a and b subject to the sole conditions

$$a^4 = 1,\ a^2 = (ab)^2 = b^2,$$

generate a group of order 8, as the reader may easily verify. This is known as the *quaternion* group. The reader may show that it is a Hamiltonian group. It has, besides the identity, six elements of order 4 and one of order 2.

We shall now prove the following theorem (by the method given in Hilton's *Finite Groups*):

II. Let G be a Hamiltonian group. Then

(1) G is the quaternion group Q; or,

(2) G is the direct product of Q and A, of Q and B, or of Q and A and B,

where A is an Abelian group of odd order k and B is an Abelian group of order 2^m and type $(1, 1, \cdots, 1)$.

Every such direct product is a Hamiltonian group.

We first prove that the direct product G_1 of Q and A and B is a Hamiltonian group. Let h be any element of a subgroup H of G_1 and write $h = abc$, where a, b, c belong, respectively, to A, B, Q. Let g be any element of G_1 and write similarly $g = \alpha\beta\gamma$, where α, β, γ belong, respectively, to A, B, Q. Then we have $g^{-1}hg = \gamma^{-1}\beta^{-1}\alpha^{-1}abc\alpha\beta\gamma = \gamma^{-1}abc\gamma = \gamma^{-1}c\gamma ab$. Since $c^4 = 1$ and $\{c\}$ is self-conjugate in Q, it follows that $\gamma^{-1}c\gamma = c$ or c^3. Hence $g^{-1}hg = h$ or c^2h. Now H contains the element $h^{2k} = (abc)^{2k} = a^{2k}b^{2k}c^{2k} = c^{2k}$. But $c^{2k} = c^2$, since $c^4 = 1$ and k is odd. Therefore H contains both h and c^2h and hence contains $g^{-1}hg$. Therefore H is self-conjugate in G_1. Therefore G_1 is a Hamiltonian group.

That the direct product of Q and A alone or of Q and B alone is also a Hamiltonian group is now evident.

Let Γ be a Hamiltonian group of order p^α, where p is a prime. Let p^λ be the lowest order of an element in Γ which is not self-conjugate in Γ, and let g be an element of Γ of order p^λ which is not self-conjugate in Γ. Let h be any element of Γ which is not permutable with g and denote the order of h by p^μ $(\mu \geqq \lambda)$.

Since Γ is Hamiltonian, it follows that $h^{-1}gh$ is in $\{g\}$. Then $h^{-1}gh$ is a power of g. Write $g^{-1} \cdot h^{-1}gh = c$. Then c is a power of g. In a similar way it may be shown that c is a power of h. Hence c is in the greatest common subgroup D of $\{g\}$ and $\{h\}$. Every subgroup (of order greater than 1) of $\{g\}$ contains $\{g^{p^{\lambda-1}}\}$, and every subgroup (of order greater than 1) of $\{h\}$ contains $\{h^{p^{\mu-1}}\}$. But, since $c \neq 1$, D does not consist of the identity alone. Therefore D contains both $\{g^{p^{\lambda-1}}\}$ and $\{h^{p^{\mu-1}}\}$. Hence $g^{p^{\lambda-1}}$ is some power of c; likewise $h^{p^{\mu-1}}$ is some power of c. Therefore $g^{p^{\lambda-1}} = h^{up^{\mu-1}}$, where u is an appropriate integer which is prime to p. Since g and h are not permutable, it follows that D does not coincide with $\{g\}$. Therefore $\lambda > 1$.

From the relation $h^{-1}gh = gc$ and the fact that g and c are permutable we have $h^{-1}g^p h = g^p c^p$. But g^p is self-conjugate in Γ by hypothesis; therefore $c^p = 1$.

Since c is permutable with both g and h and $g^{-1}h^{-1}gh = c$, we have

$$g^{-1}h^{-1}g = ch^{-1},\ \ g^{-1}h^{-\beta}g = c^{\beta}h^{-\beta},\ h^{-\beta}gh^{\beta} = gc^{\beta},\ \ h^{-\beta}g^{\alpha}h^{\beta} = g^{\alpha}c^{\alpha\beta}.$$

In particular, $gh^{\beta} = h^{\beta}gc^{\beta}$. Hence $(hg)^2 = h \cdot gh \cdot g = h \cdot hgc \cdot g = h^2g^2c$, $(hg)^3 = hgh^2g^2c = h \cdot h^2gc^2 \cdot g^2c = h^3g^3c^3$. By induction it may now be shown that $(hg)^t = h^t g^t c^{\frac{1}{2}t(t-1)}$. But from the established relation $h^{-y}g^x h^y = g^x c^{xy}$, it follows * that c^{xy} is the commutator of g^x and h^y. Hence

$$(h^y g^x)^t = h^{yt} g^{xt} c^{\frac{1}{2}xyt(t-1)},$$

as one may show from the result just preceding.

In the last relation put

$$x = 1, \quad y = -\,up^{\mu-\lambda}, \quad t = p^{\lambda-1}.$$

Then we have $(h^y g)^t = c^{\frac{1}{2}yt(t-1)}$. Hence if p is odd, or if $p = 2$ and y is even, or if $p = 2$ and $\lambda > 2$, we have $(h^y g)^t = 1$, since $c^p = 1$. Now $h^y g$ is not permutable with h; hence we cannot have $(h^y g)^t = 1$, for then we should have an element of lower order than g and yet not permutable with h, contrary to hypothesis. Therefore we must have $p = 2$, $\lambda = 2$ (since $\lambda > 1$), y an odd number, and therefore $\mu = \lambda = 2$. Then we have $g^4 = h^4 = 1$, $g^2 = h^2$, and $g^{-1}hg = h^3$. From this it follows that $\{g, h\}$ is the quaternion group.

From this it follows that any two nonpermutable elements in a Hamiltonian group Γ of order 2^{α} generate a quaternion group.

An element e of order 2 in Γ is self-conjugate, since $\{e\}$ is self-conjugate. The elements of order 2 therefore constitute an Abelian subgroup H of type $(1, 1, \cdots, 1)$. Let Q be any

* This result is of some interest in itself apart from the use made of it here.

quaternion subgroup of Γ generated by elements a and b subject to the conditions $a^4 = 1$, $a^2 = (ab)^2 = b^2$. If d is an element of Γ which is not permutable with a, then $\{a, d\}$ is a quaternion group and we have $d^2 = a^2$, in accordance with a previous result in the argument.

If γ is an element of Γ which is permutable with both a and b, then γb is not permutable with a, and hence $a^2 = (\gamma b)^2 = \gamma^2 b^2 = \gamma^2 a^2$. Therefore $\gamma^2 = 1$ and hence γ is in H.

If γ is an element of Γ which is not permutable with both a and b, then we have either (1) $\gamma^{-1} a \gamma = a$, $\gamma^{-1} b g = b^3$, (2) $\gamma^{-1} a \gamma = a^3$, $\gamma^{-1} b \gamma = b$, or (3) $\gamma^{-1} a \gamma = a^3$, $\gamma^{-1} b \gamma = b^3$. In the respective cases it may be shown that a and b are both permutable with (1) $a\gamma$, (2) $b\gamma$, (3) $ab\gamma$. In each case γ is in $\{Q, H\}$. Then Γ is generated by Q and H, and H is the central of Γ. The greatest common subgroup of Q and H is $\{a^2\}$. If B is that subgroup of H of index 2 which does not contain a^2, then B is an Abelian group of order $2^{\alpha-3}$ and of type $(1, 1, \cdots, 1)$, when $\alpha > 3$, while Γ itself is the direct product of Q and B.

From this it follows that a Hamiltonian group of order 2^α is the direct product of the quaternion group Q and an Abelian group B of order 1 when $\alpha = 3$ and of order $2^{\alpha-3}$ and type $(1, 1, \cdots, 1)$ when $\alpha > 3$.

Now any Hamiltonian group is the direct product of its Sylow subgroups. From the foregoing argument it follows that the Sylow subgroups of odd order are Abelian. The direct product of these Sylow subgroups of odd order is an Abelian group A of odd order. The Sylow subgroup of even order 2^α is either the quaternion group Q or the direct product of B and Q, as we have seen. Hence G itself is a group of one of the types described in the theorem.

This completes the proof of the theorem.

EXERCISES

1. If K is the holomorph of a cyclic group G of order 8, show that G is not a characteristic subgroup of K.

2. In the group A of inner isomorphisms of a group G no element other than the identity is a power of every other element except the identity.

3. There is no group G having the quaternion group for its group of inner isomorphisms.

4. A subgroup of a Hamiltonian group is either Hamiltonian or Abelian.

5. A factor-group of a Hamiltonian group is either Hamiltonian or Abelian.

6. The holomorph of the cyclic group of order 4 is simply isomorphic with the octic group.

7. The group of inner isomorphisms of a Hamiltonian group is an Abelian group of order 4 and type (1, 1).

8. An element of the group $\{B, Q\}$ of § **31** is of order 1 or 2 or 4.

9. If s and t are subject to the sole conditions $s^{16}=1$, $t^2=1$, $tst=s^9$, then the group $\{s, t\}$ is of order 32 and is conformal with the Abelian group of order 2^5 and type (4, 1).

10. Show that the holomorph of the cyclic group of order n contains a subgroup of order nd for every factor d of $\phi(n)$, where $\phi(n)$ denotes Euler's ϕ-function of n.

11. Show that the number of subgroups of type (2, 1) in a prime-power Abelian group of order p^6 and type (2, 2, 1, 1) is $p^2(p+1)(p^2+p+1)$.

12. In order that a prime-power group of order p^m $(m>1)$ shall be Abelian, it is necessary and sufficient that more than p^{m-1} of its elements shall correspond each to its inverse in some isomorphism of the group with itself.

13. Let $H_0, H_1, H_2, \cdots, H_p$ be the $p+1$ subgroups of order p in an Abelian group G of prime-power order p^2 and type (1, 1). Show that the group of isomorphisms of G with itself permutes these $p+1$ subgroups according to a transitive permutation group K of degree $p+1$ and order $(p+1)p(p-1)$.

14. Show that the group K of the foregoing Ex. 13 contains a transitive subgroup K_1 of degree p and order $p(p-1)$ each element of which leaves H_0 fixed; show further that K_1 has a cyclic transitive subgroup of degree and order $p-1$ each element of which leaves H_1 fixed.

15. Show that the group K of the foregoing Ex. 13 has a transitive subgroup L of index 2 such that L itself has a transitive subgroup L_1 of degree p and order $\frac{1}{2}p(p-1)$ each element of which leaves H_0 fixed.

16. Let G be a prime-power Abelian group of order p^m and type $(m_1, m_2, \cdots, m_k)$ and let r be less than or equal to k. Show that the number of subgroups in G of order p^r and type $(1, 1, \cdots, 1)$ is

$$\frac{(p^k-1)(p^{k-1}-1)\cdots(p^{k-r+1}-1)}{(p^r-1)(p^{r-1}-1)\cdots(p-1)}.$$

MISCELLANEOUS EXERCISES

1. Let G be an Abelian group of order greater than unity such that every element in it besides the identity is of one given order k. Show that k is a prime number p and that G is of order p^m and type $(1, 1, \cdots, 1)$, where m is some positive integer.

2. Let S be an element of prime order q which is permutable with a prime-power Abelian group G of order p^α but not with any proper subgroup of G except that consisting of the identity alone. Show that $q \geqq \alpha$.

3. Let G be any group of finite order. Show that a number m exists such that the group of isomorphisms of the Abelian group of prime-power order p^m and type $(1, 1, \cdots, 1)$ contains a subgroup simply isomorphic with G.

4. Let G be an Abelian group having the property that it contains a set of subgroups such that any given element of G other than the identity occurs in one and just one subgroup of the named set. Show that G is of prime-power order p^m and of type $(1, 1, \cdots, 1)$.

5. Let G be a prime-power Abelian group of order p^{2y+z} and type $(2, 2, \cdots, 2, 1, 1, \cdots, 1)$, the latter symbol containing y 2's and z 1's. Show that the number N_1 of cyclic subgroups of order p^2 in G and the number N_2 of noncyclic subgroups of order p^2 in G are given by the formulas

$$N_1 = \frac{p^y-1}{p-1}\, p^{y+z-1} \quad \text{and} \quad N_2 = \frac{(p^{y+z}-1)(p^{y+z-1}-1)}{(p^2-1)(p-1)}.$$

6. Find the number of subgroups of type $(3, 2, 1)$ in a prime-power Abelian group of order p^{12} and type $(3, 3, 2, 2, 1, 1)$.

7. Let G be an Abelian group of prime-power order p^m and type $(2, 1, 1, \cdots, 1)$. Show that the number of subgroups of index p in G is $(p^{m-1}-1)/(p-1)$.

8. If P is an element of order p^α in the group I of §§ **28** and **29**, show that $\alpha \leqq \frac{1}{2} m$ or $\alpha \leqq \frac{1}{2}(m + 1)$ according as m is even or odd.

9. Show that the group of isomorphisms of the Abelian group G of order 3^2 and type (1, 1), when represented in the usual way as a permutation group, contains two abstractly distinct regular subgroups of order 8. Show in each case that the corresponding subgroup of the holomorph of G, when represented in the usual way as a permutation group, is a transitive group of degree 9 and order $9 \cdot 8$ which contains as a subgroup a transitive group of degree 8 and order 8.

10. Show that the group of isomorphisms of the Abelian group G of order 5^2 and type (1, 1), when represented in the usual way as a permutation group, contains three abstractly distinct regular subgroups of order 24. Show in each of the three cases that the corresponding subgroup of the holomorph of G, when represented in the usual way as a permutation group, is a transitive group of degree 25 which contains as a subgroup a transitive group of degree 24 and order 24.

11. Show that the prime-power Abelian group G of order p^4 and type (1, 1, 1, 1) has a set of $p^2 + 1$ subgroups each of order p^2 such that the identity is the only element common to any two of them.

12. Show that a prime-power Abelian group G of order p^6 and type $(1, 1, \cdots, 1)$ has a set of $p^3 + 1$ subgroups each of order p^3 such that the identity is the only element common to any two of them.

13. Show that a prime-power Abelian group G of order p^6 and type $(1, 1, \cdots, 1)$ has a set of $p^4 + p^2 + 1$ subgroups each of order p^2 such that the identity is the only element common to any two of them.

14. Show that the group I of isomorphisms of the Abelian group G of order 3^3 and type (1, 1, 1) is (2, 1) isomorphic with a group H which permutes the 13 subgroups of G of order 9 according to a transitive group of degree 13 and order $13 \cdot 12 \cdot 9 \cdot 4$.

15. Show that the group I of isomorphisms of the Abelian group G of prime-power order p^3 and type (1, 1, 1) is $(p - 1, 1)$ isomorphic with a group H which permutes the $p^2 + p + 1$ subgroups of G of order p^2 according to a transitive group of degree $p^2 + p + 1$ and order $(p^2 + p + 1)(p^2 + p)p^2(p - 1)^2$.

16. Show that the group H of the foregoing Ex. 15 contains a subgroup of index $p^2 + p + 1$ which is transitive of degree $p^2 + p$.

CHAPTER V

Prime-Power Groups

32. General Properties. In § **15** we saw that any group may be generated by any set of its Sylow subgroups which contains one such subgroup of each possible order. Since these Sylow subgroups are prime-power groups, it follows that the theory of prime-power groups is of central importance in the theory of finite groups in general. In the previous chapter we have made an analysis of the prime-power Abelian groups. In this chapter we shall treat the prime-power groups without the restriction that they shall be Abelian.

The most important theorem relating to prime-power groups has already been proved in § **15**. It may be stated as follows:

> I. A prime-power * group G of order p^m contains a self-conjugate element of order p.

From this theorem we drew the following corollaries: the number of self-conjugate elements in G is a power of p; a group of order p^2 is Abelian; a group whose order is a multiple of p contains an element of order p.

In § **21** we saw that every prime-power group is soluble.

Every subgroup of a group G of order p^m has for its order a power of p (§ **10**). Hence the number of elements of G each of which is conjugate to a given element must (by Theorem VI of § **11**) be a power of p.

If G is a non-Abelian group of order p^m, its central H is a proper subgroup of order p^s, where s is a positive integer less than m. The factor-group G/H is of order p^{m-s}. We call it the *central factor-group* of G. If this group is non-Abelian, we form

* Throughout the chapter the symbol p will always denote a prime number.

its central factor-group. Continuing this process, we must finally arrive at a central factor-group which is Abelian. It is to be observed that this central factor-group is noncyclic. This follows at once from Theorems VII and VIII of § **20** and the fact that this Abelian factor-group is the factor-group of a non-Abelian group with respect to its central.

Now G is multiply isomorphic with its central factor-group G/H, the central H (of order p^s) of G corresponding to the identity in G/H. And G/H contains a self-conjugate subgroup of order p, as one sees from Theorem I. Corresponding to such a subgroup of G/H is a self-conjugate subgroup of G of order p^{s+1}, in accordance with Theorem VI of § **20**; and this self-conjugate subgroup contains the central H of G as a subgroup of index p. This subgroup of order p^{s+1} is an Abelian group, since it is generated by the central of G and one other (suitably chosen) element of G. From this result we have the following theorem:

> II. Every non-Abelian prime-power group G contains a self-conjugate Abelian subgroup some of the elements of which are not self-conjugate in G; in fact, it contains an Abelian self-conjugate subgroup having as a proper subgroup the central H of G.

Let H_1, H_2, $\cdots$, H_k be any complete set of conjugate subgroups of a group G of order p^m. Then the elements of G each of which transforms H_1 into itself form a subgroup whose order is a power of p. Therefore (Theorem VII of § **11**) the number k of subgroups in this conjugate set is itself a power of p. Let K_i be the largest subgroup of G the elements of which transform H_i into itself. Then K_i contains H_i. When $k > 1$, the elements of H_i transform at least $p - 1$ other H's of the set H_1, H_2, $\cdots$, H_k, each into itself, since the number of conjugates of H_j under transformation by the elements of H_i is a power of p. Hence we have the following theorem:

> III. The number of subgroups in any complete set of conjugate subgroups of a group G of order p^m

is a power of p. If this number is greater than one, then each subgroup in the set transforms into itself at least $p-1$ other subgroups in the set.

In particular,

IV. Every subgroup of order p^{m-1} in a group of order p^m is self-conjugate in this group.

For if H_1 and H_2 are two subgroups of order p^{m-1} in a conjugate set such that H_2 is transformed into itself by the elements of H_1, we may take g to be an element of H_1 which is not in H_2. Then $\{H_2, g\}$ coincides with G while H_2 is self-conjugate in $\{H_2, g\}$ contrary to the hypothesis that H_1 is a conjugate of H_2.

33. Some Self-conjugate Subgroups. We shall now prove the following theorem:

V. A prime-power group G of order p^m contains a set of self-conjugate subgroups $G_1, G_2, \cdots, G_{m-1}, G_m$ with $G_m \equiv G$, of orders $p, p^2, \cdots, p^{m-1}, p^m$, respectively, such that G_i is a self-conjugate subgroup of G_{i+1}, of $G_{i+2}, \cdots$, of G_m, for $i = 1, 2, \cdots, m-1$.

Let g_1 be a self-conjugate element of order p in G. Then $G/\{g_1\}$ is of order p^{m-1} and contains a self-conjugate element γ_2 of order p. In the usual multiple isomorphism of G with $G/\{g_1\}$, let g_2 be an element which corresponds to γ_2. Then $g_2{}^p$ is in $\{g_1\}$, since it corresponds to $\gamma_2{}^p$, or 1. Let g be any element of G and γ the corresponding element of $G/\{g_1\}$. Then $\gamma^{-1}\gamma_2{}^{-1}\gamma\gamma_2 = 1$, and therefore $g^{-1}g_2{}^{-1}gg_2$ is in $\{g_1\}$. Hence $\{g_1, g_2\}$ is a self-conjugate subgroup of G of order p^2 consisting of the p^2 elements

$$g_1{}^{\alpha_1}g_2{}^{\alpha_2}. \qquad (\alpha_1, \alpha_2 = 1, 2, \cdots, p)$$

It contains self-conjugately the self-conjugate subgroup $\{g_1\}$ of G.

Let γ_3 be a self-conjugate element of order p in the group $G/\{g_1, g_2\}$, and let g_3 be a corresponding element in G in the usual multiple isomorphism of G with $G/\{g_1, g_2\}$. Then $g_3{}^p$ and $g^{-1}g_3{}^{-1}gg_3$ are in $\{g_1, g_2\}$, g being any element of G. Thence it may be shown that $\{g_1, g_2, g_3\}$ is a self-conjugate subgroup of G of order p^3 consisting of the p^3 elements

$$g_1^{\alpha_1}g_2^{\alpha_2}g_3^{\alpha_3}. \qquad (\alpha_1, \alpha_2, \alpha_3 = 1, 2, \cdots, p)$$

Moreover, $\{g_1, g_2, g_3\}$ contains both $\{g_1, g_2\}$ and $\{g_1\}$ self-conjugately.

Continuing this process, we prove the existence in G of elements $g_1, g_2, \cdots, g_m$ such that the groups

$$G_i \equiv \{g_1, g_2, \cdots, g_i\} \qquad (i = 1, 2, \cdots, m)$$

have the properties named in the theorem.

COR. I. The group G ($\equiv G_m$) contains a set of elements $g_1, g_2, \cdots, g_m$ such that g_i^p and $g^{-1}g_i^{-1}gg_i$ (where g is any element of G) are in the group $G_{i-1} \equiv \{g_1, g_2, \cdots, g_{i-1}\}$ for $i = 2, 3, \cdots, m$, while G_i itself consists of the p^i elements

$$g_1^{\alpha_1}g_2^{\alpha_2} \cdots g_i^{\alpha_i}, \qquad (\alpha_k = 1, 2, \cdots, p;\ k = 1, 2, \cdots, i)$$

for each i of the set $1, 2, \cdots, m$.

COR. II. If H is any proper subgroup of order p^t in a group G of order p^m, then H is contained self-conjugately in a subgroup of G of order p^{t+1}.

If H does not contain g_1, then $\{H, g_1\}$ contains $H, Hg_1, Hg_1^2, \cdots, Hg_1^{p-1}$, and these constitute the required subgroup of order p^{t+1}. If H contains $g_1, g_2, \cdots, g_{i-1}$ but not g_i, then $\{H, g_i\}$ contains the elements $H, Hg_i, Hg_i^2, \cdots, Hg_i^{p-1}$ and these constitute the required subgroup of order p^{t+1}.

34. Number of Subgroups of Index p. We shall now prove the following theorem:

VI. Let D of order p^μ be the greatest common subgroup of the subgroups of order p^{m-1} in a group G of order p^m. Then G contains just

$$\frac{p^{m-\mu} - 1}{p - 1}$$

subgroups of order p^{m-1}.

Let $H_1, H_2, H_3, \cdots$ be the subgroups of G of index p. Then (Theorem IV of § **32**) each H_i is self-conjugate in G. Hence their greatest common subgroup D is self-conjugate in G. Let g be an element of G, γ_i the corresponding element in G/H_i in the usual multiple isomorphism of G with G/H_i, and γ the corresponding element in G/D in the usual multiple isomorphism of G with G/D. Now G/H_i is of order p, and hence $\gamma_i^p = 1$. Hence g^p is in H_i for each value of i, and therefore g^p is in D. That is, *D contains the pth power of every element in G.* Since g^p is in D, it follows that the corresponding element γ^p in G/D is the identity. Hence G/D consists of the identity and $p^{m-\mu} - 1$ elements each of order p.

To each subgroup of index p in G/D there corresponds one and just one subgroup of index p in G, in the named isomorphism of G with G/D. Therefore the number of subgroups of index p in G is the same as the number of subgroups of index p in G/D. It remains to determine the latter number.

For this purpose it is convenient to prove first that G/D is Abelian. Since G/H_i is Abelian, owing to the fact that it is of order p, it follows from Corollary II of Theorem IX of § **20** that H_i contains the commutator subgroup Δ of G; hence D contains Δ. Then from Corollary I of the same theorem it follows that G/D is Abelian. Since the elements of G/D, other than the identity, are of order p, it follows that G/D is of type $(1, 1, \cdots, 1)$. Since its order is $p^{m-\mu}$, it follows from § **28** that the number of its subgroups of index p is $(p^{m-\mu} - 1)/(p - 1)$. Hence this is the number of subgroups of index p in G, as was to be proved. (The reader may note that μ is zero when G is Abelian of type $(1, 1, \cdots, 1)$.)

Cor. I. The pth power of every element of G is in D.

Cor. II. The group G/D is Abelian of order $p^{m-\mu}$ and type $(1, 1, \cdots, 1)$.

35. Number of Subgroups of Any Given Order. We shall prove the following theorem:

VII. The number of subgroups of order p^s in a group G of order p^m is of the form $1 + kp$, where k is an integer.

In view of Theorem III of § **32** it is sufficient to prove the following, in order to establish the foregoing, theorem:

VIII. The number of self-conjugate subgroups of order p^s in a group G of order p^m is of the form $1 + kp$, where k is an integer.

From Theorem V of § **33** it follows that G has at least one self-conjugate subgroup of order p^s. Let $H_1, H_2, \cdots, H_\mu$ denote its self-conjugate subgroups of order p^s. Let $K_1, K_2, \cdots, K_\nu$ be the subgroups of G of order p^{m-1}. Then from Theorem VI of § **34** it follows that $\nu \equiv 1 \bmod p$. We have to prove that $\mu \equiv 1 \bmod p$.

Let s_i be the number of the subgroups $H_1, H_2, \cdots, H_\mu$ each of which is in K_i. Let t_j be the number of the subgroups $K_1, K_2, \cdots, K_\nu$ each of which contains H_j. Then the number of cases in which a group H is in a group K is $s_1 + s_2 + \cdots + s_\nu$; it is also $t_1 + t_2 + \cdots + t_\mu$. Hence

$$s_1 + s_2 + \cdots + s_\nu = t_1 + t_2 + \cdots + t_\mu.$$

The groups K containing a given subgroup H_j are the subgroups of G which correspond to subgroups of index p in G/H_j in the usual multiple isomorphism of G with G/H_j. But the number of these subgroups of index p in G/H_j is congruent to unity modulo p, in accordance with Theorem VI of § **34**. Hence $t_j \equiv 1 \bmod p$. Then from the result at the end of the preceding paragraph it follows that

$$s_1 + s_2 + \cdots + s_\nu \equiv \mu \bmod p.$$

Since $\nu \equiv 1 \bmod p$, it will follow that $\mu \equiv 1 \bmod p$ when it is shown that $s_i \equiv 1 \bmod p$. The latter fact we shall now prove.

From Theorem VI of § **34**, together with Theorem IV of § **32**, it follows that the number of self-conjugate subgroups of order p^s in any (whatever) given group of order p^{s+1} is congruent to unity modulo p. Let us suppose that the number of self-conjugate subgroups of order p^s contained in any (whatever) given group of order p^{s+2} has the same property; and likewise for any (whatever) given group of order $p^{s+3}, \cdots, p^{m-1}$. If from this hypothesis it follows that the same is true for any (whatever) given group of order p^m, it is clear that the truth of the theorem is established by induction. Now from the hypothesis we see that the number of self-conjugate subgroups of order p^s contained in K_i is congruent to unity modulo p. These include the s_i groups H contained in K_i and also (possibly) certain other subgroups $L_1, L_2, \cdots, L_\lambda$ of order p^s, which are self-conjugate in K_i but not in G. Since K_i is self-conjugate in G, it follows that K_i contains every subgroup conjugate in G to any of the groups $L_1, L_2, \cdots, L_\lambda$; whence we conclude that $\lambda \equiv 0 \bmod p$, since these groups fall into conjugate sets in G, the number of elements in each set being a power of p. Therefore $s_i \equiv 1 \bmod p$. From this conclusion the theorem follows, as we have already seen.

The foregoing theorem will enable us to prove an important theorem due to Frobenius which is in the nature of an extension of a part of Sylow's theorem, namely, the following:

> IX. If G is any group whose order is divisible by the prime-power p^s ($s > 0$), then the number of subgroups of order p^s in G is of the form $1 + kp$.

Let p^m be the highest power of p contained as a factor in the order of G. Let G_1 be a Sylow subgroup of order p^m contained in G. If a given subgroup of G of order p^s is not a self-conjugate subgroup of G_1, then it is transformed by the elements of G_1 into a set of conjugates whose number is a power of p, as one may easily verify. Now (Theorem VIII of this section) the number of self-conjugate subgroups of order p^s in G_1 is congruent to unity modulo p. Combining the propositions in the last two sentences, we see that the number of subgroups of G of order p^s is of the form $1 + kp$, as was to be proved.

EXERCISES

1. The central of a direct product of prime-power groups is of order greater than unity.

2. A simple prime-power group is of prime order.

3. No prime-power group can be a complete group.

4. A self-conjugate subgroup of a prime-power group G has elements in common with the central of G.

5. The central of a non-Abelian group G of order p^m contains at least p commutators of G.

6. If the commutator subgroup of a prime-power group G is of prime order, then each commutator of G is a self-conjugate element of G.

7. A prime-power group is never a perfect group.

8. If S is an element of order p in a prime-power group G and if S is not self-conjugate in G, then S is not conjugate in G to any power of S.

9. Let a and b be two nonpermutable elements in a prime-power group G each having just p conjugates in G. Show that their commutator c is of order p and is permutable with both a and b.

10. Let G be the direct product of prime-power groups and let m be any factor of the order of G. Show that G contains a self-conjugate subgroup of order m.

11. Any self-conjugate subgroup of order p^s $(s \leqq m-2)$ in a group G of order p^m is itself contained self-conjugately in self-conjugate subgroups of G of orders $p^{s+1}, p^{s+2}, \cdots, p^{m-1}$.

12. The commutator subgroup of a group G of order p^m is a subgroup of G of index equal to or greater than p^2.

13. In a group G of order p^m the number of elements of order p is of the form $kp-1$.

14. The total number of subgroups of a group G of order p^m is congruent to $1+m \bmod p$.

15. Every self-conjugate subgroup of a group G of order p^m contains a subgroup of index p which is self-conjugate in G.

16. Let μ be defined as in Theorem VI of § **34**. Then show that G contains no element of order greater than $p^{\mu+1}$.

17. If E is a self-conjugate subgroup of a group G of order p^m such that G/E is an Abelian group of type $(1, 1, \cdots, 1)$, then E contains the group D of Theorem VI of § **34**.

18. In a non-Abelian group of order p^3 an element is either self-conjugate or belongs to a complete set of p conjugates.

36. Prime-Power Groups Each with a Single Subgroup of a Given Order. We shall now prove the following two theorems:

X. If a prime-power group G of odd order p^m contains only one subgroup G_s of order p^s, where s is a given positive integer less than m, then G is a cyclic group.

XI. If a group G of order 2^m contains only one subgroup G_s of order 2^s, where s is a given integer greater than 1 and less than m, then G is a cyclic group. If G contains only one subgroup G_1 of order 2, then G is either a cyclic group or a group of the type defined by the relations

$$S^{2^{m-1}} = 1, \quad T^2 = S^{2^{m-2}}, \quad T^{-1}ST = S^{-1}. \quad (m > 2)$$

The proofs of the two theorems coincide through a certain part of the argument; therefore we carry them together as far as is convenient.

Let P be an element of G not contained in G_s. If the order of P is less than p^{s+1}, then (Corollary II of Theorem V of § **33**) G contains a subgroup of order p^s containing P, and this subgroup is necessarily different from G_s. Since this contradicts the hypothesis that G contains only one subgroup of order p^s, it follows that an element P which is not in G_s is of order p^{s+t}, where t is a positive integer. Then $\{P^{p^t}\}$ is a cyclic subgroup of G of order p^s; it must therefore coincide with G_s. Hence G_s is a cyclic group.

Now let p^r be the largest number which is the order of an element of G, and let P be an element which is of order p^r. Then

(Corollary II of Theorem V of § **33**) $\{P\}$ is either identical with G or is contained self-conjugately in a noncyclic subgroup G_{r+1} of order p^{r+1}. In the first case both theorems are granted. It remains to consider the second alternative.

The group $\{P\}$ is a self-conjugate subgroup of G_{r+1}, as we have already seen. Hence if P_1 is an element of G_{r+1} which is not contained in $\{P\}$, then integers α and β exist such that

$$P_1^{-1}PP_1 = P^{\alpha}, \quad P_1^{p} = P^{\beta}.$$

Now β is divisible by p, since, if it were not, P_1 would be an element of order p^{r+1}, contrary to hypothesis. Then write $\beta = \gamma p$, so that $P_1^p = P^{\gamma p}$. Moreover, α cannot be unity, for then $\{P, P_1\}$ would be an Abelian group of type $(r, 1)$ and would therefore contain an element of order p not occurring in $\{P\}$, contrary to the conclusion reached in the first paragraph of the proof. Let P_1^{ρ} be the lowest positive integral power of P_1 which is permutable with P. Then we have $P_1^{-\rho}PP_1^{\rho} = P$. But from the relation $P_1^{-1}PP_1 = P^{\alpha}$ we have $P_1^{-\rho}PP_1^{\rho} = P^{\alpha^{\rho}}$. Hence $P^{\alpha^{\rho}} = P$ and therefore $\alpha^{\rho} \equiv 1 \bmod p^r$. Furthermore, in the group $\{P, P_1\}$ the element P is one of a complete set of ρ conjugates. Therefore ρ is a power of p, say, $\rho = p^{\lambda}$. But we have seen that $P_1^p = P^{\gamma p}$; hence $\lambda = 1$. Therefore

$$\alpha^p \equiv 1 \bmod p^r,$$

while
$$\alpha \not\equiv 1 \bmod p^r.$$

Since $x^p \equiv x \bmod p$ for every positive integer x, we may write $\alpha = 1 + kp^{\mu}$, where μ is so chosen that k is prime to p. Then

$$\alpha^p = 1 + kp^{\mu+1} + \cdots.$$

Hence $\mu = r - 1$. Therefore we have

$$P_1^{-1}PP_1 = P^{1+kp^{r-1}}, \quad P_1^p = P^{\gamma p},$$

where k is prime to p.

From the first of the last two relations we have

$$P_1^{-1}P^xP_1 = P^{x(1+kp^{r-1})}$$

for all values of the integer x. Hence

$$\begin{aligned}
P^xP_1 &= P_1P^{x\sigma}, \text{ where } \sigma = 1 + kp^{r-1}, \\
(P^xP_1)^2 &= P_1 \cdot P^{x\sigma}P_1 \cdot P^{x\sigma} = P_1{}^2P^{x(\sigma+\sigma^2)}, \\
&\cdots\cdots\cdots\cdots \\
(P^xP_1)^p &= P_1{}^pP^{x(\sigma+\sigma^2+\cdots+\sigma^p)} \\
&= P_1{}^pP^{x[p+(1+2+\cdots+p)kp^{r-1}]} \\
&= P_1{}^pP^{x[p+\frac{1}{2}p(p+1)kp^{r-1}]}.
\end{aligned}$$

Now consider the case when p is odd. Then the last member of the foregoing equation is equal to $P_1{}^pP^{xp}$. Hence, taking $x = -\gamma$ and remembering that $P_1{}^p = P^{\gamma p}$, we see that $(P^{-\gamma}P_1)^p = 1$ while $P^{-\gamma}P_1$ is not contained in $\{P\}$. Since this contradicts a result obtained in the first paragraph of the proof, the second alternative named in the second paragraph must be excluded. Hence G is a cyclic group. This completes the proof of Theorem X.

Consider now the case of Theorem XI. From the previous argument we have

$$P^xP_1 = P_1P^{x\sigma}$$

where $\sigma = 1 + 2^{r-1}k$, k being odd; whence it follows that

$$\begin{aligned}
(P^xP_1)^4 &= P_1{}^4P^{x(\sigma+\sigma^2+\sigma^3+\sigma^4)} \\
&= P_1{}^4P^{x(4+10k \cdot 2^{r-1})} \\
&= P_1{}^4P^{4x}.
\end{aligned}$$

Again take $x = -\gamma$; then since $P_1{}^2 = P^{2\gamma}$, we have $P_1{}^4P^{-4\gamma} = 1$ and hence $(P^{-\gamma}P_1)^4 = 1$ while $P^{-\gamma}P_1$ is not in $\{P\}$. If $s \geqq 2$, we have as before a contradiction with a result obtained in the first paragraph of the proof. Thence it follows that G is cyclic when $s \geqq 2$.

It remains to consider the case when G in Theorem XI is supposed to have only one subgroup G_1 of order 2. Then G is cyclic unless $m > 2$. Hence in the further argument we suppose that $m > 2$. In the case to be considered now we put on P_1 the further restriction that its order is as small as possible consistent with the other condition already placed on it, namely, that P_1 is an element of G_{r+1} which is not contained in $\{P\}$, while P has the largest possible order 2^r of an element in G. We shall then determine what noncyclic group or groups (if any) can satisfy the named conditions. As before we have $(P^{-\gamma}P_1)^4=1$ while $P^{-\gamma}P_1$ is not in $\{P\}$. Since $P^{-\gamma}P_1$ is of order not greater than 4, it follows that P_1 is of order not greater than 4, since by hypothesis P_1 is of minimum order consistent with the fact that it is in G_{r+1} and is not in $\{P\}$. But from a result in the first paragraph of the proof it follows that the order of P_1 is not less than 4. Hence P_1 is of order 4. Since G by hypothesis contains only one subgroup of order 2, it follows that $P^{2^{r-1}}$ is identical with $P_1{}^2$. Now from the relation $P_1{}^{-1}PP_1=P^{\alpha}$ we have $P_1{}^{-2}PP_1{}^2=P^{\alpha^2}$. But $P_1{}^2$ and P are permutable. Hence $P^{\alpha^2}=P$. Hence $\alpha^2\equiv 1 \bmod 2^r$. The cases $\alpha\equiv 1$ and $\alpha\equiv\pm 1+2^{r-1}$ may now be excluded, leaving $\alpha\equiv -1 \bmod 2^r$. Therefore we have $P_1{}^{-1}PP_1=P^{-1}$. By writing S and T for P and P_1, respectively, we see that the proof of the theorem will be completed when it is further shown that $r=m-1$, since it is easy to prove the existence of a group with the defining relations given in the theorem and to show that it has the requisite property of containing but one subgroup of order 2. [To show the existence and uniqueness of a group with the given defining relations, note that its elements are S^i and S^iT for $i=0, 1, 2, \cdots, 2^{m-1}-1$ and that these elements are permuted among themselves in a determinate way when they are multiplied on the left by either S or T, the resulting permutations σ and τ having the properties assigned to S and T and generating a group of order 2^m. Then show that this group has only one element of order 2.]

Now $r<m$, since we are considering the case when G is not cyclic. If r were less than $m-1$, then (Corollary II of Theorem V of § **33**) the group $\{P, P_1\}$ would be contained self-conjugately in a subgroup of G of order 2^{r+2}. Let P_2 be an element of this latter group not contained in $\{P, P_1\}$. Since $\{P, P_1\}$ is transformed into itself by P_2 and $\{P\}$ is the only cyclic subgroup of order 2^r in $\{P, P_1\}$, then $\{P\}$ is transformed into itself by P_2. If $P_2{}^2$ is in $\{P\}$, then, by an argument like the foregoing, we show that $P_2{}^{-1}PP_2=P^{-1}$. Hence $P_1{}^{-1}P_2{}^{-1}PP_2P_1=P$. Then $\{P, P_2P_1\}$ is a noncyclic Abelian

group which contains 3 subgroups of order 2. Hence P_2^2 is not in $\{P\}$. Now $\{P, P_2\}$ is of order 2^{r+2} at most; hence P_2^4 is in $\{P\}$; it is therefore the lowest positive integral power of P_2 which is in $\{P\}$, whence it follows that $\{P, P_2\}$ is of order 2^{r+2} and that $\{P, P_2^2\}$ is of order 2^{r+1}. Now P_2^2 and P cannot be permutable; for, if so, we should have in $\{P, P_2^2\}$ three subgroups of order 2. But from the relation $P_2^{-1}PP_2 = P^\delta$ we have $P_2^{-2}PP_2^2 = P^{\delta^2}$ and $P_2^{-4}PP_2^4 = P^{\delta^4}$. Hence $\delta^2 \not\equiv 1 \bmod 2^r$, $\delta^4 \equiv 1 \bmod 2^r$. But $\delta^2 + 1 \equiv 0 \bmod 2$ and $\delta^2 + 1 \not\equiv 0 \bmod 4$. Hence $\delta^2 \equiv 1 \bmod 2^{r-1}$, while, as we have seen, $\delta^2 \not\equiv 1 \bmod 2^r$. Hence $\delta^2 = 1 + 2^{r-1}k$, where k is odd. Hence $P_2^{-2}PP_2^2 = P^{1+2^{r-1}k}$. Therefore $P_2^{-2}P^2P_2^2 = P^2$, so that P_2^2 and P^2 are permutable. Therefore the group $\{P_2^2, P^2\}$ is Abelian and contains three subgroups of order 2, contrary to hypothesis. Hence $r \nless m-1$. Then we conclude that $r = m - 1$.

This completes the proof of the theorem.

37. Groups of Order p^m Each with a Cyclic Subgroup of Index p. We now prove the following theorem:

> XII. If p is an odd prime and $m > 2$, there is one and only one abstract non-Abelian group G of order p^m containing an element of order p^{m-1}. It is the group $\{P, R\}$, where P and R are subject to the sole defining relations
>
> $$P^{p^{m-1}} = R^p = 1, \quad R^{-1}PR = P^{1+p^{m-2}}.$$

The groups of order p and p^2 are Abelian, as we have already seen.

Let P be an element of order p^{m-1} in a non-Abelian group G of order p^m, if such a group exists. The group $\{P\}$ contains just one subgroup of order p. Hence, since G is noncyclic, it follows from Theorem X of the preceding section that G contains an element Q of order p not contained in $\{P\}$. Since $\{P\}$ is self-conjugate in G, it follows that $\{P\}$ is transformed into itself by Q, and hence that $Q^{-1}PQ = P^\alpha$, where α is some positive integer between 1 and p^{m-1} exclusive of these bounds; moreover, α is prime to p.

Now $P = Q^{-p}PQ^p = P^{\alpha^p}$. Hence $\alpha^p \equiv 1 \bmod p^{m-1}$. But $\alpha^p \equiv \alpha \bmod p$. Hence $\alpha \equiv 1 \bmod p$. Then write $\alpha = 1 + kp^\mu$, where k is prime to p. It is clear that $0 < \mu < m-1$. Now $\alpha^p = 1 + kp^{\mu+1} + \cdots$. Hence $\mu = m-2$. Therefore $\alpha = 1 + kp^{m-2}$.

Now $Q^{-x}PQ^x = P^{\alpha^x}$. We have $\alpha^x = 1 + kxp^{m-2} + p^{m-1}I$, where I is an integer since $m > 2$. Let x be such that $kx \equiv 1 \bmod p$ and put R for Q^x. Then $R^{-1}PR = P^{1+p^{m-2}}$ while R itself is of order p. Then $\{P, R\}$ is the group G, in case this group exists. It is of order p^m, and its generators satisfy the conditions

$$P^{p^{m-1}} = R^p = 1, \quad R^{-1}PR = P^{1+p^{m-2}}.$$

If such a group exists, its elements are

$$P^i, P^iR, P^iR^2, \cdots, P^iR^{p-1}. \quad (i = 0, 1, 2, \cdots, p^{m-1}-1)$$

On multiplying these elements on the left by P and by R we obtain determinate permutations π and ρ respectively; and these permutations generate a group G having the requisite properties. Hence the group G exists and is unique.

XIII. If $m > 3$, there are just four abstract non-Abelian groups of order 2^m each of which contains an element of order 2^{m-1}. (See Ex. 1 on page 134.)

Let G be a non-Abelian group of order 2^m containing an element P of order 2^{m-1}, m being greater than 3.

Let us first suppose that G contains no element of order 2 except the single element of this order contained in $\{P\}$. Then G is a non-Abelian group having only a single subgroup of order 2. It is therefore of the last type defined in Theorem XI of § 36.

There remains the case in which G contains an element Q of order 2 not contained in $\{P\}$. Since $\{P\}$ is self-conjugate in G, it follows that $Q^{-1}PQ = P^\alpha$, where α is some odd positive integer between 1 and 2^{m-1} exclusive of these bounds. Then $P = Q^{-2}PQ^2 = P^{\alpha^2}$; hence $\alpha^2 \equiv 1 \bmod 2^{m-1}$. Writing $\alpha = 1 + 2^\mu k$, where k is odd, we have

$$\alpha^2 - 1 = (1 + 2^\mu k)^2 - 1 = 2^{\mu+1}(k + k^2 \cdot 2^{\mu-1}) \equiv 0 \bmod 2^{m-1}.$$

Hence (1) $\mu = m - 2$, or (2) $\mu = 1$ and $k(1+k) \equiv 0 \bmod 2^{m-3}$. In case (1) we have $\alpha = 1 + 2^{m-2}$. In case (2), since k is odd, we must have $k = -1 + 2^{m-3}\lambda$, and hence $\alpha = -1 + 2^{m-2}\lambda$, where λ is an integer. Then the only possible values for λ are $\lambda = 1$ and $\lambda = 2$. The three cases thus obtained give rise, respectively, to the following three sets of conditions:

$$(1) \qquad P^{2^{m-1}} = Q^2 = 1, \quad QPQ = P^{1+2^{m-2}};$$

$$(2) \qquad P^{2^{m-1}} = Q^2 = 1, \quad (PQ)^2 = P^{2^{m-2}};$$

$$(3) \qquad P^{2^{m-1}} = Q^2 = (PQ)^2 = 1.$$

It is not difficult to show (by methods now familiar to the reader) that each of these sets of conditions (when taken as the sole defining relations of $\{P, Q\}$) leads uniquely to an abstract group and that the three groups so defined are distinct.

From the conclusions already reached the theorem follows.

EXERCISES

1. Show that there are just two abstract non-Abelian groups of order 8 and that they have, respectively, the following defining relations:

(1) $a^4 = b^2 = (ab)^2 = 1$; (2) $a^4 = 1, \quad a^2 = (ab)^2 = b^2$.

2. Let p be an odd prime. Show that there are just two abstract non-Abelian groups of order p^3 and that they have, respectively, the following defining relations:

(1) $a^{p^2} = b^p = 1$, $b^{-1}ab = a^{1+p}$;

(2) $a^p = b^p = c^p = 1, \quad c^{-1}bc = ba, \quad c^{-1}ac = a, \quad b^{-1}ab = a$.

3. Let G be the abstract group of odd order p^m $(m > 2)$ generated by two elements a and b subject to the sole conditions

$$a^{p^{m-1}} = b^p = 1, \quad ab = ba^{1+p^{m-2}}.$$

Prove the following propositions:

(1) The elements b and a^p are permutable.

(2) The central of G is $\{a^p\}$.

(3) If $c = a^{-1}b^{-1}ab$, then c is permutable with a and with b and we have $c^p = 1$.

(4) The subgroups of G of index p^λ $(\lambda < m)$ are the p cyclic groups $\{b^i a^{p^{\lambda-1}}\}$ $(i = 0, 1, \cdots, p-1)$ and the Abelian group $\{a^{p^\lambda}, b\}$. The latter is noncyclic if $\lambda < m - 1$.

(5) The commutator subgroup of G is $\{a^{p^{m-2}}\}$ of order p.

(6) Every proper subgroup of G is Abelian.

(7) Every noncyclic subgroup of G is characteristic.

(8) A factor-group of G is an Abelian group.

4. If G is a non-Abelian group of order 2^m containing two and just two cyclic subgroups of order 2^β and no cyclic subgroup of order $2^{\beta+1}$, show that β cannot be greater than $m-2$.

5. If G is a prime-power non-Abelian group of order p^3, show that G is generated by any two noncommutative elements in it.

6. If a group of order p^{15} has its central of order p^2, then it contains an Abelian subgroup of order p^6. [SUGGESTION. Let C be the central of G and let g be an element of G corresponding to a self-conjugate element γ of order p in G/C in the usual multiple isomorphism of G with G/C. Then show that $\{C, g\}$ is Abelian of order p^3 and is contained in the central C_1 of a subgroup G_1 of G of order at least as great as p^{13}. Repeat the process with G_1 and C_1, and so on.]

7. If a group of order p^{16} has its central of order p^4, then it contains an Abelian subgroup of order p^7.

8. Let G be a non-Abelian group of order p^m containing two Abelian subgroups H and K of index p. Show that the greatest common subgroup of H and K is the central C of G. Show also that the derived group of G and the group of inner isomorphisms of G are both Abelian and of type $(1, 1, \cdots, 1)$, the latter being of order p^2.

9. The greatest common subgroup of all self-conjugate subgroups of index p^2 in a group G of order p^m contains the commutator subgroup of G.

10. Let P and Q be two noncommutative elements of a group G of odd order p^m each of which corresponds to its inverse in some isomorphism of G with itself; show that in this isomorphism the commutator of P and Q cannot correspond to its inverse.

11. Let G be a group of order 2^m containing only one cyclic subgroup of given order 2^α, where $1 < \alpha < m$; then show that it contains no more than one cyclic subgroup of order 2^β, where $\alpha < \beta < m$.

12. If a group of order 2^m contains just $1 + 2k$ cyclic subgroups of order 2^α, where $\alpha > 2$ and k is an integer, then k must be zero.

13. If G is a group of order p^m $(m > 1)$, and if $s < m$, then the number of subgroups of G of order p^{s+1} each of which contains a given subgroup of order p^s is congruent to unity modulo p.

14. If G is a non-Abelian group of order p^m, then the number of Abelian subgroups of index p in G is 0, 1, or $1+p$. In the last case the central is of index p^2.

15. If a group G of order p^m contains an Abelian subgroup of order p^3, then the number of its Abelian subgroups of order p^3 is of the form $1+kp$.

MISCELLANEOUS EXERCISES

1. There is one and just one abstract non-Abelian group of odd order p^3 all of whose elements except the identity are of order p.

2. A non-Abelian group of order p^m contains a self-conjugate commutator of order p.

3. If G is a non-Abelian group of order p^m and if every subgroup of G is self-conjugate in G, show that p must be 2.

4. If a group of order p^4 has its central of order p, then it contains just $2p^2-1$ conjugate sets of elements.

5. If a group of order p^4 has its central of order p^2, then it contains just p^3+p^2-p conjugate sets of elements.

6. A group of order p^m cannot be generated by two elements which are conjugate within it.

7. If the elements $C, A_1, A_2, \cdots, A_{4n}$ are subject to the sole defining relations

$$C^2=1,\ A_i^2=1 \qquad (i=1, 2, \cdots, 4n),$$
$$CA_iA_jA_iA_j=1 \qquad (i \neq j;\ i, j=1, 2, \cdots, 4n),$$

they generate a group G of order 2^{4n+1} whose central is the group $\{C\}$ of order 2. Moreover, the numbers of elements in G of orders 4 and 2 are, respectively,

$$2^{4n}+(-1)^{n+1}2^{2n} \quad \text{and} \quad 2^{4n}-(-1)^{n+1}2^{2n}-1.$$

8. Let G be a group of order 3^m which contains no element of order 9. Show that any two conjugate elements in G are permutable. If n is the number of elements in a set of independent generators of G, show that $2^n-1 \geqq m$.

9. Show that a group of order p^m contains a self-conjugate Abelian subgroup of order p^α if $\alpha(\alpha-1)<2m$.

10. The number of subgroups of order p in a noncyclic group of odd order p^m is congruent to $1+p \bmod p^2$.

11. Show that there are just three abstract groups of order 3^4 each of which contains three and only three cyclic subgroups of order 9.

12. Determine the abstract non-Abelian groups of odd order p^4 each of which has all its elements of order p except the identity. When $p = 3$ show that there is only one such group. When $p > 3$ show that there are two such groups, one having its central of order p and the other having its central of order p^2.

13. Let G be a noncyclic group of odd order p^m, and let α be an integer such that $1 < \alpha < m$. Show that the number of noncyclic subgroups of order p^α in G is of the form $1 + kp$.

14. Let G be a group of order p^m, and let p^n be the highest power of p contained in the order of the group of isomorphisms of G. Show that $n \leqq \frac{1}{2} m(m-1)$. Show, furthermore, that n attains the maximum value $\frac{1}{2} m(m-1)$ when G is Abelian and of type $(1, 1, \cdots, 1)$ or of type $(2, 1, 1, \cdots, 1)$.

15. Let R, S, T be three elements each of odd prime order p such that the commutators $S^{-1}T^{-1}ST$, $T^{-1}R^{-1}TR$, $R^{-1}S^{-1}RS$ are each of order p while each of them is permutable with each of the elements R, S, T. If the elements R, S, T are subject to no conditions except those implied by the conditions already stated, show that the group $\{R, S, T\}$ is of order p^6, that each of its elements besides the identity is of order p, and that any given element in the group either is self-conjugate or is one of a complete set of p^2 conjugates.

16. Let G be a non-Abelian group of order p^{m+2} $(m \geqq 2)$ which is generated by two elements P and Q of orders p^m and p^2 respectively such that the groups $\{P\}$ and $\{Q\}$ have no common element besides the identity. Show that G must belong to one of the four cases (1), (2), (3), (4) determined, respectively, by the further conditions:

$$(1) \qquad P^{-1}Q^{-1}PQ = P^{p^{m-1}},$$
$$(2) \qquad P^{-1}Q^{-1}PQ = P^{p^{m-2}},$$
$$(3) \qquad P^{-1}Q^{-1}PQ = Q^{p},$$
$$(4) \qquad P^{-1}Q^{-p}PQ^{p} = P^{p^{m-1}}, \quad P^{-1}Q^{-1}PQ = P^{p^{m-2}}Q^{\alpha p}.$$

How many abstractly distinct groups can be obtained in case (4) by suitably varying α?

CHAPTER VI

Permutation Groups

38. Introduction. In § **4** we have defined the terms *permutation group* and *degree* of a permutation group. The $n!$ permutations on n letters form (see § **4**) the symmetric group of degree n and order $n!$, and the even permutations on n letters form the alternating group of degree n and order $\frac{1}{2}(n!)$. We saw (in § **4**) that in any permutation group the permutations are all even or exactly half of them are even; in the latter case the even permutations form a subgroup of index 2 in the given group. The question of the identity of two permutation groups was also discussed in § **4**.

It is obvious that any alternating group is a self-conjugate subgroup of the symmetric group on the same letters. More generally, if G is any permutation group containing odd permutations, then the even permutations in G constitute a self-conjugate subgroup of G.

In § **12** we defined the terms *transitive* and *intransitive* as applied to permutation groups. A transitive group whose order is equal to its degree is called a regular permutation group.

Furthermore, in § **12** we showed that every group G of finite order n can be represented as a regular permutation group on n symbols, the latter group being simply isomorphic with G. In fact, we set up this representation in two ways; whenever the group G is non-Abelian (and only then) these two ways give rise to two conjugate permutation groups each of which contains permutations not in the other. Moreover, several properties concerning the relations of these two groups were determined. In particular we showed that two simply isomorphic regular groups on the same set of n letters are conjugate under the symmetric group on those letters.

It is obvious that a given group G may be represented in an unlimited number of ways as a permutation group simply isomorphic with G. In fact, if G is so represented as a permutation group on each of two distinct sets of letters, then it is also representable as a permutation group on the set composed of all the letters in the two given sets by taking as the correspondent of each element g of G the product of the two elements which correspond to g in the given permutation groups, one of the factors being taken from one of the given representations and the other from the other representation.

In the preceding chapters we have frequently employed permutation groups as a tool in the study of abstract groups, particularly in the case of the group of isomorphisms and the holomorph of a given group. Now we shall proceed to develop some properties of permutation groups as such.

39. Transitive Groups. A transitive permutation group G on the symbols $a_1, a_2, \cdots, a_n$, as we have seen in § **12**, is a permutation group on those symbols containing permutations $S_1, S_2, \cdots, S_n$ which replace a_1 by $a_1, a_2 \cdots, a_n$, respectively. Then $S_i^{-1}S_j$ replaces a_i by a_j, so that any symbol in G may be replaced by any other symbol in G by a permutation belonging to G. A permutation group G which contains a permutation replacing any whatever given ordered pair of symbols in G by any whatever other given ordered pair of symbols in G is called a *doubly transitive* group. More generally, a permutation group G which contains a permutation replacing any whatever given ordered set of k symbols in G by any whatever other given ordered set of k symbols in G is called a *k-ply transitive*, or a *k-fold transitive*, group. For $k = 3, 4, 5$ one often uses the terms *triply*, *quadruply*, *quintuply* transitive. A group which is transitive but not doubly transitive is often said to be *singly* transitive or *simply* transitive. If a group is k-ply transitive but is not $(k+1)$-ply transitive, then k is said to be the *degree of transitivity* of the group. If the degree of transitivity of a transitive group is greater than unity, the group is said to be *multiply* transitive.

If the permutation group G on the symbols $a_1, a_2, \cdots, a_n$ contains permutations replacing the given ordered set $a_1, a_2, \cdots, a_k$

of k symbols in G by every other ordered set of k symbols in G, it is evident that G is k-ply transitive in accordance with the foregoing definition; for, if P_1 and P_2 are permutations in G replacing the given ordered set $a_1, a_2, \cdots, a_k$ by any two given ordered sets, then $P_1^{-1}P_2$ replaces one of these latter by the other. Again, if G contains permutations replacing every given ordered set of k symbols in G by the ordered set $a_1, a_2, \cdots, a_k$, then G is obviously k-ply transitive.

Let G be a k-ply transitive group on n symbols. If S and T are two permutations in G each of which leaves fixed a given ordered set of k symbols in G, then ST leaves fixed the same ordered set of k symbols. Hence we are led to the following theorem:

I. The totality of permutations of a given k-ply transitive group G each of which leaves fixed a given ordered set of k symbols of G forms a subgroup H of G.

If this subgroup H is l-ply transitive, then G itself is $(k+l)$-ply transitive; for if $a_1, a_2, \cdots, a_k, a_{k+1}, \cdots, a_{k+l}$ is any ordered set of $k+l$ symbols in G and $b_1, b_2, \cdots, b_{k+l}$ is any other, then G has an element replacing $b_1, b_2, \cdots, b_k$ by $a_1, a_2, \cdots, a_k$; if $b_{k+1}, \cdots, b_{k+l}$ are replaced by this element by $c_{k+1}, \cdots, c_{k+l}$, then there is an element in H which replaces the latter ordered set by the ordered set $a_{k+1}, \cdots, a_{k+l}$; then the product of these two elements is an element in G replacing the ordered set $b_1, \cdots, b_{k+l}$ by the ordered set $a_1, \cdots, a_{k+l}$.

Now let G be any k-ply transitive group of degree n, where $k > 1$. Then G is also $(k-l)$-ply transitive, where l is any positive integer less than k. Therefore (Theorem I) G contains a subgroup H consisting of all the elements of G leaving fixed each of a given set of $k-l$ symbols. *This group H is l-ply transitive*; for if $a_1, a_2, \cdots, a_n$ are the symbols in G and if $a_1, a_2, \cdots, a_{k-l}$ are the symbols left separately fixed by the elements of H, then H contains an element replacing the ordered set $a_1, a_2, \cdots, a_k$ by the ordered set $a_1, a_2, \cdots, a_{k-l}, b_1, b_2, \cdots, b_l$, where $b_1, b_2, \cdots, b_l$ is any ordered set of l symbols in G not containing one of the symbols $a_1, a_2, \cdots, a_{k-l}$.

We shall now prove the following theorem:

II. The order of a k-ply transitive group G of degree n is $n(n-1)\cdots(n-k+1)m$, where m is the order of the largest subgroup H of G each element of which leaves fixed a given ordered set of k symbols. The subgroup H is contained self-conjugately in a subgroup of G of order $k!\cdot m$.

The number μ of ordered sets of the n symbols of G, when these symbols are taken k at a time, is $n(n-1)\cdots(n-k+1)$. Denote these ordered sets by $P_1, P_2, \cdots, P_\mu$, where P_1 is an ordered set of the k symbols left fixed by each element of H. Let $g_1, g_2, \cdots, g_\mu$ be permutations in G, such that g_i replaces the ordered set P_1 by the ordered set P_i. Then G consists of the following elements and no others: $Hg_1, Hg_2, \cdots, Hg_\mu$. For, if g and g_i replace P_1 by P_i, then gg_i^{-1} replaces P_1 by P_1 and is therefore contained in H; hence g is contained in Hg_i. The sets $Hg_1, \cdots, Hg_\mu$ of elements of G form a set of μm distinct elements. Hence the order of G is that stated in the theorem.

Let P_1 be the ordered set $a_1, a_2, \cdots, a_k$. Then each element of H leaves this ordered set unchanged. If $a'_1, a'_2, \cdots, a'_k$ is any ordered set of the same k symbols, then G contains a permutation α of the form

$$\alpha = \begin{pmatrix} a_1, & a_2, & \cdots, & a_k, & b_1, & b_2, & \cdots \\ a'_1, & a'_2, & \cdots, & a'_k, & b'_1, & b'_2, & \cdots \end{pmatrix}.$$

There are $k!$ permutations of the form α no two of which are alike as regards the ordered set $a'_1, a'_2, \cdots, a'_k$; and each of them is permutable with H, since it interchanges among themselves the symbols left unchanged by H. If α_1 and α_2 are two permutations of the foregoing class α which are alike as regards the sequence $a'_1, a'_2, \cdots, a'_k$, then $\alpha_1^{-1}\alpha_2$ is in H. Therefore the permutations α constitute a subgroup of G of order $k!\cdot m$, and this subgroup contains H self-conjugately.

This completes the proof of the theorem.

COR. I. The order of a transitive group is divisible by its degree.

COR. II. The number of elements in G each of which replaces the ordered set P_i by the ordered set P_j is m; and these m elements are the elements $g_i^{-1}Hg_j$.

If $m = 1$, then H consists of the identity alone, and there is just one permutation in G which replaces a given ordered set of k symbols by another given ordered set of k symbols. In the same case G contains elements displacing $n - k + 1$ symbols; but there is no element of G other than the identity which displaces fewer than $n - k + 1$ symbols.

By taking $k = 1$ in the foregoing theorem we have the following:

III. If G is a transitive group, the order of the subgroup H formed by all the permutations of G each of which leaves a given letter fixed is equal to the order of G divided by its degree.

Now let $S_1 = 1, S_2, \cdots, S_m$ be the elements of this group H, and form for G the following rectangular array as in § **10**:

$$\begin{array}{llll} S_1\tau_1, & S_2\tau_1, & \cdots, & S_m\tau_1, \quad (\tau_1 \equiv 1) \\ S_1\tau_2, & S_2\tau_2, & \cdots, & S_m\tau_2, \\ \cdot & \cdot & \cdot & \cdot \\ S_1\tau_n, & S_2\tau_n, & \cdots, & S_m\tau_n. \end{array}$$

Let a_1 be the letter held fixed by H, and let a_i be the letter by which τ_i replaces a_1. Then every element in the ith row of the foregoing array replaces a_1 by a_i, and no other element of G has this property. Hence a_1 is left unchanged by m permutations in G and is changed into another letter by $m(n-1)$ permutations in G. In the same way it may be shown that any other letter a_i occurs similarly in G; that is, it is left fixed by m elements of G and is changed into another letter by $m(n-1)$ elements of G. Hence $mn(n-1)$ is the total number of replacements of one letter by another in all the elements of G. But the order of G is mn. Hence we have the following theorem:

IV. The average number of letters displaced by the permutations of a transitive group is equal to the degree of the group diminished by unity.

40. Examples of Multiply Transitive Groups. Let G be a multiply transitive group of degree n and order $n(n-1)$. We shall show that n is necessarily a power of a prime number. The subgroup H of order $n-1$, leaving a given symbol fixed, is itself transitive of degree and order $n-1$. It is therefore a regular permutation group. Hence all its elements except the identity are regular permutations changing exactly $n-1$ symbols. Therefore every element in G besides the identity changes all or all but one of the symbols of G. But the average number of symbols displaced by the permutations of G is $n-1$. Hence G has exactly $n-1$ elements each of which displaces all the symbols of G. If these $n-1$ elements, together with the identity, form a subgroup, then this subgroup must be self-conjugate in G, since it obviously contains the transform of each of its elements. The order of an element leaving just one symbol unchanged is a factor of $n-1$. Hence the $n-1$ elements each of which displaces all the symbols are the only elements besides the identity which satisfy the equation $S^n = 1$. The other elements in G satisfy the equation $S^{n-1} = 1$.

No element which leaves just one symbol unchanged can be permutable with an element which displaces all the symbols. There are just $n-1$ elements each of which displaces all the symbols. Therefore these $n-1$ elements form a complete set of conjugate elements.

Let us write $n = p_1^{\alpha_1} p_2^{\alpha_2} \cdots p_s^{\alpha_s}$, where $p_1, p_2, \cdots, p_s$ are primes and (when $s > 1$) no two of them are equal and where the α_i are positive integers. The number of elements of G whose orders are factors of $n/p_i^{\alpha_i}$ is (by Theorem XII of § 22) a multiple of $n/p_i^{\alpha_i}$, say $k_i n/p_i^{\alpha_i}$. Hence the number of elements of G whose orders are multiples of p_i is $n - k_i n/p_i^{\alpha_i}$, a number necessarily different from zero since G contains an element of order p_i (by Corollary III of Theorem XVI in § 15). Each of these elements satisfies the equation $S^n = 1$; and hence each of them displaces all the symbols of G. Therefore the elements of G whose orders are multiples of p_i form a conjugate set of $n-1$ elements. Therefore $n - k_i n/p_i^{\alpha_i} = n - 1$. But $n - k_i n/p_i^{\alpha_i}$ is less than $n - 1$ unless n is a power of a prime and $k_i = 1$. Hence n is necessarily a power of a prime number, say, $n = p^\alpha$.

Now there are just $n-1$ elements of G each of which displaces all the symbols of G, and these form a conjugate set, as we have seen. Their orders are factors of p^α. Since they all have the same order (owing to the fact that they form a conjugate set) it follows that the order of each is p. There is no other element in G besides the identity whose order is a power of p, since these other elements satisfy the equation $S^{n-1} = 1$, where $n = p^\alpha$. But G contains a Sylow subgroup of order p^α. Hence the $p^\alpha - 1$ elements of order p, together with the identity, constitute the sole Sylow subgroup Γ of order p^α in G. It follows that Γ is a self-conjugate subgroup of G.

We shall next show that Γ is an Abelian group. In case $p = 2$ all the elements of Γ except the identity are of order 2. If S and T are two of these elements, we have $STST = 1$ or $T^{-1}ST = S$. Hence Γ is Abelian if $p = 2$. In the further argument suppose that p is odd. Then the group G has an element A_1 of order 2 (by Corollary III of Theorem XVI in § 15). Since the number of symbols in G is odd, A_1 must leave one letter fixed. Let a_1 be that letter. Then A_1 has a set of conjugate elements $A_1, A_2, \cdots, A_n$ $(n = p^\alpha)$ such that A_i leaves fixed the sole symbol a_i. These n elements involve $\frac{1}{2}n(n-1)$ transpositions; no two elements can have a common transposition, since their product would then leave at least two letters fixed and yet not be the identity; for this reason also the n given elements of order 2 are all the elements of order 2 in G. Now consider the set

$$A_1A_2,\ A_1A_3,\ \cdots,\ A_1A_n$$

of $n-1$ elements. Since no two A's have a common transposition, each of these elements displaces all the symbols of G. Hence these are the elements of order p in G. Now the transform of A_1A_i by A_1 is A_iA_1; hence A_1 transforms each of the elements of order p into its inverse. Then, since Γ is self-conjugate in G, it follows that Γ admits an isomorphism with itself in which each element corresponds to its inverse. Hence Γ is an Abelian group; for we have $S \sim S^{-1}$, $T \sim T^{-1}$, $ST \sim (ST)^{-1}$ and $ST \sim S^{-1}T^{-1}$, so that $(ST)^{-1} = S^{-1}T^{-1}$ or $T^{-1}S^{-1} = S^{-1}T^{-1}$, whence S and T are permutable.

Then we have the following theorem:

V. A doubly transitive group G of degree n and order $n(n-1)$ does not exist unless n is a power p^α of a prime number. In case G exists, it has just $n-1$ elements each of which displaces all the n symbols of G, and these elements, together with the identity, constitute a self-conjugate Abelian subgroup Γ of G of order p^α and type $(1, 1, \cdots, 1)$. Every element of G not in Γ is a regular permutation on just $n-1$ symbols.

Now suppose that G is a k-ply transitive group of degree n and order $n(n-1)\cdots(n-k+1)$, k being greater than unity. Then G contains a doubly transitive group of degree $n-k+2$ and order $(n-k+2)(n-k+1)$. Hence $n-k+2$ must be a power of a prime, in accordance with the preceding theorem. Therefore we have the following corollary:

COR. A k-ply transitive group G of degree n and order $n(n-1)\cdots(n-k+1)$ does not exist for k greater than unity unless $n-k+2$ is a power of a prime.

When $k=n$ the group G is obviously the symmetric group. When $k=n-2$ the group is the alternating group, as one may see by aid of Theorem VI in § **41** below. If in this corollary $k < n - 2$, then k cannot exceed 3 except when $n = 11$ and $n = 12$, a fact which is established by Jordan in Liouville's *Journal* (2) **17** (1872), pp. 357–363. [See Ex. 12 on page 151.] The actual existence of triply transitive groups of degree $p^\nu + 1$ and order $(p^\nu + 1)p^\nu(p^\nu - 1)$, where p is a prime number, will be established here for the case $\nu = 1$ and in § **68** for every positive integral value of ν.

Let p be any odd prime number and let us consider the existence of a doubly transitive group G of degree p and order $p(p-1)$. The elements of G which displace all the symbols are of order p. Let P be such an element, and let us take for P the permutation

$$P = (a_0 a_1 a_2 \cdots a_{p-1}).$$

Let α be any primitive root modulo p, and consider the permutation

$$S = (a_1 a_\alpha a_{\alpha^2} a_{\alpha^3} \cdots),$$

where it is to be understood that a subscript greater than $p - 1$ is to be reduced modulo p to a number of the set 0, 1, 2, $\cdots$, $p - 1$. Then S is of order $p - 1$, and we have

$$S^{-1}PS = (a_0 a_\alpha a_{2\alpha} a_{3\alpha} \cdots) = P^\alpha.$$

Hence the subgroup $\{P\}$ of $\{P, S\}$ is self-conjugate. Moreover, since $S^{-1}PS = P^\alpha$, it follows that all the elements of $\{P, S\}$ may be written in the form $S^\mu P^\lambda$; for $S \cdot S^\mu P^\lambda = S^{\mu+1}P^\lambda$ and $P \cdot S^\mu P^\lambda = S^\mu \cdot S^{-\mu}PS^\mu \cdot P^\lambda = S^\mu \cdot P^{\alpha^\mu} \cdot P^\lambda = S^\mu P^{\lambda + \alpha^\mu}$, whence the elements $S^\mu P^\lambda$ are merely permuted among themselves on multiplication on the left by S or by P. From these facts it follows readily that $\{P, S\}$ is of order $p(p-1)$. In order to show that this group is doubly transitive, we observe that any given ordered pair of symbols a_ρ, a_σ is changed into the fixed ordered pair a_0, a_1 by the permutation $P^{-\rho}S^{-\tau}$, where τ is suitably chosen.

Transitive subgroups of $\{P, S\}$ are readily constructed, namely, those which are generated by P and the subgroups of $\{S\}$. There is obviously such a subgroup of order pd for every divisor d of $p - 1$. Thus when $p = 13$ we obtain in this way six transitive groups of degree 13.

One may readily verify that the group {(0123456), (124)(365)} of degree 7 and order 21 displaces every unordered pair of its symbols by every other unordered pair, though the group is only singly transitive. This example shows the importance of the notion of *ordered* sets in the definition of multiply transitive groups.

Now in the general case the permutation P is completely defined by the transformation

$$x' \equiv x + 1 \bmod p$$

on the subscripts x attached to the symbols a. Similarly, the permutation S is defined by the transformation

$$x' \equiv \alpha x \bmod p$$

on these subscripts. These two transformations generate all transformations of the form

$$x' \equiv ax + b \bmod p, \quad (a \not\equiv 0 \bmod p)$$

and no others, as one may easily verify. This is a special case of the linear nonhomogeneous group modulo p introduced in § **29**. The order in this case is $p(p-1)$.

Let us now consider the set of transformations of the form

$$(A) \qquad x' \equiv \frac{ax+b}{cx+d} \bmod p, \qquad (ad - bc \not\equiv 0 \bmod p)$$

where it is to be understood that $k/0$ is to be replaced by ∞ when $k \not\equiv 0 \bmod p$ and that a corresponding a, namely, a_∞, is to be adjoined to the set of symbols a so that we now have $p+1$ symbols a.

Let us first determine the number of transformations in the set (A). If $c \equiv 0 \bmod p$ we may take $d = 1$ without loss of generality. Then the transformation is linear. We have just seen that the number of such transformations is $p(p-1)$. When $c \not\equiv 0 \bmod p$ we may take $c = 1$ without loss of generality. Then a and d may be chosen at will, each from p incongruent numbers, and then b may have any one of $p-1$ incongruent values and no more, since we must have $ad - bc \not\equiv 0 \bmod p$. Hence the number of nonlinear transformations in (A) is $p^2(p-1)$. Therefore the total number of transformations in the set (A) is $p^2(p-1)+p(p-1)$, or $(p+1)p(p-1)$. But the product of any two transformations in the set (A) is also a transformation of the same set. Thence it follows that the transformations (A) constitute a group of order $(p+1)p(p-1)$.

The transformation group (A) may be represented as a permutation group on the symbols $a_\infty, a_0, a_1, \cdots, a_{p-1}$. As such it is transitive, since any symbol may obviously be replaced by a_∞ by a suitable transformation of the form (A). Hence the largest subgroup each element of which leaves a_∞ fixed is of order $p(p-1)$. It must therefore coincide with the group $\{P, S\}$ already determined, since the elements of this group correspond to transformations leaving a_∞ unchanged. But $\{P, S\}$ is doubly transitive on $a_0, a_1, \cdots, a_{p-1}$, as we have already seen. Therefore, *the named permutation group of order* $(p+1)p(p-1)$ *on the* $p+1$ *symbols* $a_\infty, a_0, a_1, \cdots, a_{p-1}$ *is triply transitive on these symbols.*

If p is an odd prime, this triply transitive group of order $(p+1)p(p-1)$ has a doubly transitive subgroup of index 2 and degree $p+1$, consisting of even permutations alone, as one will readily verify by aid of the fact that this subgroup contains elements of order p.

41. An Upper Limit to the Degree of Transitivity. We shall now prove the following theorem:

> VI. No group of degree n, other than the symmetric and alternating groups of this degree, can be more than l-ply transitive, where l is the greatest integer not exceeding $\frac{1}{3}n+1$.

Let G be a nonsymmetric k-ply transitive group of degree n, where $1 < k < n$. Then it is obvious that $k < n-1$. Let S be any permutation of G which displaces more than k and fewer than n symbols. Suppose that the notation is so chosen that we may write

$$S = (a_1a_2 \cdots a_i) \cdots (\cdots a_{j-1}a_j)(a_{j+1} \cdots a_{k-1}a_k \cdots) \cdots.$$

Let s denote the number of symbols displaced by S. If $j < k-1$, take

$$T = \begin{pmatrix} a_1, a_2, \cdots, a_{k-1}, a_k, \cdots \\ a_1, a_2, \cdots, a_{k-1}, b_k, \cdots \end{pmatrix},$$

where b_k is some other symbol displaced by S. If $j = k - 1$, take

$$T = \begin{pmatrix} a_1, & a_2, & \cdots, & a_{k-1}, & a_k, & \cdots \\ a_1, & a_2, & \cdots, & a_{k-1}, & c_k, & \cdots \end{pmatrix},$$

where c_k is a symbol not displaced by S. In each case T is to be an element of G; such an element T certainly exists in G since G is k-ply transitive. Now in either case it may readily be shown that $T^{-1}ST \cdot S^{-1}$ is not the identity. Moreover, $T^{-1}ST \cdot S^{-1}$ displaces at most $2s - 2k + 2$ symbols, since it leaves a_1, a_2, $\cdots$, a_{k-2} unaltered in both cases and also leaves a_{k-1} unaltered in the second case and since b_k is in S.

If $2s - 2k + 2 < s$, or $s < 2k - 2$, the group G contains a permutation displacing fewer than s symbols. By continuing the process we must then arrive finally at a permutation which displaces not more than k symbols. Let Σ be such a permutation in G, where

$$\Sigma = (\alpha_1\alpha_2 \cdots \alpha_\rho) \cdots (\alpha_\sigma \cdots \alpha_\tau).$$

Then G contains a permutation of the form

$$P = \begin{pmatrix} \alpha_1\alpha_2 \cdots \alpha_{\tau-1}\alpha_\tau \cdots \\ \alpha_1\alpha_2 \cdots \alpha_{\tau-1}\beta_\tau \cdots \end{pmatrix}$$

where β_τ is different from α_τ. Then

$$\Sigma^{-1} \cdot P^{-1}\Sigma P = (\alpha_\tau\beta_\tau\alpha_\sigma).$$

Hence if G contains a permutation displacing fewer than $2k - 2$ symbols, it contains a circular permutation of order 3. If G is triply transitive, it follows from this that G must contain every circular permutation of order 3 and hence (Theorem IV of § 2) it must contain the alternating group.

Now since $k > 1$, a k-ply transitive group of degree n contains permutations displacing just $n - k + 1$ symbols, since the subgroup leaving $k - 1$ symbols fixed is of degree $n - k + 1$ and is transitive. Hence if G does not contain the alternating group on its n symbols, we must have $k = 2$ or $n - k + 1 \nless 2k - 2$, the latter condition implying that $k \ngtr \frac{1}{3}n + 1$. From this conclusion the theorem follows, since 4 is the lowest possible degree for a group which is neither alternating nor symmetric.

In the course of the proof of the preceding theorem we have also established the following result:

VII. If G is a k-ply transitive group of degree n, not containing the alternating group of this degree, and if $k \geqq 3$, then every permutation of G except the identity displaces at least $2k-2$ symbols.

A much more effective limit to the degree of transitivity of a group of degree n than that contained in Theorem VI has been given by G. A. Miller (*Bull. Amer. Math. Soc.* (2) **22** (1915): 68–71). Miller's theorem may be stated as follows:

VIII. If $n = kp + r$, where p is a prime greater than the positive integer k and where $r > k$, then a group G of degree n, not containing the alternating group of degree n, cannot be more than r-fold transitive unless $k = 1$ and $r = 2$.

We shall not give a proof of this theorem or of the following corollary which Miller (loc. cit.) derives from it:

COR. When $n > 12$, a group of degree n, not containing the alternating group of degree n, cannot be s-fold transitive if $s \geqq 3n^{\frac{1}{2}} - 2$.

EXERCISES

1. There is no transitive group of degree n whose degree of transitivity is $n-1$.

2. Construct two transitive groups and one intransitive group of degree and order 4.

3. An Abelian transitive group is regular.

4. The subgroup H of the group G in Theorem II of § **39** contains no self-conjugate subgroup of G of order greater than unity.

5. A self-conjugate element (other than the identity) in a transitive group G is a regular permutation displacing every symbol in G.

6. The order of the central of a transitive group is a factor of its degree.

7. In every transitive group on n symbols there are at least $n-1$ permutations each of which displaces all the n symbols.

8. Show that the only group of degree 2 is the symmetric group, and that the only groups of degree 3 are the alternating and symmetric groups.

9. Show that there are just seven groups of degree 4 and that they are those in the following list: (1) the symmetric group; (2) the alternating group; (3) the octic group (§ 4); (4) $\{(abcd)\}$; (5) $\{(ab)(cd), (ac)(bd)\}$; (6) $\{(ab), (cd)\}$; (7) $\{(ab)(cd)\}$.

10. Show that there are just three intransitive groups of degree 5 — one of order 12 and two of order 6. Show also that there are just five transitive groups of degree 5, their orders being, respectively, 120, 60, 20, 10, 5. Give generators for each of these eight groups of degree 5. What is the degree of transitivity of each of the transitive groups in the set?

11. Show that if a group of degree 12 is 5-fold transitive but not 6-fold transitive, then its order is $12 \cdot 11 \cdot 10 \cdot 9 \cdot 8$. (Use Theorem VII of § 41.)

12. Let us write

$$S = (x_0 x_1 x_2 \cdots x_{10}),$$
$$T = (x_4 x_5 x_3 x_9)(x_{10} x_7 x_2 x_6),$$
$$U = (x_0 x_\infty)(x_1 x_{10})(x_2 x_5)(x_3 x_7)(x_4 x_8)(x_6 x_9).$$

Show that $\{S, T\}$ is a 4-fold transitive group of degree 11 and order $11 \cdot 10 \cdot 9 \cdot 8$. Show also that $\{S, T, U\}$ is a 5-fold transitive group of degree 12 and order $12 \cdot 11 \cdot 10 \cdot 9 \cdot 8$. (These are known as Mathieu groups.)

13. Construct generators for the triply transitive group of degree 10 and order $10 \cdot 9 \cdot 8$ contained in the group $\{S, T\}$ of Ex. 12. Show that the permutations

$$(a_1 a_2 \cdots a_8), \quad (a_0 a_8 a_4)(a_1 a_2 a_7)(a_3 a_6 a_5), \quad (a_0 a_1 a_3 a_2 a_4 a_9 a_8 a_6 a_7 a_5)$$

generate a different triply transitive group of degree 10 and order $10 \cdot 9 \cdot 8$, and prove that this latter group contains a doubly transitive group of degree 10 and order $10 \cdot 9 \cdot 4$.

14. Construct two doubly transitive groups of degree 9 and order $9 \cdot 8$ and show that there is no other doubly transitive group of this degree and order.

15. Construct three doubly transitive groups of degree 25 and order $25 \cdot 24$ and show that there is no other doubly transitive group of this degree and order.

16. Construct a triply transitive group of degree 6 and order $6 \cdot 5 \cdot 4$ and show that it has a doubly transitive subgroup of degree 6 and order $6 \cdot 5 \cdot 2$. Show that these are the only multiply transitive groups of degree 6 other than the alternating and symmetric groups.

17. Let G be a transitive group of degree n and order nm each element of which (except the identity) displaces all or all but one of the symbols. Prove the following propositions:

(1) There are just $n - 1$ elements of G each of which displaces all the symbols. If these elements, together with the identity, form a group, then this group is self-conjugate in G.

(2) If H is the subgroup of order m leaving one symbol fixed, then the elements of H permute, in sets of m each, the elements which displace all the symbols. Therefore m is a factor of $n - 1$. The number of elements in a complete conjugate set of elements each of which displaces all the symbols is a multiple of m.

(3) If p^α $(\alpha > 0)$ is the highest power of a prime p which divides n, then the number of elements whose orders are multiples of p is of the form $n - k_p n/p^\alpha$ and m is a factor of the positive number $p^\alpha - k_p$.

(4) If $m \geqq \sqrt{n}$, then n is a power of a prime.

(5) If n is twice an odd number, then G is a regular group.

(6) If m is even, then G contains a self-conjugate regular Abelian group of degree and order n.

18. Show that the permutations

$$(a_1a_3)(a_2a_6)(a_5a_7), \qquad (a_1a_2a_3a_4a_5a_6a_7a_8),$$
$$(a_0a_8a_4)(a_1a_2a_7)(a_3a_6a_5), \quad (a_0a_1a_3a_2a_4a_9a_8a_6a_7a_5)$$

generate a triply transitive group of degree 10 and order $10 \cdot 9 \cdot 8 \cdot 2$ containing the two triply transitive groups of Ex. 13.

19. Construct a doubly transitive group of degree 25 and order $25 \cdot 24 \cdot 2$ containing two doubly transitive groups of degree 25 and order $25 \cdot 24$.

20. Construct a doubly transitive group of degree 49 and order $49 \cdot 48 \cdot 2$ containing two doubly transitive groups of index 2.

42. Simplicity of the Alternating Group of Degree $n \neq 4$. We shall prove the following theorem:

IX. The alternating group of degree n is simple except when $n = 4$.

When $n = 3$ the alternating group is of order 3 and is therefore simple. When $n = 2$ it consists of the identity alone. Hence in the proof we may consider only the case when $n \geqq 4$.

Now the alternating group G of degree n is $(n-2)$-ply transitive. If P is a permutation of G displacing fewer than $n-1$ symbols, then, as in § **41**, we may construct a permutation Σ such that $\Sigma^{-1}P^{-1}\Sigma \cdot P$ is a circular permutation of order 3. But $\Sigma^{-1}P^{-1}\Sigma = (\Sigma^{-1}P\Sigma)^{-1}$. Hence P and its conjugate permutations generate the group G. If S is a permutation of G displacing $n-1$ symbols, then, as in § **41**, we may construct a permutation T such that $S^{-1}T^{-1}ST$ displaces not more than $2(n-1) - 2(n-2) + 2$, or 4, symbols. If S is a permutation of G displacing n symbols, then T may be found so that $S^{-1}T^{-1}ST$ displaces not more than $2\,n - 2(n-2) + 2$, or 6, symbols.

From these considerations it follows that the group G is certainly generated by any given permutation Q of G and its conjugates, except possibly in the case of a permutation displacing $n-1$ symbols when $n = 5$ and in the case of a permutation displacing n symbols when $n = 4$, 5, or 6.

When $n = 5$ and S is an even permutation on 4 symbols, we may write $S = (12)(34)$. Then if we take $T = (12)(35)$, we have $S^{-1}T^{-1}ST = (354)$. Hence S and its conjugates generate G.

When $n = 6$ and S is an even permutation on 6 symbols, we may take for S either $(12)(3456)$ or $(123)(456)$. If T is $(12)(3645)$, we have for $S^{-1}T^{-1}ST$ the permutation (356) or (14263) in the respective cases. In either case S and its conjugates generate G.

When $n = 5$ and S is an even permutation on 5 symbols, we may take $S = (12345)$. Putting $T = (345)$, we have $S^{-1}T^{-1}ST = (134)$, so that again S and its conjugates generate G.

When $n = 4$ and S is an even permutation on 4 symbols, we may take $S = (12)(34)$. The permutations conjugate to S in G are S and $(13)(24)$ and $(14)(23)$. These generate a group of order 4 which is self-conjugate in G. Hence G is not simple when $n = 4$.

When $n > 4$, the group G is generated by any one of its elements (other than the identity) and the conjugates of that element. Hence, when $n > 4$, G contains no self-conjugate proper subgroup except that consisting of the identity alone; hence G is simple when $n > 4$, and therefore when $n \neq 4$.

43. Self-conjugate Subgroups of Symmetric Groups. We shall prove the following theorem:

> X. The alternating group of degree n is the only self-conjugate proper subgroup (of order greater than unity) contained in the symmetric group of degree n except when $n = 4$.

When $n = 4$ the self-conjugate subgroup of order 4 in the alternating group is also self-conjugate in the symmetric group, as one may easily verify. When $n = 2$ or $n = 3$ the theorem is obvious. Hence we have left to consider the case when $n > 4$.

As in the proof of the previous theorem, it may be shown that the conjugates of any even permutation (other than the identity) in the symmetric group of degree n $(n > 4)$ generate the alternating group. It is obvious that a subgroup of order 2 is not self-conjugate in the symmetric group of degree n $(n > 4)$. Any other subgroup containing odd permutations also contains an even permutation besides the identity; hence if it is self-conjugate it must contain the alternating group and therefore must coincide with the given symmetric group itself.

Since a subgroup of index 2 in a group is self-conjugate in the group, we readily obtain the following corollary:

> Cor. The alternating group of degree n is the only subgroup of index 2 in the symmetric group of degree n.

44. Representation of a Group as a Transitive Group. We have seen (in § **12**) that every finite group can be represented as simply isomorphic with a regular permutation group. It is often desirable to represent a given abstract group as a transitive group of lowest possible degree, in order to facilitate the study of the properties of the group. Therefore we shall now give some theorems concerning the representation of an abstract group as a transitive permutation group.

XI. Let G be a group of finite order g which contains a subgroup H of index m. Then G has a $(k, 1)$ isomorphism with a transitive group of degree m, where k is the order of some subgroup of H which is self-conjugate in G. The isomorphism is simple if H contains no self-conjugate subgroup of G of order greater than unity.

Let G be separated into the partitions $H\tau_1$ $(\tau_1 = 1)$, $H\tau_2, \cdots,$ $H\tau_m$ according to the second method of § **10**; and denote these partitions in order by the symbols $\gamma_1, \gamma_2, \cdots, \gamma_m$. If a is any element of G, then every element in $H\tau_i \cdot a$ belongs to the same partition, say γ'_i, as $\tau_i \cdot a$. If b is any element of G, then every element in $H\tau_i ab$ belongs to the same partition, say γ''_i, as $\tau_i ab$. Now if we write

$$S = \begin{pmatrix} \gamma_1, & \gamma_2, & \cdots, & \gamma_m \\ \gamma'_1, & \gamma'_2, & \cdots, & \gamma'_m \end{pmatrix}, \quad T = \begin{pmatrix} \gamma'_1, & \gamma'_2, & \cdots, & \gamma'_m \\ \gamma''_1, & \gamma''_2, & \cdots, & \gamma''_m \end{pmatrix},$$

we have

$$ST = \begin{pmatrix} \gamma_1, & \gamma_2, & \cdots, & \gamma_m \\ \gamma''_1, & \gamma''_2, & \cdots, & \gamma''_m \end{pmatrix}.$$

From this it follows that if the permutations S and T on $\gamma_1, \gamma_2, \cdots, \gamma_m$ correspond to a and b, respectively, then the product ST corresponds to ab. Hence all the permutations such as $S, T, \cdots$ form a permutation group $\bar{G}$ on $\gamma_1, \gamma_2, \cdots, \gamma_m$ which is isomorphic with G. This group $\bar{G}$ is transitive, since the element γ_1 is carried into the element γ_i by the permutation corresponding to the element τ_i of G.

The identity in $\overline{G}$ is the only element in $\overline{G}$ corresponding to the identity in G. The totality of elements in G each of which corresponds to the identity in $\overline{G}$ forms a self-conjugate subgroup H_1 of G, in accordance with Theorem I of § 16. Let k denote the order of H_1. Then G is $(k, 1)$ isomorphic with $\overline{G}$. If h_1 is any element of H_1, then $H\tau_i h_1$ is the same set of elements as $H\tau_i$ for each i of the set $1, 2, \cdots, m$. In particular, Hh_1 is the same set as H. Therefore h_1 is in H. Therefore H contains the self-conjugate subgroup H_1 of G. Hence when H contains no self-conjugate subgroup of G of order greater than unity, the isomorphism of G with $\overline{G}$ is simple.

Cor. If a group G contains a complete set of m conjugate elements $S_1, S_2, \cdots, S_m$, or a complete set of m conjugate subgroups $H_1, H_2, \cdots, H_m$, then G is isomorphic with a transitive permutation group of degree m.

For G contains a subgroup of index m in accordance with Theorem VI, or Theorem VII, of § 11.

If a group G of order g is a transitive group of degree n on the n letters $a_1, a_2, \cdots, a_n$, then, as we have seen, G contains subgroups $G_1, G_2, \cdots, G_n$ of index n such that G_i consists of all those elements of G each of which leaves a_i fixed. Moreover, G_i contains no self-conjugate subgroup of G of order greater than unity, as one may readily show. If G_1 leaves α letters fixed, so that it is of degree $n - \alpha$, then the groups $G_1, G_2, \cdots, G_n$ fall into sets of α each so that the α groups in each set are identical. In any case the distinct groups in the set $G_1, G_2, \cdots, G_n$ form a complete set of conjugate subgroups of G. If G is nonregular, the groups $G_1, G_2, \cdots, G_n$ cannot all coincide, so that in this case there are at least two distinct groups in the set. Hence a group cannot be represented in the form of a nonregular transitive permutation group to which it is simply isomorphic unless it contains a non-self-conjugate subgroup H which itself contains no self-conjugate subgroup of the given group except that consisting of the identity alone. Combining this result with the preceding theorem, we have the following:

XII. A necessary and sufficient condition that an abstract group G of order g may be represented as simply isomorphic with a transitive permutation group of degree n $(n < g)$ is that G shall contain a subgroup H of index n such that neither H nor any proper subgroup of H (other than that of order unity) is self-conjugate in G.

Now let G be a transitive permutation group on the n letters $a_1, a_2, \cdots, a_n$ which contains no subgroup of degree n and index n but does contain subgroups displacing just $n-1$ letters. Then G contains distinct subgroups $G_1, G_2, \cdots, G_n$ of index n such that G_i displaces all the letters except a_i. These n subgroups must correspond to these n subgroups in every isomorphism of G with itself. An element of G which replaces a_i by a_j transforms G_i to G_j; therefore a permutation P in G transforms the subgroups G_i according to a permutation which transforms to P by the permutation

$$\begin{pmatrix} G_1, & G_2, & \cdots, & G_n \\ a_1, & a_2, & \cdots, & a_n \end{pmatrix}.$$

Hence, if each G_i corresponds to itself in an isomorphism of G with itself, then every element of G corresponds to itself in that isomorphism. Therefore the group of isomorphisms of G may be represented as a permutation group on $G_1, G_2, \cdots, G_n$. Furthermore, G is simply isomorphic with its group of inner isomorphisms. Therefore the latter group may be represented as a transitive permutation group of degree n which contains G as a self-conjugate subgroup. Hence we have the following theorem:

XIII. If G is a transitive permutation group which contains subgroups of index n displacing just $n-1$ letters, but no subgroup of index n displacing all the n letters, then G is simply isomorphic with its group of inner isomorphisms, and the group of isomorphisms of G may be represented as a transitive permutation group of degree n which contains G as a self-conjugate subgroup.

45. Intransitive Groups. Let G be an intransitive group. Let x_1 be any letter on which it operates, and let $x_1, x_2, \cdots, x_r$ be the letters into which x_1 may be changed by the elements of G. Then any permutation in G merely permutes these letters among themselves. Moreover any letter x_i may be displaced by any letter x_j by a permutation of G; for if g displaces x_1 by x_i and h displaces x_1 by x_j, then $g^{-1}h$ displaces x_i by x_j. Hence the elements of G permute the letters $x_1, x_2, \cdots, x_r$ transitively. These letters form what is called a *transitive set* of letters in G.

Since G is intransitive it operates on some other letters than those contained in the transitive set $x_1, x_2, \cdots, x_r$. Let y_1 be such a letter, and let $y_1, y_2, \cdots, y_s$ be the transitive set containing y_1. If this does not exhaust the letters on which G operates, then there is another transitive set $z_1, z_2, \cdots, z_t$ among the letters of G. This process may be continued until all the letters of G are exhausted, so that the letters on which G operates are thus separated into a certain number (two or more) of independent transitive sets.

Let σ be the totality of letters in a certain number (not all) of the transitive sets of the letters on which G operates; and let τ denote the totality of the remaining letters in G. If g_1 and g_2 are any elements in G which do not displace any of the letters in the set τ, and if g is any element of G, then the letters in τ are left fixed both by g_1g_2 and by $g^{-1}g_1g$. Hence the totality of elements in G each of which leaves fixed the symbols τ forms a self-conjugate subgroup H_1 of G. Similarly, the elements which leave fixed the symbols σ form a self-conjugate subgroup H_2 of G.

Now the totality of different permutations on the letters in σ alone, each of which is produced by an element of G, evidently forms a permutation group G_1 on the letters in σ. Let g and g' be any two elements of G, and let k and k' be the elements of G_1 which permute the letters in σ in the same way as g and g' respectively. Then gg' and kk' permute the letters in σ in the same way. Hence G and G_1 are isomorphic, the elements of H_2 in G corresponding to the identity in G_1. Therefore G_1 is simply isomorphic with G/H_2. It is evident that G_1 contains H_1 as a self-conjugate subgroup.

Now the identity is the only element common to H_1 and H_2. Moreover every element in one of these groups is permutable with every element in the other. Hence $\{H_1, H_2\}$ is the direct product of H_1 and H_2. Since H_1 and H_2 are both self-conjugate in G, it follows that $\{H_1, H_2\}$ is self-conjugate in G. Moreover $G/\{H_1, H_2\}$ and G_1/H_1 are of the same order.

The permutations effected on the letters in σ by $\{H_1, H_2\}$ constitute the group H_1, while the permutations effected by G on the letters in σ constitute the group G_1. Let k_1, k_2, k_3 be elements of $\{H_1, H_2\}$, and let g_1, g_2, g_3 be elements of G such that $k_1g_1 \cdot k_2g_2 = k_3g_3$. Let $k'_1, k'_2, k'_3, g'_1, g'_2, g'_3$ be the permutations effected on the letters in σ by the elements $k_1, k_2, k_3, g_1, g_2, g_3$ respectively. Then it is evident that $k'_1g'_1 \cdot k'_2g'_2 = k'_3g'_3$. Hence the groups $G/\{H_1, H_2\}$ and G_1/H_1 are isomorphic. But we have seen that they are of the same order and that G_1 is simply isomorphic with G/H_2. Hence $G/\{H_1, H_2\}$ and G_1/H_1 are simply isomorphic.

If G_2 is the permutation group effected on the letters in τ by the group G, then it may be shown similarly that G_2/H_2 is simply isomorphic with $G/\{H_1, H_2\}$. Hence G_1/H_1 and G_2/H_2 are simply isomorphic.

Now let G be an intransitive group of degree n having just k transitive constituents. That the average number of symbols displaced by the permutations of G is $n-k$ is readily seen from the fact that the average number of letters of each transitive set displaced by the permutations of G is one less than the number of symbols in that set (Theorem IV of § **39**).

46. Primitive and Imprimitive Groups. Let G be a transitive group on n symbols. Suppose that the n symbols may be divided into r sets $\sigma_1, \sigma_2, \cdots, \sigma_r$ $(r > 1)$, each set containing s $(s > 1)$ symbols (so that $n = rs$), such that any whatever given permutation of G either permutes the s symbols of σ_i among themselves or replaces these symbols by the symbols of another set σ_j, this holding for each i of the set $1, 2, \cdots, r$. Then G is called an *imprimitive* group and the sets $\sigma_1, \sigma_2, \cdots, \sigma_r$ are called *imprimitive systems* or *systems of imprimitivity.* If no such separation of the n symbols into systems is possible, then the transitive group G is called a *primitive* group.

The group $\{(xyz)(abc), (xa)(yb)(zc)\}$ has two sets of imprimitive systems, namely, x, y, z; a, b, c and x, a; y, b; z, c.

An imprimitive group cannot be multiply transitive; for if it were as much as doubly transitive, it would contain a permutation displacing any two given symbols by any other two, and the first two could be selected from the same system of imprimitivity and the second two from different systems. Hence *every multiply transitive group is a primitive group.* There are also primitive groups which are only singly transitive; in fact it is obvious that any transitive group of prime degree is primitive.

Now let G be a nonregular transitive group on the n symbols $a_1, a_2, \cdots, a_n$, and let G_1 be the group consisting of all those permutations in G each of which leaves a_1 fixed. Let α be the number of the letters $a_1, a_2, \cdots, a_n$ left fixed by G_1 and suppose that $\alpha > 1$. Let $G_1, G_2, \cdots, G_k$ be the conjugates of G_1 in G. Then each of these subgroups leaves fixed a different set of α letters, so that $k\alpha = n$. The k sets of α letters each, left fixed by $G_1, G_2, \cdots, G_k$ respectively, form a set of systems of imprimitivity of G, since the subgroups $G_1, G_2, \cdots, G_k$ are transformed among themselves by any element of G. Hence *a necessary condition in order that a nonregular transitive group shall be primitive is that the largest subgroup which leaves fixed one given symbol shall leave fixed only that one symbol*; but this condition is not sufficient, as one may see from the corollary to Theorem XIV below.

XIV. Let $S_1, S_2, \cdots, S_m$ be a complete set of conjugate elements or conjugate subgroups of a given abstract group G. A necessary and sufficient condition that the symbols $S_1, S_2, \cdots, S_m$ shall be transformed under G according to an imprimitive permutation group is that the subgroup H_1 of G which consists of the totality of elements of G transforming S_1 into itself shall be contained in a larger proper subgroup of G.

In order to prove the condition sufficient, let us suppose that H_1 is contained in a larger proper subgroup K_1 of G. Now the number of conjugates of S_1 under K_1 is the quotient λ of the order of K_1 by the order of H_1. Moreover K_1 contains all the elements of G each of which transforms these λ conjugates among themselves. Therefore every element of G not in K_1 transforms these λ conjugates from the set $S_1, S_2, \cdots, S_m$ into another set of λ conjugates from the same set. In this way these symbols are separated into sets of λ each such that the sets remain intact as sets under transformation by the elements of G and are merely permuted among themselves. Hence they constitute a set of systems of imprimitivity of the transitive group on $S_1, S_2, \cdots, S_m$ obtained on transforming by the elements of G in the way indicated.

To prove the necessity of the condition, we notice that if the symbols $S_1, S_2, \cdots, S_m$ are transformed by the elements of G according to an imprimitive group, then there is a proper subgroup K_2 of G which contains H_1, this subgroup being formed of those elements of G each of which transforms among themselves the symbols of the imprimitive system containing S_1.

This completes the proof of the theorem.

COR. Let G be a transitive group of degree n whose largest subgroup G_1 leaving one symbol fixed is of degree $n-1$. Then a necessary and sufficient condition that G shall be imprimitive is that G_1 shall be contained in a larger proper subgroup of G.

This follows at once from the theorem and the fact that G transforms the conjugates of G_1 in exactly the same way as it permutes the symbols $a_1, a_2, \cdots, a_n$ on which G operates.

EXERCISES

1. Construct a transitive group of degree 6, an intransitive group of degree 6, and an intransitive group of degree 7, each of which is simply isomorphic with the symmetric group on 4 symbols.

2. Let $x_1, x_2, \cdots, x_r; y_1, y_2, \cdots, y_s; z_1, z_2, \cdots, z_t; \cdots$ be the transitive sets of letters in an intransitive group G. Prove the following propositions:

(1) The group G is a subgroup of the direct product of the symmetric groups on the symbols $[x_1, x_2, \cdots, x_r]$, $[y_1, y_2, \cdots, y_s]$, $\cdots$.

(2) The order of G is a factor of $r! \cdot s! \cdot t! \cdots$ and is a common multiple of $r, s, t, \cdots$.

(3) The permutations leaving x_1 fixed constitute a subgroup of index r.

3. Construct a doubly transitive group of degree 10 which is simply isomorphic with the alternating group of degree 6.

4. Construct a transitive group of degree 15 which is simply isomorphic with (*a*) the alternating group of degree 6, (*b*) the symmetric group of degree 6.

5. The alternating group of degree 5 is simple and is of order 60. Show that 60 is the lowest possible composite order of a simple group.

6. The central of a primitive group consists of the identity alone.

7. The group of inner isomorphisms of a primitive group G is simply isomorphic with G.

8. If a transitive group contains an element of prime order p greater than the largest proper factor of its degree n, then G is a primitive group.

9. Those permutations of an imprimitive group G which permute among themselves the letters in each of a given complete set of imprimitive systems of G constitute a self-conjugate subgroup of G.

10. All the primitive groups of degrees 2 to 20 have been constructed, and it has been found that their number for each degree is as follows:

DEGREE	2	3	4	5	6	7	8	9	10	11	12	13	14	15	16	17	18	19	20
NUMBER	1	2	2	5	4	7	7	11	9	8	6	9	4	6	22	10	4	8	4

Many of these can readily be found by the methods already described. For each of the degrees 2, 3, 4, 5, 6, 14, 18, 19, 20 construct as many primitive groups as are indicated for that degree in the foregoing table, and for each of the degrees 2, 3, 4, 5, 6 show that these are all the primitive groups of these degrees.

11. Show that the permutations (123)(456) and (17)(26) generate a doubly transitive group of degree 7 and order 168 and prove that this group is simple.

12. Construct seven primitive groups of degree 7 and show that these are all the primitive groups of degree 7. (See Exs. 10 and 11.)

13. A self-conjugate subgroup (of order greater than unity) in a primitive group G is transitive. Hence its order is a multiple of the degree of G.

14. The symmetric group of degree n is the only primitive group of degree n one of whose elements is a transposition.

15. The alternating and symmetric groups of degree n are the only primitive groups of degree n containing a circular permutation of order 3.

16. A regular group of composite order is imprimitive.

17. The ϕ-subgroup of a primitive group consists of the identity alone.

18. Let G be a prime-power Abelian group of order p^n and type $(1, 1, \cdots, 1)$, and let K be the holomorph of G expressed in the usual way as a permutation group of degree p^n. Show that K is doubly transitive when p is an odd prime and that it is triply transitive when $p = 2$.

19. Show that the doubly transitive group of prime degree p and order $p(p-1)$, constructed in § **40**, is simply isomorphic with its group of isomorphisms.

20. Assuming the theorem that the symmetric group of degree n contains no subgroup of degree n and index n when $n \neq 6$, prove that the symmetric group of degree n, when $n \neq 2$ and $n \neq 6$, is simply isomorphic with its group of isomorphisms.

MISCELLANEOUS EXERCISES

1. Let G_1 and G_2 be two transitive groups of degree n such that the permutations in G_1 which displace all the symbols are the same as the permutations in G_2 which displace all the symbols. Show that the two groups can differ only in the permutations which leave just one symbol unchanged.

2. Let G be a transitive group of degree n and order g. Let g_r be the number of permutations in G each of which leaves just r symbols fixed. Show that

$$\sum_{r=0}^{n} g_r = g, \qquad \sum_{r=1}^{n} r g_r = g.$$

If G is k-fold transitive, show that

$$g = \sum_{r=l}^{n} r(r-1) \cdots (r-l+1) g_r. \qquad (l = 1, 2, \cdots, k)$$

In particular, if G is triply transitive, show that

$$\sum_{r=1}^{n} r^3 g_r = 5\, g.$$

3. Let G be a transitive group of order p^m, where p is a prime number. Let H be the largest subgroup of G each element of which leaves fixed a given symbol of G. Then H leaves fixed p^α symbols of G, where α is a positive integer.

4. If ρ is the index of a proper subgroup H of the symmetric group G of degree n, then $\rho = 2$ or ρ is at least as great as the largest prime number less than n.

5. The group G of degree n $(n > 4)$ which is generated by all the permutations of the form (12)(34) on a given set of n letters is the alternating group of degree n.

6. By means of Theorem VIII of § **41** prove that, besides the alternating and symmetric groups, there are no groups of degree not greater than 100 which are as much as 8-fold transitive.

7. The totality of circular permutations of order r on m symbols generates the symmetric or the alternating group on these m symbols according as r is even or odd.

8. Write n in the form $n = k_0 p^\alpha + k_1 p^{\alpha-1} + \cdots + k_{\alpha-1} p + k_\alpha$, where $k_0, k_1, \cdots, k_\alpha$ are positive integers less than the prime p. Then a Sylow subgroup of order p^m in the symmetric group of degree n has its central of order p^l where $l = k_0 + k_1 + \cdots + k_{\alpha-1}$.

9. Let us write

$A = (x_0 x_1 x_2 x_3 \cdots x_{22})$,

$B = (x_2 x_{16} x_9 x_6 x_8)(x_4 x_3 x_{12} x_{13} x_{18})(x_{10} x_{11} x_{22} x_7 x_{17})(x_{20} x_{15} x_{14} x_{19} x_{21})$,

$C = (x_0 x_\infty)(x_1 x_{22})(x_2 x_{11})(x_3 x_{15})(x_4 x_{17})(x_5 x_9)(x_6 x_{19})(x_7 x_{13})(x_8 x_{20})$
$(x_{10} x_{16})(x_{12} x_{21})(x_{18} x_{14})$.

Show that $\{A, B\}$ is a 4-fold transitive group of degree 23 and order $23 \cdot 22 \cdot 21 \cdot 20 \cdot 16 \cdot 3$. Show also that $\{A, B, C\}$ is a 5-fold transitive group of degree 24 and order $24 \cdot 23 \cdot 22 \cdot 21 \cdot 20 \cdot 16 \cdot 3$. (These groups are known as Mathieu groups.)

10. Construct all the permutation groups of degree 6.

11. Construct all the permutation groups of degree 7.

12. A transitive group of order p^α is imprimitive if p is a prime and $\alpha > 1$.

13. A primitive group of degree n, not containing the alternating group of degree n, does not contain two transitive subgroups which can be transformed into each other by a transposition.

14. A doubly transitive group G does not contain an intransitive subgroup whose index in G is less than the degree of G.

15. A self-conjugate subgroup of a k-ply transitive group of degree n $(2 < k < n)$ is at least $(k-1)$-ply transitive except in the case of a triply transitive group of degree 2^m, in which case there may be a self-conjugate subgroup of order 2^m.

16. Construct seven primitive groups of degree 8 as follows: (1) the symmetric group; (2) the alternating group; (3) a triply transitive group of order $8 \cdot 7 \cdot 6 \cdot 4$ whose existence is asserted in Ex. 18 on page 163; (4) the triply transitive group of degree 8 and order $8 \cdot 7 \cdot 6$ whose existence is shown at the end of § **40**; (5) a doubly transitive subgroup of index 2 in the group described in (4) and hence of order $8 \cdot 7 \cdot 3$; (6) another doubly transitive group of order $8 \cdot 7 \cdot 3$; (7) a doubly transitive subgroup of the latter of order $8 \cdot 7$. Show that these are all the multiply transitive groups, and indeed all the primitive groups, of degree 8. (Compare Ex. 10 on page 162.)

17. Show that the 5-fold transitive group of degree 12 defined in Ex. 12 on page 151 contains as a subgroup a 3-fold transitive group of degree 12 and order 7920. Then construct six multiply transitive groups of degree 12 and eight primitive groups of degree 11. (Compare Ex. 10 on page 162.)

18. Construct nine primitive groups of degree 13.

19. Construct six primitive groups of degree 15.

20. Construct six multiply transitive groups of degree 16 containing, respectively, the six groups of Ex. 19 as the largest subgroups leaving one letter fixed.

CHAPTER VII

Defining Relations for Abstract Groups

47. Introduction. Two General Theorems. In § **9** we illustrated by means of examples the notion of defining relations for abstract groups. A group may have several independent sets of generators; but it is completely defined as an abstract group by means of any independent set of abstract generators and all the independent relations by which they are connected. The theory of defining relations for abstract groups, so far as it has been developed up to the present time, consists mainly of isolated theorems. In § **24** we obtained defining relations for prime-power Abelian groups; and it is obvious how one would pass from these to defining relations for abstract Abelian groups in general. In Chapter V, on prime-power groups, we have incidentally met a number of defining relations for particular classes of abstract groups. In this chapter we shall give a few additional results concerning defining relations. In the present section we prove two general theorems.

I. Let G denote an abstract finite group whose generators $t_1, t_2, \cdots, t_k$ are subject to the sole defining relations

$$f_i(t_1, t_2, \cdots, t_k) = 1, \qquad (i = 1, 2, \cdots, m)$$

where $f_i(t_1, t_2, \cdots, t_k)$ denotes a product of powers of some or all of the elements $t_1, t_2, \cdots, t_k$. Let Γ be an abstract group whose generators $\tau_1, \tau_2, \cdots, \tau_k$ are subject to the sole defining relations

$$f_i(\tau_1, \tau_2, \cdots, \tau_k) = 1, \qquad (i = 1, 2, \cdots, m)$$
$$F_i(\tau_1, \tau_2, \cdots, \tau_k) = 1, \qquad (i = 1, 2, \cdots, \mu)$$

where $F_i(\tau_1, \tau_2, \cdots, \tau_k)$ denotes a product of powers of some or all of the elements $\tau_1, \tau_2, \cdots, \tau_k$. Then the elements $F_i(t_1, t_2, \cdots, t_k)$ $(i=1, 2, \cdots, \mu)$ generate a self-conjugate subgroup H of G, and G/H is simply isomorphic with Γ.

The groups G and Γ are exhibited as isomorphic by making t_i and τ_i correspond for each value i of the set $1, 2, \cdots, k$. To each element in G there corresponds only a single element in Γ; but to the identity in Γ corresponds every element of G which is in H and no other element of G. Hence the isomorphism of G with Γ is multiple; and the subgroup H of G which corresponds to identity in Γ is (§ **16**) a self-conjugate subgroup of G, and G/H is (§ **20**) simply isomorphic with Γ.

II. If H denotes an abstract finite group whose generators $s, t_1, t_2, \cdots, t_k$ are subject to the sole defining conditions

$$f_i(s, t_1, t_2, \cdots, t_k) = 1, \qquad (i = 1, 2, \cdots, m)$$

where $f_i(s, t_1, t_2, \cdots, t_k)$ denotes a product of powers of some or all of the elements $s, t_1, t_2, \cdots, t_k$, and if ν is any number prime to the order n of s, then the generators $\sigma, t_1, t_2, \cdots, t_k$ subject to the sole defining conditions

$$t_j^{-1}\sigma^{-n}t_j\sigma^n = f_i(\sigma^\nu, t_1, t_2, \cdots, t_k) = 1,$$
$$(j = 1, 2, \cdots, k;\ i = 1, 2, \cdots, m)$$

generate an abstract group which is the direct product of H and the cyclic group of order ν.

Let h be the order of H, and let H be written as a regular permutation group on h symbols. Let S, T_j be the concrete forms of s, t_j in this representation. Since ν is prime to n, there exists a regular permutation S_1 on the same h symbols such that $S_1^\nu = S$. Define Σ by the relation $\Sigma = S_1 \cdot (b_1 b_2 \cdots b_\nu)$, where $(b_1 b_2 \cdots b_\nu)$ is a cyclic permutation on symbols distinct from the h symbols on which H is represented as a permutation group. Then $\Sigma^\nu = S_1^\nu = S$. Moreover Σ^n is the nth power of $(b_1 b_2 \cdots b_\nu)$, so that Σ^n is permutable with each of the permutations $T_1, T_2, \cdots, T_k$. Hence the group $\{\sigma, t_1, t_2, \cdots, t_k\}$ has at least as many elements as the group $\{\Sigma, T_1, T_2, \cdots, T_k\}$ and is (Theorem I) isomorphic with it. Moreover the group $\{\sigma^\nu, t_1, t_2, \cdots, t_k\}$ has at least as many elements as the group $\{\Sigma^\nu, T_1, T_2, \cdots, T_k\}$ and is isomorphic with it. Hence $\{\sigma^\nu, t_1, t_2 \cdots, t_k\}$ has at least as many elements as H and is isomorphic with it. But it cannot contain more elements than H, since $\sigma^\nu, t_1, t_2, \cdots, t_k$ satisfy all the conditions imposed on $s, t_1, t_2, \cdots, t_k$ in the definition of H. Hence $\{\sigma^\nu, t_1, t_2, \cdots, t_k\}$ is simply isomorphic with H. It may therefore be denoted by H.

Let us consider the ν sets of elements

$$H,\ H\sigma^n,\ H\sigma^{2n},\ \cdots,\ H\sigma^{(\nu-1)n},$$

each element of which belongs to the group $\{\sigma, t_1, t_2, \cdots, t_k\}$. On multiplying on the right by any t_j these sets are unaltered as sets, since σ^n is permutable with each t_j and H contains each t_j. The foregoing sets, except for order, are the same as the sets

$$H,\ H\sigma,\ H\sigma^2,\ \cdots,\ H\sigma^{\nu-1},$$

since the numbers $n, 2n, 3n, \cdots, (\nu - 1)n$ are in some order congruent modulo ν to the numbers $1, 2, \cdots, \nu - 1$ (owing to the fact that ν and n are relatively prime), and since $H\sigma^{n\nu} \equiv H$. If the last sets are multiplied on the right by σ they are permuted cyclically in the order written. The ν sets are then permuted but left intact as sets by multiplication on the right by any of the elements $\sigma, t_1, t_2, \cdots, t_k$. Hence all the elements of $\{\sigma, t_1, t_2, \cdots, t_k\}$ are contained in these sets. The latter have not more than νh distinct elements. Hence the order of $\{\sigma, t_1, t_2, \cdots, t_k\}$ is not greater than νh. But this group is isomorphic with $\{\Sigma, T_1, T_2, \cdots, T_k\}$ and contains at least as many elements as the latter. It is easy to see that the latter group is simply isomorphic with the direct product of H and the cyclic group of order ν (and hence is of order νh), since it clearly contains the subgroup $\{\Sigma', T_1, T_2, \cdots, T_k\}$, simply isomorphic with H, and the permutation $(b_1 b_2 \cdots b_\nu)$ which is on letters not in this subgroup. Thence follows readily the conclusion of the theorem.

It is clear that the theorem may be applied again to the generational relations in the conclusion so as to generalize one of the elements t_j; and that the process may be continued until each of the elements has been replaced by a new one. In this way we obtain a formal extension of the theorem which will be of use in the next section.

48. Symmetric and Alternating Groups. Several sets of abstract defining relations for the symmetric and alternating groups are known. We reproduce here in Theorems III and IV those which we consider the most pleasing.

III. If $n > 2$ and if the $n-1$ distinct elements $s_1, s_2, \cdots, s_{n-1}, s_n(=s_1)$ satisfy the relations

$$s_i^2 = (s_i s_{i+1})^3 = (s_i s_{i+1} s_i s_j)^2 = 1, \qquad [1]$$

where i and j range over the set $1, 2, \cdots, n-1$, except that j is different from i and $i+1$, and if these elements satisfy no conditions except those implied by relations [1], then they generate a group which is simply isomorphic with the symmetric group of degree n.

For the case $n = 3$ it is to be understood that these relations become $s_1^2 = s_2^2 = (s_1 s_2)^3 = 1$. From § **9** it is seen that these conditions define a group which is simply isomorphic with the symmetric group of degree 3.

In general it is easy to state descriptively the conditions on the s_i in [1]. Each element s_i is of order 2; if any two consecutive elements of the set $s_1, s_2, \cdots, s_{n-1}, s_1$ are chosen, their product is of order 3 and the transform of the second one in the pair by the first is permutable with every element s_i not in the pair.

The concrete instance $s_i = (a_1 a_{i+1})$ $(i = 1, 2, \cdots, n-1)$ shows that conditions [1] are consistent. These concrete elements generate the symmetric group on $a_1, a_2, \cdots, a_n$. Hence the abstract group $\{s_1, s_2, \cdots, s_{n-1}\}$ is isomorphic with the symmetric group of degree n; and it contains at least $n!$ elements, since the s_i are subject to no conditions except those implied by [1]. To complete the proof of the theorem we must show that the named isomorphism is simple. It is clearly sufficient to this purpose to show further (compare Theorem I) that the order of the abstract group $\{s_1, s_2, \cdots, s_{n-1}\}$ is not greater than $n!$.

For the purpose of making this proof it is convenient to establish the following lemma:

LEMMA. If $n > 3$ and the $n-1$ distinct elements $s_1, s_2, \cdots, s_{n-1}, s_n (= s_1)$ are subject to the conditions

$$s_i^2 = (s_i s_{i+1})^3 = (s_i s_{i+1} s_i s_j)^2 = 1,$$

where i and j run over the set $1, 2, \cdots, n-1$, except that j is different from i and $i+1$, then they are also subject to the larger set of similar conditions

$$s_i^2 = (s_i s_j)^3 = (s_i s_k s_i s_j)^2 = 1,$$

where the i, j, k are any three distinct numbers from the set $1, 2, \cdots, n-1$.

For $0 < k < n-1$ we have

$$\begin{aligned} s_{i+k}s_{i+k+1}s_{i+k} \cdot s_i s_{i+k} \cdot s_{i+k}s_{i+k+1}s_{i+k} &= s_i s_{i+k} s_{i+k+1} s_{i+k} s_{i+k+1} s_{i+k} \\ &= s_i s_{i+k} s_{i+k} s_{i+k+1} \\ &= s_i s_{i+k+1}. \end{aligned}$$

[We understand that subscripts greater than $n-1$ are reduced modulo $n-1$ to numbers of the set $1, 2, \cdots, n-1$.] Hence $s_i s_{i+k+1}$ has the same order as $s_i s_{i+k}$; thence by induction it follows that $s_i s_j$ has the same order as $s_i s_{i+1}$, so that $(s_i s_j)^3 = 1$ for every two distinct subscripts i and j from the set $1, 2, \cdots, n-1$.

Transforming $s_is_{i+1}s_is_j$ by $s_ks_is_k$, where j is different from i and $i+1$, and where k is different from i, $i+1$, j, we have

$$\begin{aligned} &s_ks_is_k \cdot s_is_{i+1}s_i \cdot s_ks_is_k \cdot s_ks_is_k \cdot s_j \cdot s_ks_is_k \\ &= s_ks_is_ks_ks_is_{i+1}s_is_is_k \cdot s_ks_is_k \cdot s_j \cdot s_ks_is_k \\ &= s_ks_{i+1}s_k \cdot s_ks_is_ks_j \cdot s_ks_is_k. \end{aligned}$$

Since the square of this element is the identity, we see readily that s_j is permutable with $s_ks_{i+1}s_k$ if it is permutable with $s_ks_is_k$. Hence $(s_ks_{i+1}s_ks_j)^2 = 1$ if $(s_ks_is_ks_j)^2 = 1$. But $(s_ks_{k+1}s_ks_j)^2 = 1$ if j is different from k and $k+1$. Hence we see by induction that $(s_ks_{k+\alpha}s_ks_j)^2 = 1$ if j is different from each of the numbers k, $k+1, \cdots, k+\alpha$. That is, $(s_is_ks_is_j)^2 = 1$ if $i < k$ and j does not belong to the set $i, i+1, \cdots, k$. Consider next the product $s_is_ks_is_j$, when $i < k$ and j is a number of the set $i+1, i+2, \cdots, k-1$. It has the same order as $s_is_js_is_k$. Here we have $i < j$ and k not of the set $i, i+1, \cdots, j$. Therefore $(s_is_js_is_k)^2 = 1$, and hence $(s_is_ks_is_j)^2 = 1$. Hence $(s_is_ks_is_j)^2 = 1$ if i, j, k are distinct and $i < k$. If $k < i$ and j is different from k and i, we have from the foregoing that $(s_ks_is_ks_j)^2 = 1$. But

$$s_is_ks_is_ks_js_i = s_ks_is_js_i = s_i \cdot s_i \cdot s_ks_is_j \cdot s_i.$$

Hence $(s_is_ks_is_j)^2 = 1$ in this case also. Hence we conclude finally that $(s_is_ks_is_j)^2 = 1$ whenever i, j, k are distinct numbers of the set $1, 2, \cdots, n-1$.

This completes the proof of the lemma.

Now let G_n denote the group $\{s_1, s_2, \cdots, s_{n-1}\}$ of the theorem. Then G_3 is of order 6, as we have already seen. Let k be any number such that G_k is of order not greater than $k!$. We shall then prove that G_{k+1} is of order not greater than $(k+1)!$. Let H denote the group $\{s_2, s_3, \cdots, s_k\}$. Its order is not greater than $k!$, since its elements satisfy all the conditions on the elements of G_k. Form the sets of elements

$$H,\ Hs_1,\ Hs_1s_2,\ Hs_1s_3, \cdots, Hs_1s_k.$$

If we multiply on the right by s_1, the first two sets are interchanged, and the others remain unaltered since by aid of the lemma it may be shown that $Hs_1s_\alpha s_1 = Hs_1s_1s_\alpha s_1s_\alpha = Hs_1s_\alpha$ if $\alpha > 1$. If we multiply on the right by s_α ($\alpha > 1$), the second and the $(\alpha+1)$th sets are interchanged; the remaining sets are unaltered, since for $\alpha > 1$, $\beta > 1$, $\alpha \neq \beta$, we have $Hs_1s_\beta s_\alpha = Hs_1s_\alpha s_\beta s_\alpha s_\beta = Hs_\alpha s_\beta s_\alpha s_1 s_\beta = Hs_1s_\beta$, as may be shown by aid of the lemma.

Now from the fact that the foregoing $k+1$ sets are thus interchanged among themselves as sets by multiplication on the right by any one of the elements $s_1, s_2, \cdots, s_k$, it follows that the group G_{k+1} contains not more than $k+1$ times as many elements as H, and hence not more than $(k+1)!$ elements. Thence it follows by induction that G_n contains not more than $n!$ elements, since G_3 contains just $3!$ elements. In view of the previous analysis this completes the proof of the theorem.

IV. If $n-2$ elements $s_1, s_2, \cdots, s_{n-2}$ $(n > 2)$ satisfy the relations

$$s_i^3 = 1, \qquad (i = 1, 2, \cdots, n-2) \qquad [2]$$

$$(s_is_j)^2 = 1, \qquad (i = 1, 2, \cdots, n-3; \; j = i+1, i+2, \cdots, n-2) \qquad [3]$$

and if these elements satisfy no conditions except those implied by these relations, then they generate a group which is simply isomorphic with the alternating group of degree n.

The same theorem may be formulated in descriptive terms as follows: *If k elements are subject to the sole defining conditions that each is of order 3 and the product of each pair of them is of order 2, then they generate a group which is simply isomorphic with the alternating group of degree $k+2$.*

For $n = 3$ in the theorem there is but a single element s and conditions [3] are absent. The theorem is therefore obvious for $n = 3$.

For $n = 4$ the given conditions reduce to the following: $s_1^3 = s_2^3 = (s_1s_2)^2 = 1$. In § 9 it has been shown that these are defining relations for the abstract alternating group. From this it follows that for the proof of the theorem in general it is sufficient to show that if the theorem is true for $n = k$ then it is also true for $n = k+1$.

The concrete elements

$$s_i = (a_i a_{n-1} a_n) \qquad (i = 1, 2, \cdots, n-2)$$

are generators of the alternating group on $a_1, a_2, \cdots, a_n$, as one sees from the corollary to Theorem IV of § **2**; and they satisfy the conditions on the corresponding abstract elements in the theorem. Hence the abstract group is isomorphic with the named alternating group, and it has at least $\frac{1}{2}(n!)$ elements, since the s_i are subject to no conditions except those implied by the relations in the theorem. To complete the proof of the theorem it is sufficient to show that the order of the abstract group $\{s_1, s_2, \cdots, s_{n-2}\}$ is not greater than $\frac{1}{2}(n!)$, on the hypothesis that $s_2, s_3, \cdots, s_{n-2}$ generate the abstract alternating group H of degree $n-1$ when they satisfy the sole conditions stated in the theorem for these elements alone.

Form the sets of elements

$$H, \ Hs_1, \ Hs_1^2, \ Hs_1s_2^2, \ Hs_1s_3^2, \cdots, Hs_1s_{n-2}^2. \qquad [4]$$

Now for $\alpha > 1$ we have

$$Hs_1s_\alpha^2s_1 = Hs_1s_\alpha s_\alpha s_1 = Hs_\alpha^{-1}s_1^{-1}s_1^{-1}s_\alpha^{-1} = Hs_1s_\alpha^2.$$

Hence, under multiplication on the right by s_1, the first three sets in [4] are left intact as sets and are permuted cyclically in the order H, Hs_1, Hs_1^2, while the remaining sets are unchanged as sets. For $\alpha > 1$ we have

$$Hs_\alpha = H, \ Hs_1s_\alpha^2s_\alpha = Hs_1, \ Hs_1s_\alpha = Hs_\alpha^{-1}s_1^{-1} = Hs_1^2,$$

$$Hs_1^2s_\alpha = Hs_1^{-1}s_\alpha^{-1}s_\alpha^2 = Hs_\alpha s_1s_\alpha^2 = Hs_1s_\alpha^2;$$

and for $\alpha > 1$ and $\beta \neq \alpha$ and $\beta \neq 1$ we have

$$Hs_1s_\beta^2s_\alpha = Hs_1s_\beta s_\beta s_\alpha = Hs_\beta^{-1}s_1^{-1}s_\alpha^{-1}s_\beta^{-1} = Hs_\alpha s_1s_\beta^2 = Hs_1s_\beta^2;$$

whence it follows that under multiplication on the right by s_α, $\alpha > 1$, the sets are left intact as sets and $Hs_1, Hs_1^2, Hs_1s_\alpha^2$ are permuted cyclically in the order written while the remaining sets are unchanged as sets. Hence the n sets of elements in [4] contain all the elements of $\{s_1, s_2, \cdots, s_{n-2}\}$, so that the number of them is not more than n times the number of those in H and hence is not greater than $\frac{1}{2}(n!)$.

In view of the preceding analysis this completes the proof of the theorem.

V. From Theorems II and III we have readily an abstract definition of the group which is simply isomorphic with the direct product of the symmetric group of degree n and $n-1$ cyclic groups of any odd orders $\nu_1, \nu_2, \cdots, \nu_{n-1}$ (equal to or greater than unity).

VI. From Theorems II and IV we have readily an abstract definition of the direct product of the alternating group of degree n by $n-2$ cyclic groups of any orders prime to 3, including the order unity.

It is sometimes desirable to know whether any of the conditions in the defining relations for a given abstract group are redundant in the sense that one or more of them may be deduced from the remaining ones. To show that a particular one of the relations is not redundant it is sufficient to exhibit elements failing to satisfy that one but satisfying all the other conditions. It is evident that this problem may vary greatly in complexity with variation in the form of the several conditions so as to leave the total set of conditions equivalent to their first form. We shall illustrate this matter by examining the defining relations already given for the symmetric group.

If the set of conditions in Theorem III is replaced by the equivalent set of $2n-1$ conditions

(1) $s_i^2 = 1, \qquad (i = 1, 2, \cdots, n-1)$

(2) $(s_i s_{i+1})^2 = 1, \qquad (i = 1, 2, \cdots, n-1, \ s_n = s_1)$

(3) the transform of each element in the sequence $s_1, s_2, \cdots, s_{n-1}, s_1$ by the one which precedes it in that sequence is permutable with every element s_i other than these two,

then the nonredundancy of each of the several conditions is readily shown by means of the elements indicated as follows:

(1) $i = k$: $s_k = (a_1 a_{k+1})(c_1 c_2 c_3), \ s_j = (a_1 a_{j+1}); \ (j \neq k)$

(2) $i = k$: $s_j = (a_1 a_{j+1}), \ (j = 1, 2, \cdots, k)$

$s_j = (a_1 a_{j+1})(c_1 c_{j+1}); \ (j = k+1, \cdots, n-1)$

(3) $s_j = (a_j a_{j+1}) \ (j = 1, \cdots, n-2), \ s_{n-1} = (a_1 a_{n-1}). \ (n > 4)$

Moreover, the example given under (2) shows that no one of the conditions $(s_i s_{i+1})^3 = 1$ is redundant even when the conditions are listed as in Theorem III itself, that is, when the defining equations are all taken separately and not partly combined as in condition (3) in this paragraph.

EXERCISES

1. If $n > 2$ and if two elements s and t are subject to the conditions*

$$s^{n-1} = t^2 = (st)^n = (t \cdot s^{-1}ts)^3 = (t \cdot s^{-1}ts \cdot t \cdot s^{-k}ts^k)^2 = 1,$$
$$(k = 2, 3, \cdots, n-3)$$

and to no conditions except those implied by these relations, they generate a group which is simply isomorphic with the symmetric group of degree n.

2. If $n > 2$ and if two elements s and t are subject to the conditions

$$s^n = t^2 = (st)^{n-1} = (t \cdot s^{-1}ts)^3 = (t \cdot s^{-k}ts^k)^2 = 1,$$
$$(k = 2, 3, \cdots, \tfrac{1}{2}(n-1) \text{ or } \tfrac{1}{2}n)$$

and to no conditions except those implied by these relations, they generate a group which is simply isomorphic with the symmetric group of degree n.

3. If the $n-1$ elements $\sigma_1, \sigma_2, \cdots, \sigma_{n-1}$ are subject to the conditions

$$\sigma_i^2 = 1, \qquad (i = 1, 2, \cdots, n-1)$$
$$(\sigma_i\sigma_{i+1})^3 = 1, \qquad (i = 1, 2, \cdots, n-2)$$
$$(\sigma_i\sigma_j)^2 = 1, \qquad (i = 1, 2, \cdots, n-3;\ j = i+2, i+3, \cdots, n-1)$$

and to no conditions except those implied by these relations, they generate a group which is simply isomorphic with the symmetric group of degree n.

4. The conditions on the elements $\sigma_1, \sigma_2, \cdots, \sigma_{n-1}$ in Ex. 3 are equivalent to the following:

(1) $\sigma_i^2 = 1;\ (i = 1, 2, \cdots, n-1)$

(2) $(\sigma_i\sigma_{i+1})^3 = 1;\ (i = 1, 2, \cdots, n-2)$

(3) every two nonconsecutive elements in the sequence $\sigma_1, \sigma_2, \cdots, \sigma_{n-1}$ are permutable.

* If $n = 3$ or 4 the relations involving k are absent. A convention similar to this is to be understood in several problems belonging to this set.

Show that when $n > 3$ there is no redundant condition in the set of $2n-2$ conditions counted as follows: $n-1$ conditions in (1); $n-2$ conditions in (2); one condition in (3).

5. If s and t are subject to the sole defining relations

$$s^4 = t^2 = (st)^2 = 1,$$

show that $\{s, t\}$ is simply isomorphic with the octic group.

6. If s and t are subject to the sole defining relations

$$s^6 = t^3 = (st^2)^2 = s^2(st)^2 = 1,$$

show that $\{s, t\}$ is of order 18 and discuss its properties.

7. Prove that $\{s, t\}$ is simply isomorphic with the alternating group of degree 4 if s and t are subject solely to either one of the following two sets of conditions:

(1) $s^3 = t^3 = (st)^2 = 1$, (2) $s^2 = t^3 = (st)^3 = 1$.

8. Prove that $\{s, t\}$ is simply isomorphic with the symmetric group of degree 4 if s and t are subject solely to any one of the following three sets of conditions:

(1) $s^3 = t^2 = (st)^4 = 1$, (2) $s^3 = t^4 = (st)^2 = 1$, (3) $s^2 = t^4 = (st)^3 = 1$.

9. If s and t are subject solely to any one of the three sets of defining conditions

(1) $s^2 = t^3 = (st)^5 = 1$, (2) $s^2 = t^5 = (st)^3 = 1$, (3) $s^3 = t^5 = (st)^2 = 1$,

they generate a group which is simply isomorphic with the alternating group of degree 5.

10. If a finite group is generated by two elements s and t such that t is of period 2 and s is not in the group $\{st, ts\}$, then $\{st, ts\}$ is a subgroup of $\{s, t\}$ of index 2.

11. Let n and r be relatively prime positive integers, and let k be the exponent to which r belongs modulo n. If s and t are subject to the sole defining relations

$$s^n = t^k = 1, \quad t^{-1}st = s^r,$$

show that $\{s, t\}$ is a group of order nk which is simply isomorphic with the group generated by the permutation $(a_0a_1a_2 \cdots a_{n-1})$ and the permutation which changes a_i to a_{ri} $(i = 0, 1, \cdots, n-1)$, the latter subscript being reduced modulo n.

12. If two elements s and t are subject to the sole defining relations

$$s^k = t^\mu = t^{-1}(s^{-\alpha}t^{-1}s^\alpha)t(s^{-\alpha}ts^\alpha) = 1, \quad (\alpha = 1, 2, \cdots, k-1)$$

they generate a group of order $k\mu^k$ which is simply isomorphic with the permutation group generated by

$$(a_1a_2 \cdots a_k)(a_{k+1}a_{k+2} \cdots a_{2k}) \cdots (a_{(\mu-1)k+1} \cdots a_{\mu k})$$

and
$$(a_1a_{k+1}a_{2k+1} \cdots a_{(\mu-1)k+1}).$$

13. If two elements s and t are subject to the sole defining relations

$$s^k = t^2 = (ts^{-i}ts^i)^2 = 1, \quad (i = 1, 2, \cdots, \tfrac{1}{2}(k-1) \text{ or } \tfrac{1}{2}k)$$

they generate a group of order $k \cdot 2^k$ which is simply isomorphic with the permutation group generated by

$$(a_1a_2 \cdots a_k)(a_{k+1}a_{k+2} \cdots a_{2k}) \quad \text{and} \quad (a_1a_{k+1}).$$

14. Construct abstract defining relations for each of the permutation groups of degrees 2, 3, 4, 5. (Compare Exs. 8, 9, and 10 on page 151.)

15. Construct abstract defining relations for each of the primitive groups of degree 6. (Compare Ex. 10 on page 162.)

49. Finite Groups $\{s, t\}$ such that $s^2 = t^2$. We shall now determine the finite groups $\{s, t\}$ which are generated by two elements s and t having a common square. We let m denote the order of st^{-1}. Then we have

$$s^2 = t^2, \quad (st^{-1})^m = 1.$$

Now we have $t^{-1}s^2t = t^{-1}t^2t = t^2 = s^2$. Hence s^2 is permutable with every element in $\{s, t\}$. Again, we have

$$st^{-1} = s^{-1}s^2t^{-1} = s^{-1}t, \quad ts^{-1} = t^{-1}s = (st^{-1})^{-1}.$$

From this it follows that st^{-1} is transformed into its inverse by both s and t. Hence the cyclic group $\{st^{-1}\}$ is self-conjugate in $\{s, t\}$. Moreover, it follows also that $\{s^2, st^{-1}\}$ is an Abelian group H which is self-conjugate in $\{s, t\}$.

If we suppose that α and β are integers such that we have $s^{2\alpha} = (st^{-1})^\beta$, then s is permutable with $(st^{-1})^\beta$. From the fact that $s^{-1}(st^{-1})s = (st^{-1})^{-1}$ it follows that $s^{-1}(st^{-1})^\beta s = (st^{-1})^{-\beta}$. But $s^{-1}(st^{-1})^\beta s = (st^{-1})^\beta$. Hence $(st^{-1})^\beta = (st^{-1})^{-\beta}$, whence we have $(st^{-1})^{2\beta} = 1$. Now if μ is the exponent of the lowest positive power of st^{-1} which is equal to a power of s^2, then the only powers of st^{-1} which are equal to powers of s^2 are those of the form $(st^{-1})^{\rho\mu}$. But $(st^{-1})^{2\mu} = 1$, as we have seen. Hence the cyclic groups $\{s^2\}$ and $\{st^{-1}\}$ have at most two elements in common; and they certainly have only one element in common if m is odd. Likewise it may be shown that they have only one element in common when s^2 is of odd order. Therefore the group H is of order $m\nu$ or of order $\frac{1}{2}m\nu$, where ν is the order of s^2, and the latter case cannot arise unless m and ν are both even.

If s is of odd order $2\lambda + 1$, then we have

$$s = s^{2\lambda+2} = (s^2)^{\lambda+1} = (t^2)^{\lambda+1},$$

so that s is in the group generated by t. If t is of odd order, then likewise t is in the group generated by s. Hence if either of the elements s and t is of odd order, the group $\{s, t\}$ coincides with the cyclic group generated by one of these elements.

Then consider the case when both s and t are of even order. Let $2n$ be the order of s. Since $s^2 = t^2$ it follows that t is also of order $2n$.

Now consider the sets H and Hs of elements of $\{s, t\}$. Since s^2 is in H, it follows that the sets H and Hs are interchanged on multiplying on the right by s. That they are also interchanged on multiplying on the right by t is shown by the following relations:

$$Ht = Hst^{-1} \cdot t = Hs, \quad Hst = Hst^{-1} \cdot t^2 = Ht^2 = Hs^2 = H.$$

Hence all the elements of $\{s, t\}$ are in the sets H and Hs. If s is in H these sets are identical; then t is in H and $\{s, t\}$ coincides with the Abelian group H. If s is not in H, then H and Hs are distinct sets such that no element in the one set is equal to an element in the other set; and the order of $\{s, t\}$ is then twice the order of H. We have to examine these two possibilities.

In the first case the group $\{s, t\}$ coincides with the Abelian group $\{s^2, st^{-1}\}$. In this case st^{-1} is of order 1 or 2, since $(st^{-1})^2 = s^2t^{-2} = 1$. If $st^{-1} = 1$, then $s = t$ and $\{s, t\}$ coincides with the cyclic group $\{s\}$. If st^{-1} is of order 2 and the cyclic groups $\{s^2\}$ and $\{st^{-1}\}$ have two elements in common, then t is a power of s and $\{s, t\}$ coincides with $\{s\}$. If st^{-1} is of order 2 and the cyclic groups $\{s^2\}$ and $\{st^{-1}\}$ have only one element in common, then H is of order $2n$ and again $\{s, t\}$ coincides with the cyclic group $\{s\}$. Therefore if $\{s, t\}$ coincides with H, then $\{s, t\} \equiv \{s\}$.

It remains to consider the case when $\{s, t\}$ does not coincide with H. Then s is not in H.

Suppose first that $\{s, t\}$ is Abelian. Since s is not in $\{s^2, st^{-1}\}$ it follows that s is of even order; we denote its order by $2n$. Now $(st^{-1})^2 = s^2t^{-2} = 1$. Hence st^{-1} is of order 1 or 2: in the former case $s = t$ and $\{s, t\} \equiv \{s\}$; if, in the latter case, H is of order n, then $\{s, t\}$ is of order $2n$ and is identical with $\{s\}$, while if H is of order $2n$, the group $\{s, t\}$ is of order $4n$ and is an Abelian group generated by s and st^{-1} of orders $2n$ and 2 respectively.

It remains to consider the case when s and t are not permutable. Then s is of even order $2n$. Moreover st^{-1} is of order greater than 2, since if $(st^{-1})^2 = 1$ we have $st^{-1}s = t$, $st^{-2}ts = t$, $s^{-1}ts = t$. Hence in this case we have $m > 2$. In this case also $\{s, t\}$ is of order twice the order of H and is therefore of order $2mn$ or mn, the latter case not arising unless both m and n are even.

Except in the cases named in the last paragraph the group $\{s, t\}$ is necessarily Abelian; it is evident that the named Abelian groups exist.

It is next to be shown that non-Abelian groups actually exist satisfying the named conditions for every pair of positive integers m and n with $m > 2$.

For the case when $\{s, t\}$ is of order $2mn$ $(m > 2)$ we have the following generators: *

$$s = \prod_{i=1}^{m} (a_1{}^{(i)}a_2{}^{(i)} \cdots a_{2n}{}^{(i)}),$$

$$t = \prod_{i=1}^{m} (a_1{}^{(i)}a_2{}^{(i+1)}a_3{}^{(i)}a_4{}^{(i+1)} \cdots a_{2n-1}{}^{(i)}a_{2n}{}^{(i+1)}),$$

where it is to be understood that the superscript $m+1$ is to be replaced by 1. Then

$$st^{-1} = (a_1{}^{(m)}a_1{}^{(m-1)}a_1{}^{(m-2)} \cdots a_1{}^{(2)}a_1{}^{(1)})(a_2{}^{(1)}a_2{}^{(2)}a_2{}^{(3)} \cdots a_2{}^{(m)}) \cdots$$
$$(a_{2n-1}{}^{(m)}a_{2n-1}{}^{(m-1)} \cdots a_{2n-1}{}^{(1)})(a_{2n}{}^{(1)}c_{2n}{}^{(2)}a_{2n}{}^{(3)} \cdots a_{2n}{}^{(m)}).$$

* If m were equal to 2, we should have here the case of an Abelian group $\{s, t\}$.

It is easy to see that $s^2 = t^2$ and that st^{-1} is of order m, while s is of order $2n$. Hence this permutation group $\{s, t\}$ belongs to the category of groups under investigation. Now the only power of st^{-1} which is equal to a power of s^2 is that which is equal to the identity, as one sees by the way in which the subscripts on the a's enter into the powers of st^{-1} and s^2 respectively. Hence the Abelian group $\{s^2, st^{-1}\}$ is of order mn. Moreover s is not in $\{s^2, st^{-1}\}$, since no element in the latter group displaces an a with an odd subscript by one with an even subscript. Therefore $\{s, t\}$ is of order $2mn$. Moreover, $\{s, t\}$ is non-Abelian, since we are taking m to be greater than 2.

Let us next exhibit s and t such that $\{s, t\}$ is non-Abelian and of order mn. In this case both m and n must be even, with $m > 2$; hence we write $m = 2\mu$ and $n = 2\nu$, with $\mu > 1$. Then for s and t we take the following generators:

$$s = \prod_{i=1}^{\mu} (a_1^{(i)} b_1^{(i)} a_2^{(i)} b_2^{(i)} \cdots a_{2\nu}^{(i)} b_{2\nu}^{(i)}),$$

$$t = (a_1^{(1)} b_{\nu+1}^{(\mu)} a_2^{(1)} b_{\nu+2}^{(\mu)} \cdots a_\nu^{(1)} b_{2\nu}^{(\mu)} a_{\nu+1}^{(1)} b_1^{(\mu)} a_{\nu+2}^{(1)} b_2^{(\mu)}$$

$$\cdots a_{2\nu}^{(1)} b_\nu^{(\mu)}) \cdot \prod_{i=1}^{\mu-1} (a_1^{(i+1)} b_1^{(i)} a_2^{(i+1)} b_2^{(i)} \cdots a_{2\nu}^{(i+1)} b_{2\nu}^{(i)}).$$

Then we have

$$st^{-1} = \prod_{i=1}^{\nu} (a_i^{(1)} a_i^{(2)} \cdots a_i^{(\mu)} a_{\nu+i}^{(1)} a_{\nu+i}^{(2)} \cdots a_{\nu+i}^{(\mu)})$$

$$\cdot \prod_{i=1}^{\nu} (b_i^{(\mu)} b_i^{(\mu-1)} \cdots b_i^{(1)} b_{\nu+i}^{(\mu)} b_{\nu+i}^{(\mu-1)} \cdots b_{\nu+i}^{(1)}).$$

Then s and t are of order 4ν and st^{-1} is of order 2μ, while $s^2 = t^2$ and $(st^{-1})^\mu = s^{2\nu}$. Hence the group $\{s^2, st^{-1}\}$ is of order $2\mu\nu$ and $\{s, t\}$ is of order $4\mu\nu = mn$. Therefore the groups $\{s, t\}$ are groups of the class whose existence was to be shown.

The results obtained imply the following three theorems:

VII. Let G be the finite group $\{s, t\}$ generated by two distinct elements s and t such that $s^2 = t^2$. If either s or t is of odd order, then G coincides with the cyclic group generated by the other one of these elements. If s and t are both of even order, then their orders are equal; in this case we denote their common order by $2n$. Let m be the order of st^{-1}; then $m > 1$, since $s \neq t$. Then when s and t are both of even order, we have

$$s^2t^{-2} = s^{2n} = (st^{-1})^m = 1.$$

In this case the group H, $H \equiv \{s^2, st^{-1}\}$, is an Abelian self-conjugate subgroup of G of order mn or $\frac{1}{2}mn$, the latter case not arising unless m and n are both even. Moreover, if in this case G coincides with H, then G is either the cyclic group $\{s\}$ or an Abelian group of order $4n$ generated by s and st^{-1} of orders $2n$ and 2 respectively or a non-Abelian group of order mn or $2mn$, with $m > 2$, the former of the two latter cases not arising unless both m and n are even. Moreover, in all cases named, groups actually exist having the stated properties.

VIII. Let s and t be two elements which are subject to the sole defining relations

$$s^2t^{-2} = s^{2n} = (st^{-1})^m = 1; \quad (m > 1)$$

then $\{s, t\}$ is completely defined as an abstract group of order $2mn$.

IX. Let s and t be two elements which are subject to the sole defining relations

$$s^2t^{-2} = s^{4\nu} = (st^{-1})^\mu s^{-2\nu} = 1; \quad (\mu > 1)$$

then $\{s, t\}$ is completely defined as an abstract group of order $4\mu\nu$.

50. Dihedral and Dicyclic Groups. A *dihedral* group is a group which is generated by two elements of order 2 whose product is of order m $(m > 1)$. By taking $n = 1$ in Theorem VIII of § **49**, it follows from that theorem that such a group is of order $2m$ and that there is one and just one dihedral group of each even order greater than 2. If s and t are the generators of order 2 and st is of order m $(m > 2)$, then the dihedral group $\{s, t\}$ of order $2m$ is non-Abelian, since both s and t transform st into its inverse ts.

A *dicyclic* group is a group generated by an element s of order $2n$ $(n > 1)$ and an element t of order 4 such that t^2 is in $\{s\}$ and t transforms s into its inverse. That such a group is of order $4n$ and that there is one and just one dicyclic group of each order $4n$ $(n > 1)$, is seen at once from the following theorem, which we now prove.

X. If s and t are subject to the sole defining relations

$$s^{2n} = s^n t^2 = t^{-1}st \cdot s = 1,$$

then $\{s, t\}$ is completely defined as a group of order $4n$.

From the named conditions we have $t^2 = s^{-n}$, so that t is of order 4 at most, since $s^{2n} = 1$. Moreover, we have $t^{-1}st = s^{-1}$, so that t transforms s into its inverse.

That the named conditions are consistent is seen at once from the following permutations satisfying them:

$$\begin{aligned} s &= (a_1a_2 \cdots a_{2n})(b_1b_2 \cdots b_{2n}), \\ t &= (a_1b_{2n}a_{n+1}b_n)(a_2b_{2n-1}a_{n+2}b_{n-1}) \\ &\quad \cdot (a_3b_{2n-2}a_{n+3}b_{n-2}) \cdots (a_nb_{n+1}a_{2n}b_1). \end{aligned}$$

From this and the fact that t in the abstract group $\{s, t\}$ is of order not greater than 4, it follows that this t is of order 4. The given permutations generate a group of order $4n$. Hence the abstract group in the theorem is of order at least as great as $4n$. Moreover it is isomorphic with the permutation group $\{s, t\}$. To complete the proof of the theorem it is sufficient to show that the order of the abstract group is not greater than $4n$, whence it will follow that it is simply isomorphic with the permutation group $\{s, t\}$. Let H denote the abstract group $\{s\}$, and form the sets H and Ht of elements in the abstract group $\{s, t\}$. These sets are interchanged on multiplying them on the right by t, since t^2

is in H. They are left unchanged on multiplying on the right by s, since $Hs = H$ and $Hts = Hs^{-1}t = Ht$. Hence all the elements of $\{s, t\}$ are in the sets H and Ht; therefore $\{s, t\}$ is of order $4n$ at most. This conclusion, as we have seen, completes the proof of the theorem.

Unless $n = 1$ the abstract group $\{s, t\}$ of Theorem X is non-Abelian. Hence every dicyclic group is non-Abelian.

In Theorem IX put $\nu = 1$. Then the group of that theorem is of order 4μ, with $\mu > 1$. That it is the dicyclic group of order 4μ is seen by putting $\sigma = st^{-1}$ and $\tau = s^{-1}$, whence it follows that σ and τ satisfy just the conditions imposed on s and t in Theorem X, with n replaced by μ. Hence the dicyclic as well as the dihedral groups belong to the category of groups treated in § **49**.

If in Theorem VIII we take $n = 2$ while m is odd, we have in $\{s, t\}$ the element s of order 4 and the element $st^{-1} \cdot s^2 = st^{-1} \cdot t^2 = st$ of order $2m$, while s^2 is in $\{st\}$. Moreover s transforms st into its inverse. Hence we have the dicyclic groups of order $4m$, where m is odd.

EXERCISES

1. Show that no dicyclic group can be simply isomorphic with a dihedral group.

2. Show that there are at least two abstract groups of every even order greater than two and that there are at least three abstract groups of every order which exceeds 4 and is divisible by 4.

3. Show that the dihedral group of order $2m$ may be defined as the group generated by a cyclic group H of order m and an element of order 2 which transforms each element of H into its inverse.

4. Show that the dicyclic group of order 8 is identical with the quaternion group and that the dihedral group of order 8 is identical with the octic group.

5. If a and b are subject to the sole defining relations

$$a^{2n} = 1, \quad a^n = (ab)^2 = b^2, \qquad (n > 1)$$

show that $\{a, b\}$ is the dicyclic group of order $4n$.

6. For the group $\{s, t\}$ of Theorem X of § **50** show that s^n is the square of every element not in $\{s\}$.

7. A finite group generated by two elements having a common square can also be generated by two elements one of which transforms the other into its inverse, and vice versa.

8. If a, b, c are subject to the sole defining relations

$$a^9 = b^3 = c^3 = 1, \quad b^{-1}ab = a^4, \quad c^{-1}ac = a^7, \quad bc = cb,$$

show that they generate a unique abstract group and that this group is conformal with the Abelian group of order 3^4 and type (2, 1, 1).

9. Groups $\{a, b\}$ and $\{c, d\}$ are determined by the following sole defining conditions respectively:

$$(1)\ a^{43} = b^3 = 1, \quad b^{-1}ab = a^6, \qquad (2)\ c^7 = d^3 = 1, \quad d^{-1}cd = c^2.$$

Show that $\{a, b\}$ and $\{c, d\}$ have a (43, 7) isomorphism, $\{a\}$ in $\{a, b\}$ corresponding to the identity in $\{c, d\}$, and $\{c\}$ in $\{c, d\}$ corresponding to the identity in $\{a, b\}$.

10. Let s and t be two elements which are subject to the sole conditions

$$s^p = t^{p-1} = 1, \quad t^{-1}st = s^k,$$

where p is an odd prime and k is a primitive root modulo p. Show that $\{s, t\}$ is completely defined as an abstract group and is a group of order $p(p-1)$. (Such a group is called a *metacyclic* group.) Prove the following propositions:

(1) A metacyclic group contains a dihedral subgroup.

(2) The Sylow subgroups of a metacyclic group are cyclic.

(3) A metacyclic group is a complete group.

(4) A metacyclic group of order $p(p-1)$ may be represented as simply isomorphic with a doubly transitive group of degree p.

11. Determine the order of the group $\{s_1, s_2, s_3\}$ whose sole defining relations are

$$s_1{}^2 = s_2{}^2 = s_3{}^2 = (s_1s_2)^3 = (s_2s_3)^3 = (s_2s_1s_3)^2 = 1$$

and represent it as simply isomorphic with a permutation group of lowest possible degree.

12. Let s and t be elements which are subject to the sole defining relations

$$s^3 = t^3, \quad (st)^2 = 1.$$

Show that $\{s, t\}$ is a group of order 96. Show how to adjoin other conditions to those already given so that the group $\{s, t\}$ as thus further restricted shall be simply isomorphic with (*a*) the alternating group G of degree 4, (*b*) the direct product of G and the cyclic group of order 2, (*c*) the direct product of G and the cyclic group of order 4.

Show that no other non-Abelian groups can be obtained by this process of adjoining conditions to those initially given.

13. Show that there are just four non-Abelian groups $\{s, t\}$ such that

$$s^3 = t^2, \quad (st)^3 = 1,$$

and determine their defining relations and their orders.

14. Show that there are just six non-Abelian groups $\{s, t\}$ such that $s^2 = t^3$ and st is of order 4, their orders being 24, 48, 96, 120, 240, 480, and determine their defining relations.

15. Determine the non-Abelian groups $\{s, t\}$ such that

$$s^3 = t^4, \quad (st)^2 = 1,$$

and construct defining relations for each of them.

MISCELLANEOUS EXERCISES

1. If for $n > 3$ two elements s and t are subject for odd n to the conditions

(1) $$s^{n-2} = 1, \quad t^3 = 1,$$

(2) $$(st)^n = 1,$$

(3) $$(t \cdot s^{-k}ts^k)^2 = 1, \quad (k = 1, 2, \cdots, \tfrac{1}{2}(n-3))$$

and for even n to the conditions

(1) $$s^{n-2} = 1, \quad t^3 = 1,$$

(2) $$(st)^{n-1} = 1,$$

(3) $$(t^{(-1)^k}s^{-k}ts^k)^2 = 1, \quad (k = 1, 2, \cdots, \tfrac{1}{2}(n-2))$$

and to no conditions except those implied by these, then these elements generate a group which is simply isomorphic with the alternating group of degree n.

2. Construct abstract defining relations for each of the primitive groups of degree 7. (Compare Ex. 12 on page 163.)

3. Construct abstract defining relations for each of the primitive groups of degree 8. (Compare Ex. 16 on page 165.)

4. Let s and t be two noncommutative elements each of prime order p and suppose that the elements t, $s^{-1}ts$, $s^{-2}ts^2$, $\cdots$, $s^{-p+1}ts^{p-1}$ are commutative. If s and t satisfy no conditions except those implied by these, show that $\{s, t\}$ is of order p^{p+1} and is simply isomorphic with a Sylow subgroup of order p^{p+1} in the symmetric group of degree p^2.

5. Construct abstract defining relations for a Sylow subgroup of order p^{p^2+p+1} in the symmetric group of degree p^3, where p is a prime number.

6. If k is a positive integer less than the prime p, show that there is one and but one abstract group of order p^{p+k} which can be represented as simply isomorphic with a permutation group of degree $p^2 + (k-1)p$. Show that it is non-Abelian and construct its defining relations.

7. If k is a positive integer less than the prime p, show that there is one and but one abstract group of order p^{p^2+p+k} which can be represented as simply isomorphic with a permutation group of degree $p^3 + (k-1)p$. Show that it is non-Abelian and construct its defining relations.

8. Generalize the results in Exs. 4–7.

9. If s and t are subject to the sole defining relations

$$s^{4m} = t^2 = 1, \quad tst = s^{1+2m},$$

show that $\{s, t\}$ is a group G_m of order $8\,m$, that every subgroup of G_m is either Abelian or of the type G_k, and that the group of isomorphisms of G_m with itself is of order $2\,\phi(4\,m)$ or $4\,\phi(4\,m)$ according as m is odd or even.

10. If s and t are subject to the sole defining relations

$$s^{4m} = t^2 = 1, \quad tst = s^{2m-1},$$

show that $\{s, t\}$ is a group of order $8\,m$ and that its group of isomorphisms with itself is of order $2\,m\phi(4\,m)$.

11. Show that the permutations

$$s = \prod_{i=1}^{\mu} (a_1^{(i)} b_1^{(i)} a_2^{(i)} b_2^{(i)} \cdots a_{2\nu}^{(i)} b_{2\nu}^{(i)}),$$

$$t = (a_1^{(1)} b_{2\nu}^{(\mu)} a_2^{(1)} b_1^{(\mu)} a_3^{(1)} b_2^{(\mu)} \cdots a_{2\nu}^{(1)} b_{2\nu-1}^{(\mu)}) \cdot \prod_{i=1}^{\mu-1} (a_1^{(i+1)} b_1^{(i)} a_2^{(i+1)} b_2^{(i)} \cdots a_{2\nu}^{(i+1)} b_{2\nu}^{(i)}),$$

μ being greater than 1, generate a group of order $4\,\mu\nu^2$, and construct defining relations for the abstract group which is simply isomorphic with $\{s, t\}$. Show that the groups $\{s, t\}$ include the dicyclic groups.

12. A group G whose Sylow subgroups are cyclic is a group $\{a, b\}$ such that b transforms a into a power of a. Find a group of the latter class whose Sylow subgroups are not cyclic.

13. Let a and b be elements of orders λ and μ, respectively, such that $b^{-1}ab = a^k$; let a^α be the lowest positive power of a which is equal to a power of b and write $a^\alpha = b^s$; and let b^β be the lowest positive power of b which is equal to a power of a and write $b^\beta = a^r$. Show that $\{a, b\}$ is of order $\lambda\beta$ and discuss the general properties of $\{a, b\}$.

14. Obtain abstract defining relations for the symmetric group of degree n as generated by three elements, each of order 2.

15. If for $n \geqq 3$, ν any number prime to n, and μ any odd integer, two elements σ and τ are subject to the sole defining relations

$$\sigma^{n\nu} = \tau^{\nu\mu} = \sigma^{-n}\tau^{\mu}\sigma^{n}\tau^{\mu} = \sigma^{-1}\tau^{\mu}\sigma\tau^{\mu} = (\sigma^{\nu}\tau^{\mu})^{n-1} = (\tau^{\mu} \cdot \sigma^{-\nu}\tau^{\mu}\sigma^{\nu})^3$$
$$= (\tau^{\mu}\sigma^{-k\nu}\tau^{\mu}\sigma^{k\nu})^2 = 1, \ (k = 2, 3, \cdots, \tfrac{1}{2}(n-1) \text{ or } \tfrac{1}{2}n),$$

show that they generate a group of order $\mu\nu \cdot n!$ which is simply isomorphic with the direct product of the symmetric group of degree n and the cyclic groups of orders μ and ν.

16. Construct defining relations for the abstract group which is simply isomorphic with the direct product of the symmetric group of degree n and cyclic groups of orders μ and ν, where ν is odd and μ is prime to $n-1$.

17. Construct defining relations for the abstract group which is simply isomorphic with the direct product of the symmetric group and the cyclic groups of orders μ and ν, where μ and ν are any positive integers prime to n and $n-1$ respectively.

18. If two abstract elements s and t are subject (for $m > 1$ and $k > 1$) to the sole defining relations

$$s^{mk} = t^m = (ts^{-1})^k = t^{-1} \cdot s^{-\alpha}t^{-1}s^{\alpha} \cdot t \cdot s^{-\alpha}ts^{\alpha} = 1, \ \ (\alpha = 1, 2, \cdots, k-1)$$

they generate a group of order $k \cdot m^k$ which is simply isomorphic with the permutation group

$$\{(a_1a_2 \cdots a_{mk}), \ (a_1a_{k+1}a_{2k+1} \cdots a_{(m-1)k+1})\}.$$

19. Determine all the non-Abelian groups $\{s, t\}$ such that $s^2 = t^4$, $(st)^3 = 1$, and construct defining relations for each of them.

20. Show that there are just six non-Abelian groups $\{s, t\}$ such that $s^2 = t^3$, $(st)^5 = 1$, and construct defining relations for each of them.

21. If two elements are of order 4 and their product is of order 2, while the square of one element is permutable with the other element, show that they generate a group of order 16, and represent this group as a regular group.

CHAPTER VIII

Groups of Linear Transformations

51. Properties of Linear Substitutions. The system of n linear homogeneous equations

$$y_i = \sum_{j=1}^{n} a_{ij} x_j, \qquad (i = 1, 2, \cdots, n) \qquad [1]$$

in which the n^2 coefficients a_{ij} are n^2 given (real or complex) numbers of ordinary algebra, uniquely determines the n complex variables y in terms of the n complex variables x. Such a system of equations is called a *linear homogeneous substitution*; it is said to be performed on the x's to produce the new variables y. (If to the second member of the ith equation we add the constant b_i, for $i = 1, 2, \cdots, n$, we obtain a *linear nonhomogeneous substitution* on the x's.)

In case the determinant $|a_{ij}|$ of system [1], namely,

$$|a_{ij}| = \begin{vmatrix} a_{11} a_{12} \cdots a_{1n} \\ a_{21} a_{22} \cdots a_{2n} \\ \cdot \quad \cdot \quad \cdot \quad \cdot \quad \cdot \\ a_{n1} a_{n2} \cdots a_{nn} \end{vmatrix}, \qquad [2]$$

is different from zero, that system can be solved uniquely for the x's in terms of the y's. Then we call [1] a *linear homogeneous transformation* on the x's into the y's. (In the corresponding case (namely, when $|a_{ij}| \neq 0$) the linear nonhomogeneous substitution is called a *linear nonhomogeneous transformation.*)

The array of elements in the determinant $|a_{ij}|$, as written out in [2], will be called the *matrix* of the substitution and will be denoted by $\| a_{ij} \|$. It is clear that the character of the substitution is determined by the matrix of its coefficients and is independent of the variables used in the transformation. Consequently we shall call two transformations identical if they have the same matrix of coefficients even if they are written on different sets of variables.

If A_{ij} is the cofactor of a_{ji} in the determinant $|a_{ij}|$ and if we write $\alpha_{ij} = A_{ij}/|a_{ij}|$, then we may solve for the x's in terms of the y's in the transformation A, namely,

$$A: \qquad y_i = \sum_{j=1}^{n} a_{ij}x_j, \qquad (i = 1, 2, \cdots, n) \qquad [3]$$

and so obtain the transformation A', namely,

$$A': \qquad x_i = \sum_{j=1}^{n} \alpha_{ij}y_j. \qquad (i = 1, 2, \cdots, n)$$

Then A' is called the transformation *inverse* to A. It is then easy to see that A is also the inverse of A'.

If in addition to A we have a second transformation B, which we may write in the form

$$B: \qquad z_l = \sum_{k=1}^{n} b_{lk}y_k, \qquad (l = 1, 2, \cdots, n) \qquad [4]$$

and if we eliminate from [3] and [4] the variables y, we have a new transformation C, namely,

$$C: \qquad z_t = \sum_{s=1}^{n} c_{ts}x_s, \qquad (t = 1, 2, \cdots, n)$$

where

$$c_{ts} = \sum_{k=1}^{n} b_{tk}a_{ks}.$$

We call C the *product** of A and B, and we write $AB = C$. This process of combination of transformations is called *multiplication.* From the usual rule for the multiplication of determinants we have $|c_{ts}| = |b_{ts}| \cdot |a_{ts}|$; that is, the determinant of the product of two transformations A and B is equal to the product of the determinants of A and B.

* If α, β, γ are the matrices of the transformations A, B, C, respectively, then we call γ the product of α and β and write $\alpha\beta = \gamma$. The same law of multiplication is used even if one or more of the corresponding substitutions have zero determinants.

The transformation AA we denote by A^2; more generally, we write $AA^{n-1} = A^n$ and we call the transformation A^n the nth power of A. The inverse of A we denote by A^{-1} and its nth power we denote by A^{-n}. Then we have $A^\mu A^\nu = A^{\mu+\nu}$ for all integers μ and ν, provided we use A^0 for the *identical* transformation I, namely,

$$I: \qquad y_i = x_i. \qquad (i = 1, 2, \cdots, n)$$

The product of a transformation and its inverse is the identical transformation.

If A and B are two transformations whose product AB is denoted by D, and if the product BC of B and C is denoted by E, we have $(AB)C = DC$ and $A(BC) = AE$. By a direct computation it may readily be shown that $DC = AE$. Hence we have $(AB)C = A(BC)$; that is, the associative law holds for the multiplication of transformations. (Similarly, it may be shown to hold for substitutions even when the determinants are allowed to have the value zero.)

From the various properties of transformations thus set forth and from the definition of group in § **3**, it follows that transformations with the indicated rule of multiplication are suitable to serve as the elements of groups. We may therefore take over at once (without further definition) the terminology which we have already introduced in dealing with elements of the most general kind belonging to abstract groups. As an example, if S and T are two transformations, then $S^{-1}TS$ is called the transform of S by T. We may also take over for transformations the theorems already established for general elements belonging to groups.

If A and B are defined as in [3] and [4], then the transform $A^{-1}BA$ is the transformation

$$A^{-1}BA: \qquad y_i = \sum_{j=1}^{n} \sum_{k=1}^{n} \sum_{l=1}^{n} a_{ij} b_{jk} \alpha_{kl} x_l, \qquad (i = 1, 2, \cdots, n)$$

as one shows by a direct computation. The properties of transforms in general may evidently be carried over to transforms of this type.

The two linear transformations

$$y_i = \sum_{j=1}^{n} a_{ij}x_j, \quad y_i = \sum_{j=1}^{n} a_{ji}x_j, \qquad (i = 1, 2, \cdots, n)$$

are said to be each the *transposed* of the other. If A, A_t; B, B_t; C, C_t are three pairs of transposed transformations, and if $AB = C$, it is readily shown by direct computation that $C_t = B_tA_t$ and hence that $A_t^{-1}B_t^{-1} = C_t^{-1}$. Hence if the linear homogeneous transformations I, A, B, C, $\cdots$ form a group G, then the transposed transformations I, A_t, B_t, C_t, $\cdots$ form a group G_t simply isomorphic with G, each transformation in G corresponding to the inverse of its transposed in the simple isomorphism thus indicated. Each of these groups G and G_t is called the *transposed* of the other. When we speak of the isomorphism of G and G_t, we shall always mean the one here indicated unless the contrary is expressly stated.

Using $\overline{\alpha}$ to denote the conjugate imaginary of α, we call each of the transformations

$$y_i = \sum_{j=1}^{n} \alpha_{ij}x_j, \quad y_i = \sum_{j=1}^{n} \overline{\alpha}_{ij}x_j, \qquad (i = 1, 2, \cdots, n)$$

the *conjugate imaginary* of the other. If the linear homogeneous transformations I, A, B, C, $\cdots$ form a group G, then the conjugate-imaginary transformations I, $\overline{A}$, $\overline{B}$, $\overline{C}$, $\cdots$ form a group $\overline{G}$ which is simply isomorphic with G, with the correspondences $A \sim \overline{A}$, $B \sim \overline{B}$, $\cdots$, since the relation $AB = C$ implies that $\overline{A}\overline{B} = \overline{C}$, as one may readily verify. Each of the groups G and $\overline{G}$ is called the *conjugate imaginary* of the other. When we speak of the isomorphism of G and $\overline{G}$, we shall always mean the one here indicated unless the contrary is expressly stated.

Let $k_1x_1 + k_2x_2 + \cdots + k_nx_n$ be a linear homogeneous function of the x's which is changed into a multiple of itself by a transformation A, so that we have the identity

$$\sum_{i,j=1}^{n} k_i a_{ij} x_j \equiv \lambda \sum_{j=1}^{n} k_j x_j,$$

where λ is the *multiplier* of the linear function under the named transformation; then we have

$$\sum_{i=1}^{n} k_i a_{ij} = \lambda k_j. \qquad (j = 1, 2, \cdots, n)$$

Hence λ must satisfy the *characteristic equation* of the transformation, namely, the equation

$$\begin{vmatrix} a_{11} - \lambda & a_{12} & \cdots a_{1n} \\ a_{21} & a_{22} - \lambda \cdots & a_{2n} \\ \cdot & \cdot & \cdot \\ a_{n1} & a_{n2} & \cdots a_{nn} - \lambda \end{vmatrix} = 0.$$

The determinant in this equation is called the *characteristic determinant* of A. The roots λ of this equation are the only multipliers possible for a linear homogeneous function of the x's under the transformation A; and for each root of this equation there is evidently at least one linear homogeneous function of the x's having this root as such a multiplier.

We shall now prove the following theorem:

I. A transformation has the same characteristic equation as any transformation into which it can be transformed by another transformation on the same number of variables.

Let B be the given transformation and let A be the transforming transformation. The characteristic determinant D of $A^{-1}BA$ may be put in the form

$$D \equiv \left| \sum_{j=1}^{n} \sum_{k=1}^{n} a_{ij} b_{jk} \alpha_{kl} - \lambda_{il} \right|,$$

the element written being that in the ith row and the lth column and λ_{il} denoting λ or zero according as $l = i$ or $l \neq i$. By means of the usual rule for the multiplication of determinants, and by aid of the relations existing among the quantities a_{ij} and α_{kl} in view of the definition of the latter in terms of the former, it is easy to show that

$$|b_{jk} - \lambda_{jk}| \equiv |a_{ij}| \cdot |b_{jk} - \lambda_{jk}| \cdot |\alpha_{kl}|$$

$$\equiv \left|\sum_{j=1}^{n} a_{ij}b_{jk} - a_{ik}\lambda\right| \cdot |\alpha_{kl}|$$

$$\equiv \left|\sum_{k=1}^{n}\sum_{j=1}^{n} a_{ij}b_{jk}\alpha_{kl} - \lambda_{il}\right| \equiv D.$$

Hence the characteristic equation for B is the same as that for $A^{-1}BA$.

The sum of the roots of the characteristic equation of B is $b_{11} + b_{22} + \cdots + b_{nn}$; that is, it is equal to the sum of the main diagonal elements in the matrix $\| b_{ij} \|$ of the transformation. This is called the *characteristic* of the transformation. From the foregoing theorem it follows that *the characteristic is unaltered* when the transformation is transformed into a new one by means of any transformation A on the same number of variables. Therefore, *in a group of linear homogeneous transformations any two conjugate elements have the same characteristic.* They also have the same characteristic equation.

A transformation of the form

$$y_1 = a_1x_1, \; y_2 = a_2x_2, \; \cdots, \; y_n = a_nx_n$$

is called a *multiplication.* The coefficients $a_1, a_2, \cdots, a_n$ are called the *multipliers* of the transformation. Any two multiplications are permutable and their product is a multiplication. If in the foregoing multiplication all the coefficients a_i are equal, then the transformation is called a *similarity transformation.* A transformation of the form

$$y_1 = a_1x_\alpha, \; y_2 = a_2x_\beta, \; \cdots, \; y_n = a_nx_\mu,$$

where $\alpha, \beta, \cdots, \mu$ are the symbols $1, 2, \cdots, n$ in some order, is called a *monomial* transformation. If the coefficients in a monomial transformation are all equal to unity, then the transformation is called a *permutation* and represents merely a permutation of the given symbols. Thus linear transformations afford a generalization of ordinary permutations.

52. Finite Groups of Linear Transformations. Thus far we have said nothing explicitly which would restrict our transformations to belong to finite groups or indeed to be transformations of finite order. The transformation $x' = x$, $y' = x + y$ is obviously not of finite order. In using linear transformations for the study of finite groups we shall need to know (among other things) conditions on a transformation which will ensure its being of finite order. Accordingly we now prove the following theorem:

II. A necessary condition in order that a linear homogeneous transformation A, namely,

$$A: \qquad y_i = \sum_{j=1}^{n} a_{ij} x_j, \qquad (i = 1, 2, \cdots, n)$$

shall be of finite order N is that a transformation S shall exist such that $S^{-1}AS$ shall be of the form

$$y_i = \omega_i x_i, \qquad (i = 1, 2, \cdots, n)$$

where $\omega_1, \omega_2, \cdots, \omega_n$ are Nth roots of unity.

For every S the transformations A and $S^{-1}AS$ are of the same order, if either is of finite order. Hence, whenever S exists such that $S^{-1}AS$ is a multiplication whose multipliers are roots of unity, it follows that A is of finite order.

In order to prove the theorem let us suppose that A is of finite order N. Let t_1 be a linear function of the x's which is not identically zero, let t_2 be the function into which it is changed by A, let t_3 be the function into which t_2 is changed by A, and so on; and suppose that in each case the variables $y_1, y_2, \cdots, y_n$ are replaced by $x_1, x_2, \cdots, x_n$, respectively, after the transformation, so that each t_i is a function of $x_1, x_2, \cdots, x_n$. Then, since A is of finite order, there exists a number ν such that $t_1, t_2, \cdots, t_\nu$ are all the distinct functions thus obtained from t_1. Then the sequence $t_1, t_2, \cdots, t_\nu$ is changed in cyclical order by A, t_ν going into t_1. Let us now consider the linear functions $\eta_0, \eta_1, \cdots, \eta_{\nu-1}$ defined by the following equations, where ω is a primitive νth root of unity:

$$t_1 + \omega^{-i} t_2 + \omega^{-2i} t_3 + \cdots + \omega^{-(\nu-1)i} t_\nu = \eta_i. \quad (i = 0, 1, \cdots, \nu - 1)$$

Now by hypothesis t_1 is not identically zero; hence not all the η's are identically zero, since the determinant of the coefficients in the foregoing set of equations is different from zero. Let m be the number of the η's each of which is not identically zero. If η_l is one of them, then η_l is replaced by $\omega^l \eta_l$ when the variables are changed by A. Therefore the m η's which are different from zero are linearly independent. We retain just these m η's.

If m is less than n, then there exists a linear function s_1 of the x's which is linearly independent of the retained η's. We may treat s_1 as we treated t_1 and so arrive at a new set $\zeta'_0, \zeta'_1, \cdots, \zeta'_{\rho-1}$ of linear functions of the x's which are linearly independent. These cannot all be linearly dependent on the η's, since this would imply that s_1 is linearly dependent on them, contrary to hypothesis. Retaining those which are linearly independent of the retained η's we have an enlarged set of linearly independent linear functions of the x's each of which is changed into a multiple of itself by A, the multiplier being a root of unity.

If we do not yet have n linearly independent linear functions of the x's, we may continue the process. Finally we must obtain n linearly independent functions of the x's each of which is changed by A into a product of itself by a root of unity. The existence of this set of functions may be employed in showing the existence of an S such that $S^{-1}AS$ is a multiplication with multipliers equal to roots of unity. For if these functions are denoted by the symbols $u_1, u_2, \cdots, u_n$, where

$$u_i = \sum_{j=1}^{n} s_{ij} x_j, \qquad (i = 1, 2, \cdots, n)$$

and if we write

$$v_i = \sum_{j=1}^{n} s_{ij} y_j, \qquad (i = 1, 2, \cdots, n)$$

we have

$$v_i = \sum_{j=1}^{n} s_{ij} \sum_{k=1}^{n} a_{jk} x_k, \qquad (i = 1, 2, \cdots, n)$$

$$v_i = \omega_i u_i, \qquad (i = 1, 2, \cdots, n)$$

where the ω_i are roots of unity; whence it follows that

$$\sum_{j=1}^{n} s_{ij} a_{jk} = \omega_i s_{ik}.$$

Hence if S is the transformation whose matrix is $\| s_{ij} \|$ and we denote the matrix of the inverse of S by $\| \sigma_{ij} \|$, then for $S^{-1}AS$ we have

$$S^{-1}AS: \quad y_i = \sum_{j=1}^{n} \sum_{k=1}^{n} \sum_{l=1}^{n} s_{ij} a_{jk} \sigma_{kl} x_l = \sum_{k=1}^{n} \sum_{l=1}^{n} \omega_i s_{ik} \sigma_{kl} x_l = \omega_i x_i.$$

It is obvious that the ω_i must be Nth roots of unity, since $S^{-1}AS$ is of order N. Hence S is the required transforming transformation.

COR. The characteristic of any element in a finite group of linear homogeneous transformations on n variables is a sum of n roots of unity.

In order to obtain a standard form to which any finite group of linear homogeneous transformations may be brought, it is convenient to introduce certain auxiliary considerations.

A bilinear form in the n variables $x_1, x_2, \cdots, x_n$ and their conjugates, namely,

$$\sum_{i,j=1}^{n} c_{ij} x_i \bar{x}_j,$$

is called a *Hermitian form* if the coefficients c_{ij} satisfy the relations

$$c_{ij} = \bar{c}_{ji}. \qquad (i, j = 1, 2, \cdots, n)$$

A Hermitian form is obviously real-valued for every set of (real or complex) values of the variables. We shall say that a Hermitian form is *definite* if it cannot take a negative value, whatever values are given to the variables.

It is easy to verify directly that any Hermitian form is changed into a Hermitian form when the variables in it are subjected to any linear homogeneous transformation.

We shall now reduce a definite Hermitian form to a certain standard type by means of a linear homogeneous transformation on its variables. Let H be the definite Hermitian form

$$H: \qquad \sum_{i,j=1}^{n} c_{ij} x_i \bar{x}_j. \qquad (c_{ij} = \bar{c}_{ji})$$

If c_{kk} is negative, then H has a negative value if $x_k = 1$ and the other x's are all zero. Hence $c_{kk} \geqq 0$ $(k = 1, 2, \cdots, n)$. If $c_{kk} = 0$, then we must have $c_{ki}=0$ for $i=1, 2, \cdots, n$; for if we take each x_i equal to zero except x_k and x_l, where $l \neq k$, and if $c_{kk}=0$, then the value of H reduces to the value of $c_{ll}x_l\bar{x}_l + c_{kl}x_k\bar{x}_l + c_{lk}x_l\bar{x}_k$: if $c_{ll} \neq 0$, put $x_l = c_{kl}$ and $x_k = -c_{ll}$, whence H is negative in value unless $c_{kl}=0$; if $c_{ll}=0$, put $x_k=-1$ and $x_l = c_{kl}$, whence H is negative in value unless $c_{kl}=0$. Therefore $c_{kl}=0$ if $c_{kk}=0$.

From this it follows, in particular, that at least one of the coefficients $c_{11}, c_{22}, \cdots, c_{nn}$ is different from zero unless all the coefficients in H are zero (a case which we shall exclude from consideration). By a suitable change of subscripts (equivalent to a linear homogeneous transformation) it may be brought about that $c_{11} \neq 0$; and we suppose this transformation to be already carried out. Now we put

$$\sqrt{c_{11}}\, t_1 = c_{11}x_1 + c_{21}x_2 + \cdots + c_{n1}x_n,$$
$$\sqrt{c_{11}}\, \bar{t}_1 = c_{11}\bar{x}_1 + c_{12}\bar{x}_2 + \cdots + c_{1n}\bar{x}_n.$$

Then the given Hermitian form H is changed to a new Hermitian form

$$t_1\bar{t}_1 + \sum_{i,j=2}^{n} d_{ij}x_i\bar{x}_j.$$

If the coefficients d_{ij} are not all zero, we may repeat the process as applied to the form indicated by the summation in the foregoing expression and obtain a form

$$t_1\bar{t}_1 + t_2\bar{t}_2 + \sum_{i,j=3}^{n} e_{ij}x_i\bar{x}_j.$$

It is clear that the process may be continued until we change H to the form

$$t_1\bar{t}_1 + t_2\bar{t}_2 + \cdots + t_s\bar{t}_s,$$

where $s \leqq n$. It is evident that the linear forms $t_1, t_2, \cdots, t_s$ of $x_1, x_2, \cdots, x_n$ are linearly independent, since each of them contains a variable x which is not in those that follow it. This form in t is equal to zero when and only when $t_1 = t_2 = \cdots = t_s = 0$. When $s=n$, and only in this case, this implies the conclusion that H has a zero value only when $x_1 = x_2 = \cdots = x_n = 0$. We shall follow the terminology of W. Burnside (*Theory of Groups*,

2d ed., p. 254) and call H a *nonzero* definite Hermitian form when $s = n$. When $s < n$ we shall call the form *zero* definite. It may readily be shown that the determinant $|c_{ij}|$ is equal to zero when $s < n$ and is different from zero when $s = n$.

Now let G and $\overline{G}$ be two conjugate-imaginary finite groups of linear homogeneous transformations, and denote *corresponding* elements in G and $\overline{G}$ by the respective symbols

$$y_i = \sum_{j=1}^{n} a_{ij}x_j, \quad \overline{y}_i = \sum_{j=1}^{n} \overline{a}_{ij}\overline{x}_j. \qquad (i = 1, 2, \cdots, n)$$

It is obviously legitimate to use the conjugate variables $\overline{y}$ and $\overline{x}$ in the second transformation.

By means of these transformations the form $x_1\overline{x}_1 + x_2\overline{x}_2 + \cdots + x_n\overline{x}_n$ is changed into

$$\sum_{i=1}^{n} \sum_{j=1}^{n} \sum_{k=1}^{n} a_{ij}\overline{a}_{ik}x_j\overline{x}_k.$$

The new form has a positive value for all values of the x's except the simultaneous set $x_1 = x_2 = \cdots = x_n = 0$, since this is a property of the form from which it was obtained (or the fact may be readily verified directly). Now construct such a transform of $x_1\overline{x}_1 + \cdots + x_n\overline{x}_n$ for each pair of corresponding elements in G and $\overline{G}$ and take the sum of the resulting expressions. Since each of the summands is positive except for simultaneous zero values of the variables, it follows that the same is true for this sum and hence that the sum is a nonzero definite Hermitian form. But this sum is obviously invariant when the variables x and $\overline{x}$ undergo corresponding transformations in G and $\overline{G}$.

Hence we have the following theorem:

III. If G and $\overline{G}$ are any two conjugate-imaginary finite groups of linear homogeneous transformations, then there exists a nonzero definite Hermitian form which is invariant when its two sets x and $\overline{x}$ of variables are subjected to corresponding transformations of G and $\overline{G}$.

Let H be the Hermitian form whose existence is asserted by this theorem, and let the conjugate-imaginary transformations S and $\bar{S}$, namely,

$$t_i = \sum_{j=1}^{n} t_{ij} x_j, \quad \bar{t}_i = \sum_{j=1}^{n} \bar{t}_{ij} \bar{x}_j, \qquad (i = 1, 2, \cdots, n)$$

be transformations by which H is changed into the standard form $t_1\bar{t}_1 + t_2\bar{t}_2 + \cdots + t_n\bar{t}_n$. Then this latter form is left invariant when its variables are subjected to corresponding transformations of the conjugate-imaginary groups $S^{-1}GS$ and $\bar{S}^{-1}\bar{G}\bar{S}$.

This fact will enable us to prove the following theorem:

IV. Any group G of finite order, whose elements are linear homogeneous transformations, may be transformed by means of a suitable linear homogeneous transformation S into a group $S^{-1}GS$ such that the coefficients c_{ij} in any element

$$y_i = \sum_{j=1}^{n} c_{ij} x_j \qquad (i = 1, 2, \cdots, n)$$

of $S^{-1}GS$ satisfy the conditions

$$\sum_{k=1}^{n} c_{ki}\bar{c}_{kj} = \begin{cases} 1 \text{ if } i = j, \\ 0 \text{ if } i \neq j. \end{cases}$$

Let S be a transformation (already proved existent) such that $x_1\bar{x}_1 + x_2\bar{x}_2 + \cdots + x_n\bar{x}_n$ is unaltered when its variables are subjected to corresponding transformations of $S^{-1}GS$ and $\bar{S}^{-1}\bar{G}\bar{S}$. Then we have the identity

$$\sum_{k=1}^{n} x_k\bar{x}_k \equiv \sum_{k=1}^{n} \sum_{i=1}^{n} \sum_{j=1}^{n} c_{ki}\bar{c}_{kj} x_i \bar{x}_j.$$

Equating coefficients of like terms on the two sides of this identity, we have the relations asserted in the conclusion of the theorem.

COR. The conjugate imaginary of an element C in $S^{-1}GS$ is the inverse of the transposed C_t of C; and hence the conjugate-imaginary group and the transposed group are identical.

For if $\| c_{ij} \|$ is the matrix of C, then the matrix of the product $\bar{C}C_t$ is

$$\left\| \sum_{k=1}^{n} c_{ki}\bar{c}_{kj} \right\|;$$

and this is the matrix of the identical transformation in view of the relations in the theorem.

53. Reducible and Irreducible Groups. Let G be a group of linear homogeneous transformations in the n variables $x_1, x_2, \cdots, x_n$. If for some s $(0 < s < n)$ there exist s linear functions $t_1, t_2, \cdots, t_s$ of the x's such that these s functions are transformed among themselves by each element of G according to a linear homogeneous transformation on the t's, then G is said to be *reducible*. Otherwise G is said to be *irreducible*. If for ν greater than unity there exist ν sets of linear functions of the x's such that these sets together form n linearly independent functions of the x's and such that the functions in each set are transformed among themselves by each element of G while the group of linear transformations in each set is by itself irreducible, then G is said to be *completely reducible*, and these ν sets are called *completely reduced sets* for G.

It may be shown that *the only homogeneous substitutions S on $x_1, x_2, \cdots, x_n$ which are permutable with every transformation of an irreducible group G of linear homogeneous transformations on the same variables are those in which S has the form $x'_i = ax_i$* $(i = 1, 2, \cdots, n)$. For $T^{-1}ST$ is then permutable with $T^{-1}GT$, where T is any transformation on the same variables. If λ is a root of the characteristic equation of S, then T may be chosen so that $T^{-1}ST$ replaces each of a certain number of the variables by λ times itself. Then a transformation permutable with $T^{-1}ST$ transforms these variables among themselves; hence this must be true of all the transformations in $T^{-1}GT$. Since the latter is an irreducible group, it follows that $T^{-1}ST$

replaces each of the n variables by λ times itself. Therefore S itself also has this property, as was to be proved.

> V. If G and $\bar{G}$ are two conjugate-imaginary groups of linear homogeneous transformations such that there exists a zero definite Hermitian form which is invariant when its variables are subjected to corresponding transformations of G and $\bar{G}$, then G is a reducible group.

By the process employed in the foregoing section, express the zero definite invariant Hermitian form in the form $t_1\bar{t}_1 + t_2\bar{t}_2 + \cdots + t_s\bar{t}_s$, where $s < n$, n being the number of variables on which G operates. Let $t_1, t_2, \cdots, t_s, t_{s+1}, \cdots, t_n$ be a set of n linearly independent linear functions of the original variables on which G operates. Transform G into a group H on these new variables by means of a transformation S so that $H = S^{-1}GS$. Let $\bar{H}$ be the conjugate imaginary of H so that $\bar{H} = \bar{S}^{-1}\bar{G}\bar{S}$. Then the foregoing standard form is invariant for H and $\bar{H}$. But if

$$s_i = \sum_{j=1}^{n} a_{ij}t_j, \quad \bar{s}_i = \sum_{j=1}^{n} \bar{a}_{ij}\bar{t}_j, \qquad (i = 1, 2, \cdots, n)$$

are corresponding elements of H and $\bar{H}$, then from the invariance of $t_1\bar{t}_1 + \cdots + t_s\bar{t}_s$ it follows that

$$\sum_{i=1}^{s} t_i\bar{t}_i = \sum_{i=1}^{s} \sum_{j=1}^{n} \sum_{k=1}^{n} a_{ij}\bar{a}_{ik}t_j\bar{t}_k.$$

This identity implies that

$$\sum_{i=1}^{s} a_{ij}\bar{a}_{ij} = 0 \quad \text{if} \quad j = s+1, s+2, \cdots, n.$$

Hence $a_{ij} = 0$ if $i = 1, 2, \cdots, s$ and $j = s+1,\ s+2, \cdots, n$. Therefore H transforms the variables $t_1, t_2, \cdots, t_s$ among themselves and hence is reducible. Therefore G itself is reducible.

VI. If a group G of linear homogeneous transformations is of finite order, then G is either irreducible or completely reducible.

If G is reducible, let it be transformed to a set of variables

$$x_1, x_2, \cdots, x_r, x_{r+1}, x_{r+2}, \cdots, x_{r+s}, \qquad [1]$$

such that the last s variables are transformed among themselves by the elements of the transformed group H. Let I be a nonzero definite Hermitian form which is invariant for H and $\bar{H}$. Reduce I to the standard form by the step-by-step process of § **52**, taking the variables in the order given in [1]; and let the new variables be $t_1, t_2, \cdots, t_{r+s}$. The last s of these are functions of the last s x's in [1]; hence they are transformed among themselves by H. Transform H to the new variables t and denote the group in this form by K and its conjugate imaginary by $\bar{K}$. Then $t_1\bar{t}_1 + \cdots + t_{r+s}\bar{t}_{r+s}$ is invariant for K and $\bar{K}$, while the last s t's and the last s $\bar{t}$'s are transformed among themselves by K and $\bar{K}$ respectively. Now (§ **52**, Theorem IV, corollary) $\bar{K}$ is identical with the transformed K_t of K. Hence the last s t's are transformed among themselves by K_t: therefore the first r t's are transformed among themselves by K. Hence K transforms among themselves the variables in each of the two sets

$$t_1, t_2, \cdots, t_r \quad \text{and} \quad t_{r+1}, t_{r+2}, \cdots, t_{r+s}.$$

If the group in either of these sets is reducible, the process may be repeated for that set. By continuing the process we arrive finally at a separation of variables which implies the theorem as stated.

VII. Let G be a finite group of linear homogeneous transformations on the variables $x_1, x_2, \cdots, x_n$, and let H be a simply isomorphic group of linear homogeneous transformations on the variables $y_1, y_2, \cdots, y_m$. Let f be a function of the form

$$f = X_1 Y_1 + X_2 Y_2 + \cdots + X_k Y_k, \qquad (0 < k < n)$$

where $X_1, X_2, \cdots, X_k$ are linearly independent linear homogeneous functions of $x_1, x_2, \cdots, x_n$ and $Y_1, Y_2, \cdots, Y_k$ are such functions of $y_1, y_2, \cdots, y_m$. If f is left unaltered when the x's are changed by any (every) element of G, and the y's by the corresponding element of H, then G is a reducible group.

We suppose that G and H are so transformed that f is the function $x_1y_1 + x_2y_2 + \cdots + x_ky_k$. Since this function has the stated property of invariance, it follows that $x_1, x_2, \cdots, x_k$ must be transformed into linear homogeneous functions of themselves by every element in G. Since $0 < k < n$, it follows that G is reducible.

COR. If two linearly independent functions of the form

$$\sum_{i,j=1}^{n} d_{ij}x_i\bar{x}_j$$

are left unchanged by every element of G, then G is reducible.

Let $\bar{G}$, the conjugate imaginary of G, be the group H of the theorem, and suppose that the variables are so chosen (§ **52**) that one of the forms in the corollary is I, where

$$I = x_1\bar{x}_1 + x_2\bar{x}_2 + \cdots + x_n\bar{x}_n.$$

Let F be the other form. Then F may be written

$$F = \xi_1\bar{x}_1 + \xi_2\bar{x}_2 + \cdots + \xi_n\bar{x}_n,$$

where $\xi_1, \xi_2, \cdots, \xi_n$ are linear homogeneous functions of $x_1, x_2, \cdots, x_n$. If λ is any constant, then $F + \lambda I$ is also left unchanged by all the elements of G. But λ may be so chosen that $\xi_1 + \lambda x_1, \xi_2 + \lambda x_2, \cdots, \xi_n + \lambda x_n$ are linearly dependent. We may then suppose that the notation is so chosen that $\xi_n + \lambda x_n$ is a linear function of the form

$$\xi_n + \lambda x_n = a_1(\xi_1 + \lambda x_1) + \cdots + a_{n-1}(\xi_{n-1} + \lambda x_{n-1}).$$

Then

$$F + \lambda I = (\xi_1 + \lambda x_1)(\bar{x}_1 + a_1\bar{x}_n) + \cdots + (\xi_{n-1} + \lambda x_{n-1})(\bar{x}_{n-1} + a_{n-1}\bar{x}_n).$$

This process of reducing the number of terms may be continued until we have a function possessing the properties demanded in the theorem. Then if we apply the theorem, the corollary follows at once.

54. Composition of Isomorphic Groups. Let G and G' be two simply isomorphic groups of finite order, their elements being linear homogeneous transformations, the first on n variables and the second on m variables; and let A and A', namely,

$$A: \qquad y_i = \sum_{j=1}^{n} a_{ij} x_j, \qquad (i = 1, 2, \cdots, n)$$

$$A': \qquad v_k = \sum_{l=1}^{m} a'_{kl} u_l, \qquad (k = 1, 2, \cdots, m)$$

be corresponding elements in a given simple isomorphism of G and G'. From these two systems of equations we may form the new system

$$y_i v_k = \sum_{j=1}^{n} \sum_{l=1}^{m} a_{ij} a'_{kl} x_j u_l, \qquad (i = 1, 2, \cdots, n; \ k = 1, 2, \cdots, m)$$

defining a linear homogeneous transformation α on the mn variables $x_j u_l$. If B and B' constitute another pair of corresponding elements from G and G' respectively, we may similarly form a transformation β on the mn variables $x_j u_l$. If now $AB = C$ and $A'B' = C'$ and we similarly form γ on the $x_j u_l$ corresponding to C and C', it may easily be shown by a direct computation that $\alpha\beta = \gamma$. Hence the transformations $\alpha, \beta, \gamma, \cdots$ form a group which is simply isomorphic with G and with G'.

This process of forming this third group from the two groups G and G' and a given simple isomorphism of them is called a *composition* of the two groups with respect to the given simple isomorphism, and the resulting third group is called the *compound* of the two given groups with respect to this isomorphism.

If A and A' are written as multiplications, in accordance with Theorem II of § **52**, then α is a multiplication in which the mn multipliers are the mn products formed with factors one of which is a multiplier of A, while the other is a multiplier of A'. Hence *the characteristic of α is the product of the characteristics of A and A'.*

Now suppose that a finite group G is written as a set of transformations changing x's into y's and also as a set of transformations changing u's into v's, and exhibit the two forms of G as simply isomorphic by making each transformation in the one form correspond to that transformation in the other form which has with it the same matrix of coefficients. Now carry out the process of composition on the two forms of G. If G itself is written on n variables, we obtain in this way a new group on n^2 variables which is simply isomorphic with G and we have the correspondences which imply this isomorphism. We shall call it the *first compound* of G with itself. By means of this isomorphism of G with its first compound, form the *second compound* of G with itself, namely, the group resulting from carrying out the process of composition of G with its first compound with respect to the named simple isomorphism of the two groups. It is evident that this process may be continued indefinitely and that we shall thus have a third compound, a fourth compound, and so on, of G with itself.

Now let A be any element of G and write the group on such variables as will reduce A to a multiplication with multipliers $\omega_1, \omega_2, \cdots, \omega_n$, in accordance with Theorem II of § **52**. Then the multipliers of the element corresponding to A in the first compound of G with itself will evidently be the n^2 products $\omega_i\omega_j$. In fact it is easy to see that the multipliers of the element corresponding to A in the $(\alpha - 1)$th compound of G with itself are the n^α notationally distinct products of α factors each, each factor being a number of the set $\omega_1, \omega_2, \cdots, \omega_n$.

When G and G' are two groups of linear homogeneous transformations between which exists a general isomorphism of the sort described in § **16**, then we may apply to them a process of composition similar to that applied to simply isomorphic groups at the beginning of the present section. We suppose that to every element of G there correspond p elements of G', while to every element of G' there correspond q elements of G. Let Σ_1, $\Sigma_2, \cdots$ be the elements of an abstract group which is simply isomorphic with G, and let $\Sigma'_1, \Sigma'_2, \cdots$ be the elements of an abstract group which is simply isomorphic with G', and such that each Σ_i is permutable with every Σ'_j. Let $\Sigma'_{i1}, \Sigma'_{i2}, \cdots$,

Σ'_{ip} be the p elements of the second group, each of which corresponds to Σ_i in the first in accordance with the named isomorphism. Let K of order k be the group whose elements are

$$\Sigma_i\Sigma'_{i1},\ \Sigma_i\Sigma'_{i2},\ \cdots,\ \Sigma_i\Sigma'_{ip}$$

where Σ_i varies over the elements of G; this group K is multiply isomorphic with both G and G', the isomorphism with G and G' being, respectively, $(p, 1)$ and $(q, 1)$.

Denote by S_α $(\alpha = 1, 2, \cdots, k)$ the elements of K, and let

$$y_i = \sum_{j=1}^{n} a_{ij\alpha}x_j, \qquad (i = 1, 2, \cdots, n)$$

$$v_s = \sum_{t=1}^{m} a'_{st\alpha}u_t, \qquad (s = 1, 2, \cdots, m)$$

be the transformations of G and G', respectively, which correspond to S_α in the indicated isomorphisms. With this notation, each of the elements of G appears p times and each of the elements of G' appears q times. By the method employed in the preceding case it may be shown that the k transformations on the mn products of x's and u's, namely, the transformations

$$y_iv_s = \sum_{j=1}^{n}\sum_{t=1}^{m} a_{ij\alpha}a'_{st\alpha}x_ju_t \qquad (i = 1, 2, \cdots, n;\ s = 1, 2, \cdots, m;\ \alpha = 1, 2, \cdots, k)$$

constitute a group which is simply isomorphic with K, the element written being that corresponding to S_α in this isomorphism. The group which thus results by *composition* of G and G' is called the *compound* of G and G' with respect to the named general isomorphism between G and G'.

55. Representation of a Finite Group as a Group of Linear Homogeneous Transformations. Let G be an abstract group of order g whose elements are $S_1 = 1, S_2, S_3, \cdots, S_g$. Let Γ be a group of linear homogeneous transformations to which G is $(\mu, 1)$ isomorphic, where $\mu \geqq 1$. Let the correspondences be given by which a given $(\mu, 1)$ isomorphism of G with Γ may be exhibited. Then, with respect to this explicit isomorphism, Γ is said to afford a *representation* of G as a group of linear homogeneous transformations. If Γ is a permutation group, then we have a representation of G as a permutation group.

Let Γ and Γ', each on a given number n of variables, be two representations of a given group G. Let s_i and s'_i be the elements in Γ and Γ', respectively, which correspond to S_i in G in the given isomorphisms. If there exists a linear homogeneous transformation T on n variables such that $T^{-1}s'_iT = s_i$ for $i = 1, 2, \cdots, g$, then Γ and Γ' are said to be *equivalent* representations of G; if no such T exists, then the representations are said to be *nonequivalent.*

The terms *equivalent* and *nonequivalent* are similarly used for any groups Γ and Γ' without reference to the group G.

The two groups Γ and Γ' may be identical and yet give nonequivalent representations of the group G. Thus the Abelian group G of order p^2 and type (1, 1), where p is a prime, may be represented by the transformation group $y = \omega^i x$ $(i = 0, 1, \cdots, p-1)$, where ω is a primitive pth root of unity, by making two independent generators s and t of G correspond to the transformations $y = \omega_1 x$ and $y = \omega_2 x$, respectively, where ω_1 and ω_2 are pth roots of unity, one of them at least being different from unity. Thus we have $p^2 - 1$ representations of the group G by one and the same transformation group; and it is easy to see that these $p^2 - 1$ representations are such that no two are equivalent, for no two of the relevant $p^2 - 1$ pairs of elements $y = \omega_1 x$ and $y = \omega_2 x$ have, respectively, the same characteristics.

If a finite group G is represented as a reducible group Γ of linear homogeneous transformations, and if Γ is written in such a way as to exhibit the sets of variables in each of which the variables are changed according to an irreducible group, then the transformations on each of these sets afford an *irreducible* representation of G, that is, a representation of G as an irreducible group. The most important representations of G are the irreducible representations.

Among the irreducible representations of a finite group G occurs always that afforded by the group consisting of the single element $y = x$. It is known as the *identical representation*; we denote it by Γ_1. Let us use the symbols

$$\Gamma_1, \Gamma_2, \Gamma_3, \cdots$$

to denote the totality of nonequivalent irreducible representations of G. Let Γ be any representation of G, and let Γ be written in *completely reduced* form, that is, in such a form as to exhibit the sets of variables in each of which the variables are changed according to an irreducible group. If the number of times which Γ_i occurs in this form of Γ is c_i, then Γ may be represented by the symbol

$$\Sigma c_i \Gamma_i.$$

The Γ_i which actually occur here, that is, those for each of which the coefficient c_i is different from zero, will be called the *irreducible components* of Γ.

EXERCISES

1. Show that a similarity transformation is permutable with any linear homogeneous transformation on the same variables.

2. Construct a group of linear homogeneous transformations on k variables which shall be simply isomorphic with the prime-power Abelian group of order p^m and type $(m_1, m_2, \cdots, m_k)$.

3. A similarity transformation contained in a group G of linear homogeneous transformations belongs to the central of G.

4. In a group G of order n of linear homogeneous transformations the determinant of every element is equal to an nth root of unity.

5. Let G be a finite group of linear homogeneous transformations some of the elements of which have their determinants different from unity. Show that the transformations whose determinants are unity constitute a self-conjugate subgroup H of G and that the quotient group G/H is cyclic.

6. Let G be a finite group of linear homogeneous transformations containing an element whose determinant is a primitive (p^α)th root of unity, where p is a prime number and α is a positive integer, but not containing an element whose determinant is a primitive $(p^{\alpha+1})$th root of unity. Let K be the totality of elements in G such that the determinant of each is a primitive νth root of unity where ν is not divisible by p^α but otherwise assumes every value possible for elements in G. Then show that K is a self-conjugate subgroup of G of index p.

7. Determine all the linear homogeneous transformations of order 2 on (1) one variable, (2) two variables, (3) three variables.

8. The characteristic of a transformation of order 2 is an integer.

9. A representation of a finite group G as a group Γ of linear homogeneous transformations is simply isomorphic with a factor-group of G.

10. A representation of a factor-group of G is a representation of G.

11. A permutation group is always reducible.

12. The group Γ obtained by the composition of a group G with its conjugate-imaginary group $\overline{G}$ is reducible, the isomorphism employed being the usual one for G and $\overline{G}$.

13. Show that the elements

$$x' = u,\ y' = v,\ u' = -x,\ v' = -y;\quad x' = y,\ y' = -x,\ u' = v,\ v' = -u;$$
$$x' = ix,\ y' = -iy,\ u' = -iu,\ v' = iv, \text{ where } i^2 = -1,$$

generate a group of order 16 which is reducible.

14. Show that the elements

$$x' = u,\ y' = v,\ u' = -x,\ v' = -y;\quad x' = y,\ y' = -x,\ u' = v,\ v' = -u;$$
$$x' = \alpha x,\ y' = \alpha^{-1}y,\ u' = \alpha^3 u,\ v' = \alpha^{-3}v, \text{ where } \alpha^4 = -1,$$

generate a group of order 32 which is irreducible.

15. Using δ_{ij} to denote 1 or 0 according as $j = i$ or $j \neq i$, show that the relations

$$\sum_{k=1}^{n} c_{ki}\bar{c}_{kj} = \delta_{ij} \qquad (i, j = 1, 2, \cdots, n)$$

imply and are implied by the relations

$$\sum_{i=1}^{n} c_{ki}\bar{c}_{li} = \delta_{kl}. \qquad (k, l = 1, 2, \cdots, n)$$

16. Let G be a finite group of linear homogeneous transformations on $x_1, x_2, \cdots, x_n$ such that the coefficients in each transformation are real numbers. Show that there exists a quadratic function of $x_1, x_2, \cdots, x_n$ which is invariant for all the elements of G and which vanishes for real values of the variables only when $x_1 = x_2 = \cdots = x_n = 0$.

17. Let G be the abstract group $\{s, t\}$ of order 21 whose sole defining relations are

$$s^7 = t^3 = 1, \quad t^{-1}st = s^2.$$

Construct two nonequivalent representations Γ and Γ' of G, each on three variables such that G is simply isomorphic both with Γ and with Γ' and such indeed that Γ and Γ' are the same transformation group related in two ways to G.

56. Group Characteristics. Let G be a group of linear homogeneous transformations of order g in the n variables $x_1, x_2, \cdots, x_n$, the variables into which these are changed by the elements of G being now represented by $x'_1, x'_2, \cdots, x'_n$. Denote the elements of G by $S_1 = 1, S_2, S_3, \cdots, S_g$. The characteristic of S_t we denote by $\chi(S_t)$; we have seen (§ **52**, Theorem II, corollary) that $\chi(S_t)$ is a sum of n roots of unity. Since the conjugate imaginary of a root of unity is its reciprocal, and since the multipliers of S_t^{-1} (when written as a multiplication) are the reciprocals of those of S_t, it follows that $\chi(S_t)$ and $\chi(S_t^{-1})$ are conjugate imaginaries. Hence if we denote by $\bar{\alpha}$ the conjugate imaginary of α, we have $\bar{\chi}(S_t) = \chi(S_t^{-1})$ and $\chi(S_t) = \bar{\chi}(S_t^{-1})$.

It is obvious (from Theorem I of § **51**) that the elements of a complete set of conjugate elements in G all have the same characteristic. Let r be the number of complete sets of conjugate elements in G, and let $h_1 (=1), h_2, h_3, \cdots, h_r$ be the numbers of elements in the respective conjugate sets, h_1 being the number of elements conjugate to the identity. Then G has at most r distinct characteristics, the ith conjugate set having just h_i elements, all with the same characteristic. We call this the characteristic of the corresponding conjugate set.

VIII. If l is the number of linearly independent linear homogeneous functions of $x_1, x_2, \cdots, x_n$ each of which is changed into itself by (is invariant for) every element of G, then we have

$$\sum_{i=1}^{g} \chi(S_i) = lg.$$

Let L_1 be an arbitrary linear homogeneous function of $x_1, x_2, \cdots, x_n$; and let L_i be the function into which L_1 is changed by S_i. Then the function L, $L = L_1 + L_2 + \cdots + L_g$, is changed into itself by every element of G. If L does not vanish identically, it is one such invariant as is described in the theorem. If $L_1 = \alpha_1 x_1 + \alpha_2 x_2 + \cdots + \alpha_n x_n$, then the sum of the coefficients of $\alpha_1 x_1, \alpha_2 x_2, \cdots, \alpha_n x_n$ in L_i is $\chi(S_i)$, as one may readily verify by direct computation. Hence L cannot be identically zero for all coefficients α unless $\chi(S_1)+\chi(S_2)+\cdots+\chi(S_g)=0$. Therefore $l\neq 0$ when this equation is not satisfied.

If now we suppose that $l\neq 0$, we may transform G to new variables $t_1, t_2, \cdots, t_n$ such that $t_1, t_2, \cdots, t_l$ are left unaltered by all the elements of the transformed group H. Let T_i be the element into which S_i is thus transformed, and let T'_i be the corresponding transformation on $t_{l+1}, t_{l+2}, \cdots, t_n$. Then $\chi(S_i) = \chi(T_i) = l + \chi(T'_i)$. Now $\Sigma\chi(T'_i)=0$, since otherwise we would have an additional linear invariant, so that the number would not be precisely l. Therefore $\Sigma\chi(S_i)=lg$, as was to be proved. Since this relation also holds when $l=0$, the proof of the theorem is completed.

In the case of an irreducible group it is evident that $l=0$. Hence we have the following corollary:

COR. I. *If G is an irreducible group, we have*

$$\sum_{i=1}^{g}\chi(S_i)=0.$$

Applying the theorem to the $(m-1)$th compound of G with itself (§ **54**), we readily have the following corollary:

COR. II. *If l_m is the number of linearly independent homogeneous functions of $x_1, x_2, \cdots, x_n$ of degree m $(m>1)$ each of which is changed into itself by every element of G, then*

$$\sum_{i=1}^{g}\chi(S_i^{(m)})=l_m g,$$

where $\chi(S_i^{(m)})$ denotes the sum of all the n^m notationally distinct homogeneous products of degree m in the n multipliers of S_i.

IX. *If $\overline{\chi}$ is the conjugate imaginary of χ and if G is irreducible, then we have*

$$\sum_{i=1}^{g}\chi(S_i)\overline{\chi}(S_i)=g.$$

Let $\bar{G}$ be the conjugate imaginary of G, and let K be the compound of G and $\bar{G}$ formed by means of the usual simple isomorphism between G and $\bar{G}$. If S' is the element in K corresponding to the elements S and $\bar{S}$ of G and $\bar{G}$ respectively, then $\chi(S') = \chi(S)\chi(\bar{S}) = \chi(S)\bar{\chi}(S)$ (§ **54**). Hence (Theorem VIII) $\Sigma\chi(S_i)\bar{\chi}(S_i) = lg$, where l is the number of linearly independent linear functions of the n^2 variables $x\,\bar{x}_j$ each of which is left unchanged by each element of K. From the corollary to Theorem VII in § **53** and Theorem III in § **52**, it follows that $l = 1$. Hence we have the required conclusion.

X. Let H, with elements $T_1 = 1, T_2, T_3, \cdots, T_g$, be a group of linear homogeneous transformations on the m variables $y_1, y_2, \cdots, y_m$ such that H is exhibited as simply isomorphic with G by means of the correspondences $S_i \sim T_i$ $(i = 1, 2, \cdots g)$; and let G itself be irreducible. Then if $\bar{T}_i$ is the conjugate imaginary of T_i, we have

$$\sum_{i=1}^{g}\chi(S_i)\chi(\bar{T}_i) = lg,$$

where l is a non-negative integer. If $l = 1$, then H is equivalent to G. If $l > 1$, then H is reducible, and just l of its completely reduced sets are transformed according to l groups each of which is equivalent to G.

Let K be the compound of G and $\bar{H}$ formed by means of the isomorphism between G and $\bar{H}$ gotten from the isomorphism in the theorem and the usual isomorphism between the conjugate-imaginary groups H and $\bar{H}$. Applying Theorem VIII to K and employing the result in § **54** relative to the characteristics of K, we have the required equation of the theorem where l is the number of linearly independent invariants of K of the form $a_{11}x_1\bar{y}_1 + \cdots + a_{nm}x_n\bar{y}_m$.

For the other required results we have $l \geqq 1$. We suppose that the variables of G are so chosen (§ **52**) that the form $x_1\bar{x}_1 + x_2\bar{x}_2 + \cdots + x_n\bar{x}_n$ is left unaltered by each of the elements of G. We then suppose that H is so transformed that one of the l linear invariants for K has the form $x_1\bar{y}_1 + x_2\bar{y}_2 + \cdots + x_n\bar{y}_n$, this being certainly possible since G is irreducible (as one sees by aid of Theorem VII of § **53**). Then $\bar{H}$ transforms the variables $\bar{y}_1, \bar{y}_2, \cdots, \bar{y}_n$ according to a group which is equivalent to $\bar{G}$, as one may easily verify. Therefore H transforms the variables $y_1, y_2, \cdots, y_n$ according to a group which is equivalent to G. Hence H is reducible if $m > n$ and is irreducible if $m = n$. Furthermore, when $m = n$ we must have $l = 1$, to avoid a contradiction with the corollary to Theorem VII of § **53** — since G is irreducible by hypothesis. When $m > n$ there is at least one additional invariant of K besides $x_1\bar{y}_1 + \cdots + x_n\bar{y}_n$, whence $l > 1$ in this case. Therefore H is equivalent to G when $l = 1$ and H is reducible when $l > 1$.

If $l > 1$ we may treat each of the named l invariants of K after the manner employed in the preceding paragraph and thus show that H has l completely reduced sets each of which is transformed according to a group which is equivalent to G. Moreover, H has no additional such set whose elements are so transformed among themselves; for, if so, this would give rise to an additional invariant of K, and hence there would be more than l of them.

COR. I. When G and H are equivalent, we have

$$\sum_{i=1}^{g} \chi(S_i)\chi(\bar{T}_i) = g.$$

This follows at once from Theorems IX and X and the fact that $\bar{S}_i$ and $\bar{T}_i$ have the same characteristic (owing to the equivalence of $\bar{G}$ and $\bar{H}$).

COR. II. When G and H are nonequivalent and are both irreducible, we have

$$\sum_{i=1}^{g} \chi(S_i)\chi(\bar{T}_i) = 0.$$

For in this case the number l in the theorem is necessarily equal to zero, since G and H are equivalent when $l=1$ and H is reducible when $l>1$.

From Corollary II and the meaning assigned to l in the proof of the theorem we have the following result:

Cor. III. When G and H are nonequivalent and are both irreducible, they have no (nonidentically vanishing) invariant of the form

$$a_{11}x_1\bar{y}_1 + a_{12}x_1\bar{y}_2 + \cdots + a_{nm}x_n\bar{y}_m.$$

Again, from Corollaries I and II we have the following:

Cor. IV. In order that G and H (both assumed to be irreducible) shall be equivalent it is necessary and sufficient that they shall have the same characteristics.

XI. Let Γ be an irreducible representation of a group G which contains r complete conjugate sets of elements having, respectively, h_1 $(=1)$, $h_2, \cdots, h_r$ elements of G, and let χ_i denote the characteristic of the elements of Γ corresponding to the ith set of G. Then

$$\frac{h_s\chi_s}{m}\cdot\frac{h_t\chi_t}{m}=\sum_{i=1}^{r} c_{sti}\frac{h_i\chi_i}{m}, \qquad (s, t = 1, 2, \cdots, r)$$

where the coefficients c_{sti} are non-negative integers and where m is the number of variables on which Γ operates.

Let M_i denote the matrix which is equal to the sum of the matrices of the elements corresponding to the ith complete set of conjugate elements, the number in the kth row and lth column of M_i being the sum of the numbers which stand in the kth row and lth column of the several matrices of these elements of Γ. Since any element T of Γ transforms among themselves these conjugate elements, it follows that the corresponding matrix T transforms M_i into itself so that we have $T^{-1}M_iT=M_i$. The relations thus obtained by varying T over the elements of Γ imply that the matrix M_i has the form of the matrix of a similarity transformation, as one sees from the result in the second paragraph of § **53**. To find the value of the multiplying factor α_i in the main diagonal of M_i we observe that $m\alpha_i$ is equal to the sum of the characteristics of the elements corresponding to the ith conjugate set of elements in G; hence $m\alpha_i = h_i\chi_i$, or $\alpha_i = h_i\chi_i/m$.

Now consider the product M_sM_t. We shall show that we have a relation of the form

$$M_sM_t = c_{st1}M_1 + c_{st2}M_2 + \cdots + c_{str}M_r,$$

where the c_{sti} are non-negative integers. For M_s and M_t are sums of matrices of elements of Γ, and hence their product may be written as such a sum; since the latter sum is transformed into itself by every element T in Γ (for $T^{-1}M_sM_tT = T^{-1}M_sT \cdot T^{-1}M_tT=M_sM_t$), it follows that these summands enter in sets, each set corresponding to a complete conjugate set in G. From the foregoing relation we see that

$$\alpha_s\alpha_t = c_{st1}\alpha_1 + c_{st2}\alpha_2 + \cdots + c_{str}\alpha_r.$$

In view of the relations $\alpha_i = h_i\chi_i/m$, this implies the relations to be established.

Cor. I. *The quantity α_t, or $h_t\chi_t/m$, is an algebraic integer and is the sum of a finite number of roots of unity.*

The equations

$$\alpha_s\alpha_t = c_{st1}\alpha_1 + c_{st2}\alpha_2 + \cdots + c_{str}\alpha_r, \qquad (s = 1, 2, \cdots, r)$$

for fixed t, imply that α_t is an algebraic integer, that is, a root of an equation of the form $x^\nu + a_1x^{\nu-1} + \cdots + a_\nu = 0$, where $a_1, a_2, \cdots, a_\nu$ are ordinary integers; this is readily proved by eliminating from the foregoing equations all the α's except α_t. But $m\alpha_t$ is a sum of roots of unity, since it is a sum of characteristics of Γ. The truth of the corollary is now a consequence of the following lemma:

LEMMA. If α is an algebraic integer and $\mu\alpha$ is a sum of roots of unity, μ being an integer, then α is itself a sum of roots of unity.

This lemma from the theory of numbers is a consequence of the lemma employed in § **58**.

COR. II. If G is an irreducible group of linear homogeneous transformations, the number n of variables transformed by G is a factor of the order g of G.

With the present notation the equation of Theorem IX may be written in the form

$$g = h_1\chi_1\bar{\chi}_1 + h_2\chi_2\bar{\chi}_2 + \cdots + h_r\chi_r\bar{\chi}_r;$$

or

$$\frac{g}{n} = \frac{h_1\chi_1}{n}\bar{\chi}_1 + \frac{h_2\chi_2}{n}\bar{\chi}_2 + \cdots + \frac{h_r\chi_r}{n}\bar{\chi}_r.$$

Since products and sums of algebraic integers are themselves algebraic integers, it follows that g/n is an algebraic integer. But g/n is a rational number; therefore it must be an ordinary integer.

XII. If the completely reduced form of G is denoted by the symbol $\Sigma c_i\Gamma_i$, in accordance with § **55**, then the conjugate-imaginary groups G and $\bar{G}$ have just Σc_i^2 linearly independent invariants (functions left unchanged by each element of G) of the form $\Sigma c_{ij}x_i\bar{x}_j$.

By aid of Corollary III to Theorem X it may be shown that no one of these invariants has a term of the form $as\bar{t}$, where s is a variable in one Γ_i and t is a variable in another and hence nonequivalent one. Therefore the number of these invariants is equal to the sum of the numbers of the invariants for the separate Γ_i. It is therefore sufficient to prove that the number for a particular Γ_i is c_i^2. We may suppose that the c_i sets of variables in these c_i equivalent representations are

$$x_{t1}, x_{t2}, \cdots, x_{ts}; \qquad (t = 1, 2, \cdots, c_i)$$

and we may assume that the variables have been so transformed that for each element in G these c_i sets all undergo the same transformation and that the corresponding (unique) invariants for these separate sets are

$$x_{t1}\bar{x}_{t1} + x_{t2}\bar{x}_{t2} + \cdots + x_{ts}\bar{x}_{ts}. \qquad (t = 1, 2, \cdots, c_i)$$

Let $\Sigma a_{kplq} x_{kp} \bar{x}_{lq}$ be one of the invariants in consideration; and let

$$x'_{kp} = \sum_{q=1}^{s} \alpha_{pqj} x_{kq} \qquad (p = 1, 2, \cdots, s)$$

be a typical transformation on the x's. Then we have

$$a_{kulv} = \sum_{p,q} a_{kplq} \alpha_{puj} \bar{\alpha}_{qvj}.$$

These relations imply that the form $\Sigma a_{kulv} x_u \bar{x}_v$ is invariant for the group whose transformations are

$$x'_p = \sum_{q=1}^{s} \alpha_{pqj} x_q. \qquad (p = 1, 2, \cdots, s)$$

Since $x_1\bar{x}_1 + x_2\bar{x}_2 + \cdots + x_s\bar{x}_s$ is the only invariant for this group, we have

$$a_{kplq} = 0 \text{ if } p \neq q, \quad a_{kplp} = a_{kqlq} = b_{kl} \text{ (say)}.$$

Then the most general invariant of the required form in the named $c_i s$ variables and their conjugates may be written

$$\sum_{k,l,p} b_{kl} x_{kp} \bar{x}_{lp};$$

and this is invariant for arbitrary values of the c_i^2 coefficients b_{kl}. Hence we have just c_i^2 linearly independent invariants of the specified form on these $c_i s$ variables. We have already seen that this result implies the theorem to be established.

57. Regular Permutation Groups. Let H be a regular permutation group of order g whose elements are $T_1 = 1, T_2, T_3, \cdots, T_g$. The permutation T_i defines a linear homogeneous transformation Σ_i on the g symbols on which H operates. Thus we have a group Γ whose elements $\Sigma_1 = 1, \Sigma_2, \Sigma_3, \cdots, \Sigma_g$ are linear homogeneous transformations on g variables. Since T_1 is the only element of H which leaves a symbol fixed, it follows that the matrix of Σ_i $(i > 1)$ has only zeros in its principal diagonal. Therefore $\chi(\Sigma_i) = 0$ if $i > 1$. It is obvious that $\chi(\Sigma_1) = g$. That the group Γ is reducible follows from the fact that the sum of the variables on which it operates is left unchanged by every element in Γ.

Let K be a subgroup of Γ of index α and let $g/\alpha = a$. The characteristic of the identity in K is g and that of every other element is zero. Then if we apply Theorem VIII of § **56**, we see that α is the number of linearly independent linear homogeneous functions of the variables of Γ each of which is left unchanged by every element in K. It is easy to construct a set of α such linear invariants. Let $x_1, x_2, \cdots, x_g$ be the variables of Γ and suppose that the notation is chosen so that the transitive sets in K are the following:

$$x_1, x_2, \cdots, x_a;\ x_{a+1}, x_{a+2}, \cdots, x_{2a};\ \cdots;\ x_{(\alpha-1)a+1}, \cdots, x_{\alpha a}.$$

Then the following are α linearly independent invariants of the type in consideration:

$$x_1 + x_2 + \cdots + x_a,\ x_{a+1} + \cdots + x_{2a},\ \cdots,\ x_{(\alpha-1)a+1} + \cdots + x_{\alpha a}.$$

Consider next the compound of the conjugate-imaginary groups Γ and $\bar{\Gamma}$. The characteristic of the identity is g^2 and that of every other element is zero. The g^2 variables of the group are the symbols $x_i\bar{x}_j$. Then from Theorem VIII of § **56** it follows that g is the number of linearly independent linear homogeneous functions of the g^2 variables $x_i\bar{x}_j$ each of which is left invariant by every element of this compound group. Therefore Γ *and* $\bar{\Gamma}$ *have just* g *linearly independent invariants of the form* $\Sigma c_{ij}x_i\bar{x}_j$.

Now if the completely reduced form of Γ is denoted by the symbol $\Sigma c_i\Gamma_i$, in accordance with § **55**, we see from Theorem XII of § **56** and the result in the preceding paragraph that

$$g = \Sigma c_i^2.$$

But if m_i is the number of variables on which Γ_i operates, then, since the number of variables in Γ is equal to the order g of Γ, it is obvious that

$$g = \Sigma c_i m_i.$$

Therefore

$$\Sigma c_i m_i = \Sigma c_i^2.$$

Now let G, with the elements $s_1 = 1, s_2, \cdots, s_g$, be an irreducible group of linear homogeneous transformations on n variables, and suppose that G is simply isomorphic with Γ, with the correspondences $s_i \sim \Sigma_i$ $(i = 1, 2, \cdots, g)$. Then by aid of the foregoing values of $\chi(\Sigma_i)$ we find that

$$\sum_{i=1}^{g} \chi(s_i)\chi(\overline{\Sigma}_i) = ng.$$

From this relation and Theorem X of § **56** we see that *just n of the completely reduced sets of Γ are transformed, each according to a group which is equivalent to G.*

More generally, let G be any irreducible group of linear homogeneous transformations which affords a representation of Γ (§ **55**), and let n be the number of symbols on which G operates. Then Γ is $(\mu, 1)$ isomorphic with G, where $\mu \geqq 1$. Let A be the self-conjugate subgroup of Γ which consists of those elements of Γ (μ in number) each of which corresponds to the identity in this isomorphism of Γ with G; and with respect to A separate Γ into the partitions

$$t_1A, t_2A, t_3A, \cdots, t_\lambda A, \quad (t_1 = 1)$$

by the method of § **10**. On multiplying these sets on the left by any element of Γ, the sets are permuted among themselves (compare § **20**). If this operation is performed for every element in Γ, a permutation group K on the λ sets is induced. The group K is obviously transitive, since such multiplication by t_i replaces the first set by the ith set. Now if s is any element of A, we have $st_iA = t_i \cdot t_i^{-1}st_i \cdot A = t_iA$, since $t_i^{-1}st_i$ is in A; therefore each of the λ sets is left unaltered as a set when the named operation is performed with an element of A. Therefore the order of K is not greater than λ. Since K is transitive on λ symbols, it follows that the order of K is precisely λ.

Hence K is a regular group on its symbols. It is clear that K is simply isomorphic with the quotient group Γ/A, and thence that K and G are simply isomorphic. Hence G affords an irreducible representation of K by means of a simply isomorphic group. From the result in the preceding paragraph it follows then that just n of the completely reduced sets of K are transformed, each according to a group which is equivalent to G.

We have seen that the notation may be chosen so that each of the λ functions

$$x_1 + x_2 + \cdots + x_\mu, \quad x_{\mu+1} + \cdots + x_{2\mu}, \quad \cdots, \quad x_{(\lambda-1)\mu+1} + \cdots + x_{\lambda\mu}$$

is left invariant by each element of A. Since the variables in any one of the functions constitute a transitive set for A, it follows that the notation may be further restricted so that t_i replaces x_μ by $x_{i\mu}$; and we suppose that this restriction is made. Then these λ linear functions are obviously permuted by Γ in the same way as Γ permutes the sets $t_1A, t_2A, \cdots, t_\lambda A$ in accordance with the method of the preceding paragraph. Therefore if Γ is written in the completely reduced form denoted by the symbol $\Sigma c_i\Gamma_i$, there must be a Γ_i which is equivalent to G, and the number of such Γ_i equivalent to G is at least as large as the number of symbols on which Γ_i operates, as one sees from the result attained in the preceding paragraph. Hence $c_i \geqq m_i$, where m_i is the number of variables on which Γ_i operates. But we have seen that $\Sigma c_i m_i = \Sigma c_i^2$. Then it follows readily that $c_i = m_i$. Therefore the coefficient c_s in the symbol $\Sigma c_i\Gamma_i$ is equal to the number of variables on which Γ_s operates. The order of the group Γ_s is a factor of g, since Γ is multiply isomorphic with Γ_s; the order of Γ_s is (§ **56**, Theorem XI, Corollary II) a multiple of c_s; hence c_s is a factor of g.

We are to show next that the number k of nonequivalent Γ_i in the symbol $\Sigma c_i\Gamma_i$ for Γ is equal to the number r of complete conjugate sets of elements in Γ. For this purpose we employ the symbols $M_1, M_2, \cdots, M_r$ with the meanings given to them in the proof of Theorem XI of § **56**, except that they now refer to the group Γ in its completely reduced form; and we use without further reference the properties of them deduced in the course of that proof. We denote by $h_1 (= 1), h_2, h_3, \cdots, h_r$ the numbers of elements in the respective conjugate sets, the first set consisting of the identity alone.

Let us consider the matrix M defined by the equation

$$M = u_1M_1 + u_2M_2 + \cdots + u_rM_r,$$

where $u_1, u_2, \cdots, u_r$ are independent parameters. Then M has the form of the matrix of a multiplication transformation, as we shall now show. Let $\chi_{1j}, \chi_{2j}, \cdots, \chi_{rj}$ be the characteristics of sets of elements in Γ_j corresponding to the various conjugate sets in Γ. Then, so far as the c_j variables of Γ_j are concerned, M has the form of the matrix of a similarity transformation whose multiplier β_j is

$$\beta_j = (h_1u_1\chi_{1j} + h_2u_2\chi_{2j} + \cdots + h_ru_r\chi_{rj})/c_j.$$

Since $u_1, u_2, \cdots, u_r$ are independent parameters, it follows (by aid of Corollary IV to Theorem X in § **56**) that two β_j formed for different Γ_j are distinct. Therefore we have just k different β_j, where k is the number of the groups Γ_j. A like result is true not only for M but for any transform of M by a linear homogeneous transformation. Hence the β_j cannot furnish more than k linearly independent linear homogeneous functions of $u_1, u_2, \cdots, u_r$. But M contains just r such functions, namely, $u_1, u_2, \cdots, u_r$. Hence $k \geqq r$ and just r of the β_j are linearly independent. We suppose the notation so chosen that these are $\beta_1, \beta_2, \cdots, \beta_r$.

If $k > r$ and we replace $u_1, u_2, \cdots, u_r$ by the conjugate imaginaries of the characteristics $\chi_1, \chi_2, \cdots, \chi_r$ of the elements in Γ_{r+1} corresponding to the r conjugate sets of Γ, we have (by Corollary II to Theorem X in § **56**) the relations $\beta_1 = \beta_2 = \cdots = \beta_r = 0$. But $\overline{\chi}_1, \overline{\chi}_2, \cdots, \overline{\chi}_r$ are not all zero, since one of them (that corresponding to the identity) denotes the number of variables on which Γ_{r+1} operates. This contradicts the fact that the $\beta_1, \beta_2, \cdots, \beta_r$ are linearly independent. Hence k is not greater than r. Therefore we conclude finally that $k = r$, so that the number of the Γ_i in the symbol $\Sigma c_i\Gamma_i$ is precisely r.

Among the results which we have now obtained are all of those included in the following theorem:

XIII. Let H be the representation of a given finite group of order g as a simply isomorphic regular permutation group, and let r be the number of complete conjugate sets of elements in H. Let Γ be the group of linear homogeneous transformations of order g on g variables defined by H; and let $\Sigma c_i\Gamma_i$ represent the completely reduced form of Γ. Then the number of symbols operated upon by Γ_i is c_i, so that we have

$$g = c_1^2 + c_2^2 + \cdots + c_r^2;$$

and each c_i is a factor of g. Moreover, every irreducible representation of H occurs among the groups $\Gamma_1, \Gamma_2, \cdots, \Gamma_r$.

COR. The relations

$$\sum_{i=1}^{r} a_i\chi_{ti} = 0, \qquad (t = 1, 2, \cdots, r)$$

where $a_1, a_2, \cdots, a_r$ are constants, imply that

$$a_1 = a_2 = \cdots = a_r = 0.$$

For these relations imply that

$$\sum_{i=1}^{r} a_i c_i \beta_i \equiv 0$$

as a function of $u_1, u_2, \cdots, u_r$, whereas the c_i are all different from zero and the functions $\beta_1, \beta_2, \cdots, \beta_r$ are linearly independent; whence it follows that $a_1 = a_2 = \cdots = a_r = 0$.

Let us now suppose that in the symbol $\Sigma c_i\Gamma_i$ for Γ at least two of the Γ_i operate each on a single symbol, say that Γ_1 and Γ_2 are two such groups. Then for Γ_1 we have the form $y_1 = x_1$, but for Γ_2 we have the form $y_2 = ax_2$, where a is different from unity, since we have seen (by aid of Theorem VIII in § **56**) that Γ leaves invariant just one linear homogeneous form. If Γ is simply isomorphic with Γ_2, then Γ itself is a cyclic group; if Γ is multiply isomorphic with Γ_2, then Γ has a self-conjugate subgroup different from itself and from unity. Hence Γ is a composite group unless its order is a prime number. Hence we have the following theorem:

XIV. If Γ is a group of composite order, and if in the symbol $\Sigma c_i\Gamma_i$ for Γ there are two nonequivalent groups Γ_i each of which operates on a single symbol, then Γ is a composite group.

Using $h_1 = 1, h_2, \cdots, h_r$ as before to denote the numbers of elements in the respective complete conjugate sets of Γ, we have for the order g of Γ the relations

$$g = c_1{}^2 + c_2{}^2 + \cdots + c_r{}^2, \quad g = h_1 + h_2 + \cdots + h_r,$$

where each c_i and each h_i is a factor of g. The group is composite if two c's or two h's are each equal to unity. It is simple if no partial sum of the form $h_1 + h_\alpha + h_\beta + \cdots$, containing h_1 and at least one other h, is a factor of g, since such a sum must arise from a self-conjugate proper subgroup of Γ of order greater than unity. For a given g the foregoing equations imply great restrictions on the possible values of r. If r is preassigned, the possible values of g are restricted.

Let us return to the group Γ of Theorem XIII, whose completely reduced form is $\Gamma = \Sigma c_i\Gamma_i$. As before, denote by h_1 $(= 1)$, $h_2, \cdots, h_r$ the numbers of elements in the r complete conjugate sets of elements in Γ. Let $\chi_{1i}, \chi_{2i}, \cdots, \chi_{ri}$ be the characteristics of the sets of elements in Γ_i corresponding to the various conjugate sets in Γ. The set of quantities χ_{1i}, $\chi_{2i}, \cdots, \chi_{ri}$ is called a set of *group characteristics*. If Σ_1 $(= 1)$, $\Sigma_2, \cdots, \Sigma_g$ denote the elements of Γ, we have seen that $\chi(\Sigma_i) = 0$ if $i > 1$ and that $\chi(\Sigma_1) = g$. Hence

$$\sum_{i=1}^{r} h_i\chi_{i1} = g \quad \text{and} \quad \sum_{i=1}^{r} h_i\chi_{ij} = 0 \text{ if } j > 1. \qquad [A]$$

Since χ_{1i} is the number of symbols on which Γ_i operates, it follows from Theorem XI of § **56** that we have the relations

$$h_ih_j\chi_{ik}\chi_{jk} = \chi_{1k}\sum_{s=1}^{r} c_{ijs}h_s\chi_{sk}, \qquad (i, j, k = 1, 2, \cdots, r) \qquad [B]$$

where the coefficients c_{ijs} are non-negative integers.

To each element of Γ there corresponds a single element of Γ_i and a single element of Γ_j in the usual isomorphism of Γ with these groups. By means of this fact a general isomorphism is established between Γ_i and Γ_j, an element of the one corresponding to an element of the other when and only when these two elements correspond to one and the same element in Γ. With respect to this isomorphism form the compound of Γ_i and Γ_j according to the method of § **54** and denote this compound group by $\Gamma_i\Gamma_j$ or $\Gamma_j\Gamma_i$. This compound affords a representation of Γ; and its completely reduced form may be denoted by the equation

$$\Gamma_i\Gamma_j = \Gamma_j\Gamma_i = \sum_{s=1}^{r} g_{ijs}\Gamma_s,$$

where the coefficients g_{ijs} are non-negative integers.

The condition $g_{ij1} \neq 0$ indicates the existence of one or more invariants of the form $a_{11}x_1y_1 + a_{12}x_1y_2 + \cdots$ for the groups Γ_i and Γ_j. By aid of Corollary III to Theorem X in § **56**, it may then be shown that $g_{ij1} = 0$ when Γ_i and $\bar{\Gamma}_j$ are non-equivalent, while from Theorem X itself it follows that $g_{ij1} = 1$ when Γ_i and $\bar{\Gamma}_j$ are equivalent.

The characteristic of any transformation in $\Gamma_i\Gamma_j$ is the product of the characteristics of the corresponding transformations in Γ_i and Γ_j. Then from the foregoing completely reduced form of $\Gamma_i\Gamma_j$ it follows that

$$\chi_{ki}\chi_{kj} = \sum_{s=1}^{r} g_{ijs}\chi_{ks}. \qquad (k = 1, 2, \cdots, r) \qquad [C]$$

Multiplying by h_k and summing with respect to k, we have

$$\sum_{k=1}^{r} h_k\chi_{ki}\chi_{kj} = \sum_{s=1}^{r} g_{ijs} \sum_{k=1}^{r} h_k\chi_{ks} = g_{ij1}g,$$

as one sees by aid of [A]. Then, from the already determined value of g_{ij1}, we have

$$\sum_{k=1}^{r} h_k\chi_{ki}\chi_{kj} = g \quad \text{or} \quad 0$$

according as Γ_i and $\bar{\Gamma}_j$ are or are not equivalent representations of Γ. If $\Gamma_{i'}$ is the representation which is equivalent to $\overline{\Gamma}_i$, then we have

$$\sum_{k=1}^{r} h_k \chi_{ki} \chi_{kj} = \begin{cases} g \text{ if } j = i', \\ 0 \text{ if } j \neq i'. \end{cases} \qquad [D]$$

These results will afford a ready proof of the following theorem:

XV. In order that two representations of a group of finite order as groups of linear homogeneous transformations shall be equivalent it is necessary and sufficient that the characteristic of each conjugate set shall be the same in the two.

We show first that no two distinct irreducible representations Γ_i and Γ_j have the same set of characteristics. For if they have the same set of characteristics, then we have $\chi_{ki} = \chi_{kj}$ for $k = 1, 2, \cdots, r$. If $\Gamma_{i'}$ and $\Gamma_{j'}$ are the representations equivalent to $\overline{\Gamma}_i$ and $\overline{\Gamma}_j$ respectively, then $\chi_{ki'} = \chi_{kj'}$, and we have

$$\sum_{k=1}^{r} h_k \chi_{ki} \chi_{kj'} = \sum_{k=1}^{r} h_k \chi_{ki} \chi_{ki'} = g;$$

whereas

$$\sum_{k=1}^{r} h_k \chi_{ki} \chi_{kj'} = 0 \text{ when } j' \neq i'.$$

Hence Γ_i and Γ_j have not the same set of characteristics.

Now let $\psi_1, \psi_2, \cdots, \psi_r$ be the characteristics of any representation of Γ, and let $\Sigma \gamma_i \Gamma_i$ be the completely reduced form of this representation. Then we have

$$\psi_s = \Sigma \gamma_i \chi_{si}. \qquad (s = 1, 2, \cdots, r)$$

But from the corollary to Theorem XIII it follows that the determinant $|\chi_{si}|$ is different from zero. Hence the coefficients γ_i are completely determined by the foregoing system of equations. They are therefore the same for any two representations of Γ which have the same set of characteristics. They are obviously different for any two representations which have different sets of characteristics.

Let m be the order of the elements in the jth conjugate set of Γ_i, and let S be one of the elements in that set. Then if μ is prime to m, the element S^μ is an element of a conjugate set containing h_j elements; and the characteristic of S^μ, which we denote by $\chi_{j(\mu)}$, is obtained from the characteristic χ_j of S by replacing each of the multipliers of S by its μth power and taking the sum of the resulting elements. Then consider the product P,

$$P = \prod_\mu \frac{h_j \chi_{j(\mu)}}{c_i},$$

where the product is taken for μ running over the $\phi(m)$ positive integers less than m and prime to m. Each factor in this product is an algebraic integer (§ **56**, Theorem XI, Corollary I), and hence the product itself is an algebraic integer. But P is a rational number, since the product is a symmetric function of the $\phi(m)$ primitive mth roots of unity. Since P is an algebraic integer and is a rational number, it follows that P is an ordinary integer. But

$$\prod_\mu \chi_{j(\mu)} = \prod_\mu |\chi_{j(\mu)}|$$

where $|\alpha|$ denotes the absolute value of α. We may therefore write P in the form

$$P = \left(\frac{h_j}{c_i}\right)^{\phi(m)} \prod_\mu |\chi_{j(\mu)}|.$$

Now if c_i is prime to h_j it follows that $\Pi\,|\chi_{j(\mu)}|$ must be divisible by $c_i^{\phi(m)}$. But $|\chi_{j(\mu)}|/c_i$ is either zero or a real positive number less than unity unless the c_i mth roots of unity whose sum makes up $\chi_{j(\mu)}$ are all the same. Therefore $\chi_{j(\mu)}$, and hence χ_j itself, is zero or else the c_i mth roots whose sum constitutes χ_j are all the same, provided that c_i is prime to h_j. In the latter case the multipliers of S are all the same.

It remains to prove the proposition in the last sentence of the theorem. If $c_i = 1$ this proposition follows from Theorem XIV of § **57**. In any case Γ_i contains a self-conjugate element, namely, this element whose multipliers are all equal. Hence Γ_i is composite unless it is of prime order; therefore Γ (when not of prime order) is composite if it is simply isomorphic with Γ_i, and it is evidently composite if it is multiply isomorphic with Γ_i.

COR. I. If the number of elements in some conjugate set of a group is a prime power p^n $(n > 0)$, then the group is composite.

Represent the group as a simply isomorphic regular permutation group Γ of order g, and let $\Sigma c_i \Gamma_i$ be the symbol for the complete reduction of Γ. We assume that Γ is simple and show that the hypothesis in the corollary then leads us to a contradiction. Since g is divisible by p^n and $g = c_1^2 + c_2^2 + \cdots + c_r^2$, and since $c_1 = 1$, it follows that there is at least one representation Γ_i, other than the identical one, in which the number c_i of variables is prime to p. Since Γ is assumed to be simple, it follows from the theorem that the characteristics of elements other than the identity in such a representation are equal to zero. Now if $\chi_{1i}, \chi_{2i}, \cdots, \chi_{ri}$ denote the characteristics of the elements in Γ_i corresponding to the complete conjugate sets of Γ, then, since the characteristic of an element of Γ other than the identity is zero, we have

$$\sum_{k=1}^{r} c_k \chi_{ik} = 0. \qquad (i \neq 1)$$

But we have just seen that χ_{ik} is zero when c_k is prime to p and $k > 1$. Therefore, since $c_1 = 1$ and $\chi_{i1} = 1$, and since every χ_{ik} is a sum of roots of unity, the preceding equation implies the relation

$$1 + pN = 0,$$

where N is a sum of a finite number of roots of unity. That this equation is impossible and hence that the corollary is established is implied by the following lemma:

LEMMA. If $\alpha_1 + \alpha_2 + \cdots + \alpha_s = 0$ and $\alpha_1, \alpha_2, \cdots, \alpha_s$ are s roots of unity, then these s roots fall into sets, each containing a prime number of roots such that the sum in such a set is zero and such that if q is the number of roots in any one of these sets and α is a primitive qth root of unity, then these q roots are $\epsilon, \epsilon\alpha, \epsilon\alpha^2, \cdots, \epsilon\alpha^{q-1}$, where ϵ is some root of unity.

For results implying this lemma from the theory of numbers see Kronecker, *Journ. de Math.* (1) **19** (1854): 177–192.

COR. II. A group whose order contains only two distinct prime factors is soluble.

Represent the group as a simply isomorphic regular permutation group Γ of order $g = p^\alpha q^\beta$, where p and q are distinct primes, and let $\Sigma c_i \Gamma_i$ be the symbol for the completely reduced form of Γ. Then

$$p^\alpha q^\beta = 1 + c_2^2 + c_3^2 + \cdots + c_r^2,$$

where r is the number of complete conjugate sets of elements in Γ. Then some c_i $(i > 1)$ is prime to q; if such a c_i is equal to unity, the group is composite (Theorem XIV of § **57**); if such a c_i is greater than unity, then it is of the form p^n, where $n > 0$; then from the preceding corollary it follows that Γ is composite. Therefore, in any case, Γ is composite. Then let H be a proper self-conjugate subgroup of Γ of order greater than unity. Then G/H and H (when not of prime order) are both composite, as we see from what we have already proved and the fact that a prime-power group is composite if its order is not a prime. Then from Theorem XI of § **21** we readily conclude that Γ is soluble, since it is now easy to show by induction that its composition-factors are primes.

59. Transitive Groups in Which Only the Identity Leaves Two Symbols Fixed. As another important application of the theory of group characteristics we have that involved in the proof of the following theorem:

XVII. If G is a transitive permutation group in which the identity is the only element leaving two symbols fixed, then the identity and the $n-1$ elements each of which permutes all the symbols of G constitute a self-conjugate subgroup.

That there are indeed just $n-1$ elements each of which permutes all the symbols of G follows readily from Theorem IV of § **39**.

Represent G as a simply isomorphic regular permutation group Γ, and let $\Sigma c_i\Gamma_i$ be the symbol for the completely reduced form of Γ. Let g be the order of G. Let K be a subgroup of G, of order γ ($\gamma = g/n$), each element of which leaves fixed a given symbol; represent K as a simply isomorphic regular permutation group H, and let $\Sigma\gamma_i H_i$ be the symbol for the completely reduced form of H. Then we have

$$g = c_1^2 + c_2^2 + \cdots + c_r^2, \quad \gamma = g/n = \gamma_1^2 + \gamma_2^2 + \cdots + \gamma_\rho^2, \quad [1]$$

where r is the number of complete conjugate sets of elements in Γ and ρ is the number of complete conjugate sets of elements in H.

If Γ_i is any one of the irreducible representations of G, and if we fix attention on the usual multiple isomorphism of G with Γ_i, then in this isomorphism the subgroup K of G corresponds to a subgroup L_i of Γ_i, while L_i affords a representation of K whose irreducible components are contained among the groups H_j. If H_j occurs c_{ij} times among these irreducible components, then we may represent the reduced form of L_i by means of the equation

$$L_i = c_{i1}H_1 + c_{i2}H_2 + \cdots + c_{i\rho}H_\rho. \quad [2]$$

Since $L_1 = H_1$, it follows that $c_{11} = 1, c_{12} = 0, c_{13} = 0, \cdots, c_{1\rho} = 0$.

Now let $\chi_{1i}, \chi_{2i}, \cdots, \chi_{\gamma i}$ be the characteristics of the elements of L_i corresponding, respectively, to the elements T_1 $(=1)$, $T_2, \cdots, T_\gamma$ in H, and let $\theta_{1j}, \theta_{2j}, \cdots, \theta_{\gamma j}$ be the corresponding characteristics of H_j. Then we have $\chi_{1i} = c_i$ and $\theta_{1j} = \gamma_j$. We also have $\theta_{k1} = 1$. Then from [2] we have the relation

$$\chi_{ki} = c_{i1} + c_{i2}\theta_{k2} + c_{i3}\theta_{k3} + \cdots + c_{i\rho}\theta_{k\rho}. \quad [3]$$

Now consider the sum

$$\begin{aligned} S = {} & \chi_{s1}\chi_{11}\theta_{1t} + \chi_{s1}\overline{\chi}_{21}\theta_{2t} + \cdots + \chi_{s1}\overline{\chi}_{\gamma 1}\theta_{\gamma t} \\ & + \chi_{s2}\overline{\chi}_{12}\theta_{1t} + \chi_{s2}\overline{\chi}_{22}\theta_{2t} + \cdots + \chi_{s2}\overline{\chi}_{\gamma 2}\theta_{\gamma t} \\ & \cdots\cdots\cdots\cdots\cdots\cdots \\ & + \chi_{sr}\overline{\chi}_{1r}\theta_{1t} + \chi_{sr}\overline{\chi}_{2r}\theta_{2t} + \cdots + \chi_{sr}\overline{\chi}_{\gamma r}\theta_{\gamma t}, \end{aligned} \quad [4]$$

where $1 < s \leqq \gamma$. We shall write S in two forms, one obtained on summing by columns and the other on summing by rows.

On summing by columns we have

$$S = \theta_{1t}\sum_{i=1}^{r} \chi_{si}\bar{\chi}_{1i} + \theta_{2t}\sum_{i=1}^{r} \chi_{si}\bar{\chi}_{2i} + \cdots + \theta_{\gamma t}\sum_{i=1}^{r} \chi_{si}\chi_{\gamma i}.$$

This may be simplified by means of equation [G] at the end of § **57** and the fact that $\bar{\chi}_{si} = \chi_{s'i}$. Thus we have

$$S = \gamma\theta_{st}$$

since if h' is the number of elements of K in the conjugate set containing T_s we have $h'g/\gamma$ conjugates of T_s in G.

Now in [4] substitute for the $\bar{\chi}_{ki}$ their values obtained from [3], sum by lines and simplify by aid of Corollaries I and II to Theorem X in § **56** and equation [D] of § **57**; thus we have

$$\begin{aligned} S &= \sum_{i=1}^{r} \chi_{si} \sum_{j=1}^{\gamma} \theta_{jt} \sum_{\alpha=1}^{\rho} c_{i\alpha}\bar{\theta}_{j\alpha} \\ &= \sum_{i=1}^{r} \chi_{si} \sum_{\alpha=1}^{\rho} c_{i\alpha} \sum_{j=1}^{\gamma} \theta_{jt}\bar{\theta}_{j\alpha} \\ &= \gamma \sum_{i=1}^{r} \chi_{si} c_{it} \\ &= \gamma \sum_{i=1}^{r} (c_{i1}c_{it} + \theta_{s2}c_{i2}c_{it} + \cdots + \theta_{s\rho}c_{i\rho}c_{it}). \end{aligned}$$

Equating the two values of S and omitting the common factor γ, we obtain the equation

$$A_1 + A_2\theta_{s2} + \cdots + A_\rho\theta_{s\rho} = 0, \qquad (1 < s \leqq \gamma) \qquad [5]$$

where $\quad A_s = -1 + \sum_{i=1}^{r} c^2_{it}, \quad A_\alpha = \sum_{i=1}^{r} c_{i\alpha}c_{it}$ when $\alpha \neq s$.

This will enable us to establish the relations

$$(A_1 - q) + (A_2 - q\gamma_2)\theta_{s2} + \cdots + (A_\rho - q\gamma_\rho)\theta_{s\rho} = 0, \qquad (1 \leqq s \leqq \gamma) \qquad [6]$$

where $\quad q = \gamma_t(g - \gamma)/\gamma^2.$

When $s > 1$, equations [6] are implied by [5] since the characteristic of T_s in H is zero and is also $1 + \gamma_2\theta_{s2} + \cdots + \gamma_\rho\theta_{s\rho}$, as one sees from the completely reduced form of H. In order to verify [6] when $s = 1$, we observe that the left member of [6] may then be put in the form

$$\begin{aligned}&(A_1 - q) + \gamma_2(A_2 - q\gamma_2) + \cdots + \gamma_\rho(A_\rho - q\gamma_\rho)\\ &\quad = A_1 + \gamma_2 A_2 + \cdots + \gamma_\rho A_\rho - q(1 + \gamma_2^2 + \cdots + \gamma_\rho^2)\\ &\quad = \sum_{i=1}^{r} c_{it}c_i - \gamma_t g/\gamma,\end{aligned}$$

as one sees by inserting the values of q and the A's, employing the second relation in [1] and the equation

$$c_{i1} + \gamma_2 c_{i2} + \cdots + \gamma_\rho c_{i\rho} = c_i$$

obtained from [2] by considering the characteristic of the identity. In order to establish [6] for $s = 1$, it is therefore necessary and sufficient to show that

$$\sum_{i=1}^{r} c_{it}c_i = \gamma_t g/\gamma. \qquad [7]$$

Now consider the subgroup L of Γ which corresponds to the subgroup K of G in the simple isomorphism between G and Γ. In L the group K appears g/γ $(= n)$ times, once for each subgroup of G of order γ which leaves fixed a single letter. Hence H_t occurs just $\gamma_t g/\gamma$ times in the completely reduced form of L. But H_t occurs here just $\Sigma c_{it}c_i$ times, as one sees by aid of [2] and the fact that Γ_i occurs just c_i times in the completely reduced form of Γ. Therefore the last equation is established. This completes the verification of equation [6] for all values of s.

From the corollary to Theorem XIII in § **57** it follows that [6] implies the relations

$$A_i - q\gamma_i = 0. \qquad (i = 1, 2, \cdots, \rho) \qquad [8]$$

By taking $i = 1, 2$ and $t = 1, 2$ we obtain the relations

$$c_{21}^2 + c_{31}^2 + \cdots + c_{r1}^2 = (g - \gamma)/\gamma^2, \qquad [9_1]$$

$$c_{21}c_{22} + c_{31}c_{32} + \cdots + c_{r1}c_{r2} = \gamma_2(g - \gamma)/\gamma^2, \qquad [9_2]$$

$$c_{22}^2 + c_{32}^2 + \cdots + c_{r2}^2 = \gamma_2^2(g - \gamma)/\gamma^2 + 1. \qquad [9_3]$$

Thence we have

$$(c_{22} - \gamma_2 c_{21})^2 + (c_{32} - \gamma_2 c_{31})^2 + \cdots + (c_{r2} - \gamma_2 c_{r1})^2 = 1.$$

This equation can be satisfied only when one of the terms in the first member is unity and the others are all zero (since each term is obviously a non-negative integer). We may suppose the notation so chosen that the first term is unity; then we have

$$c_{22} = \gamma_2 c_{21} \pm 1, \quad c_{32} = \gamma_2 c_{31}, \quad \cdots, \quad c_{r2} = \gamma_2 c_{r1}.$$

By substituting these values in [9_2] and combining the resulting equation with [9_1], we find that $c_{21} = 0$.

From this result and equation [3] we see that

$$\chi_{k2} = c_{22}\theta_{k2} + c_{23}\theta_{k3} + \cdots + c_{2\rho}\theta_{k\rho}. \qquad [10]$$

Now let σ denote the sum of the n characteristics of elements in Γ_2 corresponding to the identity and the $n-1$ elements of G each of which displaces all the n symbols on which G operates. Now no two different subgroups of G of order γ, each omitting one of the letters of G, can have any element in common except the identity. Then, by aid of Corollary I to Theorem VIII in § **56**, we have

$$\begin{aligned} 0 &= \sigma + n\sum_{k=2}^{\gamma}\chi_{k2} = \sigma + n(-c_2 + \sum_{k=1}^{\gamma}\chi_{k2}) \\ &= \sigma + n(-c_2 + c_{22}\sum_{k=1}^{\gamma}\theta_{k2} + \cdots + c_{2\rho}\sum_{k=1}^{\gamma}\theta_{k\rho}) \quad \text{(by [10])} \\ &= \sigma - nc_2, \end{aligned}$$

since the sums denoted by Σ in the second preceding line are all zero, owing to the fact that H is a regular permutation group. Therefore $\sigma = nc_2$, while at the same time σ is a sum of n characteristics each of which is itself a sum of c_2 roots of unity. Hence each of these roots of unity must be unity itself and therefore each of the named characteristics is c_2.

From this it follows that the corresponding transformations of Γ_2 must be the identity in each case, as one may see by aid of Theorem II in § **52**. Hence, in the multiple isomorphism of G with Γ_2, every element of G which does not belong to K or its conjugates corresponds to the identity in Γ_2. Therefore the $n-1$ elements each of which permutes all the symbols of G generate a self-conjugate subgroup G_1 of G whose order is less than g since $c_{21} = 0$. If the order of this group G_1 is not

n, apply the foregoing process to G_1 itself and thus obtain a self-conjugate proper subgroup G_2 of G_1. Continuing this process we must finally come to a group of order n which contains the $n-1$ elements of G, each of which displaces all the symbols of G. It is then obvious that this subgroup is self-conjugate. Thence we conclude to the theorem as stated.

60. Simply Transitive Groups of Prime Degree. We shall now prove the following theorem of Burnside, using a method due to I. Schur *:

> XVIII. A simply transitive group of prime degree p is contained as a proper subgroup in the doubly transitive group of degree p and order $p(p-1)$, namely, in the group
> $$\{(a_0a_1 \cdots a_{p-1}), \quad (a_1a_ta_{t^2} \cdots)\},$$
> where t is a primitive root modulo p and the subscripts in the second generator are to be reduced modulo p to numbers of the set $0, 1, \cdots, p-1$. (Compare § **40**.)

From this theorem it follows at once that a group of prime degree p containing more than one Sylow subgroup of order p is necessarily multiply transitive.

The proof is divided into four parts.

1. Let Γ be a permutation group on the n symbols $0, 1, \cdots, n-1$. The bilinear form

$$F = \sum_{i,j=0}^{n-1} a_{ij}x_iy_j$$

is said to be invariant under Γ if every permutation A in Γ transforms F into itself in case the subscripts on the x's and the y's undergo simultaneously the permutation A. If A replaces the subscripts i, j by i', j', then F is invariant under A if and only if $a_{ij} = a_{i'j'}$ for every pair i, j of subscripts. From this it

* *Jahresber. d. Deut. Math.-Ver.* **17** (1908): 171–176.

follows readily that a necessary and sufficient condition that F shall be invariant under a doubly transitive group Γ is that

$$a_{11} = a_{22} = \cdots = a_{nn},$$
$$a_{12} = a_{13} = \cdots = a_{1n} = a_{21} = a_{23} = \cdots = a_{n-1,\, n};$$

and these conditions are equivalent to the condition that F shall be the form $aE + bJ$, where a and b are constants and

$$E = \sum_{i=0}^{n-1} x_i y_i, \qquad J = \sum_{i,\, j=0}^{n-1} x_i y_j.$$

On the other hand, a simply transitive group Γ admits other invariants F, since the ordered pairs of subscripts are not permuted transitively by it.

If the two forms

$$F = \sum_{i,\, j=0}^{n-1} a_{ij} x_i y_j, \qquad G = \sum_{i,\, j=0}^{n-1} b_{ij} x_i y_j$$

are invariant under Γ, so is the form K,

$$K = \sum_{i,\, j=0}^{n-1} c_{ij} x_i y_j, \qquad \left(c_{ij} = \sum_{k=0}^{n-1} a_{ik} b_{kj}\right)$$

as one may readily verify. We denote K by the symbolic product FG. The product of λ factors each equal to F is denoted by F^{λ}. We also write F^0 for E. If

$$\phi(x) = a_0 + a_1 x + a_2 x^2 + \cdots + a_m x^m,$$

we denote by $\phi(F)$ the form

$$\phi(F) = a_0 F^0 + a_1 F + a_2 F^2 + \cdots + a_m F^m.$$

2. Now let n be the prime number p and let Γ be a transitive group. We assume, as we may without loss of generality, that Γ contains the permutation P, where

$$P = (0, 1, \cdots, p-1).$$

If F is to be invariant under Γ, then it must be invariant under P. A necessary and sufficient condition that F shall be invariant under P is that it shall have the form

$$F = a_0 \sum_{i=0}^{p-1} x_i y_i + a_1 \sum_{i=0}^{p-1} x_i y_{i+1} + a_2 \sum_{i=0}^{p-1} x_i y_{i+2} + \cdots + a_{p-1} \sum_{i=0}^{p-1} x_i y_{i+p-1},$$

the subscripts being reduced modulo p to numbers of the set 0, 1, $\cdots$, $p-1$. If we denote the second summation in this equation by R, then the $(\lambda+1)$th summation is R^λ, while $R^p = E$, as one may easily verify. Then the bilinear invariant F may be written in the form

$$F = \phi(R) \equiv a_0 E + a_1 R + a_2 R^2 + \cdots + a_{p-1} R^{p-1}.$$

The condition that F shall be invariant under the remaining permutations of Γ may be expressed by means of the fact that certain of the coefficients a_i are equal. One may therefore limit attention to those invariants F in which the coefficients a_i are rational numbers; and this we do.

3. Let us now suppose that the transitive group Γ is not doubly transitive. Then Γ admits at least one invariant $\phi(R)$ which is not of the form $aE + bJ$. In this invariant the coefficients $a_1, a_2, \cdots, a_{p-1}$ are not all equal, as one sees from the fact that J may be written in the form

$$J = E + R + R^2 + \cdots + R^{p-1}.$$

From this it follows that if ρ is a primitive pth root of unity, then the algebraic number $\phi(\rho)$ is not a rational number. Then this number $\phi(\rho)$ must satisfy an irreducible equation of degree e $(e > 1)$, where e is a factor of $p-1$. We write $p-1 = ef$. Then from the theory of roots of unity (see Weber's *Algebra*, Vol. I, 2d ed., § 175) it follows that a polynomial $\psi(x)$ exists such that

$$\psi[\phi(\rho)] = \rho + \rho^\gamma + \rho^{\gamma^2} + \cdots + \rho^{\gamma^{f-1}},$$

where γ belongs modulo p to the exponent f. This is equivalent to the equation

$$x + x^\gamma + x^{\gamma^2} + \cdots + x^{\gamma^{f-1}}$$
$$= \psi[\phi(x)] + \chi(x)\{x^0 + x + x^2 + \cdots + x^{p-1}\},$$

where $\chi(x)$ is a suitable polynomial in x. Replacing x by the bilinear form R, we have still a true equation. Hence, since $R^\lambda J = J$ (as is readily verified), we have

$$\chi(R)\{R^0 + R + \cdots + R^{p-1}\} = \chi(R) \cdot J = cJ,$$

where c is the sum of the coefficients of $\chi(R)$.

Since $\psi[\phi(R)] = \psi(F)$ and both $\phi(R)$ and cJ are invariants of Γ, it follows that H is an invariant of Γ, where

$$H = R + R^{\gamma} + R^{\gamma^2} + \cdots + R^{\gamma^{f-1}} = \psi(F) + cJ.$$

4. We next investigate what permutations A,

$$A = \begin{pmatrix} 0 & 1 & \cdots & p-1 \\ \alpha_0 & \alpha_1 & \cdots & \alpha_{p-1} \end{pmatrix},$$

can leave the bilinear form H invariant. Now H may be written in the form

$$H = \sum_{i=0}^{p-1} x_i(y_{i+1} + y_{i+\gamma} + y_{i+\gamma^2} + \cdots + y_{i+\gamma^{f-1}})$$

$$= \sum_{i=0}^{p-1} x_{\alpha_i}(y_{\alpha_i+1} + y_{\alpha_i+\gamma} + y_{\alpha_i+\gamma^2} + \cdots + y_{\alpha_i+\gamma^{f-1}}).$$

Under the permutation A the form H is to be transformed into itself. Applying this permutation to the first form of H and comparing the result with the second form, we see that for each value of i the numbers

$$\alpha_{i+1}, \quad \alpha_{i+\gamma}, \quad \alpha_{i+\gamma^2}, \quad \cdots, \quad \alpha_{i+\gamma^{f-1}},$$

taken modulo p, must be in some order the numbers

$$\alpha_i + 1, \quad \alpha_i + \gamma, \quad \alpha_i + \gamma^2, \quad \cdots, \quad \alpha_i + \gamma^{f-1}.$$

Now let $g(x)$,

$$g(x) = c_0 + c_1 x + \cdots + c_k x^k,$$

be a polynomial in x with integral coefficients and of degree k $(k < p)$ such that the congruences

$$g(i) \equiv \alpha_i \bmod p \qquad (i = 0, 1, \cdots, p-1)$$

are satisfied; such a function, for instance, is

$$g(x) = -\sum_{i=0}^{p-1} \alpha_i \frac{x(x-1)(x-2)\cdots(x-p+1)}{x-i}.$$

Then from the named properties of the numbers α_i it follows that for each exponent r we have

$$\sum_{\mu=0}^{f-1} \{g(i) + \gamma^{\mu}\}^r \equiv \sum_{\mu=0}^{f-1} \{g(i+\gamma^{\mu})\}^r \bmod p. \qquad [1]$$

Since $\gamma^{\mu f} \equiv 1 \bmod p$, it follows that

$$x^f - 1 \equiv (x-1)(x-\gamma)(x-\gamma^2)\cdots(x-\gamma^{f-1}) \bmod p.$$

Then if
$$s_\lambda = 1 + \gamma^\lambda + \gamma^{2\lambda} + \cdots + \gamma^{(f-1)\lambda}$$

it follows that s_λ is congruent to f or 0 modulo p according as λ is or is not divisible by f. Therefore if $0 < r < f$, we have

$$\sum_{\mu=0}^{f-1} \{g(i) + \gamma^\mu\}^r = \sum_{\lambda=0}^{r} \binom{r}{\lambda} s_\lambda \{g(i)\}^{r-\lambda} \equiv f \cdot \{g(i)\}^r \bmod p. \quad [2]$$

Writing $h(x)$ for $\{g(x)\}^r$ and employing Taylor's formula

$$h(x+y) = h(x) + y\frac{h'(x)}{1!} + y^2\frac{h''(x)}{2!} + \cdots$$

(the functions $h^{(\lambda)}(x)/\lambda!$ being polynomials with integral coefficients), we have

$$\sum_{\mu=0}^{f-1} h(i+\gamma^\mu) = fh(i) + s_1\frac{h'(i)}{1!} + s_2\frac{h''(i)}{2!} + \cdots$$
$$\equiv f \cdot \{h(i) + \frac{h^{(f)}(i)}{f!} + \frac{h^{(2f)}(i)}{(2f)!} + \cdots\} \bmod p.$$

Then from [1] and [2] we have

$$\frac{h^{(f)}(i)}{f!} + \frac{h^{(2f)}(i)}{(2f)!} + \cdots \equiv 0 \bmod p. \qquad (i = 0, 1, \cdots, p-1)$$

Then the function

$$\frac{h^{(f)}(x)}{f!} + \frac{h^{(2f)}(x)}{(2f)!} + \cdots$$

is divisible modulo p by $x^p - x$. If $kr < p$ and if this function does not vanish identically, then its degree is $kr - f$. Hence a number $kr - f$, where r belongs to the set $1, 2, \cdots, f-1$, is either negative or greater than $p - 1 - f$; in particular, if $f > 1$ it follows that $k - f$ is negative, since $k < p$.

We shall now show that $k = 1$. If $f = 1$, we have $\alpha_{i+1} \equiv \alpha_i + 1$ modulo p, whence $\alpha_i \equiv \alpha_0 + i \bmod p$; therefore $k = 1$. Then suppose $f > 1$. Let s be the least integer such that $ks \geqq f$. Then, if $k > 1$, we have $s < f$, while $ks > p - 1$ and $k < f$ by a result at the end of the preceding paragraph. Then $k(s-1) > p - 1 - k > p - 1 - f$. But $p - 1 = ef$ and

$e > 1$. Hence $p - 1 \geqq 2f$, whence $p - 1 - f \geqq f$. Therefore $k(s-1) > f$, contrary to the hypothesis on s. Since this contradiction is reached on supposing $k > 1$, it follows that $k = 1$.

Then $g(x)$ is of degree 1. Hence A is induced by a linear substitution modulo p. Therefore Γ is contained in the metacyclic group. This result implies the theorem as stated.

EXERCISES

1. Construct the p irreducible nonequivalent representations of a group of prime order p.

2. Construct the p^3 irreducible nonequivalent representations of an Abelian group of prime-power order p^3 and type (2, 1).

3. By means of the theory of group characteristics prove that a group of order p^2, where p is a prime, is an Abelian group.

4. Show that an irreducible representation of a group of order p^3 or p^4, where p is a prime, involves one variable or p variables.

5. By means of the theory of group characteristics prove that a group of prime-power order p^m $(m > 1)$ is composite.

6. Determine all possible groups G each of which has just two or three or four complete conjugate sets of elements.

7. Determine all possible groups G each of which has just five complete conjugate sets of elements.

8. Prove that the order of a transitive group of odd prime degree p is of the form $(kp + 1)p\mu$, where $kp + 1$ is the number of Sylow subgroups of order p and μ is some factor of $p - 1$; prove that k is zero or an odd number.

9. Show that the number of Sylow subgroups of order p in a transitive group G of odd prime degree p is completely determined by the order g of G.

10. Show that there is no group of degree 31 which is 3-fold but not 4-fold transitive.

11. If G is a transitive group of degree 13 or 61 not containing the alternating group of its degree, show that G is not triply transitive.

12. If G is a finite Abelian group of linear homogeneous transformations, show that a linear homogeneous transformation S exists such that the elements of $S^{-1}GS$ are all multiplications.

13. Let G be a group of finite order and let the commutator subgroup of G be of index α; show that there are just α nonequivalent representations of G each in a single variable.

14. Let H be a self-conjugate subgroup of a finite group G, and let ρ be the number of complete conjugate sets of elements in G/H. Show that there are at least ρ nonequivalent irreducible representations of G in each of which the identity corresponds to every element in H.

15. Prove that the group $\{s, t\}$ whose sole defining conditions are

$$s^9 = t^7 = t^{-2}s^{-1}ts = 1$$

has just 15 complete conjugate sets of elements and that its irreducible representations consist of 9 on a single variable and 6 on 3 variables.

MISCELLANEOUS EXERCISES

1. The number of abstract finite groups each having just a given number r of complete conjugate sets of elements is finite.

2. Let p and q be different primes such that p is not a factor of $q^2 - 1$. Let s and t be elements subject to the sole defining relations

$$s^{q^2} = t^p = 1, \quad t^{-1}s^{-1}ts = t.$$

Show that $\{s, t\}$ is a group of order pq^2 having just q^2 representations in a single variable. If $p < q^2$, show that the other irreducible representations are $p - 1$ in number and that each of them is on q variables. Show that the number of complete conjugate sets of elements is $q^2 + p - 1$.

3. The only substitution of zero determinant which is permutable with every element of an irreducible group of linear homogeneous transformations on the same variables is the substitution which replaces each variable by zero.

4. Let $x_1, x_2, \cdots, x_n$ be the variables operated on by an irreducible group G of linear homogeneous transformations. Show that $kx_1, kx_2, \cdots, kx_n$, where k is an arbitrary constant different from zero, are the only linear functions of the x's which, for every element of G, undergo the same linear transformation as the x's undergo in that element.

5. Show how to form the most general group of linear homogeneous transformations on a given set of variables each of whose elements is permutable with every element of a given finite group G of linear homogeneous transformations on the same variables.

6. Let Γ_i have the meaning assigned to it in Theorem XIII of § **57**. Show that Γ_i and $\overline{\Gamma}_i$ are equivalent representations of Γ when and only when each group characteristic for Γ_i is real.

7. Employing the notation of the latter part of § **57**, show that

$$g_{jik} = g_{ijk} = g_{i'kj} = g_{j'ki} = g_{i'j'k'} = g_{ik'j'} = g_{jk'i'}.$$

Show also that

$$\sum_{k=1}^{r} g_{ijk} g_{kst}$$

is unaltered by any permutation of the symbols i, j, s.

8. Employing the notation of the latter part of § **57**, show that

$$\sum_{i,j,k} g^2{}_{ijk} = g \sum_{p} \frac{1}{h_p}.$$

9. Let s be an element of order m in a group G, and let χ_s be the characteristic of s in an irreducible representation of G. Then χ_s may be written in the form

$$\chi_s = \omega^{a_1} + \omega^{a_2} + \cdots + \omega^{a_t}$$

where ω is a primitive mth root of unity and the a's are integers. The characteristic χ_{s^μ} of s^μ in the same representation is then

$$\chi_{s^\mu} = \omega^{\mu a_1} + \omega^{\mu a_2} + \cdots + \omega^{\mu a_t}.$$

If s and s^μ are conjugate under G, then these characteristics must be equal, so that in each irreducible representation of G it is true that χ_s is unchanged when ω^μ is put for ω. Show, conversely, that if this last condition is satisfied, then s and s^μ are conjugate elements of G.

10. In a group of odd order no element other than the identity is conjugate to its inverse.

11. In a group of odd order some of the characteristics of every conjugate set must be imaginary.

12. In a group of odd order the number of conjugate sets of elements is odd.

13. For a group of odd order no irreducible representation, other than the identical one, is equivalent to its conjugate imaginary.

14. A group of linear homogeneous transformations of odd order with real coefficients is necessarily reducible.

15. If G is a group of odd order g, and r is the number of complete sets of conjugate elements in G, then $g \equiv r \bmod 16$.

CHAPTER IX

Galois Fields

61. Introduction. There exist certain remarkable doubly transitive groups of prime-power degree p^n by means of whose properties many interesting results in the theory of finite groups may be obtained. They are contained as subgroups in the holomorph of the Abelian group of order p^n and type $(1, 1, \cdots, 1)$. Instead of undertaking a direct proof of their existence, based on this fact, it seems more convenient to develop first the auxiliary theory of finite fields (defined in the next section) and then to employ the tool afforded by this theory as a means of facilitating the proof of the existence of these groups and of deriving their properties. Consequently this chapter is devoted to the theory of these finite fields and to some of its immediate applications to the theory of finite groups.

62. Finite Fields. Let $u_0, u_1, u_2, \cdots, u_{s-1}$ be a set of s $(s > 1)$ distinct symbols or *marks* or elements which may be combined by addition in accordance with the formal laws

$$u_i + u_j = u_j + u_i; \quad u_i + (u_j + u_k) = (u_i + u_j) + u_k.$$

Let the sum of any two of these marks be a mark of the set. Let the set be such that for every pair u_i and u_k of the marks there exists a single mark u_j such that $u_i + u_j = u_k$; then u_j is said to be determined by subtraction, and we write $u_j = u_k - u_i$. We call u_j the difference of u_k and u_i. The set then contains every difference $u_i - u_i$; such a difference has the additive property of zero, since $u_j + (u_i - u_i) = u_j$. From the last equation we have $u_i - u_i = u_j - u_j$. Hence all the differences $u_i - u_i$ are equal; we shall suppose that the notation is so chosen that $u_i - u_i = u_0$; then u_0 is the (unique) mark having the additive property of zero, since the relation $u_i + u' = u_i$ requires that $u' = u_i - u_i = u_0$. Two marks are said to be equal if their difference is u_0; otherwise they are said to be distinct. It is obvious that the s marks form an Abelian group of order s, the law of combination in the group being that of addition as here defined. The identity in this group is u_0. This group is called the *additive* group of the field (presently to be defined).

Let us next suppose that the marks $u_0, u_1, \cdots, u_{s-1}$ may be combined by multiplication in accordance with the formal laws

$$u_i u_j = u_j u_i, \quad u_i(u_j u_k) = (u_i u_j) u_k, \quad u_i(u_j \pm u_k) = u_i u_j \pm u_i u_k.$$

Let the product of any two marks of the set be itself a mark of the set. From the relations

$$u_0 u_i = u_i u_0 = u_i(u_j - u_j) = u_i u_j - u_i u_j = u_0$$

it follows that u_0 has the multiplicative properties of zero. Let us suppose that the marks u have the further property that if any two marks u_i and u_k are given such that $u_i \neq u_0$, then there exists one and just one mark u_j of the set such that $u_i u_j = u_k$. We say that u_j is determined by division, $u_j = u_k/u_i$; and we call u_j the quotient of u_k by u_i. The set contains every quotient u_i/u_i where $u_i \neq u_0$; such a quotient has the multiplicative properties of unity, since $u_j u_i/u_i = u_j$. From this equation we see also that $u_i/u_i = u_j/u_j$ if $u_i \neq u_0$ and $u_j \neq u_0$. If $\epsilon u_i = u_i$ or $u_i \epsilon = u_i$ and $u_i \neq u_0$, we have $\epsilon = u_i/u_i$, so that there is only one mark in the set having the multiplicative properties of unity. We suppose that the notation is chosen so that this mark is u_1. It is evident that the $s - 1$ marks $u_1, u_2, \cdots, u_{s-1}$ form an Abelian group in which the law of combination is that of multiplication as here defined. The identity in this group is u_1. This group is called the *multiplicative* group of the field (presently to be defined).

A set of s distinct marks $u_0, u_1, u_2, \cdots, u_{s-1}$ satisfying the conditions named in the two preceding paragraphs is said to form a *finite field* of *order* s. A finite field is characterized by the property that the rational operations of algebra may be performed upon the marks in the field and that they lead in every case to marks of the field. We may therefore take over, without further definition, many terms of algebra and the corresponding notations and employ them for finite fields.

We may observe that the conditions named imply that a product of two factors is u_0 when and only when one of the factors is u_0. For $u_iu_0 = u_0$, as we have seen; moreover, if $u_i \neq u_0$, $u_k \neq u_0$, and $u_iu_k = u_0$, then we have

$$u_iu_j = u_iu_j + u_0 = u_iu_j + u_iu_k = u_i(u_j + u_k)$$

so that u_iu_j gives rise to two distinct quotients, u_j and $u_j + u_k$, when divided by u_i, contrary to the hypothesis that division by a nonzero element is unique.

We exhibit an example of a finite field. Let p be a prime number and let us write $u_0 = 0$, $u_1 = 1$, $u_2 = 2$, $\cdots$, $u_{p-1} = p - 1$. Let addition and multiplication of these marks be the ordinary addition and multiplication of the numbers to which they are equal followed by a reduction modulo p to a number of the set. It is easy to see that the marks so defined constitute a finite field of order p. We may easily verify the property of division, the divisor being different from u_0, by observing that the congruence

$$ax \equiv b \bmod p \quad (a \not\equiv 0 \bmod p)$$

has always a unique solution x when a and b are given.

In the general case the marks u_0 and u_1 have the properties of zero and unity, respectively, as we have already seen. Every sum of the form $u_1 + u_1 + \cdots + u_1$ is a mark of the field. The marks defined in this way are called the *integral* marks of the field. Consider the infinite sequence of symbols

$$u_{(1)} = u_1,\ u_{(2)} = u_1 + u_1,\ u_{(3)} = u_1 + u_1 + u_1,\ \cdots.$$

Since there is only a finite number of marks in the field, two of these symbols must be equal, say $u_{(r)} = u_{(s)}$ $(r > s)$. Then $u_0 = u_{(r)} - u_{(s)} = u_{(r-s)}$. Hence the named sequence contains the zero mark u_0. Let p be the least integer such that $u_{(p)} = u_0$. Then $u_{(0)}$ $(\equiv u_0)$, $u_{(1)}$, $u_{(2)}$, $\cdots$, $u_{(p-1)}$ are all distinct, while $u_{(\alpha)} = u_{(\beta)}$ if $\alpha \equiv \beta \bmod p$. Hence there are just p integral marks in the field. We suppose that the notation is so chosen that

$u_i = u_{(i)}$ $(i = 0, 1, \cdots, p-1)$, so that the integral marks of the field are $u_0, u_1, \cdots, u_{p-1}$. When there is no danger of ambiguity, we shall write $0, 1, \cdots, p-1$ for these marks in the order given. These integral marks obviously combine by ordinary addition and multiplication with a reduction modulo p. Moreover, if p is a prime, they form a field of order p, as we have already seen.

I. The number p of integral marks in the field is a prime number.

For if $p = p_1 p_2$ $(p > p_1)$, we have $u_{p_1} \neq u_0$, while $u_{p_1} u_{(p_2)} = u_{(p_1 p_2)} = u_{(p)} = u_0$; whence it follows that $u_{(p_2)} = u_0$ so that p_2 must be a multiple of p, and hence equal to p since $p_2 \leqq p$. Hence $p_1 = 1$. Therefore the only factors of p are 1 and p.

II. The number s of marks in the field is a power of the prime p, say $s = p^n$.

Let v_1 be any mark of the field different from u_0. Then

$$\gamma_1 v_1 \qquad (\gamma_1 = 0, 1, 2, \cdots, p-1)$$

give p distinct marks of the field. If $s > p$ there is a mark v_2 in the field and not in the foregoing set. Then

$$\gamma_1 v_1 + \gamma_2 v_2 \qquad (\gamma_1, \gamma_2 = 0, 1, \cdots, p-1)$$

give p^2 distinct marks of the field. If $s > p^2$ there is a mark v_3 in the field and not in the last-named set. Then

$$\gamma_1 v_1 + \gamma_2 v_2 + \gamma_3 v_3 \qquad (\gamma_1, \gamma_2, \gamma_3 = 0, 1, \cdots, p-1)$$

give p^3 distinct marks of the field. We may continue similarly till all the marks are exhibited in the form

$$\gamma_1 v_1 + \gamma_2 v_2 + \cdots + \gamma_n v_n, \ (\gamma_i = 0, 1, 2, \cdots, p-1;\ i = 1, 2, \cdots, n)$$

and these give p^n marks, so that $s = p^n$.

In § **64** we shall show that a finite field exists of every order p^n where p is a prime and n is a positive integer.

III. The additive group of a field of order p^n is an Abelian group of type $(1, 1, \cdots, 1)$.

We have seen that this group is Abelian. Its order s is p^n by Theorem II. It remains to be observed that each element (besides the identity) in the group is of order p; and this is obvious, since $u_i + u_i + \cdots + u_i = u_1 u_i + u_1 u_i + \cdots + u_1 u_i = u_i(u_1 + u_1 + \cdots + u_1)$ and this is u_0 when the number of terms in the parenthesis is p.

A rational integral function in any number of variables $x_1, x_2, \cdots, x_n$ is said to *belong to the field* if its coefficients are marks of the field. It is *irreducible in the field* if it is not identically the product of two functions belonging to the field, each involving one or more of the variables x_i. An equation between functions which belong to the field is itself said to belong to the field. Let u be any mark of the field and form the $n+1$ marks

$$u^0, u^1, u^2, \cdots, u^n.$$

These, as we have seen, may be expressed in the form

$$u^i = c_{i1}v_1 + c_{i2}v_2 + \cdots + c_{in}v_n, \qquad (i = 0, 1, \cdots, n)$$

where $v_1, v_2, \cdots, v_n$ are the marks denoted by these symbols in the proof of Theorem II and where the c_{ij} are integral marks of the field. Hence integral marks $\rho_0, \rho_1, \cdots, \rho_n$, not all zero, exist such that

$$\rho_0 u^0 + \rho_1 u^1 + \rho_2 u^2 + \cdots + \rho_n u^n = 0,$$

as one sees by eliminating $v_1, v_2, \cdots, v_n$ from the foregoing $n+1$ equations. Therefore we have the following theorem:

IV. Any mark u of a finite field of order p^n satisfies an equation of degree $k \leqq n$,

$$c_k x^k + c_{k-1}x^{k-1} + \cdots + c_1 x + c_0 = 0, \qquad (c_k \neq 0)$$

where $c_0, c_1, \cdots, c_k$ are integral marks of the field.

If k is taken to be the lowest possible degree for such an equation satisfied by a given mark u, then the equation is evidently irreducible in the sense that the first member cannot be separated into factors of positive degrees and with coefficients which are integral marks of the field. The term *irreducible equation*, when used without qualification, will have the meaning here assigned to it.

As we have already seen, the marks $u_1, u_2, \cdots, u_{s-1}$ form an Abelian group if the law of combination of symbols is that of multiplication of the marks of the field. The order of this group is $s-1=p^n-1$. The order of an element u of this group is therefore a factor of p^n-1; this order is called the *order* of the mark u in the field. Every mark u of the field, different from u_0, satisfies the equation

$$x^{p^n-1}=1,$$

as one sees from the properties of the multiplicative group of the field. Hence,

V. Every mark of a field of order p^n satisfies the equation

$$x^{p^n}-x=0;$$

and we have

$$x^{p^n}-x=\prod_{i=0}^{p^n-1}(x-u_i).$$

As in algebra, one may prove the following theorem:

VI. If an equation of degree k (and not an identity) belongs to the field it has at most k roots in the field.

VII. If d is a divisor of p^n-1, the equation

$$x^d-1=0$$

has exactly d roots in a field of order p^n.

For we have an identity of the form

$$x^{p^n-1}-1=(x^d-1)(x^{(\mu-1)d}+x^{(\mu-2)d}+\cdots+x^d+1),$$

where $\mu=(p^n-1)/d$; the last factor is zero for at most $(\mu-1)d$ marks of the field while the first member is zero for every nonzero mark of the field; whence it follows that x^d-1 is zero for d marks of the field.

Let us write

$$p^n-1=p_1^{\alpha_1}p_2^{\alpha_2}\cdots p_k^{\alpha_k},$$

where $p_1, p_2, \cdots, p_k$ are the distinct prime factors of p^n-1. Then the equations

$$x^{p_i^{\alpha_i}}-1=0 \quad\text{and}\quad x^{p_i^{\alpha_i-1}}-1=0$$

have $p_i^{\alpha_i}$ and $p_i^{\alpha_i-1}$ as roots respectively. Hence there are

$$p_i^{\alpha_i} - p_i^{\alpha_i-1}, \quad \text{or} \quad p_i^{\alpha_i}\left(1-\frac{1}{p_i}\right),$$

marks of the field having the order $p_i^{\alpha_i}$. Let ω_i be a mark having the order $p_i^{\alpha_i}$ $(i=1, 2, \cdots, k)$. Then $\omega_1\omega_2\cdots\omega_k$ has for its order $p_1^{\alpha_1}p_2^{\alpha_2}\cdots p_k^{\alpha_k}$, or p^n-1. A mark of the field having p^n-1 for its order is called a *primitive* mark of the field.

If ω is a primitive mark of the field, then the marks

$$\omega, \omega^2, \omega^3, \cdots, \omega^{p^n-1}$$

are all distinct. They are therefore in some order the marks $u_1, u_2, \cdots, u_{s-1}$.

VIII. All the marks of the field except the mark u_0 are powers of any given primitive mark of the field. Hence the multiplicative group of the field is cyclic.

Let ω be any primitive mark in a field of order p^n. Then (Theorem IV) it satisfies an equation of the form

$$c_kx^k + c_{k-1}x^{k-1} + \cdots + c_1x + c_0 = 0, \qquad (k \leqq n;\ c_k \neq 0)$$

where $c_0, c_1, \cdots, c_k$ are integral marks of the field. Then ω^k, and hence every power of ω, can be expressed in the form

$$\gamma_{k-1}\omega^{k-1} + \cdots + \gamma_1\omega + \gamma_0,$$

where $\gamma_0, \gamma_1, \cdots, \gamma_{k-1}$ are integral marks of the field not all equal to zero, as one sees readily by repeated multiplication by ω and reduction of the degree by means of the relation of degree k satisfied by ω. The number of expressions of the named form is p^k-1 and the number of distinct powers of ω is p^n-1; hence, since $k \leqq n$, we see that $k=n$. From this result and the remark following Theorem IV we have the following theorem:

IX. A primitive mark of a finite field of order p^n satisfies an irreducible equation of the form

$$x^n + c_1x^{n-1} + \cdots + c_n = 0,$$

where $c_1, c_2, \cdots, c_n$ are integral marks of the field.

COR. I. A primitive mark satisfies no equation of degree less than n the coefficients of which are integral marks of the field.

COR. II. The quotient

$$\frac{x^{p^n} - x}{x^n + c_1 x^{n-1} + \cdots + c_n}$$

can be expressed as a polynomial in x with coefficients which are integral marks of the field.

In order to establish this corollary let us apply to the functions in the numerator and the denominator of the fraction Euclid's process for finding the greatest common divisor. Every quotient and every remainder obtained by this process will be a polynomial in x with coefficients which are integral marks of the field. Hence the greatest common divisor is either a constant or a polynomial with integral coefficients. But it cannot be a constant, since the two given functions have the common factor $x - \omega$. Since it is a polynomial with integral coefficients, it must be the denominator polynomial itself, owing to the fact that that polynomial is irreducible. The named quotient can then be expressed in the form described in the theorem.

COR. III. The equation in the theorem has n distinct roots in the field.

This follows at once from Corollary II and the fact that the equation $x^{p^n} - x = 0$ has p^n distinct roots in the field.

Let ρ be any root of the equation in Theorem IX. Then every power of ρ can be expressed in the form

$$\gamma_{n-1}\rho^{n-1} + \cdots + \gamma_1\rho + \gamma_0,$$

where $\gamma_0, \gamma_1, \cdots, \gamma_{n-1}$ are integral marks of the field, the method being that employed in the proof of Theorem IX. Likewise every power of ω can similarly be expressed in the form

$$\gamma_{n-1}\omega^{n-1} + \cdots + \gamma_1\omega + \gamma_0.$$

The ordered set of coefficients in the expression for ρ^t is the same as that in the expression for ω^t, as is evident from the way in which the expressions are formed. But the p^n-1 ordered sets of coefficients γ corresponding to the powers ω, $\omega^2, \cdots, \omega^{p^n-1}$ are distinct, since ω is a primitive mark. Hence the p^n-1 ordered sets of coefficients γ corresponding to the powers $\rho, \rho^2, \cdots, \rho^{p^n-1}$ are distinct. Therefore if any two of these powers of ρ are equal, the mark ρ satisfies an equation (not an identity) of degree at most as great as $n-1$ and with integral coefficients. But this is impossible, since ρ satisfies an irreducible equation of degree n with integral coefficients and therefore satisfies no such equation of degree lower than n, as may be shown by means of Euclid's algorithm for finding the greatest common divisor. Hence the powers $\rho, \rho^2, \cdots, \rho^{p^n-1}$ are all distinct. Therefore ρ is a primitive mark of the field. Hence,

X. Every root of the equation in Theorem IX is a primitive mark of the field.

We are now in a position to prove the following fundamental theorem:

XI. Any two finite fields of the same order are abstractly identical.

Let $F[p^n]$ and $\bar{F}[p^n]$ be any two finite fields of order p^n. Each of them has the integral marks $0, 1, 2, \cdots, p-1$. We make each of these marks in one of the fields correspond to the same mark in the other field. Their laws of combination in the two fields are evidently the same. Let ω be a primitive mark of $F[p^n]$. Then (Theorem IX) ω satisfies an irreducible equation of the form

$$W_n(x) \equiv x^n + c_1x^{n-1} + \cdots + c_n = 0,$$

where $c_1, c_2, \cdots, c_n$ are integral marks of the field. The function $W_n(x)$ (Theorem IX, Corollary II) is a factor of $x^{p^n} - x$, the complementary factor having integral coefficients. The only marks of the field $F[p^n]$ which are employed in effecting the division of $x^{p^n} - x$ by $W_n(x)$ are the integral marks. Hence the same division may be effected, and in the same way, in the field $\overline{F}[p^n]$, since that field has the same integral marks as $F[p^n]$ with the same laws of combination. Hence $W_n(x)$ is a factor of $x^{p^n} - x$ in $\overline{F}[p^n]$. From Theorem V it follows then that the equation $W_n(x) = 0$ has n distinct roots in the field $\overline{F}[p^n]$. Let $\overline{\omega}$ be any one of these roots. Then we establish a correspondence between the two fields $F[p^n]$ and $\overline{F}[p^n]$ by making each power of ω correspond to the like power of $\overline{\omega}$ and by making the zero element in one field correspond to the zero element in the other. We have to show, among other things, that this is consistent with the correspondence of integral marks already set up. If a given power of ω is expressed in the form

$$\gamma_{n-1}\omega^{n-1} + \cdots + \gamma_1\omega + \gamma_0,$$

and the like power of $\overline{\omega}$ in the form

$$\overline{\gamma}_{n-1}\overline{\omega}^{n-1} + \cdots + \overline{\gamma}_1\overline{\omega} + \overline{\gamma}_0,$$

as in the proofs of Theorems IX and X, then it is evident that $\overline{\gamma}_i = \gamma_i\,(i = 0, 1, \cdots, n-1)$. From this it follows that the integral marks correspond in the way already described. As in the proof of Theorem X, it may now be shown that $\overline{\omega}$ is a primitive mark of $\overline{F}[p^n]$. Moreover, since the integral marks in the two fields have the same laws of addition, it follows from the foregoing expressions for the powers of ω and $\overline{\omega}$ that all the corresponding marks have the same laws of addition in such a way that the indicated correspondence exhibits the additive groups of the two fields as simply isomorphic. This correspondence evidently exhibits the multiplicative groups of the two fields as simply isomorphic. Since these two simple isomorphisms are exhibited by one and the same correspondence of marks in the two fields, the two fields are said to be *abstractly identical*; and the theorem is proved.

From this theorem it follows that a particular finite field, so far as its abstract properties are concerned, is completely specified by its order.

63. Galois Fields. In order to prove the existence of finite fields we develop, in this section and the next, the properties of a particular form of finite fields known as Galois fields.

Let $P(x)$ be a given polynomial in x of degree n with integral coefficients not all divisible by the given integer p. Let $F(x)$ be any polynomial in x with integral coefficients. On dividing $F(x)$ by $P(x)$ we obtain a quotient $Q(x)$ and a remainder of degree $n-1$ at most, which remainder may be written in the form $f(x)+pq(x)$, where

$$f(x) \equiv a_0 + a_1x + a_2x^2 + \cdots + a_{n-1}x^{n-1},$$

each of the coefficients a_i belonging to the set $0, 1, 2, \cdots, p-1$, and where $q(x)$ is a polynomial with integral coefficients. Then we have

$$F(x) = f(x) + p \cdot q(x) + P(x) \cdot Q(x).$$

We call $f(x)$ the residue of $F(x)$ modulis p and $P(x)$ and we write

$$F(x) \equiv f(x) \text{ [modd } p,\ P(x)].$$

This is said to be a congruence with a *double* modulus. The totality of functions $F(x)$ which can be obtained by holding $f(x)$ fixed and varying $q(x)$ and $Q(x)$ in all possible ways subject to maintaining the named properties of $q(x)$ and $Q(x)$ constitutes a class of residues which is completely determined by $f(x)$ and the given p and $P(x)$. Two polynomials in x with integral coefficients will be called congruent modulis p and $P(x)$ when and only when they belong to the same class of residues modulis p and $P(x)$. The number of distinct classes of residues modulis p and $P(x)$ is equal to the number of functions of the form $f(x)$ with the stated restrictions, and hence this number is p^n, since each of the n independent coefficients a_i may have any one of p values. If each a_i is zero, we shall denote the corresponding class by C_0; C_0 is said to be the *zero* class.

If we have

$$F_i(x) = f_i(x) + p \cdot q_i(x) + P(x) \cdot Q_i(x), \qquad (i = 1, 2)$$

then it is obvious that the class to which any one of the functions $F_1(x)+F_2(x)$, $F_1(x)-F_2(x)$, $F_1(x)F_2(x)$ belongs is completely determined by the corresponding function $f_1(x)+f_2(x)$, $f_1(x)-f_2(x)$, $f_1(x)f_2(x)$. Hence classes of residues modulis p and $P(x)$ combine uniquely under addition, subtraction, and multiplication. In order that the division of an arbitrary class by any class C different from the zero class C_0 shall lead uniquely to a third class, it is necessary that the equation $C_iC = C_0$ shall imply that $C_i = C_0$. In order that the equation $C_iC = C_0$ shall always imply that $C_i = C_0$, it is necessary that p shall be a prime number, as one may see readily from a consideration of those classes for which the coefficients $a_1, a_2, \cdots, a_{n-1}$ of the corresponding $f(x)$ are all zero (compare the proof of Theorem I in § **62**). It is also necessary that $P(x)$ shall be *irreducible* modulo p, that is, shall be incapable of verifying an equation of the form

$$P(x) = P_1(x)P_2(x) + pP_3(x)$$

where the $P_i(x)$ are polynomials in x with integral coefficients, the degrees of $P_1(x)$ and $P_2(x)$ being positive and less than the degree of $P(x)$; for, if $P(x)$ is *reducible* modulo p, so that we have an equation of the foregoing form, then the classes corresponding to $P_1(x)$ and $P_2(x)$ are both different from C_0 while their product is C_0. Hence *if the classes of residues are to constitute a finite field it is necessary that p be a prime and that $P(x)$ be irreducible modulo p.* We shall show that this condition is also sufficient.

It is convenient first to introduce a definition and demonstrate a theorem needed in the proof.

If $F(x)$ is a polynomial in x with integral coefficients, and if polynomials $G_1(x)$, $G_2(x)$, $G_3(x)$ in x with integral coefficients exist such that

$$F(x) = G_1(x)G_2(x) + pG_3(x),$$

then $F(x)$ is said to have modulo p the factors or divisors $G_1(x)$ and $G_2(x)$ and we write $F(x) \equiv G_1(x)G_2(x) \bmod p$.

XII. If $F(x)$ and $G(x)$ are two polynomials in x with integral coefficients, and if they have modulo a prime p no common factor containing x, then polynomials $F_1(x)$ and $G_1(x)$ in x with integral coefficients exist such that

$$F_1(x)F(x) - G_1(x)G(x) \equiv 1 \bmod p.$$

For every integer α prime to p there exists an integer β such that $\alpha\beta \equiv 1 \bmod p$. Hence we have congruences of the form

$$F(x) \equiv aA(x), \quad G(x) \equiv bB(x) \bmod p$$

where the coefficient of the highest power of x in $A(x)$ and in $B(x)$ is unity and where the remaining coefficients are integers. For definiteness, suppose that the degree of $A(x)$ is not less than that of $B(x)$. Now apply to $A(x)$ and $B(x)$ the usual process for finding the greatest common divisor, modified by a reduction modulo p, writing each remainder in the form $rR(x)$, where r is an integer and the leading coefficient of $R(x)$ is unity. Then we have modulo p a set of congruences of the form

$$\begin{aligned} A &\equiv BQ_1 + r_1R_1, \\ B &\equiv R_1Q_2 + r_2R_2, \\ R_1 &\equiv R_2Q_3 + r_3R_3, \\ &\cdots\cdots\cdots \\ R_{k-2} &\equiv R_{k-1}Q_k + r_kR_k. \qquad (R_k = 1) \end{aligned}$$

From these congruences we derive readily congruences modulo p of the following form:

$$\begin{aligned} r_1R_1 &\equiv A_1A - B_1B, \\ r_1r_2R_2 &\equiv A_2A - B_2B, \\ &\cdots\cdots\cdots \\ r_1r_2 \cdots r_kR_k &\equiv A_kA - B_kB, \end{aligned}$$

where the A_i and B_i are polynomials in x having integral coefficients.

Now $r_1, r_2, \cdots, r_k$ are all prime to p, since otherwise $A(x)$ and $B(x)$ would have modulo p a common divisor containing x, contrary to hypothesis. Hence an integer r exists such that $r \cdot abr_1r_2 \cdots r_k \equiv 1 \bmod p$. Then we have

$$1 \equiv rabr_1r_2 \cdots r_k \equiv rabA_kA - rabB_kB \bmod p;$$

or

$$rbA_kF - raB_kG \equiv 1 \bmod p.$$

This result implies the theorem stated.

COR. If p is a prime and $P(x)$ is irreducible modulo p and if $F(x) \not\equiv 0$ [modd p, $P(x)$], then a polynomial $F_1(x)$ with integral coefficients exists such that

$$F_1(x)F(x) \equiv 1 \text{ [modd } p, P(x)].$$

Let us now return to the classes of residues modulis p and $P(x)$, where p is a prime and $P(x)$ is irreducible modulo p.

Let C denote any one of these classes different from the zero class C_0. Then from the preceding corollary it follows that a class Γ exists such that $C\Gamma$ is the class 1, that is, the class of polynomials congruent to 1 modulis p and $P(x)$. Hence if $\overline{C}$ is any one of the classes, we have

$$\frac{\overline{C}}{C} = \frac{\overline{C}\Gamma}{C\Gamma} = \overline{C}\Gamma.$$

Since $\overline{C}\Gamma$ belongs to the class of residues, it follows that the quotient class $\overline{C}/C$ always exists when C is different from the zero class C_0. If $\overline{C} = CQ_1$ and $\overline{C} = CQ_2$, then $C_0 = \overline{C} - \overline{C} = C(Q_1 - Q_2)$, whence it follows that $Q_1 - Q_2 = \Gamma C_0 = C_0$; therefore division of these classes is unique, the divisor being different from C_0.

We have thus proved the following theorem:

> XIII. The classes of residues modulis p and $P(x)$ form a finite field of order p^n when and only when p is a prime and $P(x)$ is a polynomial with integral coefficients which is irreducible and of degree n modulo p.

The finite field formed by these p^n classes of residues is called a *Galois field* of order p^n. It is denoted by the symbol $GF[p^n]$.

It is evident that the $GF[p^n]$, when existent, contains the marks $0, 1, 2, \cdots, p-1$ and that these constitute the $GF[p]$ formed by taking x for $P(x)$.

The absence of the symbol $P(x)$ from the symbol $GF[p^n]$ for the field is justified by the following fact, a consequence of Theorem XI: If a second polynomial $\overline{P}(x)$, irreducible and of degree n modulo p with integral coefficients, is used in the formation of a Galois field of order p^n, that field is abstractly identical with the field formed by means of the given polynomial $P(x)$; whence it follows that a particular Galois field, so far as its abstract properties are concerned, is completely determined by its order. Moreover, it is abstractly identical with any finite field of the same order.

64. Existence of Galois Fields. It remains to establish the existence of Galois fields of every order p^n by proving the following theorem:

XIV. A Galois field of order p^n exists for every prime p and positive integer n.

For the proof of this theorem it is sufficient, in view of Theorem XIII, to demonstrate the following theorem:

XV. For every prime p and positive integer n there exists a polynomial $P(x)$ with integral coefficients which is irreducible and of degree n modulo p.

When $n = 1$, we may take $x + 1$ for $P(x)$. Hence the $GF[p]$ exists. We may therefore employ this field in the proof. Theorem XV will be proved by aid of a sequence of theorems which will be given next.

XVI. If $F(x)$ and $G(x)$ are polynomials belonging to the $GF[p]$ and if they have no common divisor containing x and belonging to the $GF[p]$ and if $G(x)$ is a factor of $E(x)F(x)$, then $G(x)$ is a factor of $E(x)$.

From the hypothesis we have an equation of the form

$$E(x) \cdot F(x) = G(x) \cdot S(x).$$

But from Theorem XII we have in the $GF[p]$ the equation

$$F(x)F_1(x) = 1 + G(x)G_1(x).$$

From these two equations we have

$$E(x) = G(x)\,[S(x)F_1(x) - E(x)G_1(x)],$$

whence the conclusion of the theorem follows.

XVII. A polynomial $F(x)$ in x belonging to the $GF[p]$ can be separated into factors belonging to and irreducible in the $GF[p]$ in just one way.

It is evident that there exists a factorization of the sort described; for a reducible polynomial may be separated into factors, and a reducible factor may again be so separated, and so on. If we have

$$F(x) = F_1 F_2 \cdots F_\lambda = f_1 f_2 \cdots f_\mu$$

and the $F_i(x)$ and $f_i(x)$ are irreducible in the $GF[p]$, then F_1 must (by Theorem XVI) be equivalent to one of the f_i, say f_1. Then we have $F_2 \cdots F_\lambda$ equivalent to $f_2 \cdots f_\mu$. Thence we find F_2 equivalent to f_2 in a similar way, and so on. It is now obvious that $\lambda = \mu$.

XVIII. *If $F(x)$ is a polynomial in x of degree n which belongs to and is irreducible in the $GF[p]$, then $F(x)$ is a factor of $x^{p^n} - x$, and the complementary factor belongs to the $GF[p]$.*

Since $F(x)$, by hypothesis, has integral coefficients, is of degree n, and is irreducible modulo p, it may be employed in the formation of the $GF[p^n]$. Let u be any mark of this $GF[p^n]$ different from the zero mark. Then (Theorem V)

$$u^{p^n} - u = 0;$$

that is,

$$u^{p^n} - u \equiv 0 \bmod F(x),$$

the congruence being taken in the $GF[p]$. Taking x for u, we have the result stated in the theorem, since actual division obviously leads to a complementary factor of the form stated.

XIX. *Let $f(x)$ be a polynomial in x belonging to the $GF[p]$ and let t be any positive integer; then in the $GF[p]$ we have*

$$f(x^{p^t}) = [f(x)]^{p^t}.$$

If we write $f(x) = a_0 + a_1 x + \cdots + a_k x^k$, then we have

$$[f(x)]^p = a_0{}^p + a_1{}^p x^p + \cdots + a_k{}^p x^{pk}$$
$$= a_0 + a_1 x^p + \cdots + a_k x^{pk} = f(x^p).$$

Raising to the pth power successively for t times, we have

$$[f(x)]^{p^t} = a_0 + a_1 x^{p^t} + \cdots + a_k x^{p^{t}k} = f(x^{p^t}).$$

XX. If $F(x)$ is a polynomial of degree m belonging to and irreducible in the $GF[p]$, and if $F(x)$ is a factor of $x^{p^t} - x$ in the $GF[p]$, then t is a multiple of m.

If we write $t = sm + r$ $(0 \leqq r < m)$ and employ Theorem XVIII, we have in the $GF[p]$

$$0 \equiv x^{p^t} - x \equiv (x^{p^{sm}})^{p^r} - x \equiv x^{p^r} - x \bmod F(x).$$

Then if $f(x)$ is any mark of the $GF[p^m]$ formed with $F(x)$, we have, by aid of Theorem XIX and the congruence $x^{p^r} \equiv x \bmod F(x)$, the relation

$$[f(x)]^{p^r} \equiv f(x^{p^r}) \equiv f(x) \bmod F(x).$$

Hence every mark of the $GF[p^m]$ satisfies the congruence

$$u^{p^r} - u \equiv 0 \bmod F(x).$$

Now this congruence is satisfied by p^m distinct marks, while $p^r < p^m$. Hence (Theorem VI) the congruence must be an identical congruence. Therefore $r = 0$, and hence t is a multiple of m.

From the foregoing theorem we have readily the following:

XXI. A factor of $x^{p^n} - x$ which belongs to and is irreducible in the $GF[p]$ will be of degree n if and only if it is a factor of no function of the form

$$x^{p^\nu} - x,$$

where ν is a proper divisor of n.

We next prove the following theorem:

XXII. The function $x^{p^t} - x$ contains no repeated factor belonging to and irreducible in the $GF[p]$.

To establish this proposition we suppose that $x^{p^t} - x$ contains modulo p a factor $[F(x)]^2$, where $F(x)$ is a polynomial of positive degree belonging to and irreducible in the $GF[p]$, and then show that we are led to a contradiction. Let $G(x)$ be a polynomial of degree p^t such that $[F(x)]^2$ is a factor of $G(x)$ in the ordinary sense of algebra while at the same time $G(x) \equiv x^{p^t} - x \bmod p$. Then the derivative $G'(x)$ of $G(x)$ with respect to x is divisible by $F(x)$ in the ordinary sense of algebra, as one sees from the usual theory of multiple roots of polynomials. Hence $G'(x)$ is divisible by $F(x)$ in the $GF[p]$. But $G'(x) \equiv -1 \bmod p$, so that $G'(x) = -1$ in the $GF[p]$. But -1 is obviously not divisible, in the $GF[p]$, by a polynomial of the form of $F(x)$, for we should then have a contradiction with Theorem XVII. Since we are thus led to such a contradiction, we conclude to the truth of the theorem.

We are now able to determine the number of polynomials in x of degree n each of which belongs to and is irreducible in the $GF[p]$. For this purpose let $q_1, q_2, \cdots, q_\lambda$ be all the distinct prime factors of n, and form the expression

$$V_n = \frac{[n] \cdot \Pi\left[\frac{n}{q_i q_j}\right] \cdot \Pi\left[\frac{n}{q_i q_j q_k q_l}\right] \cdot \cdots}{\Pi\left[\frac{n}{q_i}\right] \cdot \Pi\left[\frac{n}{q_i q_j q_k}\right] \cdot \cdots},$$

where $[\mu]$ denotes the expression $[\mu] = x^{p^\mu} - x$ and where the products Π are taken for all the combinations of distinct q's in the numbers indicated, each product Π in the numerator referring to an even number of the q's and each one in the denominator to an odd number of the q's. Let $F(x)$ be a factor of $x^{p^n} - x$ of degree ν $(\nu < n)$ belonging to and irreducible in the $GF[p]$. Then ν is a proper factor of n (Theorem XX). Let t be the number of the primes q_i each of which enters into n to a higher power than that to which it enters into ν. Then $F(x)$ enters into the numerator of the expression for V_n to a power whose exponent is

$$1 + C_{t2} + C_{t4} + \cdots$$

and in the denominator to a power whose exponent is

$$C_{t1} + C_{t3} + C_{t5} + \cdots,$$

where C_{tk} denotes the number of combinations of t things taken k at a time. The last two sums are equal, since their difference is equal to $(1-1)^t$. Hence (Theorem XXI) every factor of V_n which belongs to and is irreducible in the $GF[p]$ is of degree n. If N_n denotes the number of such factors, each with leading coefficient unity, then nN_n is the degree of V_n; hence

$$nN_n = p^n - \Sigma p^{n/q_i} + \Sigma p^{n/q_i q_j} \cdots + (-1)^\lambda p^{n/q_1 q_2 \cdots q_\lambda}.$$

The number in the second member is not zero, since its quotient by its last term is congruent to 1 modulo p. Therefore $N_n > 0$. Hence there exists a polynomial in x of degree n which belongs to and is irreducible in the $GF[p]$; and N_n is the number of such polynomials, as one sees by aid of Theorems XXII and XVIII.

This conclusion contains the proposition stated in Theorem XV. Therefore a Galois field exists of order p^n for every prime p and positive integer n. But we have seen that the order of any finite field is of the form p^n (Theorem II) and that any two fields of the same order are abstractly identical (Theorem XI). From these considerations we have the following theorem:

> XXIII. A finite field of order p^n exists for every prime p and positive integer n, and every such field is abstractly identical with the Galois field of the same order.

Hereafter we shall use the symbol $GF[p^n]$ to denote indifferently the Galois field or the abstract field of order p^n.

65. Inclusion of One Finite Field within Another. We shall now prove the following theorem:

> XXIV. A finite field of order p^n contains a finite field of order p^k when and only when k is a factor of n.

The larger field is said to contain the included field as a *subfield*.

If u is a mark of the field $F[p^n]$ of order p^n and is a primitive mark of an included field $F[p^k]$ of order p^k, then u is of order

$p^k - 1$, and therefore $p^k - 1$ is a factor of $p^n - 1$. Write $n = \alpha k + \beta$, where α and β are integers and $0 < \beta \leqq k$. Then

$$p^n - 1 \equiv p^{\alpha k + \beta} - 1 \equiv (p^k)^\alpha p^\beta - 1 \equiv p^\beta - 1 \bmod p^k - 1.$$

Hence $k = \beta$, since $p^k - 1$ is a factor of $p^n - 1$ and therefore of $p^\beta - 1$; hence k is a factor of n.

Let v and w be marks of $F[p^n]$ such that

$$v^{p^k} = v, \qquad w^{p^k} = w.$$

Then $\quad (vw)^{p^k} = vw, \qquad (v \pm w)^{p^k} = v^{p^k} \pm w^{p^k} = v \pm w.$

Moreover, if $v \neq 0$ and v_1 is the mark of the field $F[p^n]$ such that $vv_1 = 1$, then we have

$$v^{p^k - 1} v_1{}^{p^k - 1} = 1, \text{ whence } v_1{}^{p^k - 1} = 1.$$

From these results it follows that the zero mark and the marks whose orders are factors of $p^k - 1$ constitute a field. This field contains a mark of order $p^k - 1$, since $p^k - 1$ is a factor of $p^n - 1$; and it does not contain any mark of order higher than $p^k - 1$. Hence the field is of order p^k.

These results imply the truth of the theorem.

COR. The integral marks in the field constitute a field of order p.

EXERCISES

1. For the case of the field $GF[2^2]$ show that the function $P(x)$ of § **64** is $x^2 + x + 1$.

2. For the case of the $GF[3^2]$ show that for the function $P(x)$ of § **64** we may take $x^2 + 1$, $x^2 + x + 2$, or $x^2 + 2x + 2$.

3. Construct addition and multiplication tables for the $GF[2^2]$, $GF[5]$, and $GF[3^2]$.

4. The number of primitive marks in the $GF[p^n]$ is $\phi(p^n - 1)$, where ϕ denotes Euler's ϕ-function.

5. If ω is a primitive mark of the $GF[p^n]$ and d is any factor of $p^n - 1$, then $\omega^{(p^n - 1)/d}$ is a mark of order d; and the number of marks of order d is $\phi(d)$.

6. A nonzero mark of the $GF[p^n]$ is called a *square* if it is the square of some mark in the field; otherwise it is called a *not-square*. Prove the following propositions:

(1) If $p = 2$ every nonzero mark in the field is a square.

(2) If p is odd the even powers of a primitive mark are squares and the odd powers are not-squares; and the reciprocal of a square [not-square] is a square [not-square].

7. Show that a root ω of the equation $x^5 - x + 1 = 0$ in the $GF[3^5]$ is a primitive mark in the field.

8. In the $GF[2^9]$ show that a root x of the equation $x^9 + x + 1 = 0$ is of order 73 while $x + x^4 + x^6 + x^7 + x^8$ is of order 7, and thence show that $x(x + x^4 + x^6 + x^7 + x^8)$, or $1 + x + x^2 + x^5 + x^7 + x^8$, is a primitive mark in the field and that it satisfies the equation

$$y^9 + y^8 + y^4 + y^3 + y^2 + y + 1 = 0.$$

9. In the Galois fields indicated below, the given equations have as roots primitive marks of the corresponding fields, n in each case denoting the degree of the given equation:

$GF[2^n]$: $x^2 = x + 1$, $x^3 = x + 1$, $x^4 = x + 1$, $x^5 = x^2 + 1$, $x^6 = x + 1$, $x^7 = x + 1$, $x^8 = x^4 + x^3 + x^2 + 1$, $x^9 = x^8 + x^4 + x^3 + x^2 + x + 1$;

$GF[3^n]$: $x^2 = 2x + 1$, $x^3 = x + 2$, $x^4 = 2x^3 + 2x^2 + x + 1$, $x^5 = x + 2$, $x^6 = x + 1$;

$GF[5^n]$: $x^2 = 2x + 2$, $x^3 = 2x + 3$, $x^4 = x^3 + x + 2$, $x^5 = x + 2$, $x^6 = x^5 - x^4 + x^3 - 2x - 2$;

$GF[7^n]$: $x^2 = x - 3$, $x^3 = x - 2$, $x^4 = 2x^3 + 2x + 2$, $x^5 = 6x + 3$;

$GF[11^n]$: $x^2 = 4x - 2$;

$GF[13^n]$: $x^2 = x + 1$.

Verify at least a part of this table of equations having primitive marks as roots.

10. Show that the group G generated by the transformations

$$x' = x + 1, \quad x' = x^7, \quad x' = x + x^3$$

in the $GF[3^3]$ permutes the 24 nonintegral marks of the $GF[3^3]$ according to an imprimitive (transitive) group of degree 24.

11. Consider the totality of transformations of the form

$$x' = P(x)$$

in the $GF[p^n]$ $(n > 1)$, where $P(x)$ is a polynomial in x whose coefficients belong to the included field $GF[p^\nu]$, ν being a proper divisor of n, and $P(x)$ is such that the transformation induces a permutation on the marks of the $GF[p^n]$. Show that this totality of transformations induces a permutation group on those marks of the $GF[p^n]$ which are not in the included field $GF[p^\nu]$, and prove that this cannot be a primitive group.

12. Show that the transformations $x' = x + 1$, $x' = -x^5 - 2x^2$ in the $GF[7]$ generate a group which permutes the seven marks of the field according to a doubly transitive group of degree 7 and order 168.

13. Using ∞ to represent $i/0$ when $i \neq 0$ and adjoining ∞ to the $GF[7]$, show that the transformations in Ex. 12 and the transformation $x' = -1/x$ induce on the eight symbols named a triply transitive group of degree 8 and order $8 \cdot 7 \cdot 6 \cdot 4$.

14. Show that in the $GF[11]$ to which ∞ has been adjoined to stand for $i/0$, where $i \neq 0$, the transformations

$$x' = x + 1, \quad x' = 4x^2 - 3x^7, \quad x' = -\frac{1}{x}$$

induce a quintuply transitive group of degree 12 and order $12 \cdot 11 \cdot 10 \cdot 9 \cdot 8$, and that this group contains as a subgroup a triply transitive group of degree 12 and order $12 \cdot 11 \cdot 10 \cdot 6$ induced by the first and third of the given transformations and the square of the second, namely, the transformation $x' = 7x^4 - 6x^9$. (Compare Ex. 12 on page 151 and Ex. 17 on page 165.)

15. Show that in the $GF[23]$ to which ∞ has been adjoined to stand for $i/0$, where $i \neq 0$, the transformations

$$x' = x + 1, \quad x' = -3x^{15} + 4x^4, \quad x' = -\frac{1}{x}$$

induce a quintuply transitive group of degree 24 and order $24 \cdot 23 \cdot 22 \cdot 21 \cdot 20 \cdot 16 \cdot 3$. (Compare Ex. 9 on page 164.)

66. Analytical Representation of Permutations. Let $u_0, u_1, u_2, \cdots, u_{s-1}$ $(s = p^n)$ denote the marks of the $GF[p^n]$. Let any given permutation on these marks be denoted by the symbol

$$\begin{pmatrix} u_0 & u_1 & u_2 & \cdots & u_{s-1} \\ u_{\phi(0)} & u_{\phi(1)} & u_{\phi(2)} & \cdots & u_{\phi(s-1)} \end{pmatrix}.$$

An analytic representation of this permutation is afforded by the Lagrange formula for interpolation. In fact it is easy to verify that the equation

$$\psi(x) = \sum_{i=0}^{s-1} \frac{u_{\phi(i)} F(x)}{(x - u_i)F'(u_i)},$$

where

$$F(x) = \prod_{i=0}^{s-1} (x - u_i)$$

and $F'(x)$ denotes the derivative of $F(x)$ with respect to x, defines a function $\psi(x)$ such that the transformation $x' = \psi(x)$ induces precisely the given permutation of marks of the field. It is obvious that $\psi(x)$ is a polynomial in x, of degree less than p^n, whose coefficients belong to the $GF[p^n]$. A polynomial $\psi(x)$ belonging to the $GF[p^n]$ and such that the transformation $x' = \psi(x)$ induces a permutation on the marks of the field is called a *substitution polynomial* in $GF[p^n]$. We shall always suppose that the degree of such a polynomial is less than p^n, since any polynomial in $GF[p^n]$ may be reduced to one of such degree by means of the relation $x^{p^n} = x$, which is verified by every mark in the field.

XXV. Two distinct substitution polynomials, $\psi_1(x)$ and $\psi_2(x)$, both belonging to the $GF[p^n]$, cannot induce the same permutation on the marks of the field.

If we assume $\psi_1(u_i) = \psi_2(u_i)$ $(i = 0, 1, \cdots, p^n - 1)$, then the equation $\psi_1(x) - \psi_2(x) = 0$ has p^n roots in the field, while its degree is less than p^n; a result in contradiction with Theorem VI of § 62.

XXVI. A necessary and sufficient condition that $\psi(x)$ shall be a substitution polynomial in the $GF[p^n]$ is that $\psi(x)$ shall be a polynomial in the $GF[p^n]$, of degree less than p^n, such that each of the equations

$$\psi(x) = u_i \qquad (i = 0, 1, 2, \cdots, p^n - 1)$$

shall have a solution.

For in this case the marks $\psi(u_0), \psi(u_1), \cdots, \psi(u_{s-1})$ are in some order the marks $u_0, u_1, \cdots, u_{s-1}$, since the former set contains at most s distinct marks and contains all the s marks in the second set.

COR. I. The condition in the theorem is equivalent to the requirement that the marks $\psi(u_0), \psi(u_1), \cdots, \psi(u_{s-1})$ shall all be distinct.

COR. II. If m is less than $p^n - 1$, then a necessary and sufficient condition that x^m shall be a substitution polynomial is that m shall be prime to $p^n - 1$.

When m and $p^n - 1$ have a common divisor greater than unity, the marks $u_0{}^m, u_1{}^m, \cdots, u_{s-1}{}^m$ are not all distinct (Theorem VII, § 62). If m and $p^n - 1$ are relatively prime, then integers α and β exist such that $\alpha m + \beta(p^n - 1) = 1$. Then if ξ and η are nonzero marks of the field such that $\xi^m = \eta^m$, we have $\xi^{\alpha m} = \eta^{\alpha m}$, whence $\xi^{\alpha m + \beta(p^n - 1)} = \eta^{\alpha m + \beta(p^n - 1)}$, whence $\xi = \eta$. Thence the required result follows by aid of Corollary I.

67. Linear Groups in One Variable in $GF[p^n]$. Let us consider the totality of transformations of the form

$$x' = ax + b \qquad (a \neq 0)$$

on the marks of the $GF[p^n]$, the coefficients a and b being marks of this field. Each of these induces a permutation of the marks of the field (Theorem XXVI), since the equation $ax + b = \beta$ obviously has a solution x in the $GF[p^n]$ whenever a, b, β are marks of this field and $a \neq 0$. The product of two transformations of the given set obviously belongs to the set. Since the number of transformations in the set is finite, it follows that the named totality constitutes a group. The order of this group is $p^n(p^n - 1)$, since a and b range independently over all the marks of the field except that a must not be the zero mark.

Now if α and β are any two given distinct marks of the field, the transformation

$$x' = (\beta - \alpha)x + \alpha$$

replaces the values 0 and 1 of x by the respective values α and β of x'. Therefore the permutation group induced on the p^n marks of the field by the transformation group in consideration is a doubly transitive group. The subgroup leaving the mark zero unchanged is induced by the transformations $x' = ax$; and this is a cyclic group, since it is generated by the transformation $x' = \omega x$, where ω is a primitive mark of the $GF[p^n]$. Hence we have the following theorem (generalizing a result obtained in § **40**):

XXVII. For every prime p and positive integer n there exists a doubly transitive group of degree p^n and order $p^n(p^n - 1)$ which contains a cyclic subgroup of degree and order $p^n - 1$.

68. Linear Fractional Groups in One Variable in $GF[p^n]$. Let us now adjoin to the $GF[p^n]$ the symbol ∞ to represent any formal quotient $u/0$, where u is a nonzero mark of the field. Then we have all told $p^n + 1$ symbols. It is easy to show that these symbols are permuted among themselves by every transformation of the form

$$x' = \frac{ax + b}{cx + d}, \qquad (ad - bc \neq 0)$$

where a, b, c, d are marks of the $GF[p^n]$ and x and x' are variables ranging over these marks and the symbol ∞. The number of transformations of this form is obviously finite, while it is easy to show that the product of any two of them is also a transformation of the same form. Hence the totality of transformations of this form constitutes a group; and this group induces a permutation group on the named $p^n + 1$ symbols.

The order of the transformation group is readily determined. If $c = 0$ we may take $d = 1$ without loss of generality; then we obtain the $p^n(p^n - 1)$ transformations employed in the previous section. If $c \neq 0$ we may take $c = 1$ without loss of generality. Then a and d may range independently over the p^n marks of the field, while for each pair of values of a and d the symbol b may take just $p^n - 1$ values, since $ad - bc \neq 0$; thus, when $c \neq 0$ we have just $p^n \cdot p^n(p^n - 1)$ transformations. Adding this number to the number of linear transformations, we obtain the sum $(p^n+1)p^n(p^n-1)$; and this number is the order of the transformation group.

Now the corresponding permutation group G on the p^n+1 symbols is transitive, since it is transitive on the symbols exclusive of ∞ and contains the element $x'=1/x$ which replaces ∞ by 0. The largest subgroup of G each element of which leaves ∞ fixed is the doubly transitive group described in the preceding section. Hence we have the following theorem (generalizing a result obtained in § **40**):

XXVIII. For every prime p and positive integer n there exists a triply transitive group of degree p^n+1 and order $(p^n+1)p^n(p^n-1)$ which contains a cyclic subgroup of degree and order p^n-1.

69. Certain Doubly Transitive Groups of Degree p^n. Let us consider the totality of transformations of the form

$$x' = ax^{p^t} + b, \qquad (a \neq 0;\ t = 0, 1, \cdots, n-1)$$

where a and b are marks of the $GF[p^n]$ and x and x' are variables running over the marks of the $GF[p^n]$. It is easy to see that each of these transformations induces a permutation on the marks of the field, that the product of two transformations in the set is a member of the set, and hence that these transformations form a group which induces a permutation group G of degree p^n on the marks of the field. It is evident from § **67** that this group is doubly transitive and that its order is $p^n(p^n-1)n$. The elements

$$x' = x+1, \quad x' = \omega x, \quad x' = x^p,$$

where ω is a primitive mark of the field, obviously generate the group G; for the last two generate a group of order $(p^n-1)n$ which is transitive on the nonzero marks of the field, whence it follows that the three elements generate the entire group. The last generator transforms each of the others into itself. Therefore, if α is any factor of n, the first two of the given generators and the αth power of the last generate a group which is contained in G as a subgroup of index α, and this subgroup is doubly transitive. Hence we have the following theorem:

XXIX. In the $GF[p^n]$ the transformations

$$x' = x + 1, \quad x' = \omega x, \quad x' = x^{p^\alpha},$$

where ω is a primitive mark of the field and α is a factor of n, generate a group of order $p^n(p^n - 1)n/\alpha$ whose transformations consist of the totality

$$x' = ax^{p^t} + b, \qquad \left(a \neq 0;\ t = \alpha, 2\,\alpha, \cdots, \frac{n}{\alpha}\,\alpha\right)$$

where a and b are marks of the field. This group induces on the marks of the field a doubly transitive group of degree p^n and order $p^n(p^n - 1)n/\alpha$.

When $\alpha = n$ this is the doubly transitive group of degree p^n and order $p^n(p^n - 1)$ described in Theorem XXVII. We shall now determine the other doubly transitive groups of this degree and order contained in the group of Theorem XXIX for the case $\alpha = 1$. Such a group contains a regular permutation group M of degree and order $p^n - 1$ on the nonzero marks of the field. It is obvious that the corresponding transformation group T consists of transformations of the form

$$x' = a_i x^{p^{t_i}}. \qquad (i = 1, 2, \cdots, p^n - 1;\ 0 \leqq t_i < n)$$

Such a transformation replaces the mark $x = 1$ by the mark $x' = a_i$. Since M is regular on the nonzero marks of the $GF[p^n]$, it follows that the coefficients a_i are in some order the nonzero marks of the field without repetition

Now the totality of linear transformations in T constitutes a subgroup of T; and this subgroup is contained in the cyclic group generated by the transformation S,

$$S: \qquad x' = \omega x,$$

where ω is a primitive mark of the field. Then there exists a least positive integer σ such that this linear subgroup is generated by S^σ. It is clear that σ is a factor of the order $p^n - 1$ of S. If $\sigma = 1$ we recover the case of § **67**; therefore, in what follows, we shall suppose that $\sigma > 1$. Then some of the exponents t_i are positive.

Let t be the least positive value of t_i appearing among the exponents t_i in the transformations of T; and let the transformation U,

$$U: \qquad x' = ax^{p^t},$$

be one of the transformations in which $t_i = t$. By taking successive powers of U we obtain transformations with the exponents $t, 2t, 3t, \cdots$ on p. Since these are to be reduced modulo n (on account of the equation $u^{p^n} = u$ for marks of the $GF[p^n]$), it follows that t is a factor of n. Moreover, since t is the least positive value of an exponent t_i, each t_i must be a multiple of t; whence one concludes that the exponents t_i are $t, 2t, 3t, \cdots$. If T_1 and T_2 are two transformations in T with the same value of the exponent t_i, then $T_1^{-1}T_2$ is a linear transformation and hence is in $\{S^\sigma\}$. Therefore all transformations in T having a given value of t_i are products of the form T_1S_1, where S_1 is in $\{S^\sigma\}$. Therefore T is generated by S^σ and U. The smallest positive value of λ such that U^λ is in $\{S^\sigma\}$ is $\lambda = n/t$. Since T and $\{S^\sigma\}$ are of orders $p^n - 1$ and $(p^n - 1)/\sigma$, it follows that $\sigma = n/t$ and hence that σ is a factor of n.

We have now to determine the further conditions on σ, t, and a such that the group $\{S^\sigma, U\}$ shall indeed induce a permutation group of the type prescribed for M. If d is the greatest divisor of σ such that a is a dth power of a mark in the $GF[p^n]$, then every coefficient in $\{S^\sigma, U\}$ is a dth power. Since d is a factor of $p^n - 1$ and every mark of the $GF[p^n]$ occurs among the coefficients in the transformations belonging to $\{S^\sigma, U\}$, it follows that $d = 1$. Therefore if γ is such that $a = \omega^\gamma$, we must have γ prime to σ. We may now combine the transformation U with an appropriate power of S^σ such that in the resulting transformation $U_{l,t}$ of the form U (with the same value of t) we shall have the corresponding coefficient of the form ω^l, where $0 < l < \sigma$ and l is prime to σ. Then we have

$$U_{l,t}: \qquad x' = \omega^l x^{p^t}. \qquad (0 < l < \sigma;\ l \text{ prime to } \sigma;\ \sigma t = n)$$

Then $\{S^\sigma, U\} \equiv \{S^\sigma, U_{l,t}\}$.

The sth power of $U_{l,t}$ may be written in the form

$$U_{l,t}{}^s: \qquad x' = \omega^{l(1+p^t+p^{2t}+\cdots+p^{(s-1)t})} x^{p^{st}}.$$

The least positive value of s for which this is in $\{S^\sigma\}$ is $s = n/t = \sigma$. In order that the induced permutation group M shall be regular, it is further necessary that the least value of s for which

$$1 + p^t + p^{2t} + \cdots + p^{(s-1)t}$$

shall be a multiple of σ is $s = \sigma$, since otherwise at least one mark of the $GF[p^n]$ would occur as a coefficient in two transformations belonging to $\{S^\sigma, U_{l,t}\}$.

When the necessary conditions now obtained are satisfied, we shall easily show that $\{S^\sigma, U_{l,t}\}$ permutes the nonzero marks of the $GF[p^n]$ according to a regular permutation group M. The coefficients in the transformations belonging to $\{S^\sigma, U_{l,t}\}$ are the marks

$$\omega^{k\sigma} \cdot \omega^{l(1+p^t+p^{2t}+\cdots+p^{(s-1)t})}, \qquad (k = 1, 2, \cdots, (p^n - 1)/\sigma; \; s = 1, 2, \cdots, \sigma - 1)$$

together with the σth power marks appearing as coefficients in the transformations of $\{S^\sigma\}$. No two of these coefficients are equal, since the second exponent on ω in the foregoing expressions is not a multiple of σ and no two such exponents have their difference a multiple of σ. Therefore no two transformations in $\{S^\sigma, U_{l,t}\}$ have the same coefficient, and hence that group replaces the value 1 of x by every nonzero mark of the field; whence it follows that $\{S^\sigma, U_{l,t}\}$ induces a regular permutation group M on the nonzero marks of the field.

Since $\sigma > 1$ it is easy to verify that the group $\{S^\sigma, U_{l,t}\}$ is non-Abelian; for the equation $S^{-\sigma}U_{l,t}S^\sigma = U_{l,t}$ would imply that $\sigma(p^t - 1) \equiv 0 \bmod p^n - 1$, and this is impossible, since

$$\sigma(p^t - 1) < (p^\sigma - 1)(p^t - 1) = (p^{n/t} - 1)(p^t - 1) < p^n - 1$$

when $\sigma < n$.

Among the results now established we have the following:

XXX. Every noncyclic group T which is contained in the transformation group G,

$$x' = ax^{p^t} + b, \qquad (a \neq 0; \; t = 0, 1, 2, \cdots, n - 1)$$

where a and b are marks of the $GF[p^n]$, subject to the condition that T shall be of order $p^n - 1$ and shall permute according to a regular permutation group M the nonzero marks of the $GF[p^n]$, is a non-Abelian group $\{S^\sigma, U_{l,t}\}$, where σ ($\sigma > 1$) is a common factor of n and $p^n - 1$ such that $s = \sigma$ is the least value of s for which $1 + p^t + p^{2t} + \cdots + p^{(s-1)t}$ is divisible by σ, where $t = n/\sigma$; and every such group $\{S^\sigma, U_{l,t}\}$ is such a group T.

The following corollary is now immediate:

COR. I. If the elements of $\{S^\sigma, U_{l,t}\}$ are the transformations

$$x' = a_i x^{p^{ti}}, \qquad (i = 1, 2, \cdots, p^n - 1)$$

then the transformations

$$x' = a_i x^{p^{ti}} + b_i, \qquad (i = 1, 2, \cdots, p^n - 1)$$

where for each value of i the symbol b_i runs over all the marks of the $GF[p^n]$, induce a doubly transitive group of degree p^n and order $p^n(p^n - 1)$ on the marks of the $GF[p^n]$, in which M is the largest subgroup each element of which leaves zero fixed.

COR. II. If $n = \sigma t$ ($\sigma > 1$) and p is a prime of the form $\sigma z + 1$, then there exists a doubly transitive group of degree p^n and order $p^n(p^n - 1)$ whose subgroups of degree and order $p^n - 1$ are non-Abelian.

COR. III. Whenever n and $p^n - 1$ are not relatively prime, there exist* at least two doubly transitive groups of degree p^n and order $p^n(p^n - 1)$.

* This is in contradiction with a conjecture of Burnside (*Messenger of Mathematics*, **25** (1896): 147–153; see also the footnote on page 184 of the second edition of his *Theory of Groups*) to the effect that, with an exception in the case when $p^n = 3^2$, there is always one and just one doubly transitive group of degree p^n and order $p^n(p^n - 1)$, and in particular with the cases $n = 2$ and $n = 3$ in which he offered a supposed proof of the conclusion.

The existence of one of these groups is asserted by Theorem XXVII of § **67**. The existence of another is asserted by the foregoing Corollary I, as may be seen by taking for σ a common prime factor of n and $p^n - 1$. For if $p^{\sigma t} - 1$ is divisible by the prime σ, it follows that $p^t \equiv p^{\sigma t} \equiv 1 \bmod \sigma$; whence $s = \sigma$ is the smallest value of s for which $1 + p^t + p^{2t} + \cdots + p^{(s-1)t}$ is divisible by σ.

From this corollary it follows that there are at least two distinct doubly transitive groups of degree p^2 and order $p^2(p^2 - 1)$ for every odd prime p. (See Ex. 15 on page 152 and Ex. 12 on page 286.) For every p of the form $3z + 1$ there are at least two distinct doubly transitive groups of degree p^3 and order $p^3(p^3 - 1)$.

70. Certain Doubly and Triply Transitive Groups of Degree $p^n + 1$. The totality of transformations of the form

$$x' = \frac{ax^{p^t} + b}{cx^{p^t} + d}, \quad (ad - bc \neq 0;\ t = 0, 1, 2, \cdots, n - 1)$$

where a, b, c, d are marks of the $GF[p^n]$ and x and x' are variables running over these marks and the symbol ∞, constitutes a group G which induces a permutation group Γ on the $p^n + 1$ symbols involved. It is easy to show (compare § **68**) that the order of G is $(p^n + 1)p^n(p^n - 1)n$ and that the induced group Γ is a triply transitive group of degree $p^n + 1$ and order $(p^n + 1)p^n(p^n - 1)n$. Moreover, if t is confined to the multiples of a divisor α of n, then we obtain a subgroup of G or Γ of index α, this subgroup of Γ being triply transitive. The corresponding doubly transitive subgroups of degree p^n are evidently those defined in Theorem XXIX of § **69**. Hence we have the following theorem:

XXXI. The transformations

$$x' = \frac{ax^{p^t} + b}{cx^{p^t} + d}, \quad \left(ad - bc \neq 0;\ t = \alpha, 2\alpha, \cdots, \frac{n}{\alpha}\alpha\right)$$

in the $GF[p^n]$ induce on ∞ and the marks of the field a triply transitive group Γ_α of degree $p^n + 1$ and order $(p^n + 1)p^n(p^n - 1)n/\alpha$, α being a given factor of n.

When p is odd each of these groups Γ_α contains transformations having determinants which are not squares of marks in the field. In such a case just half the elements have determinants which are squares, since the product of an element with a square [not-square] determinant by one with a not-square determinant is an element with a not-square [square] determinant. The elements in Γ_α, each of which has a square determinant, then constitute a subgroup of Γ_α of index 2. It is easy to see that the elements in such a subgroup may be written so that $ad - bc = 1$; for if $ad - bc = k^2$, then on replacing a, b, c, d by $k^{-1}a, k^{-1}b, k^{-1}c, k^{-1}d$, we have a transformation of the named form. Moreover, it is easy to see that such a subgroup of index 2 in Γ_α induces a doubly transitive group on the $p^n + 1$ symbols, since 0 and ∞ may be replaced by any given elements λ and μ respectively by a suitably chosen element of the group. Hence we have the following corollary:

Cor. *When p is an odd prime each of these groups Γ_α contains a subgroup of index 2 whose transformations have square determinants; such a subgroup induces a doubly transitive permutation group of degree $p^n + 1$ and order $\frac{1}{2}(p^n + 1)p^n(p^n - 1)n/\alpha$ on ∞ and the marks of the field.*

For the case when n is even and p is an odd prime the permutation group induced by the group Γ_1 of Theorem XXXI contains one or more additional triply transitive subgroups in accordance with the following theorem:

XXXII. *Let p be an odd prime and n be an even integer, and let ρ be any factor of $\frac{1}{2}n$. Consider the totality of transformations of the two forms*

$$(1) \quad x' = \frac{ax^{p^{2s\rho}} + b}{cx^{p^{2s\rho}} + d}, \qquad (2) \quad x' = \frac{ax^{p^{(2s+1)\rho}} + b}{cx^{p^{(2s+1)\rho}} + d},$$

where $2s\rho$ and $(2s+1)\rho$ together run over all the multiples of ρ in the set $0, 1, 2, \cdots, n-1$ and where

$ad - bc$ is a square in case (1) and is a not-square in case (2). These transformations form a group H_ρ of index 2 in the group Γ_ρ of Theorem XXXI. This group H_ρ induces on ∞ and the marks of the field a triply transitive permutation group of degree $p^n + 1$ and order $\frac{1}{2}(p^n + 1)p^n(p^n - 1)n/\rho$.

That these transformations form a group H_ρ follows from the readily verified fact that the product of any two of them is a transformation of the set. It is obvious that H_ρ is a subgroup of Γ_ρ; to see that it is of index 2 it is sufficient to observe that H_ρ contains just half the elements of Γ_ρ of each of the forms (1) and (2), a fact which is readily verified. To show that the permutation group induced by H_ρ on ∞ and the marks of the field is triply transitive, we observe first that it is at least doubly transitive, since it obviously contains the subgroup of index 2 in $\Gamma_{2\rho}$ described in the preceding corollary. Then there is an element of the group which takes any two distinct symbols λ and μ to zero and ∞ respectively, and hence an element which takes any three distinct symbols λ, μ, ν to 0, ∞, $\bar{\nu}$ respectively, where $\bar{\nu}$ is some symbol distinct from 0 and ∞; then there is an element in H_ρ which leaves 0 and ∞ fixed and replaces $\bar{\nu}$ by 1; hence there is an element in H_ρ which replaces λ, μ, ν in order by 0, ∞, 1; and therefore the induced group is triply transitive. It is now obvious that this permutation group has the named order.

It is obvious that each of the groups H_ρ contains $H_{\frac{1}{2}n}$. In the case of $H_{\frac{1}{2}n}$ we have a triply transitive group of degree $p^n + 1$ and order $(p^n + 1)p^n(p^n - 1)$. The subgroup of degree and order $p^n - 1$ contained in this group and leaving 0 and ∞ fixed is induced by the elements

$$(1) \quad x' = ax, \qquad (2) \quad x' = ax^{p^{\frac{1}{2}n}},$$

where a is a square in case (1) and a not-square in case (2). That this subgroup is non-Abelian is readily verified. Hence the triply transitive group induced by $H_{\frac{1}{2}n}$ is different from the triply transitive group of the same degree and order described in Theorem XXVIII of § **68**. But it is easy to verify that the two groups have a common subgroup of index 2, this subgroup in each case being induced by the transformations having square determinants.

From these conclusions we have the following theorem:

XXXIII. When p is an odd prime and n is an even integer, there exist two triply transitive groups of degree p^n+1 and order $(p^n+1)p^n(p^n-1)$. In one of these the regular subgroups of degree and order p^n-1 are cyclic; in the other these subgroups are non-Abelian and contain cyclic subgroups of index 2.

We shall now prove the following theorem:

XXXIV. The triply transitive groups described in Theorems XXVIII and XXXIII are the only triply transitive groups of degree p^n+1 and order $(p^n+1)p^n(p^n-1)$ contained as subgroups in the permutation group induced by the group Γ_1 of Theorem XXXI.

Let G be a triply transitive group of order $(p^n+1)p^n(p^n-1)$ contained as a subgroup in the permutation group induced by the group Γ_1 of Theorem XXXI, and let G_1 be the subgroup of G which consists of the elements of G each of which leaves ∞ fixed. Then G_1 must contain the cyclic group induced by the transformation $x'=\omega x$, where ω is a primitive mark of the field, or it must contain a group M described in Theorem XXX.

Now elements exist in G_1 which are of order p and replace 0 by ω and by 1 respectively, where ω is a primitive mark of the field. The corresponding transformations have the form

$$x'=\lambda x^{p^\mu}+\omega, \quad x'=lx^{p^m}+1,$$

where μ and m are non-negative integers less than n. Since these must be permutable (Theorem V of § **40**) it follows readily that $m=0$. Then $l^p=1$ and hence $l=1$. Therefore G_1 contains the permutations induced by the transformation $x'=x+1$ and its inverse $x'=x-1$.

Now G contains an element which interchanges 0 and ∞ and leaves 1 fixed. The corresponding transformation is of the form $x'=1/x^{p^\tau}$. This transforms the transformation $x'=x-1$ into the transformation

$$x'=\frac{x}{-x+1},$$

from which τ is absent. Forming the product of the transformations

$$x'=x+1, \quad x'=\frac{x}{-x+1}, \quad x'=x+1,$$

we find that the transformation group by which G is induced contains the transformation

$$x'=-\frac{1}{x}.$$

Hence G is generated by the permutation which corresponds to this transformation and any *suitable* doubly transitive group G_1 of degree p^n and order $p^n(p^n-1)$.

If G_1 contains a cyclic subgroup of order and degree p^n-1, then we have the triply transitive group described in Theorem XXVIII. Otherwise G_1 contains a group $\{S^\sigma, U_{l,t}\}$ of Theorem XXX. Since the transformation $x'=-1/x$ interchanges 0 and ∞, it must transform the last-named group into itself. Now this transformation transforms $U_{l,t}$ into the transformation

$$x'=\omega^{-l}x^{p^t}.$$

In order that this shall be in the group $\{S^\sigma, U_{l,t}\}$, an integer k must exist such that $\omega^{l+k\sigma}=\omega^{-l}$, whence $l+k\sigma \equiv -l \bmod p^n-1$. Since σ is greater than unity and is a factor of p^n-1, while $0<l<\sigma$ and l is prime to σ, the foregoing congruence requires that we must have $\sigma=2$ and $l=1$. Hence G_1 is uniquely determined by Theorem XXX and its first corollary. Then G is uniquely determined as the second group described in Theorem XXXIII. Thus we have established the given proposition.

71. A Class of Simple Groups. We shall now prove the following theorem:

XXXV. The group consisting of all the transformations of the form

$$x' = \frac{ax + b}{cx + d},$$

where a, b, c, d are marks of the $GF[p^n]$ such that $ad - bc$ is the square of a nonzero mark of the field, is a simple group when $p^n > 3$.

When $p^n = 2$ or 3 this group has a self-conjugate subgroup of order $p^n + 1$.

When $p^n > 3$ we denote by G either the named transformation group or the induced permutation group on ∞ and the marks of the field. This permutation group is doubly transitive when p is odd and is triply transitive when $p = 2$ (see Theorem XXXI and its corollary, § **70**). Let H be the largest subgroup of the permutation group G each element of which leaves ∞ fixed, and let K be the largest subgroup of H each element of which leaves zero fixed.

Let P be any element in G other than the identity, and let L be the group generated by P and its conjugates in G; we consider L both as a transformation group and as a permutation group. Since G is doubly transitive, the group L contains, as a conjugate of P, an element which replaces ∞ by 0. The conjugates under H of such an element replace ∞ by each other symbol in G, since H is transitive on its p^n symbols. Therefore the permutation group L is transitive. Since K is not the identity, it follows that L has more than one element replacing ∞ by 0; if S and T are two of these, then ST^{-1} leaves ∞ fixed and is not the identity. Hence the largest subgroup L_1 of L each element of which leaves ∞ fixed is of order greater than unity. Let Q be an element of L_1 other than the identity; if Q leaves fixed two symbols of G, then a transform of Q by some element in H displaces one of these symbols; therefore L_1 is of degree p^n.

From this it follows that L_1 contains an element R replacing 0 by some other symbol, and hence elements replacing 0 by each of the other symbols when $p = 2$ and by at least half of them when p is odd, as one sees by transforming R by the elements of K. Similarly it may be shown that L_1 replaces any mark of the field by the same number of symbols. Thence it follows that L_1 is transitive on its p^n symbols, since any transitive set contains all the symbols when $p = 2$ and at least $\frac{1}{2}(p^n - 1) + 1$ of them when p is odd. Therefore L is doubly transitive. Its order is then a multiple of p^n. Hence L contains a Sylow subgroup of G of order p^n, and therefore all the Sylow subgroups of G of this order, since these subgroups form a single conjugate set. Therefore L contains every element of order p in G.

In particular, L contains the transformation $x' = x + \alpha$ and the transform of $x' = x - \beta$ by $x' = -1/x$, where α and β are any marks of the field. Then L contains the product of these transformations, namely,

$$x' = \frac{x + \alpha}{\beta x + \alpha\beta + 1}.$$

Then it may be shown that L contains the transformation $x' = \omega^2 x$, where ω is a primitive mark of the field; for this purpose take the product of the two transformations gotten from the foregoing by putting $\alpha = -\omega^{-1}$, $\beta = \omega - 1$ for one and $\alpha = 1$, $\beta = \omega^{-1} - 1$ for the other. Since L is doubly transitive and contains this transformation, it follows that L coincides with G. Hence G is a simple group. The theorem is therefore established.

XXXVI. Let T and S_λ, where λ ranges over the p^n marks of the $GF[p^n]$, be abstract elements subject to the sole defining relations

$$T^2 = 1, \quad S_0 = 1, \quad S_\rho S_\sigma = S_{\rho+\sigma}, \qquad [1]$$

$$TS_{\frac{\mu-1}{\lambda\mu-1}} TS_{-(\lambda\mu-1)} TS_{\frac{\lambda-1}{\lambda\mu-1}} TS_\mu TS_\lambda = 1, \qquad [2]$$

where ρ, σ, λ, μ range independently over all the marks of the field except that $\lambda\mu \neq 1$. Then the abstract group Γ generated by these elements is simply isomorphic with the group G of linear fractional transformations in the $GF[p^n]$ whose elements have their determinants equal to squares of nonzero marks in the field.

We shall denote this linear fractional group by $LF(2, p^n)$.

By means of the concrete forms,

$$T: \quad x' = -\frac{1}{x}; \qquad S_\rho: \quad x' = x + \rho,$$

of T and S_ρ it may be verified directly that the given defining relations are consistent. That G is the group generated by these concrete elements may be seen by observing that ∞ and the marks of the field are permuted according to a doubly transitive group and then employing the argument used in the last paragraph preceding the theorem. Therefore, in order to prove the theorem, it is sufficient to show further that the order of Γ is not greater than that of G.

For this purpose we consider the following sets of elements in Γ:

$$TS_\sigma TS_\alpha TS_\tau, \quad S_{\alpha^{-1}}TS_\alpha TS_\tau, \qquad (\alpha \neq 0) \qquad [3]$$

where σ, α, τ run independently over all the marks of the field except that $\alpha \neq 0$.

We shall first show that these two sets contain all the elements of Γ by proving that the elements in these sets are permuted among themselves on multiplication on the left by T and by each of the elements S_ρ.

On multiplying the second set on the left by T we obviously have part of the first set. If in the first set we take $\sigma = \alpha^{-1}$ and then multiply on the left by T we obtain the second set. When $\sigma \neq \alpha^{-1}$ the first set, when multiplied on the left by T, gives rise to the elements

$$S_\sigma TS_\alpha TS_\tau. \qquad (\alpha\sigma \neq 1;\ \alpha \neq 0) \qquad [4]$$

If in [2] we take $\lambda = -\sigma$, $\mu = -\alpha$ and solve for $S_\sigma TS_\alpha TS_\tau$, we obtain these elements in the form of elements in the first set in [3]. Hence the elements [3] are permuted among themselves on multiplication on the left by T.

Since $S_0 = 1$, we next multiply on the left by S_ρ, with $\rho \neq 0$. The second set in [3] then gives rise to the set $S_{\rho+\alpha^{-1}}TS_\alpha TS_\tau$;

this is of the type [4], since $\alpha\rho \neq 0$, and hence the set is in the first set in [3]. Then consider the elements

$$S_\rho T S_\sigma T S_\alpha T S_\tau$$

obtained by multiplying the first set in [3] on the left by S_ρ. When $\alpha\sigma \neq 1$, we put

$$\mu = 1 - \alpha\sigma \quad \text{and} \quad \lambda = \frac{1-\alpha}{1-\alpha\sigma}$$

and then obtain from [2] the relation

$$\begin{aligned} S_\rho \cdot T S_\sigma T S_\alpha T \cdot S_\tau &= S_\rho \cdot S_{-\frac{1-\alpha}{1-\alpha\sigma}} T S_{\alpha\sigma-1} T S_{\frac{\sigma-1}{1-\alpha\sigma}} \cdot S_\tau \\ &= S_{\rho-\frac{1-\alpha}{1-\alpha\sigma}} T S_{\alpha\sigma-1} T S_{\frac{\sigma+\tau-1-\alpha\sigma\tau}{1-\alpha\sigma}}. \end{aligned}$$

When
$$\left(\rho - \frac{1-\alpha}{1-\alpha\sigma}\right)(\alpha\sigma - 1)$$

is different from 1, the last member is of the form [4] and hence is in the first set in [3]; when this product is 1, the last member is of the form of the second set in [3]. Hence the named multiplication of the elements [3] by S_ρ permutes these elements when $\alpha\sigma \neq 1$.

In the excluded case $\sigma = \alpha^{-1}$ we have to consider the product elements

$$S_\rho T S_{\alpha^{-1}} T S_\alpha T S_\tau.$$

We shall prove that these elements belong to the first set in [3] by establishing the equation

$$S_\rho T S_{\alpha^{-1}} T S_\alpha T = T S_{\alpha^{-1}} T S_\alpha T S_{\rho\alpha^{-2}}. \qquad [5]$$

We consider separately the two cases $\rho \neq \alpha$ and $\rho = \alpha$.

When $\rho \neq \alpha$ we put $\lambda = \rho\alpha^{-2}$ and $\mu = \alpha$ in [2] and thus obtain the equation

$$T S_{\frac{\alpha-1}{\rho\alpha^{-1}-1}} T S_{-(\rho\alpha^{-1}-1)} T S_{\frac{\alpha^{-1}-1}{\rho\alpha^{-1}-1}} T \cdot T S_{\alpha^{-1}} T S_\alpha T S_{\rho\alpha^{-2}} = 1,$$

as one easily verifies by replacing T^2 by 1 and then combining the two adjacent S's. Thence it follows that [5] is verified if the following relation is true:

$$T S_{\frac{\alpha-1}{\rho\alpha^{-1}-1}} T S_{-(\rho\alpha^{-1}-1)} T S_{\frac{\alpha^{-1}-1}{\rho\alpha^{-1}-1}} \cdot T \cdot S_\rho T S_{\alpha^{-1}} T S_\alpha T = 1.$$

Taking $\lambda = \alpha^{-1}$ and $\mu = \rho$ in [2], one readily verifies this relation.

Taking $\rho = \alpha$ in [5], we interchange the members of the equation and make obvious reductions to obtain the following relation to be established:

$$S_{-\alpha}TS_{\alpha^{-1}}TS_{\alpha}T = TS_{\alpha^{-1}}TS_{\alpha}TS_{-\alpha^{-1}}. \qquad [6]$$

This is relation [5], with $\rho = -\alpha$, and hence it is established by the argument in the foregoing paragraph when $-\alpha \neq \alpha$. Since $\alpha \neq 0$, it follows that [6] is established except when $p = 2$. But we may write [6] in the form

$$S_{\alpha^{-1}}TS_{\alpha}TS_{\alpha^{-1}}T = TS_{\alpha}TS_{\alpha^{-1}}TS_{\alpha}.$$

This is the special case of [5] when α is replaced by α^{-1} and $\rho = \alpha^{-1}$; and hence the relation is established except when $\alpha^{-1} = \alpha$ and $p = 2$; but in this case we have $\alpha = 1$. Then [6] follows from the fact that $(TS_1)^3 = 1$, a relation which follows from [2] by taking $\lambda = 1$ and $\mu = 0$.

Therefore all the elements of Γ are in the sets [3].

Now in [3] σ and τ may range over the p^n marks of the field and α over all these marks except 0. Hence the number of distinct elements in the sets [3] is not greater than

$$p^{2n}(p^n - 1) + p^n(p^n - 1) = (p^n + 1)p^n(p^n - 1). \qquad [7]$$

When $p = 2$ this is the order of G; and therefore Γ and G are simply isomorphic when $p = 2$. When $p > 2$ the order of G is just half the number in [7], while the order of Γ is a multiple of that of G and is not greater than the number in [7]. Hence G and Γ are simply isomorphic when $p > 2$ in case it is true that two notationally distinct elements in [3] represent the same element of Γ; and this is true of the two elements

$$TS_1TS_1TS_1 \quad \text{and} \quad TS_{-1}TS_{-1}TS_{-1},$$

since these are notationally distinct when $p > 2$ but both denote the element 1 since $(TS_1)^3 = 1$, as we have seen, whence $(S_{-1}T)^3 = 1$ and $(TS_{-1})^3 = 1$. Hence Γ and G are simply isomorphic in all cases.

When $n = 1$ the group G is generated by two elements of orders 2 and 3 respectively; and in terms of such elements an abstract definition of considerable interest may be given as in the following theorem:

XXXVII. Let p be an odd prime, let ρ be a primitive root modulo p, and let σ be such that $\rho\sigma \equiv 1 \bmod p$. In terms of two abstract elements T and S define R by the relation

$$R = T(TS)^{\rho}T(TS)^{\sigma}T(TS)^{\rho}.$$

Then if T and S satisfy the sole defining relations

$$T^2 = S^3 = (TS)^p = R^{-1}(TS)^{-1}R(TS)^{\rho^2}$$
$$= R^{-\nu} \cdot T(TS)^{\rho^\nu}T(TS)^{\sigma^\nu}T(TS)^{\rho^\nu} = 1,$$

for $\nu = 2, 3, \cdots, p-1$, they generate an abstract group $\{S, T\}$ which is simply isomorphic with the group G of linear fractional transformations of determinant unity in the $GF[p]$.

Consider the concrete elements

$$t:\ x' = \frac{-1}{x} \qquad \text{and} \qquad s:\ x' = \frac{x-1}{x};$$

then we have $\qquad ts:\ x' = x + 1.$

Form r, $\qquad r = t(ts)^{\rho}t(ts)^{\sigma}t(ts)^{\rho}:\ x' = \rho^2 x.$

Then it is easy to see that $\{s, t\}$ is the group G of order $\frac{1}{2}(p+1)p(p-1)$. Moreover, s and t satisfy the conditions on S and T in the theorem, as one may readily verify; whence it follows that $\{S, T\}$ is simply isomorphic with $\{s, t\}$, or G, if it is true that the order of $\{S, T\}$ is not greater than $\frac{1}{2}(p+1)p(p-1)$; and we shall establish the theorem by showing that this condition is indeed satisfied.

Let H be the subgroup $\{R, TS\}$. From the given conditions we see that

$$(TS)^p = 1, \quad R^{-1}(TS)R = (TS)^{\rho^2}.$$

Taking $\nu = \frac{1}{2}(p-1)$ in the conditions of the theorem and remembering that $\rho^{\frac{1}{2}(p-1)} \equiv -1 \bmod p$, we find that

$$R^{\frac{1}{2}(p-1)} = 1.$$

But r and ts are of orders $\frac{1}{2}(p-1)$ and p respectively; and therefore these are the orders of R and TS. The conditions now established for R and TS imply that H is of order $\frac{1}{2}p(p-1)$.

Now consider the $p+1$ sets of $\frac{1}{2}p(p-1)$ elements each, namely:

$$HT, \quad H(ST)^i. \qquad (i=0, 1, \cdots, p-1)$$

These are distinct, since the corresponding elements of $\{s, t\}$ are distinct. Now $HT \cdot ST = HTS \cdot T = HT$, $H(ST)^i \cdot ST = H(ST)^{i+1}$; hence these sets are permuted among themselves on multiplication on the right by ST. That they are also permuted among themselves by multiplication on the right by T follows from the relations

$$HT \cdot T = H = H(ST)^0, \quad H \cdot T = HT,$$

$$\begin{aligned} H(ST)^{\rho^\nu}T &= H(ST)^{\rho^\nu}T(ST)^{\sigma^\nu}(TS)^{\rho^\nu}(TS)^{-\rho^\nu}(ST)^{-\sigma^\nu} \\ &= HT(TS)^{\rho^\nu}T(TS)^{\sigma^\nu}T(TS)^{\rho^\nu} \cdot (TS)^{-\rho^\nu}(ST)^{-\sigma^\nu} \\ &= HR^\nu(TS)^{-\rho^\nu}(ST)^{-\sigma^\nu} \\ &= H(ST)^{-\sigma^\nu}. \end{aligned}$$

Hence these $p+1$ sets contain all the elements $\{S, T\}$. Therefore the order of $\{S, T\}$ is not greater than $\frac{1}{2}(p+1)p(p-1)$, a proposition from which the theorem follows, as we have already seen.

EXERCISES

1. Show that each of the groups $LF(2, 5)$ and $LF(2, 2^2)$ is simply isomorphic with the alternating group of degree 5.

2. Show that $LF(2, 3^2)$ is simply isomorphic with the alternating group of degree 6.

3. Show that the fourfold transitive group of degree 11 and the fivefold transitive group of degree 12 are both simple groups. (See Ex. 12 on page 151.)

4. Show that Mathieu's fivefold transitive group of degree 24 and the fourfold and threefold transitive groups of degrees 23 and 22 contained in it are all simple groups. (See Ex. 9 on page 164.)

5. Show that the totality of linear transformations of the form

$$x_i' = a_i x_1 + b_i x_2 + c_i x_3 \qquad (i = 1, 2, 3)$$

in the $GF[p^n]$, with nonzero determinants Δ,

$$\Delta \equiv \begin{vmatrix} a_1 & b_1 & c_1 \\ a_2 & b_2 & c_2 \\ a_3 & b_3 & c_3 \end{vmatrix},$$

constitute a group and prove that its order is

$$(p^{3n}-1)(p^{3n}-p^n)(p^{3n}-p^{2n}).$$

[SUGGESTION. Show first that the number of transformations leaving x_1 fixed is $(p^n+1)p^n(p^n-1)^2p^{2n}$, and then that x_1 may be changed by the elements of the set into just $p^{3n}-1$ distinct linear functions $\lambda x_1 + \mu x_2 + \nu x_3$.]

6. Show that the totality of linear homogeneous transformations of the form

$$\rho x'_i = a_i x_1 + b_i x_2 + c_i x_3 \qquad (i = 1, 2, 3)$$

in the $GF[p^n]$, with nonzero determinants Δ (see Ex. 5), constitute a group of order

$$(p^{3n}-1)p^{2n}(p^{2n}-1)p^n.$$

If the determinants are further restricted to be cubes of elements in the field, show that the resulting transformations form a subgroup (denoted by $H(3, p^n)$) whose order is

$$\epsilon(p^{3n}-1)p^{2n}(p^{2n}-1)p^n,$$

where ϵ is $1/3$ or 1 according as p^n-1 is or is not divisible by 3.

7. Consider the $p^{2n}+p^n+1$ distinct symbols (λ, μ, ν), where λ, μ, ν range independently over the marks of the $GF[p^n]$ except that they are not simultaneously zero, and where (λ, μ, ν) and $(\rho\lambda, \rho\mu, \rho\nu)$ are considered identical if ρ is a nonzero mark of the field. Show that these symbols are permuted by the group $H(3, p^n)$ of Ex. 6 according to a simply isomorphic doubly transitive group of degree $p^{2n}+p^n+1$ and order

$$\epsilon(p^{2n}+p^n+1)(p^{2n}+p^n)p^{2n}(p^n-1)^2,$$

where $\epsilon = 1/3$ or 1 according as p^n-1 is or is not divisible by 3.

8. It is known that the group $H(3, p^n)$ of Exs. 6 and 7 is simple in all cases. Verify this for the cases in which the order is less than 1,000,000; that is, for $p^n = 2, 3, 2^2, 5$. Show that $H(3, 2)$ is simply isomorphic with $LF(2, 7)$, and that $H(3, 2^2)$ is not simply isomorphic with the alternating group of degree 8. [SUGGESTION. Show that the elements of order 2 in $H(3, 2^2)$ form a single conjugate set, while this is not true of the alternating group of degree 8.]

9. Dickson (*Linear Groups*, pp. 309–310) has given a list of the 53 known simple groups of composite orders less than 1,000,000. By means of the foregoing exercises and of Theorems XXXV of § **71** and IX of § **42** form a list of 48 of these simple groups. Then complete a list of 53 by establishing the following five propositions:

(1) In the case $p^n = 3^2$ just 28 of the symbols (λ, μ, ν) of Ex. 7 satisfy the equation $\lambda^4 + \mu^4 + \nu^4 = 0$. The largest subgroup of the group $H(3, 3^2)$ of Ex. 6 which permutes these among themselves induces on them a doubly transitive group of degree 28 and order $28 \cdot 27 \cdot 8$, and this group is simple.

(2) In the case $p^n = 2^4$ just 65 of the symbols (λ, μ, ν) of Ex. 7 satisfy the equation $\lambda^5 + \mu^5 + \nu^5 = 0$. The largest subgroup of the group $H(3, 2^4)$ of Ex. 6 which permutes these among themselves induces on them a doubly transitive group of degree 65 and order $65 \cdot 64 \cdot 15$, and this group is simple.

(3) In the case $p^n = 5^2$ just 126 of the symbols (λ, μ, ν) of Ex. 7 satisfy the equation $\lambda^6 + \mu^6 + \nu^6 = 0$. The largest subgroup of $H(3, 5^2)$ of Ex. 6 which permutes these among themselves induces on them a doubly transitive group of degree 126 and order $126 \cdot 125 \cdot 8$, and this group is simple.

(4) In the $GF[2^2]$ just 45 of the symbols $(\lambda, \mu, \nu, \rho)$, where λ, μ, ν, ρ are not simultaneously zero and $(\lambda, \mu, \nu, \rho) \equiv (\sigma\lambda, \sigma\mu, \sigma\nu, \sigma\rho)$ if $\sigma \neq 0$, satisfy the equation $\lambda^3 + \mu^3 + \nu^3 + \rho^3 = 0$. Show that the totality of linear homogeneous transformations of the form

$$\sigma x'_i = \sum_{j=1}^{4} a_{ij} x_j \qquad (i = 1, 2, 3, 4)$$

in the $GF[2^2]$, and of nonzero determinant, each of which permutes these 45 symbols among themselves induces on them a transitive group of degree 45 and order 25920, and prove that this group is simple.

(5) Consider the totality of transformations

$$x'_i = \sum_{j=1}^{4} a_{ij} x_j, \quad y'_i = \sum_{j=1}^{4} a_{ij} y_j \qquad (i = 1, 2, 3, 4)$$

of nonzero determinants, in the $GF[2^2]$, each of which leaves formally invariant the function $y_2x_1 + y_1x_2 + y_4x_3 + y_3x_4$. Show that this totality constitutes a simple group of order

$$979200 = (2^8 - 1)2^6(2^4 - 1)2^2 = 256 \cdot 255 \cdot 15.$$

10. Show that each of the 53 known simple groups of composite order less than 1,000,000 (see Ex. 9) is simply isomorphic with a multiply transitive permutation group, with the possible exceptions of the groups named in parts (4) and (5) of Ex. 9.

11. Prove the existence of two triply transitive and four doubly transitive groups of degree 28, and of four triply transitive and three doubly transitive groups of degree 65.

12. Show that there are three and just three doubly transitive groups of degree 49 and order $49 \cdot 48$.

13. For every positive integer L and prime p there exists a positive integer n such that the number of triply transitive groups of degree $p^n + 1$ is greater than L.

14. For every positive integer L there exist a prime p and a positive integer n such that the number of doubly transitive groups of degree p^n and order $p^n(p^n - 1)$ is greater than L. [SUGGESTION. Let n be a product of suitably chosen distinct primes and take p to be of the form $nx + 1$. Use Theorem XXX and consider the centrals of the groups whose existence is asserted by that theorem.]

15. For every integer m greater than 2 prove, by aid of the $GF[2^2]$, the existence of a non-Abelian group of order 3^m which contains an Abelian subgroup of order 3^{m-1} and type $(1, 1, \cdots, 1)$. [SUGGESTION. Let the Abelian subgroup of order 3^{m-1} consist of the transformations $\rho x'_i = \alpha_i x_i$ for $i = 1, 2, \cdots, m$.]

MISCELLANEOUS EXERCISES

1. If ω is a primitive mark of the $GF[p^n]$, show that $\omega, \omega^p, \omega^{p^2}, \cdots, \omega^{p^{n-1}}$ are roots of the same irreducible equation of degree n and with integral coefficients.

2. If ω is a primitive mark of the $GF[p^n]$ satisfying the equation $\omega^n = c_1\omega^{n-1} + c_2\omega^{n-2} + \cdots + c_n$, where the coefficients c_i are integers, and if we define the sequences $u_0^{(i)}, u_1^{(i)}, u_2^{(i)}, u_3^{(i)}, \cdots$ by means of the relation

$$\omega^x = u_x^{(1)}\omega^{n-1} + u_x^{(2)}\omega^{n-2} + \cdots + u_x^{(n)},$$

where the $u_x^{(i)}$ have integral values, show that we have modulo p the relations,

$$u_{x+1}^{(1)} = c_1 u_x^{(1)} + u_x^{(2)},$$
$$u_{x+1}^{(2)} = c_2 u_x^{(1)} + u_x^{(3)},$$
$$\cdots\cdots\cdots\cdots$$
$$u_{x+1}^{(n-1)} = c_{n-1} u_x^{(1)} + u_x^{(n)},$$
$$u_{x+1}^{(n)} = c_n u_x^{(1)},$$

and that for $0 \leqq x < n$ we have $u_x^{(i)}$ equal to zero except when $x = n - i$, in which case the value is 1. Show, moreover, that each of the functions $u_x^{(i)}$ of x satisfies modulo p the recurrence relation

$$u_{x+n} = c_1 u_{x+n-1} + \cdots + c_{n-1} u_{x+1} + c_n u_x.$$

3. Consider a recurrence relation of the form

$$u_{x+n} = c_1 u_{x+n-1} + \cdots + c_{n-1} u_{x+1} + c_n u_x \qquad (x = 0, 1, 2, \cdots)$$

in which the coefficients c_i are integers belonging to the set $0, 1, 2, \cdots, p-1$, where p is a prime; and let $u_x^{(i)}$ $(i = 1, 2, \cdots, n)$ be the solution satisfying the initial conditions $u_x^{(i)} = 0$ for $0 \leqq x < n$ except that $u_x^{(n-i)} = 1$. Let $R_x^{(i)}$ be the least non-negative residue of $u_x^{(i)}$ modulo p. Suppose that $c_n \neq 0$. Show that the sequence $R_0^{(i)}, R_1^{(i)}, R_2^{(i)} \cdots$ is periodic for each i of the set $1, 2, \cdots, n$, and prove that for just $\phi(p^n - 1)/n$ sets $c_1, c_2, \cdots, c_n$ the period of each of these sequences is $p^n - 1$.

4. Let $F_n(x)$ be the polynomial with leading coefficient unity whose roots are the primitive nth roots of unity without repetition. Let $p_1, p_2, \cdots, p_\nu$ be the distinct prime factors of n. Show that

$$F_n(x) = \frac{(x^n - 1) \cdot \Pi\,(x^{n/p_ip_j} - 1) \cdot \Pi(x^{n/p_ip_jp_kp_l} - 1) \cdots}{\Pi(x^{n/p_i} - 1) \cdot \Pi(x^{n/p_ip_jp_k} - 1) \cdots},$$

where the products Π are taken for all the combinations of distinct p's in the numbers indicated, each product Π in the numerator referring to an even number of the p's and each one in the denominator to an odd number of the p's. Thence show that the coefficients in the polynomial $F_n(x)$ are integers.

5. With the notation of Ex. 4 show that

$$x^n - 1 = \Pi F_d(x),$$

where the product Π is taken for all divisors d of n.

6. Show that the irreducible factors modulo p of $x^{p^n} - x$ are x and the irreducible factors modulo p of the polynomials $F_r(x)$ (see Ex. 4), where r runs over the divisors of $p^n - 1$.

7. In the $GF[p^n]$ there exists a mark ρ such that $F_r(\rho) = 0$, r being any factor of $p^n - 1$ (see Ex. 6). A mark ρ such that $F_r(\rho) = 0$ is of order r. It is therefore primitive when and only when $r = p^n - 1$.

8. Let ω be a mark of the $GF[p^n]$ satisfying the equation

$$A(x) \equiv x^n + a_1 x^{n-1} + \cdots + a_n = 0,$$

where the a_i are integral marks of the field. A necessary and sufficient condition that ω shall be a primitive mark is that $A(x)$ shall be a factor modulo p of $F_{p^n-1}(x)$ (see Exs. 4–7).

9. Let $g_1(\alpha, \beta)$ and $g_2(\alpha, \beta)$ be the polynomials

$$g_1(\alpha, \beta) = \frac{f(a) - f(b)}{a - b}, \quad g_2(\alpha, \beta) = \frac{af(b) - bf(a)}{a - b}, \quad (f(x) \equiv F_{p^2-1}(x))$$

where $a + b = -\alpha$ and $ab = \beta$. Show that a necessary and sufficient condition that the polynomial $x^2 + \alpha x + \beta$ with integral coefficients shall be irreducible modulo p and shall have for a solution in the $GF[p^2]$ a primitive mark of that field is that both $g_1(\alpha, \beta)$ and $g_2(\alpha, \beta)$ shall be congruent to zero modulo p. (See Exs. 4–7.)

10. Show that a necessary and sufficient condition that the sequences in Ex. 3 shall have modulo p the period $p^n - 1$ is that

$$x^n - c_1 x^{n-1} - c_2 x^{n-2} - \cdots - c_n$$

shall be a factor modulo p of the polynomial $F_{p^n-1}(x)$ (compare Ex. 4).

11. Let p and q be odd primes such that $p = 2q + 1$. Let g be a primitive root modulo p; and let m and n be primitive roots modulo q. Let β be any odd integer. Let x_t $(t = 0, 1, 2, \cdots, p-1)$ be a set of p letters. Consider the transformations

$$S: \qquad t' = t + 1,$$
$$S_0: \qquad t' = \tfrac{1}{2}\{(g^{\beta(p-n)}t^{n-m} + 1)t^m - (g^{\beta(p-n)}t^{n-m} - 1)t^{m+q}\}$$

in the $GF[p]$ and the permutations S and S_0 induced by them on the x's. Let $S_k = S^{-k}S_0S^k$ $(k = 0, 1, \cdots, p-1)$. Show that each permutation S_k leaves three x's fixed while each x is left fixed by just three of the permutations $S_0, S_1, \cdots, S_{p-1}$.

12. When $p = 11$, $g = m = n = 2$, $\beta = 3$, show that the permutation group $\{S, S_0\}$ of Ex. 11 is the Mathieu fourfold transitive group of degree 11.

13. In the same case (Ex. 12) show that $\{S, S_0{}^2\}$ is the doubly transitive group of degree 11 and order $11 \cdot 10 \cdot 6$.

14. When $p = 23$, $g = -2$, $m = n = 2$, $\beta = 1$, show that the permutation group $\{S, S_0{}^2\}$, and hence $\{S, S_0\}$ of Ex. 11, is the alternating group of degree 23.

15. When $p = 23$, $g = 5$, $m = n = 2$, $\beta = 1$, show that the permutation group $\{S, S_0{}^2\}$ of Ex. 11 is the Mathieu fourfold transitive group of degree 23.

CHAPTER X

Groups of Isomorphisms of Abelian Groups of Order p^m and Type $(1, 1, \cdots, 1)$

72. Analytical Representation of Elements and Subgroups. Let $G_{(k+1)n}$, or G, be an Abelian group of order $p^{(k+1)n}$ and type $(1, 1, \cdots, 1)$, where p is any prime and $k+1$ and n are any positive integers. We shall represent the elements of G and certain subgroups of G by a sort of "systems of co-ordinates" based on the Galois field $GF[p^n]$, thus generalizing certain representations employed in § 29.

Let us denote a particular set of $(k+1)n$ independent generating elements of $G_{(k+1)n}$ by

$$\begin{array}{l} a_{01}, a_{02}, a_{03}, \cdots, a_{0n}, \\ a_{11}, a_{12}, a_{13}, \cdots, a_{1n}, \\ \cdot \quad \cdot \quad \cdot \quad \cdot \quad \cdot \quad \cdot \\ a_{k1}, a_{k2}, a_{k3}, \cdots, a_{kn}. \end{array}$$

Then any given element in G may be written uniquely in the form

$$\prod_{i=0}^{k} a_{i1}^{s_{i1}} a_{i2}^{s_{i2}} \cdots a_{in}^{s_{in}},$$

where the exponents s are integers taken modulo p. The element denoted by this product for a fixed set of exponents s will be represented by the symbol

$$\{\mu_0, \mu_1, \mu_2, \cdots, \mu_k\},$$

where μ_i $(i = 0, 1, 2, \cdots, k)$ denotes that mark of the Galois field $GF[p^n]$ which may be written in the form

$$\mu_i = s_{i1} + s_{i2}\omega + s_{i3}\omega^2 + \cdots + s_{in}\omega^{n-1},$$

ω being a fixed primitive mark of $GF[p^n]$. This correspondence of elements and symbols is unique in the sense that to each element there corresponds a single symbol and to each symbol there corresponds a single element. The marks μ_i in the symbol $\{\mu_0, \mu_1, \cdots, \mu_k\}$ are obviously analogous to nonhomogeneous co-ordinates, while the elements of G represented by these symbols are analogous to points in a Euclidean space of $k+1$ dimensions.

For the multiplication of these symbols, corresponding to the multiplication of elements in G, we have the following obvious formula:

$$\{\mu_0, \mu_1, \cdots, \mu_k\}\{\nu_0, \nu_1, \cdots, \nu_k\} = \{\mu_0 + \nu_0, \mu_1 + \nu_1, \cdots, \mu_k + \nu_k\}.$$

Now suppose that $\mu_0, \mu_1, \cdots, \mu_k$ is any fixed set of $k+1$ marks of $GF[p^n]$, at least one of them being different from zero; and consider the set of elements

$$\{\mu\mu_0, \mu\mu_1, \cdots, \mu\mu_k\},$$

where μ is a variable running over the p^n marks of $GF[p^n]$. It is obvious that the p^n elements in this set are all distinct. Moreover, the product of any two of them is in the set, as one sees immediately from the law of multiplication and the properties of the marks of a Galois field. This set of elements therefore constitutes a subgroup of G of order p^n. The elements

$$\{\omega^i\mu_0, \omega^i\mu_1, \cdots, \omega^i\mu_k\} \qquad (i = 0, 1, 2, \cdots, n-1)$$

constitute a set of independent generators of this subgroup. If σ is any nonzero mark of $GF[p^n]$, the same subgroup consists of the set of elements

$$\{\mu\sigma\mu_0, \mu\sigma\mu_1, \cdots, \mu\sigma\mu_k\},$$

where μ varies as before. The subgroup itself may therefore be represented by the symbol

$$(\mu_0, \mu_1, \cdots, \mu_k),$$

where $\mu_0, \mu_1, \cdots, \mu_k$ are interpreted as the "homogeneous co-ordinates" of the subgroup. On multiplying each of the co-ordinates by one and the same nonzero mark of the field, we have merely proportional homogeneous co-ordinates of the same subgroup. To each ordered set of co-ordinates, at least one of them being different from zero, there corresponds a subgroup of G of order p^n. [The geometric interpretation which is implicit here will be developed in the next chapter.]

The number of subgroups in the total set denoted by $(\mu_0, \mu_1, \cdots, \mu_k)$ for varying sets of μ's is readily determined. The symbols μ may be chosen independently, each in p^n ways, except that they cannot all be zero in any given set. Hence the number of choices is $p^{(k+1)n} - 1$. To obtain the number of subgroups we must divide this by the number $p^n - 1$ of possible factors of proportionality in the various notations for the same subgroup. Hence the number of subgroups $(\mu_0, \mu_1, \cdots, \mu_k)$ is

$$\frac{p^{(k+1)n} - 1}{p^n - 1}, \quad \text{or} \quad 1 + p^n + p^{2n} + \cdots + p^{kn}.$$

Once G has been given, this selection of subgroups depends on two things: the ordered set of $(k+1)n$ independent generators and the primitive mark ω by means of which the marks μ_i were first introduced. With reference to this selected basis of determination we shall call the set of subgroups just determined a geometric set of subgroups. The reason for this terminology will appear in the next chapter. By means of other sets of generators and other primitive marks we might, in cases not too restricted, select other geometric sets of subgroups of G. Since we shall have no occasion to change the basis in any particular discussion, we shall speak of the foregoing geometric set of subgroups without reference to the basis on which it has been defined.

For the case when $n = 1$ a geometric set of subgroups consists of all the subgroups of order p.

No two subgroups of a geometric set of subgroups have any element in common except the identity, as one readily shows by means of the symbols which represent their elements. Moreover, any given element of G occurs in some subgroup of a geometric set, as is obvious from the way in which such a set is defined.

73. The General Linear Homogeneous Group $GLH(k+1, p^n)$. Let us consider the totality of linear homogeneous transformations

$$x'_i = \sum_{j=0}^{k} a_{ij}x_j, \qquad (i = 0, 1, 2, \cdots, k)$$

where the coefficients a_{ij} are marks of the $GF[p^n]$ such that the determinant $|a_{ij}|$ is different from zero. The product of any two of these transformations is in the set, whence it follows readily that the totality constitutes a group. It is called the general linear homogeneous group on $k+1$ variables with coefficients in the $GF[p^n]$. We shall denote the group by $GLH(k+1, p^n)$ and its order by $GLH[k+1, p^n]$.

Let us determine the order of this group. The number of distinct linear functions $\alpha_0 x_0 + \alpha_1 x_1 + \cdots + \alpha_k x_k$ by which the transformations of this group can replace x_0 is $p^{(k+1)n} - 1$, since the coefficients may be chosen independently, each from the p^n marks of $GF[p^n]$, except that they cannot all be simultaneously zero. Let $R_1, R_2, \cdots, R_N$ be all the transformations in the group each of which leaves x_0 fixed, and let T be any transformation of the group. Then the transformations $TR_1, TR_2, \cdots, TR_N$ all replace x_0 by that linear function by which T replaces x_0. If U is any transformation in the group which has the property of replacing x_0 by the same linear function as that by which T replaces x_0, then $T^{-1}U$ leaves x_0 fixed and hence is some R_i so that $U = TR_i$, and hence U is in the set $TR_1, TR_2, \cdots, TR_N$. Therefore the order of $GLH(k+1, p^n)$ is

$$GLH[k+1, p^n] = N(p^{(k+1)n} - 1).$$

The transformations R_ν have the form

$$x'_0 = x_0, \quad x'_i = \sum_{j=0}^{k} a_{ij} x_j, \qquad (i = 1, 2, \cdots, k)$$

where the coefficients $a_{10}, a_{20}, \cdots, a_{k0}$ are arbitrary while the remaining coefficients are such that their determinant is different from zero. Therefore

$$N = p^{nk} GLH[k, p^n],$$

whence it follows that

$$GLH[k+1, p^n] = p^{nk}(p^{(k+1)n} - 1) GLH[k, p^n].$$

Now $GLH[1, p^n] = p^n - 1$. From this fact and the preceding recursion relation we have

$$\begin{aligned} GLH[k+1, p^n] &= p^{nk}(p^{(k+1)n} - 1) p^{n(k-1)}(p^{nk} - 1) \cdots p^n(p^{2n} - 1)(p^n - 1) \\ &= (p^{n(k+1)} - 1)(p^{n(k+1)} - p^n)(p^{n(k+1)} - p^{2n}) \cdots (p^{n(k+1)} - p^{kn}). \end{aligned}$$

If in a particular transformation of $GLH(k+1, p^n)$ the symbols $x_0, x_1, \cdots, x_k$ vary so that $\{x_0, x_1, \cdots, x_k\}$ runs over all the elements of the group $G_{(k+1)n}$ of the preceding section, then $\{x_0', x'_1, \cdots, x'_k\}$ likewise runs over all the elements of G. The transformation thus establishes a one-to-one correspondence of the elements of the group to its elements in some order. The identity $(0, 0, \cdots, 0)$ corresponds to itself. Moreover, if $\{\mu_0, \mu_1, \cdots, \mu_k\}$ and $\{\nu_0, \nu_1, \cdots, \nu_k\}$ correspond respectively to $\{\mu'_0, \mu'_1, \cdots, \mu'_k\}$ and $\{\nu'_0, \nu'_1, \cdots, \nu'_k\}$, then the product $\{\mu_0 + \nu_0, \cdots, \mu_k + \nu_k\}$ of the first pair of elements corresponds to the product $\{\mu'_0 + \nu'_0, \cdots, \mu'_k + \nu'_k\}$ of the second pair. Hence the correspondence of elements brought about by the given transformation effects an isomorphism of the group with itself. It is obvious that two distinct transformations effect different isomorphisms. Hence the group $GLH(k+1, p^n)$ induces a set of isomorphisms of $G_{(k+1)n}$ with itself, and this set constitutes a subgroup of the group I of isomorphisms of G with itself. This is a proper subgroup when and only when $n > 1$, since (§ 28) the order of I is

$$(p^{(k+1)n} - 1)(p^{(k+1)n} - p)(p^{(k+1)n} - p^2) \cdots (p^{(k+1)n} - p^{(k+1)n-1}).$$

Let us consider more closely those isomorphisms of G with itself which are thus induced by $GLH(k+1, p^n)$. Let $\{\mu_0, \mu_1, \cdots, \mu_k\}$ be any element of G other than the identity and let $\{\mu'_0, \mu'_1, \cdots, \mu'_k\}$ be the element to which it corresponds under a given transformation belonging to $GLH(k+1, p^n)$. Then the element $\{\mu\mu_0, \mu\mu_1, \cdots, \mu\mu_k\}$ corresponds to the element $\{\mu\mu'_0, \mu\mu'_1, \cdots, \mu\mu'_k\}$ under the same transformation. Hence the subgroup $(\mu_0, \mu_1, \cdots, \mu_k)$ corresponds to the subgroup $(\mu'_0, \mu'_1, \cdots, \mu'_k)$. Therefore every transformation in $GLH(k+1, p^n)$ induces an isomorphism of G with itself such that every subgroup in the geometric set of subgroups corresponds to a subgroup of this set. Moreover, the multiplication of each coefficient a_{ij} in the transformation by one and the same nonzero mark σ of the field gives a new transformation in which the correspondence of subgroups in the geometric set is unaltered, whereas any other modification of the transformation leads to a different correspondence of these subgroups.

Then consider the transformations

$$\rho x'_i = \sum_{j=0}^{k} a_{ij}x_j, \qquad (i = 0, 1, \cdots, k; \ |a_{ij}| \neq 0)$$

where two transformations are treated as identical if it is possible to write them with the same coefficients a_{ij} even though in order to do this it is necessary to have different values for ρ. Then two distinct transformations of this set induce different correspondences of subgroups in the geometric set of subgroups. This transformation group, and the simply isomorphic permutation group induced by it on the symbols $(x_0, x_1, \cdots, x_k)$ for subgroups, will be denoted by $P(k, p^n)$. From the foregoing paragraph it follows that $GLH(k+1, p^n)$ has $(p^n - 1, 1)$ isomorphism with $P(k, p^n)$. Hence the order of $P(k, p^n)$ is

$$\frac{1}{p^n - 1} \prod_{i=0}^{k} (p^{(k+1)n} - p^{in}).$$

As a permutation group on the symbols $(x_0, x_1, \cdots, x_k)$ the group $P(k, p^n)$ is of degree

$$1 + p^n + p^{2n} + \cdots + p^{kn}.$$

When $k = 0$ it consists of the identity alone. When k is positive we shall show that it is doubly transitive. The transformation

$$\rho x'_i = \sum_{j=0}^{k} a_{ij}x_j \qquad (i = 0, 1, \cdots, k; \ |a_{ij}| \neq 0)$$

replaces $(1, 0, 0, \cdots, 0)$ and $(0, 1, 0, \cdots, 0)$ by

$$(a_{00}, a_{10}, a_{20}, \cdots, a_{k0}) \quad \text{and} \quad (a_{01}, a_{11}, a_{21}, \cdots, a_{k1})$$

respectively. It is evident that the a's may be chosen so that these symbols represent any two distinct subgroups belonging to the geometric set. Therefore the permutation group is doubly transitive. That $P(1, p^n)$ is triply transitive follows from the readily verified fact that $P(1, p^n)$ is identical with the group Γ_n of Theorem XXXI of § **70**; or the result may be easily established directly.

In the next two chapters the group $P(k, p^n)$ will be treated in detail from another point of view.

74. Analytical Representations of the Group *I* of Isomorphisms of the Group $G_{(k+1)n}$ with Itself. Let us now consider the transformation

$$x'_i = \sum_{s=1}^{n} \sum_{j=0}^{k} a_{ijs} x_j^{p^{n-s}} \qquad (i = 0, 1, 2, \cdots, k)$$

where the coefficients a_{ijs} are marks of $GF[p^n]$ such that these transformation equations have a unique solution for the symbols x_i in terms of the symbols x'_i. (See Ex. 12 on page 305.) If

$$x'_i = \sum_{s=1}^{n} \sum_{j=0}^{k} b_{ijs} x_j^{p^{n-s}} \qquad (i = 0, 1, 2, \cdots, k)$$

is a second transformation of the same kind, the product of the two may be written in the form

$$\begin{aligned} x'_i &= \sum_{s=1}^{n} \sum_{j=0}^{k} a_{ijs} \left(\sum_{\sigma=1}^{n} \sum_{\lambda=0}^{k} b_{j\lambda\sigma} x_\lambda^{p^{n-\sigma}} \right)^{p^{n-s}} \\ &= \sum_{s=1}^{n} \sum_{j=0}^{k} a_{ijs} \left(\sum_{\sigma=1}^{n} \sum_{\lambda=0}^{k} b_{j\lambda\sigma}^{p^{n-s}} x_\lambda^{p^{2n-s-\sigma}} \right) \\ &= \sum_{\sigma=1}^{n} \sum_{\lambda=0}^{k} \sum_{s=1}^{n} \sum_{j=0}^{k} a_{ijs} b_{j\lambda\sigma}^{p^{n-s}} x_\lambda^{p^{2n-s-\sigma}} \\ &= \sum_{t=1}^{n} \sum_{l=0}^{k} \alpha_{ilt} x_l^{p^{n-t}}, \qquad (i = 0, 1, 2, \cdots, k) \end{aligned}$$

the α's being defined in a way which is obvious from a comparison of the last two members of the equation in the light of the fact that $x_\lambda^{p^n} = x_\lambda$. Thus the product of two transformations of the class in consideration belongs also to the class. The named class of transformations therefore constitutes a group. This we shall call the group T. We shall show that T induces the group I of isomorphisms of $G_{(k+1)n}$ with itself.

Let $\{\mu'_0, \mu'_1, \cdots, \mu'_k\}$ and $\{\nu'_0, \nu'_1, \cdots, \nu'_k\}$ be the elements of $G_{(k+1)n}$ corresponding to $\{\mu_0, \mu_1, \cdots, \mu_k\}$ and $\{\nu_0, \nu_1, \cdots, \nu_k\}$ respectively, under the given transformation with coefficients

a_{ijs}. Then under the same transformation we have

$$\mu'_i + \nu'_i = \sum_{s=1}^{n} \sum_{j=0}^{k} a_{ijs}(\mu_j^{p^{n-s}} + \nu_j^{p^{n-s}})$$
$$= \sum_{s=1}^{n} \sum_{j=0}^{k} a_{ijs}(\mu_j + \nu_j)^{p^{n-s}}. \qquad (i = 0, 1, 2, \cdots, k)$$

Hence $\{\mu'_0 + \nu'_0, \cdots, \mu'_k + \nu'_k\}$ corresponds to $\{\mu_0 + \nu_0, \cdots, \mu_k + \nu_k\}$ under the same transformation. Thence we see that if two given elements of G correspond respectively to two other given elements of G under a given transformation belonging to T, then under the same transformation the product of the first pair of elements of G corresponds to the product of the second pair. Hence the transformation sets up an isomorphism of G with itself. Therefore T induces on G a group which is contained in the group I of isomorphisms of G with itself. It remains to be shown that every element of I is in this induced group.

For the latter purpose it is convenient to represent the group T in a different form. We retain the symbol ω to denote a primitive mark of the $GF[p^n]$. Then any mark of $GF[p^n]$ may be written in the form

$$\gamma_0 + \gamma_1\omega + \gamma_2\omega^2 + \cdots + \gamma_{n-1}\omega^{n-1}$$

where each γ_i is a mark of the $GF[p]$ and hence is an integer taken modulo p. Then we may write

$$x_i = \sum_{\lambda=0}^{n-1} \xi_{i\lambda}\omega^\lambda, \quad x'_i = \sum_{\lambda=0}^{n-1} \xi'_{i\lambda}\omega^\lambda, \quad a_{ijs} = \sum_{\lambda=0}^{n-1} a_{ijs\lambda}\omega^\lambda,$$

where the $\xi_{i\lambda}$, $\xi'_{i\lambda}$, $a_{ijs\lambda}$ are integers taken modulo p. Then the transformation τ of T which has the coefficients a_{ijs} may be written in the form

$$\sum_{\lambda=0}^{n-1} \xi'_{i\lambda}\omega_\lambda = \sum_{s=1}^{n} \sum_{j=0}^{k} \sum_{\lambda=0}^{n-1} a_{ijs\lambda}\omega^\lambda \left(\sum_{\mu=0}^{n-1} \xi_{j\mu}\omega^\mu\right)^{p^{n-s}}$$
$$= \sum_{s=1}^{n} \sum_{j=0}^{k} \sum_{\lambda=0}^{n-1} \sum_{\mu=0}^{n-1} a_{ijs\lambda}\xi_{j\mu}{}^{p^{n-s}}\omega^{\mu p^{n-s}+\lambda}$$
$$= \sum_{s=1}^{n} \sum_{j=0}^{k} \sum_{\lambda=0}^{n-1} \sum_{\mu=0}^{n-1} a_{ijs\lambda}\xi_{j\mu}\omega^{\mu p^{n-s}+\lambda}. \qquad (i = 0, 1, 2, \cdots, k)$$

Now every power of ω can be expressed linearly in terms of $\omega^0, \omega^1, \omega^2, \cdots, \omega^{n-1}$ with coefficients which are integers taken modulo p, since ω satisfies an equation of degree n with coefficients which are integers taken modulo p. On effecting this reduction we may write the last equation in the form

$$\sum_{\sigma=0}^{n-1} \xi'_{i\sigma}\omega^\sigma = \sum_{\mu=0}^{n-1}\sum_{\sigma=0}^{n-1}\sum_{j=0}^{k} \alpha_{ij\mu\sigma}\xi_{j\mu}\omega^\sigma \qquad (i = 0, 1, \cdots, k)$$

where the $\alpha_{ij\mu\sigma}$ are integers taken modulo p. Equating coefficients of like powers of ω, we have

$$\xi'_{i\lambda} = \sum_{\mu=0}^{n-1}\sum_{j=0}^{k} \alpha_{ij\mu\lambda}\xi_{j\mu}. \qquad (i = 0, 1, \cdots, k;\ \lambda = 0, 1, \cdots, n-1)$$

Thus we have a linear transformation on the $(k+1)n$ quantities $\xi_{i\lambda}$, the coefficients of the transformation being integers taken modulo p. Since the x_i are uniquely expressible in terms of the x'_i, it follows that the $\xi_{i\lambda}$ are uniquely expressible in terms of the $\xi'_{i\lambda}$ and thence that the transformation on the ξ's is nonsingular. Now the condition that the transformation on the ξ's shall be nonsingular is equivalent to the condition that the determinant of that transformation shall be different from zero.

The totality of such linear transformations on the $\xi_{i\lambda}$ is simply isomorphic with the group I of isomorphisms of G with itself, as we see from a result in § **73** when n of that section is 1 and $k+1$ is our present $(k+1)n$. Hence in order to complete the proof that T induces the whole group I it is sufficient to prove that each nonsingular linear homogeneous transformation on the $\xi_{i\lambda}$ with coefficients in the $GF[p]$ is equivalent to a corresponding transformation in T.

In order to attain this end let the last foregoing transformation now be any nonsingular linear homogeneous transformation on the $\xi_{i\lambda}$ with coefficients which are integers taken modulo p. Change λ to σ, in the resulting equation (for fixed σ) multiply both sides by ω^σ, then sum as to σ from 0 to $n-1$. Thus we have the preceding system of equations. From it we may go to the one which next precedes provided that we are able to write

$$\sum_{\mu=0}^{n-1}\sum_{\sigma=0}^{n-1}\sum_{j=0}^{k} \alpha_{ij\mu\sigma}\xi_{j\mu}\omega^{\sigma} = \sum_{s=1}^{n}\sum_{j=0}^{k}\sum_{\lambda=0}^{n-1}\sum_{\mu=0}^{n-1} a_{ijs\lambda}\xi_{j\mu}\omega^{\mu p^{n-s}+\lambda},$$

$$(i = 0, 1, \cdots, k)$$

where the coefficients $a_{ijs\lambda}$ are integers taken modulo p. If we have this relation we may readily continue the reverse transformations through the equations written till we reach a transformation in the group T, with the coefficients a_{ijs}, these being marks in $GF[p^n]$. Hence in order to show that every transformation on the $\xi_{i\lambda}$, of the type now in consideration, leads to an equivalent transformation of the group T, it is sufficient to prove the existence of integers $a_{ijs\lambda}$ modulo p such that the last foregoing system of equations reduces to an identity in the $\xi_{j\mu}$. For this purpose it is necessary and sufficient to show that integers $a_{ijs\lambda}$ modulo p exist such that the equation

$$\sum_{\sigma=0}^{n-1} \alpha_{ij\mu\sigma}\omega^{\sigma} = \sum_{s=1}^{n}\sum_{\lambda=0}^{n-1} a_{ijs\lambda}\omega^{\mu p^{n-s}+\lambda}$$

is valid for each set of values of i, j, μ. Let us write

$$\omega^{\mu p^{n-s}+\lambda} = \sum_{\sigma=0}^{n-1} \rho_{\mu\sigma s\lambda}\omega^{\sigma},$$

where the coefficients $\rho_{\mu\sigma s\lambda}$ are integers taken modulo p. Then for the existence of the quantities $a_{ijs\lambda}$ it is necessary and sufficient that we have the relations

$$\sum_{s=1}^{n}\sum_{\lambda=0}^{n-1} \rho_{\mu\sigma s\lambda}a_{ijs\lambda} = \alpha_{ij\mu\sigma}$$

for every i, j, μ, σ. If i and j are held fixed, these become n^2 equations in the n^2 unknown quantities $a_{ijs\lambda}$ ($s = 1, 2, \cdots, n$; $\lambda = 0, 1, \cdots, n-1$). In order that they shall have a solution, it is sufficient that their determinant D shall not vanish modulo p.

In order to prove that D does not vanish modulo p, we show that we are led to a contradiction if we suppose that $D \equiv 0 \bmod p$.

If $D \equiv 0 \bmod p$, then integers $t_{s\lambda}$ exist, not all congruent to zero modulo p, such that

$$\sum_{s=1}^{n} \sum_{\lambda=0}^{n-1} t_{s\lambda} \rho_{\mu\sigma s\lambda} = 0. \qquad (\mu, \sigma = 0, 1, \cdots, n-1)$$

For fixed σ multiply both members by ω^{σ}; then, summing as to σ, we have a result which may be put in the form

$$\sum_{s=1}^{n} \sum_{\lambda=0}^{n-1} t_{s\lambda} \sum_{\sigma=0}^{n-1} \rho_{\mu\sigma s\lambda} \omega^{\sigma} = 0; \qquad (\mu = 0, 1, \cdots, n-1)$$

or, in view of the definition of the quantities ρ,

$$\sum_{s=1}^{n} \sum_{\lambda=0}^{n-1} t_{s\lambda} \omega^{\mu p^{n-s+\lambda}} = 0;$$

or

$$\sum_{s=1}^{n} \omega^{\mu p^{n-s+\lambda}} \left(\sum_{\lambda=0}^{n-1} t_{s\lambda} \omega^{\lambda} \right) = 0. \qquad (\mu = 0, 1, \cdots, n-1)$$

Now no given one of the sums in the parenthesis can be zero unless every $t_{s\lambda}$ in that sum is zero. Hence, since not every $t_{s\lambda}$ is zero, one at least of these sums in the parenthesis is different from zero. Then the consistency of the foregoing system of equations requires that the determinant

$$\Delta = \begin{vmatrix} 1 & 1 & \cdots & 1 \\ \omega^{p^{n-1}} & \omega^{p^{n-2}} & \cdots & \omega^{p} \\ \omega^{2p^{n-1}} & \omega^{2p^{n-2}} & \cdots & \omega^{2p} \\ \cdot & \cdot & \cdot & \cdot \\ \omega^{(n-1)p^{n-1}} & \omega^{(n-1)p^{n-2}} & \cdots & \omega^{(n-1)p} \end{vmatrix}$$

shall vanish. But this determinant is, apart from a nonvanishing factor, equal to a product of factors each of which is of the form

$$\omega^{p^{n-\alpha}} - \omega^{p^{n-\beta}},$$

where α and β are distinct numbers from the set $1, 2, \cdots, n-1$. Since ω is a primitive mark of $GF[p^n]$ it follows that no one of these factors can vanish. Hence $\Delta \neq 0$. We have been led to this contradiction by assuming that $D \equiv 0 \bmod p$. Hence this congruence is not valid.

Summing up the argument, we have the following result:

The transformation group T, defined at the beginning of this section, induces the group I of isomorphisms of $G_{(k+1)n}$ with itself, and the two groups are simply isomorphic.

If G is an Abelian group of order p^m and type $(1, 1, \cdots, 1)$, then we have an analytical representation of the group I of isomorphisms of G with itself for each factorization of m in the form $m = (k+1)n$. For the group I itself we have the simplest representation when $n = 1$. The different possible representations, however, will furnish varying information concerning certain subgroups of I.

75. On Certain Subgroups of *I*. When the group I of isomorphisms of G is written in the form of the transformation group T of § **74**, certain interesting classes of subgroups become obvious. Let d be any divisor of n and write $n = d\nu$. Then in the typical transformation of T put a_{ijs} equal to zero when s is not divisible by d. Then the transformation takes the special form

$$x'_i = \sum_{t=1}^{\nu} \sum_{j=0}^{k} \bar{a}_{ijt} x_j^{p^{d(\nu-t)}}. \qquad (i = 0, 1, \cdots, k)$$

The product of this transformation by another of the same form may be written as a transformation of this form, the method of reduction being the same as that employed at the beginning of § **74**. The named transformations therefore form a group T_d which is a subgroup of T. It induces a corresponding simply isomorphic subgroup of the group I of isomorphisms of $G_{(k+1)n}$ with itself. It is obvious that T_1 is identical with T.

That the group T_d is equivalent to a corresponding linear homogeneous group with coefficients in the $GF[p^d]$ may be shown by an easy generalization of the method employed in the preceding section to establish this fact for the case $d = 1$. It is sufficient merely to sketch the argument. By means of a primitive mark ω of the $GF[p^n]$ any mark of this field may be written in the form

$$\gamma_0 + \gamma_1\omega + \cdots + \gamma_{\nu-1}\omega^{\nu-1},$$

where each γ_i is a mark of $GF[p^d]$; for these symbols are $p^{\nu d}$ in number and no two of them represent the same mark, since if two of them represented the same mark the primitive mark ω would satisfy an equation of order $\nu - 1$ at most with coefficients in the $GF[p^d]$, and this is easily shown to be impossible (by the method used in proving the special case of this result given in connection with the demonstration of Theorem IX of § **62**). Then we may write

$$x_i = \sum_{\lambda=0}^{\nu-1} \xi_{i\lambda}\omega^\lambda, \quad x'_i = \sum_{\lambda=0}^{\nu-1} \xi'_{i\lambda}\omega^\lambda, \quad \bar{a}_{ijt} = \sum_{\lambda=0}^{\nu-1} \bar{a}_{ijt\lambda}\omega^\lambda,$$

where the $\xi_{i\lambda}$, $\xi'_{i\lambda}$, $\bar{a}_{ijt\lambda}$ are marks of $GF[p^d]$. The argument now proceeds in the same way as in the previous case, and we find that

$$\xi'_{i\lambda} = \sum_{\mu=0}^{\nu-1} \sum_{j=0}^{k} \bar{\alpha}_{ij\mu\lambda}\xi_{j\mu}, \qquad (i = 0, 1, \cdots, k; \lambda = 0, 1, \cdots, \nu - 1)$$

where the $\bar{\alpha}_{ij\mu\lambda}$ are marks of $GF[p^d]$. Thus a given transformation in T_d may be put into the form just written. Conversely, any transformation of the latter form may be put into the form of a transformation belonging to T_d, the method of proof being that employed in the preceding section.

We have thus exhibited the group T_d as a general linear homogeneous group in the $GF[p^d]$.

We shall now determine certain subgroups of I the elements of which induce correspondences among the subgroups of $G_{(k+1)n}$ which belong to the geometric set of subgroups. Let us consider the transformation

$$x'_i = \sum_{j=0}^{k} \alpha_{ijt}x_j^{p^t} \qquad (i = 0, 1, \cdots, k)$$

belonging to the group T of § **74**. On combining this transformation with the similar transformation

$$x'_i = \sum_{j=0}^{k} \beta_{ij\tau}x_j^{p^\tau}, \qquad (i = 0, 1, \cdots, k)$$

we have
$$x'_i = \sum_{j=0}^{k} \alpha_{ijt}\left(\sum_{\lambda=0}^{k} \beta_{j\lambda\tau} x_\lambda^{p^\tau}\right)^{p^t}$$
$$= \sum_{\lambda=0}^{k} \sum_{j=0}^{k} \alpha_{ijt}\beta_{j\lambda\tau}^{p^t} x_\lambda^{p^{t+\tau}}$$
$$= \sum_{\lambda=0}^{k} \gamma_{i\lambda} x_\lambda^{p^{t+\tau}}, \qquad (i = 0, 1, \cdots, k)$$

where the definition of the $\gamma_{i\lambda}$ is obvious and where the exponent $t + \tau$, when not less than n, is to be reduced modulo n.

From this it follows that the foregoing set of transformations constitutes a group Γ if the coefficients α_{ijt} are marks of $GF[p^n]$ and t varies over the set $0, 1, 2, \cdots, n-1$. If d is any divisor of n and t ranges over the multiples of d in the set $0, 1, 2, \cdots, n-1$, we have a subgroup Γ_d of the group Γ. Thus we have a group Γ_d for each divisor d of n. Evidently Γ_1 is the same as Γ. We denote by Γ_0 the group in which t has the value 0 alone, this being a linear group.

Now in any particular transformation belonging to Γ the quantities x_i enter homogeneously. Hence Γ has $(p^n - 1, 1)$ isomorphism with the group of transformations

$$\rho x'_i = \sum_{j=0}^{k} \alpha_{ijt} x_j^{p^t}, \qquad (i = 0, 1, \cdots, k;\ t = 0, 1, \cdots, n-1)$$

where it is understood that two transformations are to be treated as identical if the exponent t is the same in the two and if it is possible to write them with the same coefficients α_{ijt}, even though in order to do this it is necessary to have different values for ρ. This new group we denote by $C(k, p^n)$. The subgroup corresponding to the subgroup Γ_d of Γ we shall denote by $C_d(k, p^n)$. The group $C_0(k, p^n)$ is identical with the group $P(k, p^n)$ introduced in § **73**.

It is easy to show that the element

$$\rho x'_i = x_i^p \qquad (i = 0, 1, \cdots, k)$$

transforms $C_0(k, p^n)$ into itself. Hence $C(k, p^n)$ is generated by this element and $C_0(k, p^n)$, while $C_d(k, p^n)$ is generated by the dth power of this element and $C_0(k, p^n)$. Then from the known order of $C_0(k, p^n)$, or $P(k, p^n)$ (§ **73**), it follows that the order of $C(k, p^n)$ is

$$\frac{n}{p^n - 1} \prod_{i=0}^{k} (p^{(k+1)n} - p^{in}).$$

It is easy to see that $C(k, p^n)$, and hence each $C_d(k, p^n)$, permutes among themselves the symbols $(\mu_0, \mu_1, \cdots, \mu_k)$ for the subgroups in the geometric set of subgroups, and hence induces on them a permutation group. Such a permutation group we shall denote by the same symbol as the corresponding transformation group. Since $C_d(k, p^n)$ contains $P(k, p^n)$, it follows that $C_d(k, p^n)$ is triply transitive when $k = 1$ and is doubly transitive when $k > 1$.

In the next two chapters the groups $C_d(k, p^n)$ will be treated in detail from another point of view.

76. The Holomorph of G. The set of transformations of the form

$$x'_i = x_i + a_i, \qquad (i = 0, 1, \cdots, k)$$

where the a_i are marks of $GF[p^n]$, clearly form an Abelian group $\overline{G}$ of order $p^{(k+1)n}$ and type $(1, 1, \cdots, 1)$. It is therefore simply isomorphic with the Abelian group $G_{(k+1)n}$ and may be taken as a representation of it. The group generated by this group and the group T of § **74** is a representation of the holomorph of $G_{(k+1)n}$ — a fact which generalizes a result obtained in § **29**. The holomorph of $G_{(k+1)n}$ may therefore be represented by the set of nonsingular transformations of the form

$$x'_i = \sum_{s=1}^{n} \sum_{j=0}^{k} a_{ijs} x_j^{p^{n-s}} + a_i, \qquad (i = 0, 1, \cdots, k)$$

where the a's are marks of the $GF[p^n]$. The transformation group so defined will be represented by the symbol H.

It is evident that the group $\overline{G}$ is a self-conjugate subgroup of H. It is therefore a self-conjugate subgroup of every subgroup of H which contains $\overline{G}$. In particular, $\overline{G}$ is transformed into itself by the group T_d defined in § **75**. Hence the group $\{T_d, \overline{G}\}$ is a subgroup of H of the same index as that of T_d in T. We thus have a ready means of constructing it. An analytical representation of $\{T_d, \overline{G}\}$ is afforded by the set of nonsingular transformations

$$x'_i = \sum_{t=1}^{\nu} \sum_{j=0}^{k} \overline{a}_{ijt} x_j^{p^{d(\nu-t)}} + a_i, \qquad (i = 0, 1, \cdots, k)$$

where the a's are marks of $GF[p^n]$ and d is any factor of n and $\nu = n/d$.

Again we may form other subgroups of H in a similar manner by taking the groups Γ_d of § **75** and combining each of them with $\overline{G}$. The forms of the analytical representations of these groups are obvious.

EXERCISES

1. By means of the groups $C(2, 2^2)$ and $P(2, 2^2)$ show the existence of four doubly transitive groups of degree 21, their orders being $21 \cdot 20 \cdot 16 \cdot 9 \cdot 2$, $21 \cdot 20 \cdot 16 \cdot 9$, $21 \cdot 20 \cdot 16 \cdot 3 \cdot 2$, $21 \cdot 20 \cdot 16 \cdot 3$, respectively.

2. The powers of the permutation $(ABCDEFGHIJKLMNOPQRSTU)$ replace the quintuple A, B, G, I, S by a set of 21 quintuples. Show that the largest permutation group on the 21 letters each element of which permutes these quintuples among themselves is conjugate to the permutation group $C(2, 2^2)$.

3. The permutation group $P(3, 2)$ is a doubly transitive group of degree 15 and order $15 \cdot 14 \cdot 12 \cdot 8 = \frac{1}{2}(8!)$. Prove that this group is simply isomorphic with the alternating group of degree 8 by showing that the latter group has a conjugate set of 15 triply transitive subgroups of order $8 \cdot 7 \cdot 6 \cdot 4$ and that these are transformed by the elements of this alternating group according to a permutation group which is conjugate to $P(3, 2)$.

4. Employ the results of the foregoing Ex. 3 in constructing four primitive groups of degree 15, their orders being $15 \cdot 14 \cdot 12 \cdot 8$, $15 \cdot 14 \cdot 12$, $15 \cdot 48$, $15 \cdot 24$, respectively; show that the first two are doubly transitive and that the last two are singly transitive. (See Ex. 10 on page 162.)

5. Prove the existence of at least twelve transitive groups of degree 31.

6. Prove that $P(2, 5)$ is generated by any two elements in it of order 31, provided that neither of them is a power of the other, and show that there are 7,198,200,000 such pairs of generators of $P(2, 5)$.

7. Construct four doubly transitive groups of degree 121.

8. When p is a prime of the form $p=2^\nu-1$ ($\nu>2$), show that there exists a doubly transitive group of degree p and order

$$\prod_{i=0}^{\nu-1}(2^\nu-2^i).$$

Show that the number of Sylow subgroups of order p in this group is

$$\rho\prod_{i=2}^{\nu-1}(2^\nu-2^i),$$

where ρ is a factor of $p-1$.

9. When p is a prime of the form $p=2^{2^m}+1$, show that there exist $m+1$ triply transitive groups of degree p, their orders being

$$p(p-1)(p-2)2^i. \qquad (i=0, 1, 2, \cdots, m)$$

Show that the number of Sylow subgroups of order p in each of these groups is $\frac{1}{2}(p-3)p+1$.

10. Construct at least thirteen doubly (but not triply) transitive groups of prime degrees less than 1000, no one of them being the metacyclic group of its degree.

11. Construct ten transitive groups of degree 17. (See Ex. 10 on page 162.)

12. Determine a necessary and sufficient condition on the coefficients a_{ijs} such that the transformation at the beginning of § 74 shall have a unique solution for the x_i in terms of the x'_i. [SUGGESTION. From the given equations form new equations by successively raising both members to the pth power, and thus make the determination of the condition depend on linear equations in the symbols

$$x_i,\ x_i^p,\ x_i^{p^2},\ \cdots,\ x_i^{p^{n-1}};$$

express the condition by means of a determinant.]

13. The Abelian group of order 5^3 and type (1, 1, 1) has 31 subgroups of order 5 and 31 subgroups of order 25; each subgroup of order 25 contains 6 of these subgroups of order 5; form the 31 sets of six subgroups thus indicated and show that these sets constitute a configuration of the 31 symbols such that $P(2, 5)$ is the largest permutation group on these 31 symbols each element of which leaves this configuration invariant.

14. Formulate and solve a similar problem for the Abelian group of order 3^3 and type (1, 1, 1).

15. Show that there exists a triply transitive group of degree 32 and order $32 \cdot 31 \cdot 30 \cdot 28 \cdot 24 \cdot 16$. [SUGGESTION. Consider the group I of isomorphisms and the holomorph of the Abelian group of order 2^5 and type (1, 1, 1, 1, 1) and the relation of I to the permutation group $P(4, 2)$.]

77. Doubly Transitive Groups of Degree p^n and Order $p^n(p^n-1)$. Let G be a doubly transitive group of degree p^n and order $p^n(p^n-1)$. Then (Theorem V of § **40**) G contains a single Sylow subgroup H of order p^n, and this subgroup is Abelian of type $(1, 1, \cdots, 1)$. Let $a_0, a_1, \cdots, a_m$ $(m = p^n - 1)$ be the p^n symbols permuted by G. Then H permutes these symbols among themselves according to a regular group. Hence there is one and just one element h_i of H which replaces a_0 by any given symbol a_i.

Let us denote by M the subgroup of order $p^n - 1$ in G each element of which leaves a_0 fixed. It is a regular group on $a_1, a_2, \cdots, a_m$. Hence there is one and just one element m_i of M which replaces a_1 by any given symbol a_i.

Now each element of M transforms H into itself. Hence the correspondences $h_i \sim m_j^{-1}h_im_j$, where in a particular correspondence j is fixed and i runs over the set $0, 1, \cdots, m$, exhibit an isomorphism of H with itself. On giving to j the values $1, 2, \cdots, m$, we have thus m distinct isomorphisms of H with itself; for if $m_j^{-1}h_im_j = m_t^{-1}h_im_t$, we have $h_i = (m_tm_j^{-1})^{-1}h_i(m_tm_j^{-1})$ and hence $m_tm_j^{-1} = 1$ and therefore $t = j$.

The totality of these isomorphisms of H with itself constitutes a subgroup I_1 of order m of the group I of isomorphisms of H with itself. Since $m_j^{-1}h_1m_j = h_j$, it follows that the isomorphism induced by m_j replaces h_1 by h_j. If we represent the isomorphism (in the usual way) as a permutation on $h_1, h_2, \cdots, h_m$, then the isomorphism induced by m_i is transformed by the permutation P,

$$P = \begin{pmatrix} h_0, & h_1, & \cdots, & h_m \\ a_0, & a_1, & \cdots, & a_m \end{pmatrix},$$

into a permutation σ_i which replaces a_1 by a_i. Now the correspondence $m_i \sim \sigma_i$ sets up a simple isomorphism between M and the group consisting of the permutations $\sigma_1, \sigma_2, \cdots, \sigma_m$, while both m_i and σ_i replace a_1 by a_i. Hence the permutations m_i and σ_i are identical for each i of the set $1, 2, \cdots, m$; for if m_i replaces a_k by a_l, we have $m_i = m_k^{-1}m_l$, whence $\sigma_i = \sigma_k^{-1}\sigma_l$ and therefore σ_i replaces a_k by a_l. Therefore the permutation group on $h_1, h_2, \cdots, h_m$, induced by the group I_1 of isomorphisms, is conjugate to the group M. Now the holomorph of H contains a single subgroup of order $p^n(p^n - 1)$ generated by I_1 and H, each being written in the usual way as a permutation group on $h_0, h_1, \cdots, h_m$. This subgroup is transformed into G by the permutation P, since its regular subgroups on $h_0, h_1, \cdots, h_m$ and $h_1, h_2, \cdots, h_m$ are transformed into the corresponding subgroups of G.

Thus we are led to the following theorem:

> I. Every doubly transitive group G of degree p^n and order $p^n(p^n - 1)$ is contained in the holomorph of the Abelian group H of order p^n and type $(1, 1, \cdots, 1)$ when that holomorph is written in the usual way as a permutation group. Moreover, the regular subgroup M of G, consisting of those elements which leave one symbol fixed, is contained in the group I of isomorphisms of H.

Now let I_1 be any regular group of degree and order $p^n - 1$ contained in the group I of isomorphisms of an Abelian group H of order p^n and type $(1, 1, \cdots, 1)$. The holomorph of H has a $(p^n, 1)$ isomorphism with I. Let G_1 be the subgroup of this holomorph which corresponds to I_1 in the named isomorphism. Then G_1 is a doubly transitive group of degree p^n and order $p^n(p^n - 1)$, such that its singly transitive subgroup of degree $p^n - 1$ is conjugate to I_1.

Hence we have the following theorem:

> II. For every regular group I_1 of degree and order $p^n - 1$ contained in the group I of isomorphisms of an Abelian group of order p^n and type $(1, 1, \cdots, 1)$ there exists a doubly transitive group G of degree p^n and order $p^n(p^n - 1)$ containing I_1 as a subgroup.

Let G and $\overline{G}$ be two permutation groups on $a_0, a_1, \cdots, a_m$ $(m = p^n - 1)$ each of which is doubly transitive and of order $p^n(p^n - 1)$, and let them be such that their respective subgroups M and $\overline{M}$ of order $p^n - 1$ on $a_1, a_2, \cdots, a_m$ are simply isomorphic. Let the notation be so chosen that G and $\overline{G}$ have a common Abelian subgroup H of order p^n and type $(1, 1, \cdots, 1)$; and let h_i be the element in H which replaces a_0 by a_i. Let S_i be the element in M which replaces a_1 by a_i; then $h_i = S_i^{-1}h_1S_i$. Let $\overline{S}_i$ be the element in $\overline{M}$ which corresponds to S_i in M in the simple isomorphism postulated in the hypothesis; and let a_{k_i} be the element by which $\overline{S}_i$ replaces a_1; then $h_{k_i} = \overline{S}_i^{-1}h_1\overline{S}_i$. Now the permutation P,

$$P \equiv \begin{pmatrix} a_0, & a_1, & a_{k_2}, & \cdots, & a_{k_m} \\ a_0, & a_1, & a_2, & \cdots, & a_m \end{pmatrix},$$

transforms $\overline{S}_i$ into S_i, as one sees from the proof of the corollary to Theorem XII in § **12**. Also, P transforms H into itself; for we have

$$h_{k_i} = \overline{S}_i^{-1}h_1\overline{S}_i = \overline{S}_i^{-1} \cdot S_ih_iS_i^{-1} \cdot \overline{S}_i = (S_i^{-1}\overline{S}_i)^{-1}h_i(S_i^{-1}\overline{S}_i),$$

whence it follows that P belongs to the group of isomorphisms of H (when written on the a's) and therefore transforms H into itself. From these results and from the relations $G \equiv \{H, M\}$ and $\overline{G} \equiv \{H, \overline{M}\}$ it follows that P transforms $\overline{G}$ into G. Therefore G and $\overline{G}$ are identical as permutation groups.

Hence we have the following theorem:

III. If G and $\overline{G}$ are two doubly transitive permutation groups of degree p^n and order $p^n(p^n - 1)$ whose regular subgroups of order $p^n - 1$ are simply isomorphic, then G and $\overline{G}$ are identical (conjugate) as permutation groups.

A doubly transitive group of degree μ and order $\mu(\mu - 1)$ exists (Theorem V of § **40**) when and only when μ is a prime-power. From the results in this section it follows therefore that the problem of constructing all doubly transitive groups of degree μ and order $\mu(\mu - 1)$ is equivalent to the problem of constructing all regular subgroups I_1 of degree $p^n - 1$ contained in the group I of isomorphisms of the Abelian group H of order p^n and type $(1, 1, \cdots, 1)$ when this group I is written in the usual way as a permutation group. (In § **103** it is shown that these problems are also equivalent to the problem of constructing all finite algebras of a certain type.) These equivalent problems have been only partially solved; it seems to be difficult to effect a complete solution.

78. Analytical Forms of M. Employing the notation of the preceding section, let $n = k\nu$, where k and ν are positive integers (either or both of which may be unity). Then (§§ **28** and **74**) the group I of isomorphisms of H with itself is of order

$$(p^{k\nu} - 1)(p^{k\nu} - p)(p^{k\nu} - p^2) \cdots (p^{k\nu} - p^{k\nu - 1})$$

and is simply isomorphic with the transformation group T of all transformations of the form

$$x'_i = \sum_{s=1}^{\nu} \sum_{j=1}^{k} a_{ijs} x_j^{p^{n-s}}, \qquad (i = 1, 2, \cdots, k)$$

where the coefficients a_{ijs} are marks of the $GF[p^\nu]$ such that the transformation equations have a unique solution for the symbols x_i in terms of the symbols x'_i

There are two particular forms of the transformations which are of special use: the first is that in which $k = 1$, and the second is that in which $\nu = 1$. The advantage of the first lies in the fact that there is but one variable x (and related variable x') and that we have at our disposal the largest possible Galois field. The advantage of the other lies in the fact that the transformations are linear.

Now we have seen (§ **77**) that the group M is simply isomorphic with a subgroup I_1 of I. Therefore in the case when $k = 1$, and hence $\nu = n$, the elements of the group M may be represented analytically in the form

$$T_i: \qquad x' = \sum_{s=1}^{n} a_s^{(i)} x^{p^{n-s}}. \qquad (i = 0, 1, 2, \cdots, p^n - 2)$$

Since the group M is regular, it follows that the mark 1 must be carried to any given nonzero mark by one and just one transformation T_i. Hence we may (and we do) suppose the notation so chosen that

$$a_1^{(i)} + a_2^{(i)} + \cdots + a_n^{(i)} = \omega^i. \qquad (i = 0, 1, 2, \cdots, p^n - 2)$$

When $\nu = 1$, and hence $k = n$, the transformations may be written in the form

$$S_\alpha: \qquad x'_i = \sum_{j=1}^{n} a_{ij}^{(\alpha)} x_j, \qquad (i = 1, 2, \cdots, n)$$

where α runs over the set $0, 1, 2, \cdots, p^n - 2$.

In developing the theory of these groups we shall sometimes use the transformations T_i and sometimes the transformations S_α.

79. On Certain Elements and Subgroups of M. The transformation group T of § **78**, when $k = 1$ and hence $\nu = n$, contains the element $x' = \omega x$ of order $p^n - 1$, where ω is a primitive mark of the $GF[p^n]$. Hence T has a cyclic subgroup of order $p^n - 1$. Now let q (when existent) be any prime factor of $p^n - 1$ which is not a factor of any $p^t - 1$ for $1 \leqq t < n$, and let q^α be the highest power of q contained in $p^n - 1$. Then q^α is the highest power of q contained in the order of T. Hence the Sylow subgroups of T of order q^α are cyclic. Therefore the group M contains a cyclic Sylow subgroup of order q^α.

This result may be extended. Suppose, if possible, that M contains a noncyclic subgroup K of order ρ^2, where ρ is a prime. If H is transformed by the elements of K, then the elements of H are permuted transitively in sets of ρ^2 elements each. So far as one of these sets is concerned, the generators of these isomorphisms of H may be written in the form

$$P_1 = (a_{11}a_{12} \cdots a_{1\rho})(a_{21}a_{22} \cdots a_{2\rho}) \cdots (a_{\rho 1}a_{\rho 2} \cdots a_{\rho\rho}),$$
$$P_2 = (a_{11}a_{21} \cdots a_{\rho 1})(a_{12}a_{22} \cdots a_{\rho 2}) \cdots (a_{1\rho}a_{2\rho} \cdots a_{\rho\rho}).$$

Then in $P_1P_2^i$ the cycle containing a_{11} is

$$(a_{11}\, a_{1+i,\,2}\, a_{1+2i,\,3} \cdots a_{1-i,\,\rho}),$$

the subscripts being reduced modulo ρ. The identity is the only element in H left fixed by any of these isomorphisms;

hence the product of the elements of H in any cycle must be the identity E. Therefore

$$\begin{aligned} a_{11}a_{12} \cdots a_{1\rho} &= E, \\ a_{11}a_{21} \cdots a_{\rho 1} &= E, \\ a_{11}a_{1+i,2} \cdots a_{1-i,\rho} &= E, \qquad (i = 1, 2, \cdots, \rho - 1) \end{aligned}$$

Hence

$$a_{11}{}^{\rho} \prod_{i,j=1}^{\rho} a_{ij} = E, \quad \text{or} \quad a_{11}{}^{\rho} = E.$$

But this is impossible. Hence M contains no noncyclic subgroup of order ρ^2. Therefore a Sylow subgroup of order ρ^α in M contains only a single subgroup of order ρ; for it contains a self-conjugate subgroup of order ρ (Theorem I of § **32**) and hence contains a noncyclic subgroup of order ρ^2 in case there is in it a second subgroup of order ρ. Applying Theorems X and XI of § **36**, we conclude to the following result:

I. If M is a regular subgroup of order $p^n - 1$ in a doubly transitive group G of degree p^n and order $p^n(p^n - 1)$, then the Sylow subgroups of M of odd order are cyclic and those of even order are either cyclic or of the sole noncyclic type containing a single element of order 2.

The part of this theorem which relates to elements of order 2 is extended in the following theorem:

II. The group I of isomorphisms of an Abelian group H of odd order p^n and type $(1, 1, \cdots, 1)$, when represented in the usual way as a permutation group on the elements of H other than the identity, contains just one element of period 2 which leaves fixed none of the $p^n - 1$ symbols of I. This element is therefore self-conjugate in I. The corresponding isomorphism of H with itself is that in which each element corresponds to its inverse.

In order to prove this, we represent the group I, as in § **29**, by the transformations

$$x'_i = \sum_{j=1}^{n} a_{ij} x_j, \qquad (i = 1, 2, \cdots, n)$$

where the a_{ij} are marks of the $GF[p]$. Now let the transformation

$$x'_i = \sum_{j=1}^{n} \alpha_{ij} x_j \qquad (i = 1, 2, \cdots, n)$$

be of period 2 and let it leave fixed no element of H except the identity. The square of the transformation is

$$x'_i = \sum_{j=1}^{n} \alpha_{ij} \sum_{s=1}^{n} \alpha_{js} x_s = \sum_{s=1}^{n} \left(\sum_{j=1}^{n} \alpha_{ij} \alpha_{js} \right) x_s. \qquad (i = 1, 2, \cdots, n)$$

Since this is to be the identity, we must have

$$\sum_{j=1}^{n} \alpha_{ij} \alpha_{js} = \delta_{is} = \begin{cases} 0 \text{ if } i \neq s, \\ 1 \text{ if } i = s. \end{cases}$$

Since the identity is the only element of H left fixed by the transformation under consideration, it follows that the system

$$\sum_{j=1}^{n} (\alpha_{ij} - \delta_{ij}) x_j = 0 \qquad (i = 1, 2, \cdots, n)$$

has no solution except that in which each x_i is zero. Therefore the determinant $| \alpha_{ij} - \delta_{ij} |$ is different from zero. Now we have

$$\sum_{j=1}^{n} (\alpha_{ij} - \delta_{ij})(\alpha_{js} + \delta_{js}) = \sum_{j=1}^{n} \alpha_{ij} \alpha_{js} - \alpha_{is} + \alpha_{is} - \delta_{is} = 0.$$

Therefore we must have $\alpha_{js} + \delta_{js} = 0$. These conditions uniquely determine the transformation under consideration to be the following:

$$x'_i = - x_i. \qquad (i = 1, 2, \cdots, n)$$

From this the theorem follows readily.

The elements of H besides the identity are permuted transitively under transformation by the elements of M, as we have seen; therefore if P is any element of order p in H and λ is any primitive root modulo p, then there is an element S in M such that $S^{-1}PS = P^{\lambda}$. Then S^{p-1} transforms P into itself, while no lower power of S transforms P into itself. Then the order of S is at least as great as $p-1$. But the identity is the only element in M which transforms P into itself. Hence S^{p-1} is the identity and the order of S is $p-1$. Therefore,

III. The subgroup M of G contains a cyclic subgroup of order $p-1$.

Applying Theorem III of § 77, we have the following corollary:

COR. There is one and just one doubly transitive group of degree p and order $p(p-1)$.

This is a special case of the following theorem, which is an immediate corollary of results in Chapter XIII (see Ex. 11 on page 403):

IV. If a regular subgroup M of order $p^n - 1$ in a doubly transitive group G of degree p^n and order $p^n(p^n - 1)$ is Abelian, then M is cyclic and the group G is uniquely determined (see Theorem XXVII in § 67).

80. The Case of Certain Invariant Subgroups of M. Let us now consider those doubly transitive groups G of degree p^n and order $p^n(p^n-1)$ in which it is true that a regular subgroup M of degree $p^n - 1$ contained in G has an invariant subgroup of order q^β $(\beta > 0)$, where q is a prime factor of $p^n - 1$ which is not a divisor of any $p^\rho - 1$ for $1 \leqq \rho < n$. For this purpose it is convenient to represent the elements of M analytically in the form T_i of § 78, namely:

$$T_i: \quad x' = \sum_{s=1}^{n} a_s^{(i)} x^{p^{n-s}}. \qquad (i = 0, 1, 2, \cdots, p^n - 2)$$

An invariant subgroup of M of order q^β is contained in a Sylow subgroup of M of order q^α. Since such a Sylow subgroup of M is also a Sylow subgroup of the group I of isomorphisms of H with itself (in the notation of § 77), and since Sylow subgroups of a given order constitute a single conjugate set, it follows that we may without loss of generality suppose that M contains any given Sylow subgroup of order q^α, since any such case is conjugate to any other such case under I. Now if we write $p^n - 1 = q^\alpha \mu$ and if ω is any primitive mark of the $GF[p^n]$, then a Sylow subgroup of I of order q^α is generated by the transformation $x' = \omega^\mu x$. We take this to be a Sylow subgroup of M, as we may without loss of generality. Then the invariant group of order q^β in M is contained in this Sylow subgroup. Hence if we write $p^n - 1 = q^\beta \lambda$, it follows that this invariant subgroup of order q^β is generated by the transformation $x' = \omega^\lambda x$.

Let T be a particular transformation T_i of M and let U be the transformation $x' = \omega^\lambda x$. Since $\{U\}$ is invariant in M, it follows that $T^{-1}UT = U^\tau$ for a suitable value of τ. Hence $UT = TU^\tau$. Writing T in the form

$$T: \qquad x' = \sum_{s=1}^{n} a_s x^{p^{n-s}},$$

we have for UT and TU^τ the transformations

$$UT: \qquad x' = \sum_{s=1}^{n} a_s \omega^\lambda x^{p^{n-s}},$$

$$TU^\tau: \qquad x' = \sum_{s=1}^{n} a_s \omega^{\lambda \tau p^{n-s}} x^{p^{n-s}}.$$

These two transformations are to be identical. This requires that

$$a_s \omega^\lambda = a_s \omega^{\lambda \tau p^{n-s}}. \qquad (s = 1, 2, \cdots, n)$$

Now $a_s \neq 0$ for at least one s. Let l be such that $a_l \neq 0$. Then we have

$$\omega^\lambda = \omega^{\lambda \tau p^{n-l}}, \text{ or } \omega^{\lambda(\tau p^{n-l} - 1)} = 1, \text{ or } \lambda(\tau p^{n-l} - 1) \equiv 0 \bmod p^n - 1.$$

Since $p^n - 1 = q^\beta \lambda$, we then have $\tau p^{n-l} - 1 \equiv 0 \bmod q^\beta$, or $\tau p^n \equiv p^l \bmod q^\beta$, or $\tau \equiv p^l \bmod q^\beta$. If $a_{l_1} \neq 0$ for $l_1 \neq l$, then we have also $\tau \equiv p^{l_1} \bmod q^\beta$, and therefore $p^l \equiv p^{l_1} \bmod q^\beta$, where both l and l_1 belong to the set $1, 2, \cdots, n$. But this is impossible, since q is a divisor of $p^n - 1$, which is not a divisor of any $p^\rho - 1$ for $1 \leqq \rho < n$.

From this it follows that T has the form

$$x' = a_l x^{p^{n-l}}.$$

Therefore the transformations T_i are all of the form $x' = ax^{p^t}$. Hence all the possible groups M of the class now under consideration (and indeed all those whose transformations are of the last foregoing form) are contained among those determined in § **69**. There is just one case in which M is cyclic. All possible non-cyclic groups M are described in Theorem XXX of § **69**.

Thus we have a complete determination of all groups G whose subgroups M have the property stated at the beginning of the section. That there are other groups G besides those here determined is shown by the cases $p^n = 5^2$ and $p^n = 7^2$. The theorems of this section yield exactly two doubly transitive groups G of every odd degree p^2 and order $p^2(p^2 - 1)$. But for $p^n = 5^2$ and for $p^n = 7^2$ there are just three groups G (see Ex. 15 on page 152 and Ex. 12 on page 286).

In connection with the determination of certain finite algebras (see our Chapter XIII) Dickson (Göttingen *Nachrichten*, 1905) has conjectured the following theorem:

> Any group G of order $p^n - 1$, where p is a prime and n is an odd integer greater than unity, contains an invariant subgroup of order a power of a prime q, where q is a factor of $p^n - 1$ but not of any $p^\rho - 1$ for $1 \leqq \rho < n$.

Dickson verified this empirical theorem for all groups of each of 144 orders of the named form $p^n - 1$. The author has extended the verification to 15 additional orders. In so far as this theorem is true, the determination of the groups G is complete. In fact this determination is complete when the conclusion of the theorem holds for groups of the named order $p^n - 1$ which are restricted to satisfy conditions developed in § **79**.

The determination of groups G is also complete in so far as the following (extended) proposition is true:

> Let K be a group of order $p^n - 1$, where p is a prime and n is an integer greater than two (the cases $n = 4, 6$ being excluded). Then K contains a self-conjugate subgroup of order q^β ($\beta > 0$), where q is a prime factor of $p^n - 1$ but is not a factor of any number of the form $p^\rho - 1$ for $1 \leqq \rho < n$.

That $p^n - 1$ (in the cases named) always has such a prime factor q is known from the theory of numbers (see *Annals of Mathematics*, **15** (1913), 30–70, especially page 61). The verifications of the next preceding empirical theorem afford 159 verifications of this one. The latter has been verified in 24 additional cases, no exception having been found. The presence of the exceptional cases in the theorem as stated indicates that it is probably not universally true. But it is true in a sufficiently wide range of cases to be significant for the present problem.

Since these empirical theorems are of interest on their own account, and since no like theorem in the theory of groups seems to have been demonstrated, it may be well to record here certain related empirical results. The principal one is contained in the following empirical proposition:

> Let r and s be real numbers, not both numerically equal to unity, such that $r + s$ and rs are relatively prime integers. Let n be an integer greater than two. Let $D_n(r, s)$ denote the integer
>
> $$D_n(r, s) = \frac{r^n - s^n}{r - s},$$
>
> and let n be further restricted (see *Annals*, loc. cit., Theorem XXI) so that $D_n(r, s)$ shall have at least one prime factor q which is not a factor of any $D_\rho(r, s)$ for $1 \leqq \rho < n$. Then a group of order $D_n(r, s)$ has a

self-conjugate subgroup whose order is of the form q^α ($\alpha > 0$), where q is a factor of $D_n(r, s)$ subject to the conditions just named.

This theorem has been verified for 285 orders $D_n(r, s)$ and no case of exception has been found. From certain considerations arising from the theory of numbers it seems that the most probable cases of exception are those for which $n = 6$. But no such case of exception has been found.

Another related empirical proposition is the following:

Let r, s, n have the same meanings as in the foregoing proposition. Let $F_n(r, s) = (s^{\phi(n)})P_n(r/s)$, where $P_n(x)$ is the polynomial with leading coefficient unity whose roots are the $\phi(n)$ primitive nth roots of unity without repetition. Then a group of order $F_n(r, s)$ has a self-conjugate subgroup of order q^α ($\alpha > 0$), where q is a prime factor of $F_n(r, s)$ but is not a factor of n.

This theorem has been verified for 639 orders $F_n(r, s)$ and no case of exception has been found.

For none of these empirical theorems have the verifications suggested any method of general proof.

Let us next consider those doubly transitive groups G of degree $p^{2\nu}$ and order $p^{2\nu}(p^{2\nu} - 1)$ in which it is true that a regular subgroup M of degree $p^{2\nu} - 1$ contained in G has an invariant subgroup of order q^β ($\beta > 0$), where q is an odd prime factor of $p^\nu - 1$ which is not a divisor of any $p^\rho - 1$ for $1 \leqq \rho < \nu$. We denote by H the regular Abelian subgroup of G of order $p^{2\nu}$ and by I the group of isomorphisms of H with itself. If q^α is the highest power of q contained in $p^\nu - 1$, then $q^{2\alpha}$ is the highest power of q contained in the order of I, as one sees by inspection of the order of I (§ 78).

We now make a further restriction, namely, that the invariant subgroup of order q^β in M is contained in the group generated by the transformation $x' = \omega x$, where ω is a primitive mark of the $GF[p^{2\nu}]$. If we write $p^{2\nu} - 1 = q^\beta \lambda$, then M contains self-conjugately the subgroup generated by the transformation $x' = \omega^\lambda x$. We denote this transformation by U.

Any transformation T of M may be written in the form

$$T: \qquad x' = \sum_{s=1}^{2\nu} a_s x^{p^{2\nu - s}},$$

where the coefficients are in the $GF[p^{2\nu}]$. An integer τ exists such that $T^{-1}UT = U^\tau$, whence $UT = TU^\tau$. For UT and TU^τ we have transformations similar to those denoted by the same symbols in the earlier part of the section. Proceeding as in the former case, we show that if $a_l \neq 0$ and $a_{l_1} \neq 0$, then we have $p^l \equiv p^{l_1} \bmod q^\beta$. From this relation and the assumed property of q we see that l and l_1, when not equal, differ by ν. Hence T has the form

$$T: \qquad x' = ax^{p^{2\nu - l}} + bx^{p^{\nu - l}}.$$

Since M is of order $p^{2\nu} - 1$ and permutes the nonzero marks of the field transitively and hence must have just one element which replaces the mark 1 by any given nonzero mark ω^i, the transformations of M may be written in the form

$$S_i: \ x' = \alpha_i x^{p^{\nu + \sigma_i}} + \beta_i x^{p^{\sigma_i}}, \qquad (\alpha_i + \beta_i = \omega^i; \ i = 0, 1, \cdots, p^{2\nu} - 2)$$

The coefficients α_i and β_i are in the $GF[p^{2\nu}]$.

We shall now consider all the groups M whose transformations may be written in the foregoing form S_i whether or not these groups M have the properties employed in arriving at this form. [If $\nu = 1$ we have $\sigma_i = 0$. Comparing with § **78**, one sees that we have here all cases M of degree $p^2 - 1$.]

Let us consider the set Γ of all transformations of the form

$$A: \qquad x' = \alpha x^{p^{n + \sigma}} + \beta x^{p^\sigma},$$

where α and β range over the marks of the $GF[p^{2\nu}]$ and σ runs over the set $0, 1, 2, \cdots, \nu - 1$. The condition on α and β in order that A shall be nonsingular is that

$$\alpha^{p^\nu + 1} \neq \beta^{p^\nu + 1}.$$

Since the product of two transformations of the form A is also of this form, the set Γ constitutes a group. There are ν possible values for σ. When $\alpha = 0$ we have for β any one of $p^{2\nu} - 1$ marks; when $\beta = 0$ we have for α any one of $p^{2\nu} - 1$ marks; when $\alpha\beta \neq 0$ we have for α any one of $p^{2\nu} - 1$ marks, while for each α we have for β any one of $p^{2\nu} - p^{\nu} - 2$ marks. Hence the order of Γ is

$$(p^{2\nu} - 1)(p^{2\nu} - p^{\nu})\nu.$$

If σ is further restricted to be a multiple of d, where d is a divisor of ν ($\nu = d\delta$), then the resulting group is a subgroup of Γ of index δ. Each of these groups is in the group I of isomorphisms of H. The corresponding subgroup of the holomorph of H, in its usual isomorphism with I, is doubly transitive. Hence,

For every divisor d of ν there exists a doubly transitive group of degree $p^{2\nu}$ and order

$$p^{2\nu}(p^{2\nu} - 1)(p^{2\nu} - p^{\nu})d.$$

The groups M under consideration here are subgroups of the group Γ. We shall not attempt a general determination of them but shall content ourselves with applications of the results attained.

In order to construct a doubly transitive group of degree 25 and order $25 \cdot 24$, we seek a transformation of order 4 of the form

$$x' = \alpha x^5 + \beta x.$$

Its square (§ **79**) must be $x' = -x$. Hence we have $\alpha^6 + \beta^2 = -1$, $\alpha\beta(\beta^4 + 1) = 0$. These conditions are satisfied by the transformation

$$x' = \omega^{12}x^5 + \omega^{21}x,$$

where $\omega^2 = \omega + 3$. Adjoining the transformations $x' = \omega^8 x$ and $x' = x + 1$, we have the required doubly transitive group.

In a similar way one may find doubly transitive groups of degree p^2 and order $p^2(p^2 - 1)$ when p is a suitable odd prime.

EXERCISES

1. By the method of § **80** construct three doubly transitive groups of degree p^2 and order $p^2(p^2-1)$ for each value p of the set 7, 11, 23.

2. Determine all the doubly transitive groups G of degree n and order $n(n-1)$ for which $n < 81$.

3. Show that there is just one doubly transitive group G of degree p^n and order $p^n(p^n-1)$ when $p^n = 2^7, 2^9, 2^{11}, 2^{13}, 2^{17}, 2^{19}, 3^5, 3^7, 3^9, 3^{13}$.

4. Show that there are just two distinct doubly transitive groups of degree 81 and order $81 \cdot 80$. Show that each of them has a cyclic Sylow subgroup of order 16.

5. Prove the existence of at least seven doubly (but not triply) transitive groups of degree 81.

6. Show that there are just $2^n + 1$ conjugate sets of elements in the triply transitive group of degree $2^n + 1$ and order $(2^n+1)2^n(2^n-1)$ whose regular subgroups of degree $2^n - 1$ are cyclic.

7. Show that the symmetric group of degree 8 contains 30 triply transitive subgroups of degree 8 and order $8 \cdot 7 \cdot 6 \cdot 4$ and that in the alternating group of degree 8 these subgroups fall into two distinct conjugate sets of 15 each.

8. Show that the alternating group of degree 8 may be represented as simply isomorphic with a transitive group of degree 15 in such a way that the subgroups each of which leaves just one symbol fixed constitute one of the conjugate sets of 15 subgroups mentioned in Ex. 7 while the other set of 15 subgroups of order $8 \cdot 7 \cdot 6 \cdot 4$ are permuted in two transitive sets of 7 and 8 symbols respectively.

9. When the alternating group of degree 8 is represented as a transitive group of degree 15, as in Ex. 8, show that there is a set of seven of the 15 symbols which takes only 15 values under the permutations of the group. Construct this group of degree 15 and form the indicated configuration consisting of 15 sets of seven symbols each from the indicated 15 symbols.

10. The Abelian group G of order 2^4 and type (1, 1, 1, 1) has 15 subgroups of order 8. Show that the fifteen elements of order 2 in G fall into 15 sets of 7 each so that each set of 7 with the identity constitutes a subgroup of G of order 8, and prove that this configuration is conjugate to that described in Ex. 9.

11. Show that any two sets of 7 in the configuration in Ex. 10 have just three symbols in common and that these three symbols also occur in a third set of 7 in the configuration. There are just 35 of these sets of three each.

12. Represent the alternating group of degree 8 as simply isomorphic with a transitive group of degree 35 (see Ex. 11).

MISCELLANEOUS EXERCISES

1. Discuss the number of ways in which it is possible to select a geometric set of subgroups of order p^n in the group $G_{(k+1)n}$ of § **72**.

2. The group of isomorphisms of an Abelian group G can always be represented in just one way as a transitive permutation group on letters corresponding to the elements of G except when the order of G is twice an odd number, in which case there are just two such transitive representations.

3. In order that the group of isomorphisms of an Abelian group G shall itself be Abelian it is necessary and sufficient that G shall be cyclic.

4. If m is the highest order for an element of an Abelian group G, then the group of isomorphisms of G contains just $\phi(m)$ self-conjugate elements, $\phi(m)$ being Euler's ϕ-function.

5. If G is a non-Abelian group, then G cannot be represented as simply isomorphic with a permutation group on symbols corresponding to a set of relatively permutable elements of G.

6. If the group I of isomorphisms of a given group G is represented as a simply isomorphic permutation group on symbols corresponding to elements of G, then I is at most doubly transitive.

7. Exhibit a group G containing a self-conjugate subgroup H such that the group of isomorphisms of H is of greater order than the group of isomorphisms of G.

8. If G is a group which admits an isomorphism with itself in which each element corresponds to the square of that element, then G is an Abelian group of odd order.

9. If G is a group which admits an isomorphism with itself in which each element corresponds to its cube, then G is an Abelian group whose order is prime to 3.

10. The group of isomorphisms of an Abelian group cannot be a non-Abelian group whose only representation as a simply isomorphic transitive permutation group is that afforded by a regular group.

11. The order of the group I of isomorphisms of an Abelian group G is of the form mk, where m is the number of elements of highest order. A necessary and sufficient condition that the order of I shall be m is that G shall be cyclic.

12. Show that just two of the five groups of order 8, namely, the cyclic group and the quaternion group, have each the property that it cannot be the group of isomorphisms of any group with itself.

CHAPTER XI

Finite Geometries

81. Definition of the Finite Projective Geometries. Abelian groups of order $p^{(k+1)n}$ and type $(1, 1, \cdots, 1)$ admit of an interpretation which affords a representation of the so-called finite projective geometries $PG(k, p^n)$; and these groups and these geometries throw light each upon the other. The object of this chapter is to develop that part of the theory of the finite geometries which will be useful to us in its applications to the theory of groups.

Veblen and Bussey (*Trans. Amer. Math. Soc.* **7** (1906), 241–259) have defined a finite projective geometry in the following way. It consists of a set of elements, called points for suggestiveness, which are subject to the following five conditions or postulates:

I. The set contains a finite number of points. It contains one or more subsets called lines, each of which contains at least three points.

II. If A and B are distinct points, there is one and only one line that contains both A and B.

III. If A, B, C are noncollinear points and if a line l contains a point D of the line AB and a point E of the line BC but does not contain A or B or C, then the line l contains a point F of the line CA.

IV$_k$. If m is an integer less than k, not all the points considered are in the same m-space.

V$_k$. If IV$_k$ is satisfied, there exists in the set of points considered no $(k+1)$-space.

The geometry so defined is said to be a geometry of a k-dimensional space.

In the foregoing system of postulates the terms point and line are left undefined. A point is called a 0-space and a line is called a 1-space. An m-space, or a space of m dimensions, may be defined inductively as follows. A point is a 0-space. If $P_1, P_2, \cdots, P_{m+1}$ are points not all in the same $(m-1)$-space, then the set of all points each of which is collinear with P_{m+1} and some point of the $(m-1)$-space $(P_1, P_2, \cdots, P_m)$ is the m-space $(P_1, P_2, \cdots, P_{m+1})$. A 2-space is called a plane.

82. Representation of Finite Geometries by Means of Galois Fields. By means of the marks of a Galois field we shall now give a concrete representation of a finite k-dimensional projective geometry. We denote a point of the geometry by the ordered set of *homogeneous coordinates*

$$(\mu_0, \mu_1, \cdots, \mu_k)$$

where $\mu_0, \mu_1, \cdots, \mu_k$ are marks of the $GF[p^n]$ at least one of which is different from zero, and where it is understood that the foregoing symbol denotes the same point as the symbol $(\mu\mu_0, \mu\mu_1, \cdots, \mu\mu_k)$, where μ is any one of the $p^n - 1$ nonzero marks of the field. Since the ordered set of marks $\mu_0, \mu_1, \cdots, \mu_k$ may be chosen in $p^{(k+1)n} - 1$ ways, and since each point is represented in $p^n - 1$ ways by $p^n - 1$ sets of symbols in this totality, it follows that the number of points defined is

$$1 + p^n + p^{2n} + \cdots + p^{kn}.$$

For the line containing the two distinct points $(\mu_0, \mu_1, \cdots, \mu_k)$ and $(\nu_0, \nu_1, \cdots, \nu_k)$ we take the set of points

$$(\mu\mu_0 + \nu\nu_0, \mu\mu_1 + \nu\nu_1, \cdots, \mu\mu_k + \nu\nu_k),$$

where μ and ν run independently over the marks of the $GF[p^n]$ subject to the condition that μ and ν shall not be simultaneously zero. The number of possible combinations of the μ and ν is then $p^{2n} - 1$; and for each of these the corresponding symbol denotes a point, since not all the $k+1$ coordinates are zero. But the same point is represented by $p^n - 1$ of these combinations of μ and ν, owing to the factor of proportionality involved in the definition of points. Therefore a line as so defined contains $p^n + 1$ points. It is obvious that any two points on the line may be used in this way to define the same line.

It must now be shown that the five postulates given in § **81** are satisfied by the concrete elements thus introduced. The existence of lines containing $p^n + 1$ points each is sufficient to show that Postulate I is satisfied. That Postulate II is satisfied is evident from the way in which a line containing two given points has been defined.

Let $(\lambda_0, \lambda_1, \cdots, \lambda_k)$, $(\mu_0, \mu_1, \cdots, \mu_k)$, $(\nu_0, \nu_1, \cdots, \nu_k)$ be any three noncollinear points A, B, C. Let l be a line containing a point D, say $(\lambda\lambda_0 + \mu\mu_0, \cdots, \lambda\lambda_k + \mu\mu_k)$, of the line AB and a point E, say $(\rho\mu_0 + \sigma\nu_0, \cdots, \rho\mu_k + \sigma\nu_k)$, of the line BC, and suppose that l does not contain A or B or C, whence it follows that λ, μ, ρ, σ are all different from zero. In order to prove that Postulate III is satisfied we have to show that l contains a point of CA. Now l consists of the points

$$(\alpha\lambda\lambda_0 + \alpha\mu\mu_0 + \beta\rho\mu_0 + \beta\sigma\nu_0, \cdots, \alpha\lambda\lambda_k + \alpha\mu\mu_k + \beta\rho\mu_k + \beta\sigma\nu_k)$$

where α and β run independently over the marks of the $GF[p^n]$ subject to the condition that they shall not be simultaneously zero. Now, whatever nonzero marks μ and ρ may be, there exist nonzero marks α and β such that $\alpha\mu + \beta\rho = 0$. For such values of α and β we have the point

$$(\alpha\lambda\lambda_0 + \beta\sigma\nu_0, \cdots, \alpha\lambda\lambda_k + \beta\sigma\nu_k)$$

on l; and this point is on CA. Hence Postulate III is satisfied.

It is convenient, before verifying the other two postulates, to determine the number of points in an m-space belonging to the concrete representation of the geometry which we are considering.

Let $(\mu_{00}, \mu_{01}, \cdots, \mu_{0k})$, $(\mu_{10}, \mu_{11}, \cdots, \mu_{1k})$, $(\mu_{20}, \mu_{21}, \cdots, \mu_{2k})$ be three noncollinear points in the geometry, such points being surely existent if $k > 1$. The first two of these determine a line l; and this line and the third point determine a 2-space. It is obvious that the points on this 2-space are the points

$$(\mu_0\mu_{00} + \mu_1\mu_{10} + \mu_2\mu_{20}, \cdots, \mu_0\mu_{0k} + \mu_1\mu_{1k} + \mu_2\mu_{2k}),$$

where μ_0, μ_1, μ_2 run independently over the p^n marks of the $GF[p^n]$ except that they cannot be simultaneously equal to zero. The number of the sets μ_0, μ_1, μ_2 is therefore $p^{3n}-1$; taking out the factor p^n-1, due to the factor of proportionality, we have for the number of points in a 2-space the number

$$1+p^n+p^{2n}.$$

It is obvious that any three noncollinear points in this 2-space define the same 2-space.

In general, if the points $(\mu_{i0}, \mu_{i1}, \cdots, \mu_{ik})$ $(i=0, 1, 2, \cdots, m)$ are any $m+1$ points not in the same $(m-1)$-space (certainly existent in the geometry if $m \leqq k$), they may be used in the same way to define an m-space consisting of the points

$$\left(\sum_{i=0}^{m} \mu_i\mu_{i0}, \cdots, \sum_{i=0}^{m} \mu_i\mu_{ik}\right),$$

where μ_0, μ_1, $\cdots$, μ_m run independently over the marks of the $GF[p^n]$ except that they shall not be simultaneously zero. Then the m-space consists of

$$1+p^n+p^{2n}+\cdots+p^{mn}$$

points, as one sees by noting that there are $p^{(m+1)n}-1$ combinations of the μ_i and that these fall into sets of p^n-1 each such that all the symbols in a set represent the same point.

Now the points of the m-dimensional geometry so defined may be represented uniquely by the homogeneous co-ordinates $(\mu_0, \mu_1, \cdots, \mu_m)$, once the base set of $m+1$ points has been chosen. Thence it is not difficult to see that this m-dimensional geometry is of the same general character as the k-dimensional geometry which contains it.

From the foregoing results it follows that if $m<k$ there are points in the geometry which are not in any given m-space and that the geometry does not contain any $(k+1)$-space. Therefore the last two postulates in § **81** are satisfied by the concrete representation which we have given of the geometry.

The concrete finite projective k-dimensional geometry so defined by means of the $GF[p^n]$ we denote by the symbol $PG(k, p^n)$. We shall also use the same symbol to denote any finite projective geometry which is abstractly equivalent to the concrete geometry so defined, that is, is such that a one-to-one correspondence may be established between the points of the two geometries in such a way that the points which form a line in one geometry always correspond to points which form a line in the other.

Veblen and Bussey (loc. cit.) proved that when $k > 2$ every finite projective k-dimensional geometry satisfying the definition reproduced in the foregoing § **81** is a geometry of points whose homogeneous co-ordinates may be taken as the marks of the $GF[p^n]$ in precisely the same way as we have used homogeneous co-ordinates to represent the points of the $PG(k, p^n)$. Hence, when $k > 2$, we have in the $PG(k, p^n)$ geometries which are abstractly identical with all possible finite projective geometries of more than two dimensions. Since we do not require to make explicit use of this interesting theorem, we shall not give a proof of it here. (See § **108** for finite plane geometries of types different from the $PG(2, p^n)$.)

It is convenient to insert here the determination of the number of m-spaces $PG(m, p^n)$ $(m < k)$ contained in the given k-space $PG(k, p^n)$. The number of ways in which a given set of $m+1$ base points for the $PG(m, p^n)$ may be selected in a given order from the points of the $PG(k, p^n)$, subject as they are to the condition that they do not all lie in any given $(m-1)$-dimensional space, is

$$(1+p^n+p^{2n}+\cdots+p^{kn})(p^n+p^{2n}+\cdots+p^{kn})$$
$$(p^{2n}+\cdots+p^{kn})\cdots(p^{mn}+p^{(m+1)n}+\cdots+p^{kn}),$$

the factors in this expression, in the order written, being the number of ways in which the first point, the second point, the third point, $\cdots$, the $(m+1)$th point, respectively, may be selected. The number of ways in which $m+1$ points of a given $PG(m, p^n)$ may be selected in a given order so that they do not all lie in any $(m-1)$-dimensional space is similarly shown to be

$$(1+p^n+\cdots+p^{mn})(p^n+p^{2n}+\cdots+p^{mn})$$
$$\cdots(p^{(m-1)n}+p^{mn})(p^{mn}).$$

The number of m-dimensional spaces $PG(m, p^n)$ in the given $PG(k, p^n)$ is the quotient of the first of the foregoing two products by the second; hence this number is equal to

$$\frac{(p^{(k+1)n}-1)(p^{kn}-1)(p^{(k-1)n}-1)\cdots(p^{(k-m+1)n}-1)}{(p^{(m+1)n}-1)(p^{mn}-1)\cdots(p^{2n}-1)(p^n-1)}.$$

83. Representation of Finite Geometries by Means of Abelian Groups. Let G be an Abelian group of prime-power order $p^{(k+1)n}$ and type $(1, 1, \cdots, 1)$. In § **72** we introduced a set of subgroups of G, each of order p^n, and represented these subgroups by the symbols $(\mu_0, \mu_1, \cdots, \mu_k)$, where in each symbol the μ's are marks of $GF[p^n]$ and at least one of them is different from zero. Such a set of subgroups we called a geometric set of subgroups.

These subgroups $(\mu_0, \mu_1, \cdots, \mu_k)$ of order p^n, constituting the geometric set of subgroups of G, will be taken as the points of the finite geometry in the concrete representation of the geometry which is now to be set up. An m-space in this geometry will be defined as the set of points denoted by the groups of the geometric set which are contained as subgroups in the group generated by $m+1$ of the groups in the geometric set, these $m+1$ groups being such that no one of them is contained in the group generated by the other m. Again we call a point a 0-space; a 1-space is called a line. With point and line thus defined, it is evident that the definition of an m-space here given is equivalent to the inductive definition given in § **81**.

If $(\mu_0, \mu_1, \cdots, \mu_k)$ and $(\nu_0, \nu_1, \cdots, \nu_k)$ are two distinct points in this set, then the line determined by them consists of the p^n+1 points

$$(\mu\mu_0+\nu\nu_0, \mu\mu_1+\nu\nu_1, \cdots, \mu\mu_k+\nu\nu_k),$$

where μ and ν run independently over the marks of the $GF[p^n]$ except that they are not simultaneously zero.

Since the points and lines of the geometry are now represented by the same symbols as the points and lines in § **82**, it follows readily that the elements here set up constitute the $PG(k, p^n)$. Hence every $PG(k, p^n)$ is capable of a concrete representation by means of an Abelian group G of order $p^{(k+1)n}$ and type $(1, 1, \cdots, 1)$.

From this it follows that every abstract theorem relating to $PG(k, p^n)$ may be translated into a corresponding theorem about the group G. Conversely, a certain class of theorems about the group G are likewise individually capable of interpretation as theorems in the $PG(k, p^n)$. This interaction of two theories, in the first place apparently quite distinct, affords a matter of considerable interest.

84. Euclidean Finite Geometries $EG(k, p^n)$. Let us consider the subset $(\mu_0, \mu_1, \cdots, \mu_k)$ of points in the $PG(k, p^n)$, for each of which $\mu_0 \neq 0$. Without loss of generality we take $\mu_0 = 1$. Then the points considered are $(1, \mu_1, \mu_2, \cdots, \mu_k)$. Since the marks $\mu_1, \mu_2, \cdots, \mu_k$ may run independently over the p^n marks of the $PG(k, p^n)$, it is evident that the points in consideration are p^{kn} in number. They are said to constitute a Euclidean finite geometry; this Euclidean finite geometry is denoted by $EG(k, p^n)$. The excluded points $(0, \mu_1, \mu_2, \cdots, \mu_k)$ obviously constitute a $PG(k-1, p^n)$ the homogeneous co-ordinates of whose points are of the form $(\mu_1, \mu_2, \cdots, \mu_k)$. More generally, if we omit from the $PG(k, p^n)$ any given $PG(k-1, p^n)$ contained in it, the retained points are said to constitute a Euclidean finite geometry $EG(k, p^n)$; and this geometry contains just p^{kn} points.

The particular form of the $EG(k, p^n)$ first mentioned in the preceding paragraph has for the homogeneous co-ordinates of its points those of the form $(1, \mu_1, \mu_2, \cdots, \mu_k)$. When considering the $EG(k, p^n)$ alone, it is therefore possible to represent its points by the nonhomogeneous co-ordinates

$$\{\mu_1, \mu_2, \cdots, \mu_k\}.$$

But we have seen that the elements of the Abelian group of order p^{kn} and type $(1, 1, \cdots, 1)$ may be represented by nonhomogeneous co-ordinates $\{\mu_1, \mu_2, \cdots, \mu_k\}$. Hence the elements of this group afford concrete representations of the $EG(k, p^n)$.

From the definition of points and lines of the $PG(k, p^n)$, given in § **82**, it follows that the $PG(k, p^n)$ is transformed into itself when its points $(x_0, x_1, \cdots, x_k)$ are transformed in accordance with any transformation of the form

$$\rho x'_i = \sum_{j=0}^{k} \alpha_{ij} x_j, \qquad (i = 0, 1, \cdots, k)$$

where the α_{ij} are marks of the $GF[p^n]$ such that the determinant $|\alpha_{ij}|$ is different from zero. By such a transformation the $PG(k-1, p^n)$ defined by the equation $x_0 = 0$, that is, the $PG(k-1, p^n)$ consisting of the points $(0, \mu_1, \mu_2, \cdots, \mu_k)$, is replaced by a $PG(k-1, p^n)$ whose equation is $x'_0 = 0$, or

$$\alpha_{00}x_0 + \alpha_{01}x_1 + \cdots + \alpha_{0k}x_k = 0.$$

At least one of these coefficients α_{0i} is different from zero. Conversely, if we have any equation of the foregoing form, with at least one coefficient different from zero, then there exists a transformation of the named type by which the $PG(k-1, p^n)$ defined by the equation $x_0 = 0$ is transformed into the given equation. Therefore every equation of the named form defines a $PG(k-1, p^n)$ contained in the given $PG(k, p^n)$. Furthermore, every $PG(k-1, p^n)$ contained in the given $PG(k, p^n)$ consists of points $(x_0, x_1, \cdots, x_k)$ whose co-ordinates satisfy an equation of the form

$$\beta_0x_0 + \beta_1x_1 + \cdots + \beta_kx_k = 0;$$

for (§ **82**) such a $PG(k-1, p^n)$ consists of a set of points of the form

$$\left(\sum_{i=0}^{k-1} \mu_i\mu_{i0}, \cdots, \sum_{i=0}^{k-1} \mu_i\mu_{ik}\right),$$

where the points $(\mu_{i0}, \cdots, \mu_{ik})$ $(i = 0, 1, \cdots, k-1)$ are a set of base points for defining the given $PG(k-1, p^n)$, and for every such set of points the coefficients β exist such that these points are just the points $(x_0, x_1, \cdots, x_k)$ whose co-ordinates satisfy the last foregoing equation. From these considerations it follows that a transformation of the named type exists by which any given $PG(k-1, p^n)$ contained in the $PG(k, p^n)$ may be transformed into any other such $PG(k-1, p^n)$. Therefore all the $EG(k, p^n)$ contained in $PG(k, p^n)$ have the same structure.

85. The Principle of Duality. In the postulates in § **81** the terms *point* and *line* are undefined. Therefore we may give these names to any entities having the properties assigned to point and line in the postulates. We shall establish the property of duality by showing that certain other entities in the $PG(k, p^n)$ have the properties of points and lines respectively. To prevent confusion we shall temporarily use the terms *punct* and *rect* for the entities having the properties of point and line respectively. During the argument we shall suppose that $k > 1$.

A $(k-1)$-space in $PG(k, p^n)$ we shall call a punct; and a $(k-2)$-space we shall call a rect. We shall now show that two given puncts have one and only one rect in common. Let $(\mu_{i0}, \mu_{i1}, \cdots, \mu_{ik})$ $(i=1, 2, \cdots, k)$ be a set of k points in $PG(k, p^n)$ which are not on the same $(k-2)$-space. They may be used as the base points by means of which to define a $(k-1)$-space, or a punct, as in § **82**. Let a second punct be defined by the set $(\nu_{i0}, \nu_{i1}, \cdots, \nu_{ik})$ $(i=1, 2, \cdots, k)$ of k base points which are not on the same $(k-2)$-space. Then the points contained in these two puncts are

$$\left(\sum_{i=1}^{k} \mu_i\mu_{i0}, \cdots, \sum_{i=1}^{k} \mu_i\mu_{ik}\right) \text{ and } \left(\sum_{i=1}^{k} \nu_i\nu_{i0}, \cdots, \sum_{i=1}^{k} \nu_i\nu_{ik}\right)$$

respectively, where the μ_i, and likewise the ν_i, run over the marks of the $GF[p^n]$ except that neither all the μ_i nor all the ν_i can be simultaneously zero.

Let us consider the system of equations

$$\sum_{j=0}^{k} a_j\mu_{ij} = 0 \qquad (i = 1, 2, \cdots, k)$$

in the unknown quantities $a_0, a_1, \cdots, a_k$. Since the k points of the first system of base points do not lie on a $(k-2)$-space, it follows that the matrix

$$\begin{Vmatrix} \mu_{10} & \mu_{11} & \cdots & \mu_{1k} \\ \mu_{20} & \mu_{21} & \cdots & \mu_{2k} \\ \cdot & \cdot & \cdot & \cdot \\ \mu_{k0} & \mu_{k1} & \cdots & \mu_{kk} \end{Vmatrix}$$

is of rank k. Hence the foregoing system of equations has a solution for the a's which is unique except for a factor of proportionality belonging to the $GF[p^n]$. Thence it follows that the points of the first punct are precisely the points $(x_0, x_1, \cdots, x_k)$ for which the equation

$$a_0x_0 + a_1x_1 + \cdots + a_kx_k = 0$$

is satisfied. We may therefore denote this punct uniquely by the "homogeneous co-ordinates" $[a_0, a_1, \cdots, a_k]$. Likewise there exists an equation

$$c_0x_0 + c_1x_1 + \cdots + c_kx_k = 0$$

whose solutions $(x_0, x_1, \cdots, x_k)$ afford precisely the points of the second punct, whence we denote the second punct by $[c_0, c_1, \cdots, c_k]$. Then the common solutions of these two equations define precisely the points which are common to the two given puncts. Since the two given puncts are different (by hypothesis), it follows that the matrix

$$\begin{Vmatrix} a_0 & a_1 & \cdots & a_k \\ c_0 & c_1 & \cdots & c_k \end{Vmatrix}$$

is of rank two. Hence the common solutions of the two equations can be expressed linearly and homogeneously in terms of $k-1$ suitably determined solutions, and the $k-1$ points defined by these particular solutions do not all lie on the same $(k-3)$-space. Therefore the solutions define a $(k-2)$-space, or a rect. Hence the two puncts have one and only one rect in common.

We shall say that the puncts which may be used in thus determining a given rect are the puncts on that rect; and we shall say also that the rect contains these puncts.

Putting punct and rect for point and line, respectively, in the postulates of § **81**, we see that the results just proved indicate that Postulates I and II in their new form are satisfied.

In order to show that Postulate III in the new form is satisfied, let us consider three puncts A, B, C with the respective defining equations

$$a_0x_0 + a_1x_1 + \cdots + a_kx_k = 0,$$
$$b_0x_0 + b_1x_1 + \cdots + b_kx_k = 0,$$
$$c_0x_0 + c_1x_1 + \cdots + c_kx_k = 0,$$

no one of these puncts being on the rect common to the other two. Let l be a rect such that one of the puncts D on l is also on the rect AB which is common to A and B and such that one of the puncts E on l is also on the rect BC, while l does not contain A or B or C. There exist nonzero marks d_1 and d_2 of the $GF[p^n]$ such that the equation

$$(d_1a_0 + d_2b_0)x_0 + \cdots + (d_1a_k + d_2b_k)x_k = 0$$

is the defining equation for the punct D. Likewise nonzero marks e_1 and e_2 exist in the $GF[p^n]$ such that the equation

$$(e_1b_0 + e_2c_0)x_0 + \cdots + (e_1b_k + e_2c_k)x_k = 0$$

is the defining equation for the punct E. The puncts on the rect DE, this being the rect l, have defining equations of the form

$$\{\alpha(d_1a_0 + d_2b_0) + \beta(e_1b_0 + e_2c_0)\}x_0 + \cdots = 0,$$

where α and β are marks of the $GF[p^n]$. Now nonzero marks α and β exist such that $\alpha d_2 + \beta e_1 = 0$. For these values of α and β the last named punct is on CA. This is the punct F called for in the new form of Postulate III. Hence that postulate is satisfied.

Now the rect which contains the two given puncts $[\alpha_0, \alpha_1, \cdots, \alpha_k]$ and $[\beta_0, \beta_1, \cdots, \beta_k]$ consists of the puncts $[\lambda\alpha_0 + \mu\beta_0, \cdots, \lambda\alpha_k + \mu\beta_k]$, where λ and μ run independently over the marks of the $GF[p^n]$ except that they cannot be simultaneously zero. It is this fact on which the proof in the preceding paragraph rests; and that proof is evidently abstractly the same as a corresponding proof given in § **82**.

That the new forms of the Postulates IV_k and V_k are satisfied may now be proved by means of an argument which is abstractly the same as that employed in a corresponding proof in § **82**. This proof will not be given.

Furthermore, we have incidentally given an analytical representation of puncts and rects which is in all abstract respects the same as that which we gave for points and lines in § **82**.

From these considerations it follows that the puncts and rects of a $PG(k, p^n)$ may be employed in place of points and lines in setting up a new representation of the same abstract $PG(k, p^n)$.

Now a 0-space (or punct) in the new sense is a $(k-1)$-space in the old sense, and a 1-space (or rect) in the new sense is a $(k-2)$-space in the old sense. More generally, we shall show that an l-space in the new sense is a $(k-l-1)$-space in the old sense. For an l-space in the new sense consists of the points $(x_0, x_1, \cdots, x_k)$ whose co-ordinates satisfy $l+1$ independent equations of the form

$$\sum_{j=0}^{k} c_{ij}x_j = 0; \qquad (i = 1, 2, \cdots, l+1)$$

and these equations have $k-l$ independent solutions in terms of which all their solutions may be expressed linearly and homogeneously, whence it follows that these equations define a $(k-l-1)$-space of points in the old sense.

From these considerations it follows that every theorem relating to $PG(k, p^n)$ may be translated into a new theorem relating to $PG(k, p^n)$ by replacing 0-space by $(k-1)$-space, 1-space by $(k-2)$-space, and, in general, l-space by $(k-l-1)$-space for every value of l less than k. This is the *principle of duality*. We have established this principle for $k > 1$; it obviously holds (in a trivial way) when $k = 1$.

Since the $PG(k, p^n)$ may be represented by means of a geometric set of subgroups of the Abelian group G of order $p^{(k+1)n}$ and type $(1, 1, \cdots, 1)$, we see that any theorem concerning the geometric set of subgroups of G may be translated into a new theorem by means of the principle of duality.

The new theorem obtained in either of these cases is called the *dual* of the original theorem. It is clear that the original theorem is then the dual of the new theorem. In case the dual of a theorem is that theorem itself, the theorem is said to be *self-dual*. In all other cases the truth of one of the theorems implies the truth of the other without further argument, so that the principle of duality gives rise to economy of thought. It also exhibits clearly certain aspects of beauty which might not be realized without its aid.

86. Finite Geometries Contained within Finite Geometries. Let us consider the finite projective geometry $PG(k, p^n)$, where $n > 1$. Let ν be any proper divisor of n (including the possibility that ν shall be unity). Then the $GF[p^n]$ contains a subfield $GF[p^\nu]$, as we saw in § **65**. Let us consider the set of points

$$(\rho_0, \rho_1, \cdots, \rho_k)$$

in $PG(k, p^n)$, where the ρ_i run independently over the p^ν marks of the $GF[p^\nu]$ except that they shall not be simultaneously zero. This set of points constitutes a finite projective geometry $PG(k, p^\nu)$, and this geometry is contained within the $PG(k, p^n)$ as a subgeometry. Therefore, when $n > 1$ the $PG(k, p^n)$ always contains one or more subgeometries $PG(k, p^\nu)$, one for each proper divisor ν of n.

Let us consider as an illustrative example the $PG(2, 2^2)$ based on the $GF[2^2]$ defined by means of the function $x^2 + x + 1$. The marks of the $GF[2^2]$ may be denoted by 0, 1, ω, ω_1, where $\omega_1 = \omega + 1$. Then we have the following relations:

$$1 + \omega = \omega_1, \;\; 1 + \omega_1 = \omega, \;\; \omega + \omega_1 = 1, \;\; 1 + \omega + \omega_1 = 0,$$
$$\omega\omega = \omega_1, \;\; \omega_1\omega_1 = \omega, \;\; \omega\omega_1 = 1.$$

The points of $PG(2, 2^2)$ are 21 in number, since $1 + 2^2 + 2^4 = 21$. They will be denoted by letters in accordance with the following scheme:

(001)	(010)	(011)	(01ω)	$(01\omega_1)$	(100)	(101)
A	*B*	*C*	*D*	*E*	*F*	*G*
(10ω)	$(10\omega_1)$	(110)	(111)	(11ω)	$(11\omega_1)$	$(1\omega 0)$
H	*I*	*J*	*K*	*L*	*M*	*N*
$(1\omega 1)$	$(1\omega\omega)$	$(1\omega\omega_1)$	$(1\omega_1 0)$	$(1\omega_1 1)$	$(1\omega_1\omega)$	$(1\omega_1\omega_1)$
O	*P*	*Q*	*R*	*S*	*T*	*U*

The 21 lines are those given in the following scheme, the letters in a given column denoting a line:

A	*A*	*A*	*A*	*A*	*B*	*B*	*B*	*B*	*C*	*C*	*C*	*C*	*D*	*D*	*D*	*D*	*E*	*E*	*E*	*E*
B	*F*	*J*	*N*	*R*	*F*	*G*	*H*	*I*	*F*	*G*	*H*	*I*	*F*	*G*	*H*	*I*	*F*	*G*	*H*	*I*
C	*G*	*K*	*O*	*S*	*J*	*K*	*L*	*M*	*K*	*J*	*M*	*L*	*L*	*M*	*J*	*K*	*M*	*L*	*K*	*J*
D	*H*	*L*	*P*	*T*	*N*	*O*	*P*	*Q*	*P*	*Q*	*N*	*O*	*Q*	*P*	*O*	*N*	*O*	*N*	*Q*	*P*
E	*I*	*M*	*Q*	*U*	*R*	*S*	*T*	*U*	*U*	*T*	*S*	*R*	*S*	*R*	*U*	*T*	*T*	*U*	*R*	*S*

The points *A*, *B*, *C*, *F*, *G*, *J*, *K*, in the junction into lines defined by this scheme, constitute the $PG(2, 2)$ of 7 points whose lines are denoted by the columns in the following scheme:

$$\begin{matrix} A & B & F & C & J & K & G \\ B & F & C & J & K & G & A \\ C & J & K & G & A & B & F \end{matrix}$$

This is a subgeometry $PG(2, 2)$ contained within the given $PG(2, 2^2)$.

EXERCISES

1. Show directly from the postulates in § **81** that a two-dimensional finite projective geometry having just three points on a line consists of a set of seven points which may be labeled A, B, C, D, E, F, G in such a way that the lines of the geometry are the sets of three each in the columns of the following scheme:

$$\begin{matrix} A & B & C & D & E & F & G \\ B & C & D & E & F & G & A \\ D & E & F & G & A & B & C \end{matrix}$$

Show that the largest permutation group on A, B, C, D, E, F, G each element of which transforms this geometry into itself in the sense that points are replaced by points and lines are replaced by lines is the doubly transitive group $\{(ABCDEFG), (BD)(EF)\}$ of degree 7 and order 168. Denoting the lines of this geometry, in the order in which they appear in the foregoing scheme, by a, b, c, d, e, f, g, set up the dual form of the geometry; find the group on a, b, c, d, e f, g induced by the group $\{(ABCDEFG), (BD)(EF)\}$ and examine the relation between these groups. Are the two groups conjugate as well as isomorphic?

2. Treat similarly the two-dimensional finite projective geometries having (*a*) just four points on a line, (*b*) just five points on a line.

3. Determine the 12 lines of 3 points each belonging to the $EG(2, 3)$ of 9 points. Determine the largest permutation group on these nine points each element of which transforms this $EG(2, 3)$ into itself.

4. Denote the 15 points of the $PG(3, 2)$ by the symbols $A, B, C, \cdots, O$, as follows:

(0001)	(0010)	(0011)	(0100)	(0101)	(0110)	(0111)	(1000)
A	B	C	D	E	F	G	H

(1001)	(1010)	(1011)	(1100)	(1101)	(1110)	(1111)
I	J	K	L	M	N	O

Determine the 15 planes of 7 points each contained in this $PG(3, 2)$; and then determine its 35 lines by means of the intersections of its planes in pairs.

5. Show that the largest permutation group on the 15 points of the $PG(3, 2)$, each element of which transforms this geometry into itself, is a doubly transitive group of degree 15 and order $15 \cdot 14 \cdot 12 \cdot 8$.

6. Note that the points H, I, J, K, L, M, N, O in Ex. 4 constitute an $EG(3, 2)$ of 8 points. Find the largest subgroup of the doubly transitive group named in Ex. 5 which subgroup has the property that its elements permute among themselves the points of the named $EG(3, 2)$. Show that this subgroup permutes the points of the $EG(3, 2)$ according to a triply transitive group of degree 8 and order $8 \cdot 7 \cdot 6 \cdot 4$.

7. Show that the doubly transitive group of degree 15 named in Ex. 5 can be represented as simply isomorphic with a transitive group on the 35 lines of the $PG(3, 2)$.

8. By aid of the principle of duality in the finite geometries show that an Abelian group of order p^m and type $(1, 1, \cdots, 1)$ has just as many subgroups of index p^l, $0 < l < m$, as it has subgroups of order p^l.

9. Arrange the 35 lines of the $PG(3, 2)$ (see Ex. 4) in seven sets of five each so that each point appears once and just once in each set of five lines.

10. Show how 15 girls may go walking in five sets of three each on each of seven consecutive days so that any whatever given two of the girls shall be together in a set of three on one and just one of the seven days.

11. Show that successive powers of the permutation $(x_0 x_1 x_2 \cdots x_{12})$ change the set x_0, x_1, x_3, x_9 into 13 distinct sets defining the lines of the $PG(2, 3)$ whose points are $x_0, x_1, x_2, \cdots, x_{12}$.

12. Show that successive powers of the permutation $(x_0 x_1 x_2 \cdots x_{30})$ change the set $x_1, x_5, x_{11}, x_{24}, x_{25}, x_{27}$ into 31 distinct sets defining the lines of the $PG(2, 5)$ whose points are $x_0, x_1, x_2, \cdots, x_{30}$.

87. Interrelations of Finite Geometries and Abelian Groups. We begin this section with a proof of the following theorem:

THE THEOREM OF DESARGUES. Let ABC and abc be two triangles in the same plane in a $PG(k, p^n)$ and let them be perspective from a point O so that O, A, a

are collinear, O, B, b are collinear, and O, C, c are collinear. Let γ be the point of intersection of AB and ab, β that of AC and ac, and α that of BC and bc. Then the points α, β, γ are collinear.

An analytical proof of the theorem may be readily developed by means of the analytical geometry of the $PG(k, p^n)$ exhibited in the preceding pages. But we prefer to give a geometric proof.

Let A_1, A_2, A_3, A_4, A_5 be a set of five points in $PG(k, p^n)$ $(k \geqq 3)$ no four of which lie on the same plane. Then these points define 10 lines A_iA_j and 10 planes $A_iA_jA_k$. Let us take a plane section of this configuration of points and lines in such a way that the section contains no one of the points A_i. If π denotes the cutting plane, then π is pierced in 10 points by the 10 lines A_iA_j; it is also cut in 10 lines by the planes $A_iA_jA_k$. We may suppose the figure so made that the points A_3, A_4, A_5 project from A_1 into the points A, B, C, respectively, and from A_2 into the points a, b, c, respectively, of the theorem, while the line A_1A_2 pierces π in the point O. Then the points α, β, γ of the theorem are on the line in which the plane $A_3A_4A_5$ cuts the plane π. From these considerations the truth of the theorem follows.

Let us translate this result into a theorem concerning the Abelian group G of order $p^{(k+1)n}$ and type $(1, 1, \cdots, 1)$, viewed as in § **83** in the light afforded by the geometry $PG(k, p^n)$, it being assumed now that $k > 1$.

Let A, B, C be three subgroups of a geometric set of subgroups of G such that no one of them is in the group generated by the other two. We select other subgroups of the geometric set as follows, each of them to be in the group $\{A, B, C\}$: O is any such subgroup which is not contained in any one of the subgroups $\{A, B\}$, $\{B, C\}$, $\{C, A\}$; a, b, c are such subgroups different from O, A, B, C and contained, respectively, in the groups $\{O, A\}$, $\{O, B\}$, $\{O, C\}$. Let γ, α, β be the subgroups of the geometric set of subgroups common to the respective pairs of groups

$$\{A, B\}, \{a, b\}; \ \{B, C\}, \{b, c\}; \ \{C, A\}, \{c, a\}.$$

Then each of the subgroups α, β, γ is in the subgroup generated by the other two.

The generalizations of the theorem of Desargues to higher dimensions yield likewise interesting theorems concerning Abelian groups. As phrased abstractly, the theorems seem to be rather complicated; but in their geometric formulation they are easily comprehended and retained in mind.

As affording another illustration of this method of translating geometric theorems into theorems about Abelian groups, let us consider the following which gives rise to the configuration of Pappus (Veblen and Young, *Projective Geometry*, Vol. I, p. 98): If A, B, C are any three distinct points of a line l, and A', B', C' are any three additional distinct points on another line l' meeting l in O, then the three points γ, α, β of intersections of the respective pairs of line

$$AB', A'B;\ BC', B'C;\ CA', C'A$$

are collinear.

We shall not give a proof of this geometric theorem but shall content ourselves with translating it into a theorem concerning the group G.

Let O, A, A' be three subgroups of a geometric set of subgroups of G such that no one of them is in the group generated by the other two. Let B and C be two additional subgroups contained in the group $\{O, A\}$ and belonging to the geometric set, and let B' and C' be two additional such subgroups contained in the group $\{O, A'\}$, these groups being existent when and only when $p^n > 2$ and $k > 1$. Let γ, α, β be the subgroups of the geometric set which are common to the respective pairs of groups

$$\{A, B'\},\ \{A', B\};\ \{B, C'\},\ \{B', C\};\ \{C, A'\},\ \{C', A\}.$$

Then each of the subgroups α, β, γ is in the subgroup generated by the other two.

The analysis and development of projective geometry given by O. Veblen and J. W. Young (*Projective Geometry*, Vol. I, 1910; Vol. II, 1918) afford a convenient means of ascertaining what geometries have direct applications to the theory of Abelian groups by means of the representations of finite geometries given in the foregoing pages. In Volume II (p. 36) of this work Veblen describes nine classes of geometries characterized by means of the assumptions which underlie them. Using capital letters to denote assumptions and employing the notation of Veblen and Young (see the index to Volume II under the word "assumption"), we select for our purposes four of these geometries, as follows: A space satisfying assumptions

A, E is a general projective space;
A, E, P is a proper projective space;
$A, E, \overline{H}$ is a modular projective space;
$A, E, \overline{H}, Q$ is a rational modular projective space.

It is easy to verify that the assumptions involved in these four geometries are all valid in the case of the geometry $PG(k, p^n)$, except that Q is valid when and only when $n = 1$. Since the points of this geometry have been represented by certain subgroups of the Abelian group G (see § **83**), it follows that every theorem in any one of the four geometries named is capable of immediate translation into a theorem concerning the given Abelian group. In many cases a given theorem is capable of being so translated in a variety of ways, there being at least one such translation for every factorization of the number $(k+1)n$ into a product of two factors $k+1$ and n such that k and n are positive integers.

Each of the four geometries may be divided into two parts. In one part we have the assumption H_0, namely:

H_0. The diagonal points of a complete quadrangle are non-collinear.

In the other we have the assumption that these diagonal points are collinear. The consequences of this latter assumption are not developed in detail by Veblen and Young, but many of the theorems given as dependent on A, E, P, H_0 (so far as the given proofs go) are provable without the use of H_0 (compare Vol. I, p. 261, exercise). We shall presently show that H_0 is valid in $PG(k, p^n)$ when and only when the prime p is different from 2.

Now in Volume I of the work named no assumptions are used except those which are valid for $PG(k, p^n)$. Hence every theorem in Volume I may be translated, in the way indicated, into a theorem about Abelian groups. The same remarks may be made about certain parts of Volume II, and in particular about Chapter III and the first part of Chapter IV. It is thus apparent that the representation of the $PG(k, p^n)$ by means of Abelian groups carries at once a large part of the results of projective geometry into the domain of Abelian groups and that they there become theorems about Abelian groups. Thus by a single act of thought a significant extension is given to the theory of Abelian groups and a method is made apparent by which the theory may be further developed. Conversely, a certain part of the theory of Abelian groups can be translated into corresponding results in the finite geometries.

In the finite projective geometries $PG(k, p^n)$, as we have already said, an important distinction is to be made according as the prime p is equal to 2 or is odd. This distinction will become apparent from an examination of the diagonal points of a complete quadrangle, that is, the figure formed by the six lines A_iA_j defined by means of four points A_1, A_2, A_3, A_4 on the same plane but with no three on the same line. Anticipating Theorem I in § **92**, we see that we may without loss of generality take k to be 2 and choose for the points A the following:

$$A_1, (100);\ A_2, (010);\ A_3, (001);\ A_4, (111).$$

The three diagonal points of the quadrangle are then the intersections of the following pairs of lines:

$$A_1A_2,\ A_3A_4;\ A_1A_3,\ A_2A_4;\ A_1A_4,\ A_2A_3.$$

Hence they are the points (110), (101), (011). These are collinear when and only when $p = 2$. Therefore, *the diagonal points of a complete quadrangle in* $PG(k, p^n)$ *are collinear when and only when* $p = 2$. Thus an important and simple geometric fact sharply distinguishes between two cases of these finite geometries.

This difference in the geometries according as p is odd or even is reflected in an important way in the theory of Abelian groups of order p^m and type $(1, 1, \cdots, 1)$. Early in the development of the theory of these groups it became apparent that their properties differ according as p is 2 or is an odd prime. From the geometric interpretation of these groups and the facts just adduced, the fundamental basis for this difference is apparent. Hence, in investigating these groups, one sees precisely from what place to begin for developing those features of the theory which depend on the odd or even character of p.

For the case of the Abelian group G, with the geometry $PG(k, p^n)$ constructed from it in § **83**, the distinguishing difference of the two cases may be stated in group-theory language as follows (it being assumed now that $k > 1$): Let A, B, C, D be four subgroups of a geometric set of subgroups of G such that no one of them is contained in the group generated by another two, while D is contained in the group $\{A, B, C\}$. Let E be the (unique) subgroup of the geometric set common to the groups $\{A, B\}$ and $\{C, D\}$, F that common to the groups $\{A, C\}$ and $\{B, D\}$, and G that common to the groups $\{A, D\}$ and $\{B, C\}$. Then each of the subgroups E, F, G is in the group generated by the other two when and only when $p = 2$.

A large part of the theory of the geometry $PG(k, p^n)$, as we have seen, may be developed independently of any hypothesis as to the collinearity or noncollinearity of the diagonal points of a complete quadrangle. These theorems will give rise to corresponding theorems about Abelian groups of order p^m and type $(1, 1, \cdots, 1)$ which are independent of the odd or even character of p.

88. Some Generalizations. Let us now consider more generally an Abelian group A whose order is a power of a prime p and whose type is $(m_1, m_2, \cdots, m_{(k+1)n})$. Let us denote a set of independent generators of A by

$$\begin{array}{l} a_{01}, a_{02}, a_{03}, \cdots, a_{0n}, \\ a_{11}, a_{12}, a_{13}, \cdots, a_{1n}, \\ \cdot \quad \cdot \quad \cdot \quad \cdot \quad \cdot \quad \cdot \\ a_{k1}, a_{k2}, a_{k3}, \cdots, a_{kn}, \end{array}$$

these being chosen so that a_{ij} is of period $p^{m_{in+j}}$. Then every element of A may be represented uniquely in the form

$$\prod_{i=0}^{k} a_{i1}^{s_{i1}} a_{i2}^{s_{i2}} \cdots a_{in}^{s_{in}},$$

where the exponent s_{ij} is a number of the set 0, 1, 2, $\cdots$, $p^{m_{in+j}}-1$.

Consider the following subset of these elements, namely,

$$\prod_{i=0}^{k} a_{i1}^{\sigma_{i1}} a_{i2}^{\sigma_{i2}} \cdots a_{in}^{\sigma_{in}},$$

where each σ runs over the set 0, 1, 2, $\cdots, p-1$, or, more generally, the exponent σ_{ij} runs over the set $lp^{\alpha_{ij}}$ for $l=0, 1, 2, \cdots, p-1$, the fixed integer α_{ij} being non-negative and less than m_{in+j}. An element of this sort, for the fixed set of exponents

$$\sigma_{ij} = l_{ij}p^{\alpha_{ij}},$$

the a_{ij} and the α_{ij} having been chosen once for all, may be uniquely represented by the symbol

$$\{\mu_0, \mu_1, \cdots, \mu_k\},$$

where μ_i ($i=0, 1, 2, \cdots, k$) denotes that mark of the $GF[p^n]$ which may be written in the form

$$\mu_i = l_{i1} + l_{i2}\omega + l_{i3}\omega^2 + \cdots + l_{in}\omega^{n-1},$$

ω being a fixed primitive mark of the field.

Now let $\mu_0, \mu_1, \cdots, \mu_k$ be a fixed set of $k+1$ marks of the $GF[p^n]$, at least one of them being different from zero; and consider the set of elements

$$\{\mu\mu_0, \mu\mu_1, \cdots, \mu\mu_k\},$$

where μ is a variable running over the p^n-1 nonzero marks of the field. These elements generate a certain subgroup of A which we denote by the symbol $(\mu_0, \mu_1, \cdots, \mu_k)$. The same subgroup is denoted by the symbol $(\sigma\mu_0, \sigma\mu_1, \cdots, \sigma\mu_k)$, where σ is any nonzero mark of the field. The total set of such subgroups we shall call a geometric set of subgroups of A.

The subgroups each of which is denoted by a symbol of the type $(\mu_0, \mu_1, \cdots, \mu_k)$ will be taken as the points of the geometry we are constructing. The point corresponding to the subgroup $(\mu_0, \mu_1, \cdots, \mu_k)$ will be denoted by the symbol $(\mu_0, \mu_1, \cdots, \mu_k)$, and $\mu_0, \mu_1, \cdots, \mu_k$ will be called the homogeneous co-ordinates of the point. In the geometry thus constructed the points are denoted by the same symbols as those employed in § **82** in constructing the geometry $PG(k, p^n)$, and the number system, namely the $GF[p^n]$, bears the same relation to the geometry in the new case as in the old. Hence the two geometries are abstractly the same, provided we employ (as we shall agree to do) a definition of lines similar to that employed in § **82**. That is to say, the geometry constructed in this section is but another concrete representation of the abstract geometry $PG(k, p^n)$.

It follows that certain properties of the group A in the general case are identical with those for the special case when the type is $(1, 1, \cdots, 1)$; namely, those properties which may be expressed in terms of the points (and classes of points—lines, etc.) of the geometry $PG(k, p^n)$. For simplicity we shall deal with the special case when the group is of type $(1, 1, \cdots, 1)$; but the results will have the obvious extension indicated.

89. Geometric Sets of Subgroups. In §§ **72** and **83** we have given an analytic method for determining geometric sets of subgroups of G. It is desirable to have such a set characterized by means of properties which are immediately group-theoretic in character. The subgroups of a given geometric set have the following properties, as we have already seen:

I. Each of these subgroups is of order p^n.

II. No two of them have a common element except the identity.

III. Any given element of G is contained in some subgroup of a geometric set.

IV. If A, B, C are three subgroups of a geometric set such that no one of them is in the group generated by the other two, and if D is a subgroup of $\{A, B\}$ and is different from A and B and belongs to the geometric set, and finally if E is a subgroup of the group $\{B, C\}$ and is different from B and C and belongs to the geometric set, then the groups $\{C, A\}$ and $\{D, E\}$ have in common a group F which belongs to the geometric set.

Any set of subgroups of G which have these properties alone satisfy the postulates of § **81**. They therefore afford a representation of a finite geometry. But Veblen and Bussey (as cited in § **81**) have shown that every finite projective k-dimensional geometry is a $PG(k, p^n)$, provided that $k > 2$. Hence one can introduce co-ordinates into this geometry by means of the $GF[p^n]$. On doing this in the case of the given group-theoretic representation of the geometry, we may exhibit the geometric set of subgroups in the notation employed in § **83**. Therefore when $k > 2$ the properties I, II, III, IV furnish a complete group-theoretic characterization of a geometric set of subgroups. The conclusion will also hold for $k = 1$ or 2 if we suppose that the geometric set of subgroups is so chosen that it may be taken as a part of the geometric set of subgroups in a group of order p^{4n} and type $(1, 1, \cdots, 1)$ which contains the given group G for $k = 1$ or 2.

90. Another Analytical Representation of $PG(k, p^n)$. Another analytical representation of $PG(k, p^n)$ may be obtained as follows. Denote the points of the geometry by the symbols (ρ), where ρ is a nonzero mark of the $GF[p^{(k+1)n}]$ and where $(\rho) \equiv (\alpha\rho)$ for every nonzero mark α of the included field $GF[p^n]$. Since the symbols (ρ) are $p^{(k+1)n} - 1$ in number, and since the factor α of proportionality has $p^n - 1$ values, it follows readily that the number of points defined by the symbols (ρ) is

$$1 + p^n + p^{2n} + \cdots + p^{kn}.$$

If (ρ_1) and (ρ_2) are any two distinct points of the geometry, then a line of the geometry will by definition be the set of points $(\lambda_1\rho_1 + \lambda_2\rho_2)$, where λ_1 and λ_2 are marks of the included field $GF[p^n]$ and are not simultaneously zero; then the number of points on a line is $1 + p^n$. Then one defines planes, 3-spaces, 4-spaces, etc., inductively, as in § **81**. Thus the points $(\mu_1\rho_1 + \mu_2\rho_2 + \mu_3\rho_3)$ constitute a plane containing the noncollinear points (ρ_1), (ρ_2), (ρ_3), provided that μ_1, μ_2, μ_3 run independently over the marks of the included $GF[p^n]$ except that they shall not be simultaneously equal to zero.

It is easy to show that the points and lines so defined lead to a finite projective geometry. That Postulates I, II, IV, V of

§ **81** are satisfied follows at once. That Postulate III is verified may be shown by a method in all respects similar to that employed in § **82**. That this geometry is the $PG(k, p^n)$ follows from the fact that there is only one finite projective k-dimensional geometry when $k > 2$; or it may be shown directly that what we have here defined is equivalent to the more usual representation of $PG(k, p^n)$ by means of $k+1$ co-ordinates from the $GF[p^n]$.

Since we shall not further employ the present form of $PG(k, p^n)$ we shall not develop these results in detail.

91. Configurations in $PG(k, p^n)$. By a *tactical configuration of rank two* is meant a combination of l elements into m sets, each set containing λ distinct elements and each element occurring in μ distinct sets; it is to be understood that order of sets and order within a set are both immaterial. For such a configuration we use the symbol

$$\Delta_{l, m}^{\lambda, \mu}.$$

It is obvious that $l\mu = m\lambda$. A general development of the properties of these configurations is reserved for Chapter XIV. A few of the configurations arising from the $PG(k, p^n)$ will be here indicated.

The finite geometries $PG(k, p^n)$ $(k > 1)$ furnish at once a certain infinite class of these tactical configurations. The points of the geometry constitute the l elements, and the lines of the geometry constitute the m classes. Then we have a configuration with the symbol $\Delta_{l, m}^{\lambda, \mu}$, where l is the number of points in the geometry, m is the number of lines, λ is the number of points on a line, and μ is the number of lines on a point; whence it follows that we have

$$l = 1 + p^n + p^{2n} + \cdots + p^{kn}, \quad \lambda = 1 + p^n, \quad \mu = l - p^{kn}, \quad m = l\mu/\lambda.$$

When $k = 2$ and $p^n = 2, 3, 4$ we have configurations with the respective symbols $\Delta_{7,7}^{3,3}$, $\Delta_{13,13}^{4,4}$, $\Delta_{21,21}^{5,5}$. For $k = 3$ and $p^n = 2$ we have $\Delta_{15,35}^{3,7}$.

From the Euclidean geometry $EG(k, p^n)$ $(k > 1)$ we may readily construct other tactical configurations of rank two. Let an $EG(k, p^n)$ be formed from the $PG(k, p^n)$ by omitting a given

$(k-1)$-space S_{k-1}. Each line of the $EG(k, p^n)$ will contain one point which is in the omitted S_{k-1}, leaving p^n points on the line and in $EG(k, p^n)$. Now let the p^{kn} points of $EG(k, p^n)$ be the elements from which the tactical configuration is to be constructed, and let the sets of points be made up by taking for a set the p^n points of $EG(k, p^n)$ which lie on a given line, doing this for each line of the $EG(k, p^n)$. Thus we are led to a configuration $\Delta_{l,m}^{\lambda,\mu}$, where

$$l = p^{kn}, \quad \lambda = p^n, \quad \mu = 1 + p^n + p^{2n} + \cdots + p^{(k-1)n}, \quad m = l\mu/\lambda.$$

For $k = 2$ and $p^n = 2, 3$ we have the respective configurations $\Delta_{4,6}^{2,3}$, $\Delta_{9,12}^{3,4}$.

This configuration $\Delta_{4,6}^{2,3}$ belongs also to another infinite class of tactical configurations of rank two. It consists of four things taken in pairs; since the number of pairs is six, it follows that all possible pairs appear. Now from n elements one can form $\frac{1}{2}n(n-1)$ pairs, each element occurring in $n-1$ pairs. This gives rise to a configuration with the symbol

$$\Delta_{n,\frac{1}{2}n(n-1)}^{2,n-1}.$$

The last configuration may readily be generalized. From n given elements form all sets consisting each of a combination of k distinct elements, k being less than n. This gives rise to a configuration $\Delta_{l,m}^{\lambda,\mu}$ with

$$l = n, \quad \lambda = k, \quad m = \frac{n(n-1)(n-2)\cdots(n-k+1)}{k!},$$

$$\mu = \frac{(n-1)(n-2)\cdots(n-k+1)}{(k-1)!}.$$

The first configuration of this section was obtained by grouping the points of $PG(k, p^n)$ into the sets defined by the lines of the geometry. We may similarly group the points into the sets formed by the subspaces of a given number s of dimensions, where s is any positive integer less than k; and in each case we shall be led to a tactical configuration of rank two. The case when $s = k-1$ is of particular interest, since the configuration then has a certain dual character owing to the dual character of points and $(k-1)$-spaces. This configuration has the symbol $\Delta_{l,m}^{\lambda,\mu}$ where

$$l = m = 1 + p^n + p^{2n} + \cdots + p^{kn},$$
$$\lambda = \mu = 1 + p^n + p^{2n} + \cdots + p^{(k-1)n}.$$

In a similar manner configurations may be obtained from $EG(k, p^n)$. In particular the p^{kn} points of $EG(k, p^n)$ fall $p^{(k-1)n}$ at a time on the $(k-1)$-spaces of $PG(k, p^n)$ other than the one omitted in forming the $EG(k, p^n)$, thus giving rise to a configuration $\Delta_{l,m}^{\lambda,\mu}$ where

$$l = p^{kn}, \quad \lambda = p^{(k-1)n}, \quad \mu = 1 + p^n + \cdots + p^{(k-1)n},$$
$$m = p^n + p^{2n} + \cdots + p^{kn}.$$

In the case when $p^n = 2$ and $k > 1$ we have in $EG(k, 2)$ the number 2^k of points. Any three points in $EG(k, 2)$ determine a plane of $EG(k, 2)$, and this plane contains just one additional point of $EG(k, 2)$. Moreover, any three of the points in such a quadruple uniquely determines the quadruple itself. Hence the 2^k points of $EG(k, 2)$ may be taken in fours, in the way indicated, so that any given triple of these 2^k points occurs in one and in just one of the named quadruples. Thus we have a tactical configuration $\Delta_{l,m}^{\lambda,\mu}$ where, as is easily shown, we have

$$l = 2^k, \quad \lambda = 4, \quad \mu = \tfrac{1}{3}(2^k - 1)(2^{k-1} - 1),$$
$$m = \tfrac{1}{3} \cdot 2^{k-2}(2^k - 1)(2^{k-1} - 1).$$

Thus for $k = 2$ we have just one quadruple — a trivial case. For $k = 3$ we have 14 quadruples, containing each triple just once. For $k = 4$ we have 140 quadruples of 16 things.

We have already determined certain dual configurations by means of the $PG(k, p^n)$. It is of interest to construct certain others from the special case of $PG(2, p^n)$. From $PG(2, p^n)$ omit a line and all the points on that line; also omit an additional point and all the lines on that point. Then we have left $p^{2n} - 1$ points and $p^{2n} - 1$ lines; there are p^n retained points on a retained line and also p^n retained lines on a retained point. Considering the points as elements and the lines as sets of elements, we are thus led to a configuration with the symbol $\Delta_{l,m}^{\lambda,\mu}$ where

$$l = m = p^{2n} - 1, \quad \lambda = \mu = p^n.$$

For $p^n = 2, 3$ these configurations are $\Delta_{3,3}^{2,2}$, $\Delta_{8,8}^{3,3}$. The latter configuration may be exhibited explicitly by the symbols

136, 147, 158, 238, 245, 267, 357, 468,

where the 8 digits are the elements and the triples are those indicated.

Let us next consider the configuration obtained from $PG(2, p^n)$ by omitting all the points on a line and all the lines on one point of this line. There remain p^{2n} points and p^{2n} lines; each retained line contains p^n of the retained points, and each retained point is on p^n of the retained lines. Thus we have a $\Delta_{l,m}^{\lambda,\mu}$ with $l = m = p^{2n}$, $\lambda = \mu = p^n$. For $p^n = 3$ we have a configuration $\Delta_{9,9}^{3,3}$ of considerable interest.

Let us now consider the dual configuration formed from the $PG(2, p^n)$ in the following manner. We omit all the points on two lines, leaving $p^{2n} - p^n$ points. We also omit all the lines on the common point of these first two lines and also all the lines on one other point of one of these lines. We have thus omitted two lines of points, these two lines having a common point, and also two bundles of lines, these two bundles having a common line. The omitted configuration is dual in character. Hence the points which remain form a set that is dual in character. Grouping these remaining $p^{2n} - p^n$ points in collinear sets on the retained lines, we have a dual configuration $\Delta_{l,m}^{\lambda,\mu}$ where

$$l = m = p^{2n} - p^n, \quad \lambda = \mu = p^n - 1,$$

as one may readily verify. For $p^n = 4$ this gives rise to an interesting configuration $\Delta_{12,12}^{3,3}$ formed from the $PG(2, 2^2)$. Using the scheme of § **86** for this geometry, and omitting the lines *BFJNR* and *AFGHI* with their points and also the lines on *A* and *F*, we have a concrete representation of $\Delta_{12,12}^{3,3}$ in the form

CLO, *CQT*, *CMS*, *DKT*, *DMP*, *DOU*,
EPS, *ELU*, *EKQ*, *MQU*, *KQS*, *LPT*.

Let us next omit from $PG(2, p^n)$ three noncollinear points and all the points on the three lines determined by pairs of them, and also all the lines on each of these three points. There remain of the $PG(2, p^n)$ the same number of lines and of points, namely, $(p^n - 1)^2$; they fall into sets of $p^n - 2$ each on $p^n - 2$ lines, thus giving a configuration $\Delta_{l, m}^{\lambda, \mu}$ with $l = m = (p^n - 1)^2$, $\lambda = \mu = p^n - 2$. Special cases of this configuration have the symbols $\Delta_{9, 9}^{2, 2}$ and $\Delta_{16, 16}^{3, 3}$.

This configuration may readily be generalized. Let P_r denote a polygon in $PG(2, p^n)$ whose vertices are $A_1, A_2, \cdots, A_r$ and whose sides are A_1A_2, A_2A_3, A_3A_4, $\cdots$, $A_{r-1}A_r$, A_rA_1. Omit all the points on these r lines and also all the lines on these r vertices. The number of omitted points [omitted lines] is rp^n. Each of the retained lines holds $p^n - r + 1$ of the retained points, while each of the retained points is on the same number of retained lines. We suppose that r is such that $p^n - r + 1$ is an integer s greater than unity and less than $p^n - 1$ (in order to avoid trivial cases). Then we have a dual configuration

$$\Delta_{l, m}^{s, s}. \qquad (s = p^n - r + 1; \quad l = m = sp^n + 1)$$

Let us now consider the $PG(2, 2^n)$ $(n > 2)$. Let Q be any complete quadrangle in this plane. Since its diagonal points are collinear, it consists of seven points and seven lines. Omitting all the lines on these seven points and all the points on these seven lines, we have from the retained points and lines a $\Delta_{l, m}^{\lambda, \mu}$ for which one readily shows that

$$l = m = 2^{2n} - 6 \cdot 2^n + 8, \quad \lambda = \mu = 2^n - 6.$$

For $n = 3$ we have a $\Delta_{24, 24}^{2, 2}$.

Several of the configurations which we have obtained from $PG(2, p^n)$ are readily extended to the case of $PG(k, p^n)$ for $k > 1$. We shall now exhibit two of these generalizations.

Let us omit from the $PG(k, p^n)$ $(k > 1)$ one particular $(k-1)$-dimensional subspace $PG(k - 1, p^n)$, together with all its points. There remains an $EG(k, p^n)$ containing p^{kn} points. Omit one of these points and each of the $(k - 1)$-dimensional subspaces $PG(k - 1, p^n)$ which contain this omitted point. The number of $(k-1)$-dimensional subspaces retained is then $p^{kn}-1$; in each of these we take only those points which are in the named $EG(k, p^n)$. By means of these subspaces we have thus grouped the $p^{kn}-1$ retained points into $p^{kn}-1$ sets, each set containing $p^{(k-1)n}$ points and each point appearing in $p^{(k-1)n}$ sets. Thus we are led to a dual configuration $\Delta_{l,m}^{\lambda,\mu}$ where

$$l = m = p^{k\iota} - 1, \quad \lambda = \mu = p^{(k-1)n}.$$

In constructing another configuration Δ, let us omit from the $PG(k, p^n)$ $(k > 1)$ one particular $(k-1)$-space $PG(k-1, p^n)$, together with its points, thus forming an $EG(k, p^n)$ of p^{kn} points. Omit also all $(k-1)$-spaces on a particular one of the points already omitted, retaining the remaining p^{kn} $(k-1)$-spaces. Each of these remaining $(k-1)$-spaces has $p^{(k-1)n}$ points of the $EG(k, p^n)$ on it, while each of these points is on $p^{(k-1)n}$ such spaces. Thus we are led to a dual configuration $\Delta_{l,m}^{\lambda,\mu}$ where

$$l = m = p^{kn}, \quad \lambda = \mu = p^{(k-1)n}.$$

Of particular interest are the cases $p^n = 2, k = 3$; $p^n = 2, k = 4$; $p^n = 3, k = 3$: these lead to configurations with the respective symbols

$$\Delta_{8,8}^{4,4}, \quad \Delta_{16,16}^{8,8}, \quad \Delta_{27,27}^{9,9}.$$

It is possible to construct various other dual configurations generalizing several of those here given. In particular, configurations may be constructed in which the elements are lines or other subspaces. But these seem to be of less interest than those already given.

On pages 351–354 are numerous exercises concerning the groups characterized by the foregoing configurations.

EXERCISES

1. From the $PG(3, 2)$ construct the $\Delta_{15,35}^{3,7}$ described in the second paragraph of § **91** and determine the largest permutation group on its letters leaving it invariant.

2. Construct a configuration of 7 triples and also a configuration of 7 quadruples left invariant by the group $\{(a_0a_1 \cdots a_6), (a_1a_2a_4)(a_3a_6a_5)\}$ and in each case determine the largest group leaving the configuration invariant.

3. Treat the similar problem for a configuration of 13 quadruples left invariant by $\{(a_0a_1 \cdots a_{12}), (a_1a_3a_9)(a_2a_6a_5)(a_4a_{12}a_{10})(a_7a_8a_{11})\}$. Note that these permutations may be defined by the congruences

$$t' \equiv t + 1 \bmod 13, \quad t' \equiv 3\,t \bmod 13$$

on the subscripts.

4. Solve the similar problem for configurations of 31 sextuples left invariant by the permutation group defined similarly by the congruences

$$t' \equiv t + 1 \bmod 31, \quad t' \equiv 5\,t \bmod 31.$$

5. The group $\{(a_0a_1 \cdots a_{10}), (a_1a_4a_5a_9a_3)(a_2a_8a_{10}a_7a_6)\}$ permutes the set a_1, a_3, a_4, a_5, a_9 into 11 sets, thus forming a tactical configuration $\Delta_{11,11}^{5,5}$. Determine the largest permutation group on its symbols which leaves this configuration invariant.

6. From $PG(2, 3)$ construct the $\Delta_{9,12}^{3,4}$ described in the third paragraph of § **91** and determine the largest permutation group on its symbols which leaves the configuration invariant.

7. Construct the groups determined by the configurations $\Delta_{8,8}^{3,3}$ and $\Delta_{16,16}^{3,3}$ of § **91**.

8. Construct from $PG(2, 2^2)$ the configuration $\Delta_{15,15}^{4,4}$ of § **91** and the group characterized by it.

9. Construct from the $PG(2, 3)$ the configuration $\Delta_{9,9}^{3,3}$ of § **91** and the group characterized by it.

10. Construct from the $PG(2, 2^2)$ the configuration $\Delta_{12,12}^{3,3}$ of § **91** and the group characterized by it.

11. Discuss the properties of the configuration $\Delta_{l,m}^{s,s}$ of § **91**, where $l = m = sp^n + 1$.

12. Form from the $PG(3, 2)$ the configuration $\Delta_{8,8}^{4,4}$ described at the end of § **91**, and construct the group characterized by it.

MISCELLANEOUS EXERCISES

1. In the $PG(3, 3)$ determine the 16 points which lie on the quadric surface $x^2 + y^2 + z^2 + t^2 = 0$. Show that these fall seven at a time on 16 planes, and construct the resulting configuration. Determine the largest permutation group on these 16 points each element of which leaves this configuration invariant, and discuss its properties.

2. The set $ABCEHLQW$ is permuted into 29 sets of eight symbols each by the cyclic permutation $(ABC \cdots XYZ\,\alpha\beta\gamma)$ of order 29. Show that the resulting configuration characterizes a group of order 29.

3. In the $PG(2, 2^2)$ let the point (001) be denoted by A, and choose the notation for points so that the transformation

$$x' = y, \quad y' = \omega x + \omega y + \omega z, \quad z' = x,$$

where ω is a primitive mark of the $GF[2^2]$, shall permute the points of the $PG(2, 2^2)$ according to the cyclic permutation $(ABC \cdots STU)$. Show that $ABGIS$ constitutes one line of this geometry and that the powers of the given permutation permute this line into the 21 lines of the geometry. Thence determine the largest permutation group on the points of the geometry whose elements permute among themselves the lines of the geometry.

4. Form from 8 things a set of 14 quadruples such that any (whatever) triple of these 8 things appears in one and just one quadruple of the set, and show that the resulting configuration characterizes the triply transitive group of degree 8 and order $8 \cdot 7 \cdot 6 \cdot 4$.

5. Form from 16 things a set of 140 quadruples such that any (whatever) triple of these 16 things appears in one and just one quadruple of the set, and construct the permutation group characterized by the configuration.

6. Form from 10 things a set of 30 quadruples such that any (whatever) triple of these 10 things appears in one and just one quadruple of the set and such that the group characterized by the configuration is the triply transitive group of degree 10 and order $10 \cdot 9 \cdot 8 \cdot 2$. Determine how many distinct (that is, nonconjugate) systems of 30 quadruples can be formed from 10 things so that each triple appears in one and just one quadruple of each system.

7. Show that in the $GF[13]$ to which ∞ has been adjoined (as in § **68**) the general linear fractional group permutes the quadruple 0, 1, 3, 9 into 182 quadruples such that each triple of the 14 marks is in just two quadruples. From these 182 quadruples select four sets of 13 quadruples each so that each set shall form the geometry $PG(2, 3)$, the quadruples being the lines of the geometry.

8. For the $GF[31]$ formulate and solve a problem similar to that in Ex. 7 for the $GF[13]$.

9. From 32 symbols form a system of quadruples such that each triple occurs in one and just one quadruple of the system.

10. Exhibit in detail the analytical representation of the geometries $PG(2, 2)$ and $PG(2, 3)$ by the method of § **90**.

11. From the $\Delta_{11, 11}^{5, 5}$ of Ex. 5 on page 352 form a set of 66 quintuples as follows: retain the 11 quintuples of the $\Delta_{11, 11}^{5, 5}$; from every pair of quintuples in $\Delta_{11, 11}^{5, 5}$ form a new quintuple by taking the two elements common to this pair and the three elements not in either quintuple of the pair, thus obtaining the remaining 55 quintuples.

12. Determine the group characterized by the 66 quintuples of Ex. 11 and by aid of it investigate the properties of the configuration formed by the 66 quintuples. In particular, show that each quadruple of the 11 symbols appears in one and just one of the quintuples.

CHAPTER XII

Collineation Groups in the Finite Geometries

92. The Projective Group in $PG(k, p^n)$. We have seen (§ 73) that the totality of transformations of the form

$$A: \qquad \rho x'_i = \sum_{j=0}^{k} \alpha_{ij} x_j, \qquad (i = 0, 1, 2, \cdots, k)$$

on the symbols $(x_0, x_1, \cdots, x_k)$ constitutes a group $P(k, p^n)$, the coefficients α_{ij} (in each case) being marks of the $GF[p^n]$ such that the determinant $|\alpha_{ij}|$ is different from zero. If the symbols $(x_0, x_1, \cdots, x_k)$ are taken to represent the points of a $PG(k, p^n)$, then this $P(k, p^n)$ is a group of point transformations in the $PG(k, p^n)$. In § **84** we saw that the $PG(k, p^n)$ is transformed into itself by each element of the linear group $P(k, p^n)$ in the sense that lines are transformed into lines. Therefore we shall call $P(k, p^n)$ *the projective group in the* $PG(k, p^n)$. By *a projective transformation in* $PG(k, p^n)$ we shall mean a transformation in the group $P(k, p^n)$.

In § **73** we saw that the order of $P(k, p^n)$ is

$$\frac{1}{p^n - 1} \prod_{i=0}^{k} (p^{(k+1)n} - p^{in}).$$

Let us consider the particular ordered set S of $k + 2$ points in $PG(k, p^n)$:

$$S: \qquad (1, 0, 0, \cdots, 0), (0, 1, 0, \cdots, 0), \cdots, (0, 0, \cdots, 0, 1), (1, 1, \cdots, 1)$$

the last having all its co-ordinates equal to 1 and each of the others having a single co-ordinate 1 while the other co-ordinates are all zero. By a transformation of the form A the points of the set S are carried in order to the set T:

$$(\alpha_{0i}, \alpha_{1i}, \cdots, \alpha_{ki}); \qquad (i = 0, 1, \cdots, k)$$

$$T: \qquad \left(\sum_{j=0}^{k} \alpha_{0j}, \sum_{j=0}^{k} \alpha_{1j}, \cdots, \sum_{j=0}^{k} \alpha_{kj}\right).$$

Now the set S consists of $k+2$ points no $k+1$ of which are on the same $(k-1)$-space. We shall show that the coefficients α_{ij} may be so chosen that the set T will coincide with any given set of $k+2$ points no $k+1$ of which are on the same $(k-1)$-space.

Let B,

$$B: \qquad (\gamma_{0i}, \gamma_{1i}, \cdots, \gamma_{ki}), \qquad (i = 0, 1, \cdots, k)$$

be any set of $k+1$ points in $PG(k, p^n)$. Any $(k-1)$-space contained in $PG(k, p^n)$ is (§ **85**) the locus of an equation of the form

$$c_0 x_0 + c_1 x_1 + \cdots + c_k x_k = 0,$$

where the c_i are constants not all equal to zero. If the given points B are on this $(k-1)$-space, then we have

$$c_0 \gamma_{0i} + c_1 \gamma_{1i} + \cdots + c_k \gamma_{ki} = 0. \qquad (i = 0, 1, \cdots, k)$$

Since at least one of the c_i must be different from zero, it follows that a necessary and sufficient condition that the given set B of $k+1$ points shall be on a $(k-1)$-space is that the determinant $|\gamma_{ij}|$ of order $k+1$ shall be zero.

On applying this criterion to each of the $k+2$ sets of $k+1$ points each contained in the $k+2$ points in the set T, and remembering that the determinant $|\alpha_{ij}|$ is different from zero, we see that no $k+1$ points of the set T are on the same $(k-1)$-space.

Let U,

$$U: \qquad (\sigma_{0i}, \sigma_{1i}, \cdots, \sigma_{ki}), \qquad (i = 0, 1, \cdots, k+1)$$

be any ordered set of $k+2$ points no $k+1$ of which are on any $(k-1)$-space. A necessary and sufficient condition that this given set shall coincide in order with the set T is that nonzero marks $\rho_0, \rho_1, \cdots, \rho_{k+1}$ shall exist such that

$$\rho_i \sigma_{li} = \alpha_{li}, \qquad (i, l = 0, 1, \cdots, k) \qquad [1]$$

$$\rho_{k+1} \sigma_{l,\, k+1} = \sum_{j=0}^{k} \alpha_{lj}. \qquad (l = 0, 1, \cdots, k) \qquad [2]$$

We are to show that coefficients α_{ij} in the transformation exist such that these relations are satisfied. Substituting in [2] the values of the α_{lj} from [1], we have

$$\sum_{j=0}^{k} \frac{\rho_j}{\rho_{k+1}} \sigma_{lj} = \sigma_{l,\, k+1}. \qquad (l = 0, 1, \cdots, k)$$

Since the determinant $|\sigma_{lj}|$ of this system of equations is different from zero, owing to the nonincidence of $k+1$ of the points U on a $(k-1)$-space, it follows that these equations may be solved uniquely for ρ_j/ρ_{k+1} $(j = 0, 1, \cdots, k)$ in the usual form of quotients of determinants. Moreover, no one of these quantities can be zero, since no numerator determinant in these solutions is zero, owing to the properties of the points U. Taking ρ_{k+1} to be any nonzero mark of the $GF[p^n]$, we have suitable values for the marks ρ_i. Then if the α_{li} are determined by [1], we have the coefficients α_{ij} for the transformation, and they have the property that the determinant $|\alpha_{ij}|$ is different from zero. Moreover, the α_{ij} are uniquely determined except for a single factor of proportionality. For these values of the α_{ij} the set T coincides in order with the set U.

From this it follows that the ordered set S can be carried by a transformation of $P(k, p^n)$ into any given ordered set of $k+2$ points no $k+1$ of which are on the same $(k-1)$-space. Moreover, the transformation is completely determined by the set of points U into which the set S is carried.

Now let T_1 and T_2 be any two ordered sets of $k+2$ points each in $PG(k, p^n)$, each set having the property that no $k+1$ points in the set are in the same $(k-1)$-space. Let R_1 and R_2 be the (unique) transformations in $P(k, p^n)$ which carry the set S in order into the sets T_1 and T_2 respectively. Then the transformation $R_1^{-1}R_2$ carries the ordered set T_1 into the ordered set T_2. Moreover, $R_1^{-1}R_2$ is the only transformation in $P(k, p^n)$ having this property; for if R carries the set T_1 in order into the set T_2, then RR_2^{-1} carries T_1 into S, so that $RR_2^{-1} = R_1^{-1}$, whence $R = R_1^{-1}R_2$.

The principal results obtained may be summarized into the following theorem:

I. The projective group $P(k, p^n)$ in $PG(k, p^n)$, consisting of the homogeneous transformations

$$\rho x'_i = \sum_{j=0}^{k} \alpha_{ij} x_j, \qquad (i = 0, 1, \cdots, k)$$

where the α_{ij} are marks of the $GF[p^n]$, subject to the condition that the determinant $|\alpha_{ij}|$ shall be different from zero, is a group of order

$$\frac{1}{p^n - 1} \prod_{i=0}^{k} (p^{(k+1)n} - p^{in}).$$

If T_1 and T_2 are any two ordered sets of $k + 2$ points each in $PG(k, p^n)$, each set having the property that no $k + 1$ points in it lie on a $(k - 1)$-space, then $P(k, p^n)$ contains one and just one transformation which carries the set T_1 in order into the set T_2. In particular, a transformation of $P(k, p^n)$ is completely determined when the ordered set of points is given into which the ordered set

$$(1, 0, 0, \cdots, 0), (0, 1, 0, \cdots, 0), \cdots,$$
$$(0, 0, \cdots, 0, 1), (1, 1, 1, \cdots, 1)$$

is carried.

93. The Collineation Group in $PG(k, p^n)$. We have seen that a projective transformation in $PG(k, p^n)$ transforms the lines of the geometry into its lines. Hence a projective transformation is a collineation, in accordance with the following definition:

A *collineation in* $PG(k, p^n)$ is a point transformation in $PG(k, p^n)$ which has the property that it transforms the lines of $PG(k, p^n)$ into its lines.

When $n > 1$, the (nonprojective) transformation

$$\rho x'_i = x_i^p, \qquad (i = 0, 1, \cdots, k)$$

is also a collineation, as we shall now prove. It transforms the points

$$(\mu\mu_0 + \nu\nu_0, \cdots, \mu\mu_k + \nu\nu_k)$$

of the line joining

$$(\mu_0, \mu_1, \cdots, \mu_k) \quad \text{and} \quad (\nu_0, \nu_1, \cdots, \nu_k)$$

into the points

$$(\mu^p\mu_0^p + \nu^p\nu_0^p, \cdots, \mu^p\mu_k^p + \nu^p\nu_k^p);$$

these are the same as the points

$$(\rho\mu_0^p + \sigma\nu_0^p, \cdots, \rho\mu_k^p + \sigma\nu_k^p)$$

of the line joining the points

$$(\mu_0^p, \cdots, \mu_k^p) \quad \text{and} \quad (\nu_0^p, \cdots, \nu_k^p),$$

since λ^p ranges over all the marks of the $GF[p^n]$ when λ ranges over all these marks. Hence the special transformation given is a collineation.

The product of any two collineations is evidently a collineation. If we combine the powers of the special transformation of the preceding paragraph with the transformations of $P(k, p^n)$, we get all transformations of the following form and no others:

$$\rho x'_i = \sum_{j=0}^{k} \beta_{ij\tau} x_j^{p^\tau}, \qquad (i = 0, 1, \cdots, k;\ \tau = 0, 1, \cdots, n-1)$$

where the $\beta_{ij\tau}$ are marks of the $GF[p^n]$ such that the determinant Δ_τ,

$$\Delta_\tau = |\beta_{ij\tau}|, \qquad (i, j = 0, 1, \cdots, k)$$

is different from zero for each value $0, 1, \cdots, n-1$ of τ. Hence all these transformations are collineations. They constitute the group $C(k, p^n)$ introduced in § 75. When $n = 1$ the groups $C(k, p^n)$ and $P(k, p^n)$ are obviously identical.

The group $C(k, p^n)$ is called the *collineation* group in the $PG(k, p^n)$ on account of the following theorem, which will now be proved:*

II. Every collineation in the $PG(k, p^n)$ is in the group $C(k, p^n)$; and every element in this group is a collineation in the $PG(k, p^n)$.

Let S be the ordered set of points

$$S: \quad (1, 0, 0, \cdots, 0), (0, 1, 0, \cdots, 0), \cdots, (0, 0, \cdots, 0, 1), (1, 1, \cdots, 1).$$

It is a set of $k+2$ points no $k+1$ of which are on a $(k-1)$-space. Any collineation V must replace this ordered set S by some ordered set S_1 having the same property that no $k+1$ of its points are on a $(k-1)$-space. From Theorem I it follows that a projective transformation U exists which also replaces the ordered set S by the ordered set S_1. Then VU^{-1} is a collineation T which leaves fixed each of the points of S.

We are next to determine the collineations T having this property of leaving fixed each of the points S. We first carry out the demonstration for the case $k = 2$. Then the set S is the set

$$S: \quad (1, 0, 0), (0, 1, 0), (0, 0, 1), (1, 1, 1).$$

The intersection point of two lines each through fixed points of T is also a fixed point of T. By means of this fact it may be shown that the points $(0, \rho, 1)$ of the line joining $(0, 0, 1)$ and $(0, 1, 0)$ are fixed, where ρ is an integral mark of the field. Denote the points of the line $x_0 = 0$ by the nonhomogeneous co-ordinates $\infty, 0, 1, \cdots$, where these symbols (except ∞) are the marks of the $GF[p^n]$ and denote the ratios x_1/x_2. Then the points $\infty, 0, 1, 2, \cdots, p-1$ are fixed. From the quadrangle construction, and the fact that a collineation transforms a complete quadrangle into a complete quadrangle, it may be shown that if three points a, b, c of this line are so related that

$$a + b = c \quad \text{or} \quad ab = c,$$

* See Veblen, *Trans. Amer. Math. Soc.* **8** (1907), 366–368.

then the points, with co-ordinates $\phi(a)$, $\phi(b)$, $\phi(c)$ into which they are respectively transformed, are so related that

$$\phi(a)+\phi(b)=\phi(c) \quad \text{or} \quad \phi(a)\phi(b)=\phi(c).$$

Hence the transformation of the points of this line is subject to the conditions

$$\phi(a)+\phi(b)=\phi(a+b),$$
$$\phi(a)\cdot\phi(b)=\phi(ab),$$
$$\phi(0)=0,\ \phi(1)=1, \quad \phi(\infty)=\infty.$$

If ω is a primitive mark of the $GF[p^n]$, then every nonzero mark of the field may be written in the form ω^k. From the conditions on ϕ it follows then that

$$\phi(\omega^k)=[\phi(\omega)]^k.$$

Hence if $\phi(\omega)=\omega^m$, we have

$$\phi(\omega^k)=\omega^{mk}=(\omega^k)^m.$$

Since $\phi(0)=0$, it follows from this that every mark of the field is transformed into its mth power.

But for an integral mark ρ we have $\phi(\rho)=\rho$; therefore, since $\rho=\rho^m$ for every integral mark ρ, we must have for the value of m a power p^l of p. Then all the required conditions on ϕ are satisfied.

Going back to homogeneous co-ordinates, we see that the resulting transformation T, so far as it affects points on the line $x_0=0$, must be of the form

$$x'_0=x_0^{p^l}, \quad x'_1=x_1^{p^l}, \quad x'_2=x_2^{p^l}.$$

When this transformation is applied to the whole plane, it induces a collineation in the plane, as we have already seen.

Now the transformation T is completely determined by the named transformation on the line $x_0=0$ and the fact that it leaves (1, 0, 0) and (1, 1, 1) fixed, as one may see from the fact that it completely determines the lines into which the lines through (1, 0, 0) and (1, 1, 1) are displaced.

Among the transformations T is the transformation

$$x'_0=x_0^p, \quad x'_1=x_1^p, \quad x'_2=x_2^p;$$

all other transformations T are powers of this transformation; and this itself is a collineation, as we have already seen. Therefore all the collineations are generated by this particular one together with the projective transformations of the plane.

This implies the theorem for the case $k = 2$.

By means of the theorem for $k = 2$ one readily establishes it for $k = 3$, by a process similar to the latter arguments for $k = 2$. Then it is readily extended by induction to a general value of k.

94. Subgroups of the Collineation Group. We are now in position to prove the following theorem concerning the collineation group in $PG(k, p^n)$ and certain of its subgroups:

III. (1) The collineation group $C(k, p^n)$ in $PG(k, p^n)$ is represented analytically by the homogeneous transformations

$$(A)\quad \rho x'_i = \sum_{j=0}^{k} \beta_{ij\tau} x_j^{p^\tau}, \quad (i = 0, 1, \cdots, k; \tau = 0, 1, \cdots, n-1)$$

where the $\beta_{ij\tau}$ are marks of the $GF[p^n]$ such that the determinant Δ_τ,

$$\Delta_\tau \equiv \begin{vmatrix} \beta_{00\tau} \beta_{01\tau} \cdots \beta_{0k\tau} \\ \beta_{10\tau} \beta_{11\tau} \cdots \beta_{1k\tau} \\ \cdot \quad \cdot \quad \cdot \quad \cdot \quad \cdot \quad \cdot \\ \beta_{k0\tau} \beta_{k1\tau} \cdots \beta_{kk\tau} \end{vmatrix},$$

is different from zero for each value of τ. Its order is n times the order of its projective subgroup $P(k, p^n)$, or $C_0(k, p^n)$, made up of those transformations of (A) in each of which $\tau = 0$, and is therefore

$$\frac{n}{p^n - 1} \prod_{i=0}^{k} (p^{(k+1)n} - p^{in}).$$

The group G is generated by C_0 and the collineation

$$\rho x'_i = x_i^p. \qquad (i = 0, 1, \cdots, k)$$

The last element transforms C_0 into itself.

(2) If d is any proper divisor of n, then we have a subgroup $C_d(k, p^n)$ of $C(k, p^n)$ (with $C_1 \equiv C$) generated by C_0 and the collineation

$$\rho x'_i = x_i^{p^d}, \qquad (i = 0, 1, \cdots, k)$$

and C_d is of index d in C. The transformations in C_d are of the form of (A), with the restriction on τ that it shall be confined to the multiples of d belonging to the sequence $0, 1, 2, \cdots, n-1$.

(3) Those transformations in C_d whose determinants Δ_τ are $(k+1)$th powers in the $GF[p^n]$ form a subgroup $\overline{C}_d(k, p^n)$ of C_d of index μ, where μ is the greatest common divisor of $k+1$ and $p^n - 1$.

(4) The projective group $P(k, p^n)$, considered as a permutation group on the points of $PG(k, p^n)$, is triply transitive when $k = 1$ and is doubly transitive when $k > 1$. The same property of transitivity belongs to each of the previously named groups which contains $P(k, p^n)$ as a subgroup.

(5) The group $\overline{C}_d(k, p^n)$ is doubly transitive when considered as a permutation group on the points of $PG(k, p^n)$.

(6) Finally, in a special case, we have another subgroup of C defined as follows. Let $k+1$ be a divisor of n, and let σ be a fixed divisor of $n/(k+1)$. Moreover, let $k+1$ be a factor of $p^\sigma - 1$. Any multiple of σ in the set $0, 1, \cdots, n-1$ can be written in just one way in the form $\{(k+1)s + \alpha\}\sigma$, where $0 \leqq \alpha \leqq k$ and s is a non-negative integer. For every such multiple of σ form the entire set of homogeneous transformations

$$(B) \quad \rho x'_i = \sum_{j=0}^{k} \beta_{ijs\alpha} x_j^{p^{\{(k+1)s+\alpha\}\sigma}}, \qquad (i = 0, 1, \cdots, k)$$

in which each determinant $|\beta_{ijs\alpha}|$ of a transformation (s and α being fixed for a particular determinant) is equal to ω^α times a $(k+1)$th power in the $GF[p^n]$,

ω being a primitive mark of the $GF[p^n]$. The totality of these transformations forms a subgroup $H_\sigma(k, p^n)$ of $C(k, p^n)$ which is of index $(k+1)\sigma$ in C. Moreover, H_σ is contained in C_σ and is of index $k+1$ in C_σ. The group H_σ is generated by C_0 and the transformations of the form

$$(C) \quad \rho x_i' = \omega^{t_i} x_i^{p^{\{(k+1)s+\alpha\}\sigma}}, \qquad (i = 0, 1, \cdots, k)$$

where $t_0 + t_1 + \cdots + t_k \equiv \alpha \bmod (k+1)$. When considered as a permutation group on the points of $PG(k, p^n)$, the group $H_\sigma(k, p^n)$ is triply transitive when $k = 1$ and is doubly transitive when $k > 1$.

The results in paragraph (1) of the theorem were proved in the preceding two sections.

The proof of the statement in paragraph (2) of the theorem is almost immediate; it is therefore omitted.

If two transformations in C_d have their determinants equal to $(k+1)$th powers in the $GF[p^n]$, then their product has its determinant equal to such a $(k+1)$th power, as one may prove easily by combining these transformations and making use of the fact that the pth power of a determinant D whose elements are in the $GF[p^n]$ is equal to a determinant $\bar{D}$ whose elements are the pth powers of the corresponding elements of D. This proves the existence of the groups named in paragraph (3) of the theorem.

That $\bar{C}_0$ is of index μ in C_0 is proved in the following manner: By multiplying each coefficient in a given transformation of C_0 by λ $(\lambda \neq 0)$ we obtain another form of the same transformation; the determinant in the new form is λ^{k+1} times that in the original form; hence if $\lambda = \omega^\rho$ and if ω^α is the original value of the determinant, its new value is $\omega^{\alpha+\rho(k+1)} = \omega^{\alpha+\rho(k+1)+\sigma(p^n-1)}$, and this may be made equal to a number of the set $1, \omega, \omega^2, \cdots, \omega^{\mu-1}$, since integers ρ and σ exist such that $\rho(k+1) + \sigma(p^n - 1)$ is any given multiple of the greatest common factor μ of $k+1$ and $p^n - 1$. We now suppose that each transformation in C_0 is taken in such form that its determinant is one of the numbers $1, \omega, \omega^2, \cdots, \omega^{\mu-1}$. Then $\bar{C}_0$ is evidently the subgroup of C_0 whose elements have their determinants equal to unity. Let T_1 and T_2 be any two transformations in $C_0(k, p^n)$ whose determinants have any given preassigned value ω^τ from the set $1, \omega, \omega^2, \cdots, \omega^{\mu-1}$. Then $T_2T_1{}^{-1}$ has the determinant unity and hence belongs to $\bar{C}_0$. Hence every transformation T_2 with determinant ω^τ belongs to the set $\bar{C}_0T_1$, and every transformation of this set is of determinant ω^τ. *Therefore the number of transformations in $C_0(k, p^n)$ having determinant ω^τ is equal to the number having determinant unity.* Hence C_0 is of index μ in C_0.

If d is any proper factor of n, then C_0 and the transformation $\rho x'_i = x_i^{p^d}$ $(i = 0, 1, \cdots, k)$ generate the group C_d; and the order of C_d is n/d times that of C_0. It is readily proved that $\bar{C}_0$ and the same transformation generate the group $\bar{C}_d$ and that the order of $\bar{C}_d$ is n/d times that of $\bar{C}_0$. Since $\bar{C}_0$ is of index μ in C_0, it follows that $\bar{C}_d$ is of index μ in C_d.

This completes the proof of the proposition in paragraph (3).

The transitivity properties named in paragraph (4) of the theorem are immediate consequences of the fact that (§ **92**, Theorem I) there exists in $P(k, p^n)$ a transformation which carries any ordered set of $k+2$ points of $PG(k, p^n)$, no $k+1$ of which are in the same $(k-1)$-space, into any like ordered set of $k+2$ points.

To show that $\bar{C}_d$ is doubly transitive, in accordance with paragraph (5) of the theorem, we note first that the transformation (A) carries the points $(1, 0, 0, \cdots, 0)$ and $(0, 1, 0, \cdots, 0)$ into the points $(\beta_{00\tau}, \beta_{10\tau}, \cdots, \beta_{k0\tau})$ and $(\beta_{01\tau}, \beta_{11\tau}, \cdots, \beta_{k1\tau})$ respectively. Call these the points C and D respectively. The transformation may be so chosen that C and D are any two assigned points of $PG(k, p^n)$. Since C and D are different points, there exist integers λ and μ such that the determinant $\beta_{\lambda0\tau}\beta_{\mu1\tau} - \beta_{\lambda1\tau}\beta_{\mu0\tau}$ is different from zero. Suppose now that $k > 1$. From the transformations (A), which carry the first-named points into C and D respectively, choose one as follows: take $\beta_{\lambda s\tau} = 0 = \beta_{\mu s\tau}$ for $s = 2, 3, \cdots, k$; choose the remaining $\beta_{ij\tau}$ for which $j > 1$ so as to give to the determinant Δ_τ any preassigned value different from zero. It is obvious that this can be done. Hence the choice of the β's and τ can be made so that the transformation (A) thus constructed belongs to the group $\bar{C}_d$. Hence $\bar{C}_d$ is doubly transitive when $k > 1$. Suppose next that $k = 1$. We have to see that any two points $(\alpha_{00}, \alpha_{10})$ and $(\alpha_{01}, \alpha_{11})$ can be represented as $(\beta_{00\tau}, \beta_{10\tau})$ and $(\beta_{01\tau}, \beta_{11\tau})$ respectively in such a way that $\beta_{00\tau}\beta_{11\tau} - \beta_{01\tau}\beta_{10\tau}$ is a square; and this is obvious, as one sees by utilizing the factor of proportionality in the co-ordinates of the points. Hence the group $\bar{C}_d(k, p^n)$ is doubly transitive in all cases.

It remains to prove the statements in the last paragraph of the theorem.

To show that the system of transformations named constitutes a group, consider two transformations of the named form, in one of which s and α are replaced by s_1 and α_1 and in the other of which they are replaced by s_2 and α_2. A product of these two transformations may be written in the form

$$\rho x'_i = \sum_{j=0}^{k} \beta_{ijs_1\alpha_1} \left\{ \sum_{\mu=0}^{k} \beta_{j\mu s_2\alpha_2} x_\mu^{p^{\{(k+1)s_2+\alpha_2\}\sigma}} \right\}^{p^{\{(k+1)s_1+\alpha_1\}\sigma}}$$

$$= \sum_{\mu=0}^{k} \left\{ \sum_{j=0}^{k} \beta_{ijs_1\alpha_1} (\beta_{j\mu s_2\alpha_2})^{p^{\{(k+1)s_1+\alpha_1\}\sigma}} \right\} x_\mu^{p^{\{(k+1)(s_1+s_2)+\alpha_1+\alpha_2\}\sigma}}$$

for $i = 0, 1, \cdots, k$. The determinant of this product transformation may be written as a product of determinants in the form

$$| \beta_{ijs_1\alpha_1} | \cdot | \beta_{j\mu s_2\alpha_2} |^{p^{\{(k+1)s_1+\alpha_1\}\sigma}}.$$

Now the exponent on the second determinant is congruent to 1 modulo $k+1$, since $p^\sigma - 1$ is divisible by $k+1$. Hence the determinant of the last written transformation is of the form of a $(k+1)$th power in the $GF[p^n]$ times $| \beta_{ijs_1\alpha_1} | \cdot | \beta_{ijs_2\alpha_2} |$. But these two determinants (by hypothesis) are equal to $(k+1)$th powers in the $GF[p^n]$ times ω^{α_1} and ω^{α_2} respectively. Hence the determinant of the product transformation is equal to such a $(k+1)$th power times $\omega^{\alpha_1+\alpha_2}$. From this and the fact that n is a multiple of $(k+1)\sigma$ it follows that the product transformation belongs to the set of transformations defined in the last paragraph of the theorem. That set therefore forms a group H_σ. It is obviously contained in C_σ and hence in C.

It is obvious that a product of any given transformation (B) of H_σ and a suitably chosen transformation (C) is a transformation belonging to $\bar{C}_0$. From this and the fact that every transformation (C) is in H_σ it follows readily that H_σ has the named generators.

The general transformation in C_σ has its determinant restricted to be different from 0, while a like transformation in H_σ has a further restriction that the value of its determinant shall be of a certain form relative to $(k+1)$th powers, so that the possible values for the determinants of transformations in C_σ of given form are $k+1$ times as many in number as the possible values for the determinants of the corresponding transformations in H_σ. From this it follows without difficulty that H_σ is of index $k+1$ in C_σ. It is therefore of index $(k+1)\sigma$ in C.

It remains to establish the transitivity properties of the group $H_\sigma(k, p^n)$. For the case when $k>1$ the same type of argument may be used as that by means of which the double transitivity of $\bar{C}_d$ was established, and with the conclusion that $H_\sigma(k, p^n)$ is doubly transitive when $k>1$. When $k=1$ we may write $n=2\nu$, since n is then even. Then σ is a factor of ν and we have to show that $H_\sigma(1, p^{2\nu})$ is triply transitive. In this case the transformation (B) carries the points (01), (10), (11) into the points

$$(\beta_{01s\alpha}, \beta_{11s\alpha}), \quad (\beta_{00s\alpha}, \beta_{10s\alpha}), \quad (\beta_{00s\alpha}+\beta_{01s\alpha}, \beta_{10s\alpha}+\beta_{11s\alpha})$$

respectively, while at the same time the determinant

$$\beta_{00s\alpha}\beta_{11s\alpha}-\beta_{10s\alpha}\beta_{01s\alpha}$$

is equal to ω^α times a square in the $GF[p^{2\nu}]$. Subject to this condition the β's can be chosen so that for an appropriate value of α the last ordered set of three points is any given ordered set of three points in $PG(1, p^{2\nu})$. Hence $H_\sigma(1, p^{2\nu})$ is triply transitive.

This completes the proof of the theorem.

The transformation groups appearing in the foregoing theorem have been interpreted in it as permutation groups on the points of $PG(k, p^n)$. But these groups transform lines into lines; therefore they transform the m-spaces $PG(m, p^n)$ contained in $PG(k, p^n)$ among themselves for each value m of the set 0, 1, 2, $\cdots$, $k-1$. (Here we are taking k to be greater than unity.) Hence they may be interpreted as permutation groups on symbols denoting the m-spaces for each particular value of m.

In particular, the $(k-1)$-spaces are transformed among themselves. The corresponding permutation group is of the same degree as that on the points of $PG(k, p^n)$, since the number of $(k-1)$-spaces in $PG(k, p^n)$ is equal to the number of points in this k-space. In view of the principle of duality it is not difficult to show that these two permutation groups arising from $C(k, p^n)$ are identical as permutation groups; for every transformation (A) on the points of $PG(k, p^n)$ can be expressed in the form of a transformation of the same general type on the co-ordinates which represent in a dual way the $(k-1)$-spaces $PG(k-1, p^n)$ in $PG(k, p^n)$. Moreover, the transformations (A) themselves set up a one-to-one correspondence among the elements of $C(k, p^n)$ when interpreted on the one hand as permutations on the points of $PG(k, p^n)$ and on the other hand as permutations on the $(k-1)$-spaces in $PG(k, p^n)$. Furthermore, it may be seen that this correspondence is not the identical correspondence; for there are transformations leaving fixed the $(k-1)$-space $x_k = 0$ without leaving fixed any point of $PG(k, p^n)$. Detailed evidence of this fact will appear in the next section; it is involved in the fact that both the subspace $x_k = 0$ and the corresponding Euclidean space $EG(k, p^n)$ may have all its points permuted among themselves by one and the same transformation of $C(k, p^n)$.

The results of the last paragraph may be generalized to the case of l-spaces and their duals the $(k-l-1)$-spaces. Each of these sets of spaces is permuted by the transformations of $C(k, p^n)$, and the two permutation groups thus arising are identical as permutation groups. Again, the simple isomorphism which is established between them is not the identical isomorphism, except in the special case of self-dual spaces. This may be seen by observing that a space of the one type may be held fixed while no space of the other type is held fixed.

Hence we have the following theorem:

IV. The collineation group $C(k, p^n)$, when $k > 1$, transforms the $(k-1)$-spaces $PG(k-1, p^n)$ in $PG(k, p^n)$ according to the same permutation group as that according to which it transforms the points of $PG(k, p^n)$; it sets up a simple isomorphism of this permutation group with itself which is different from the identical isomorphism. More generally it sets up a like correspondence between two identical permutation groups the letters of one of which are the symbols for the l-spaces of $PG(k, p^n)$ while the letters of the other are the symbols for the dual $(k-l-1)$-spaces (except that the isomorphism may be identical in the case of self-dual spaces). These several permutation groups (of different degrees) are all simply isomorphic with $C(k, p^n)$ itself.

It is obvious that similar results are valid for each of the subgroups of $C(k, p^n)$ described in Theorem III. Of particular interest is the corresponding theorem for the case of the projective group $P(k, p^n)$. Thus *Theorem IV becomes a new theorem of interest if throughout it we replace* $C(k, p^n)$ by $P(k, p^n)$ *wherever the former occurs.*

For the case when $k > 1$ the lines of $PG(k, p^n)$ are permuted among themselves by $P(k, p^n)$ or $C(k, p^n)$ according to a transitive group, since any $k+2$ points no $k+1$ of which are on a $(k-1)$-space may be transformed into any such set of $k+2$ points by either of the named groups. If $k > 2$ the $PG(k, p^n)$ has pairs of intersecting lines and pairs which do not intersect: since a pair of one of these sorts cannot be transformed into a pair of the other sort, it follows that this permutation group on the lines of $PG(k, p^n)$ cannot be doubly transitive when $k > 2$. When $k = 2$ the lines are transformed according to the same permutation group as the points, the latter being the duals of the former in this case. Hence the lines of $PG(2, p^n)$ are transformed among themselves according to a doubly transitive group by both $C(2, p^n)$ and $P(2, p^n)$ and in fact by their subgroup $\bar{C}_0(2, p^n)$.

More generally, it may be shown in the same way that the m-spaces $PG(m, p^n)$ in $PG(k, p^n)$, when $m < k$ and $k > 1$, are permuted according to a transitive group by either $P(k, p^n)$ or $C(k, p^n)$. If $0 < m < \frac{1}{2} k$, this group is simply transitive, since there exist two sorts of pairs of m-spaces, namely pairs in which the two spaces intersect and those in which they do not intersect, and a pair of one sort cannot be transformed into a pair of the other sort by either group in consideration. Thence by means of the principle of duality it is seen that this permutation group is also simply transitive when $\frac{1}{2} k < m < k-1$. We have to consider further the case when k is even and $m = \frac{1}{2} k$. Since this case has already been treated when $k = 2$, we shall now suppose that $k > 2$. Then for this case we have $m \geqq 2$. It is clear, then, that there exist again two sorts of pairs of m-spaces, namely pairs in which the elements have an $(m-1)$-space in common and pairs in which the common elements constitute a space of fewer dimensions. Since a pair of one of these sorts cannot be transformed into a pair of the other sort by a collineation, we conclude in this case also that the permutation group on the m-spaces as symbols is simply transitive.

Since $\bar{C}_0(k, p^n)$ is doubly transitive on the points of $PG(k, p^n)$, it follows that the lines of $PG(k, p^n)$ are permuted transitively by $\bar{C}_0(k, p^n)$. We shall show more generally that the m-spaces of $PG(k, p^n)$ are permuted transitively by $\bar{C}_0$. For this purpose it is sufficient to show that $\bar{C}_0(k, p^n)$ contains a transformation which replaces the m-space $(0 < m < k)$ containing the points $P_0, P_1, \cdots, P_m$ by any given m-space S_m, P_i being the point whose $(i+1)$th co-ordinate is unity and whose remaining co-ordinates are all zero. Now any transformation, of determinant unity, which is contained in $P(k, p^n)$ belongs to $\bar{C}_0(k, p^n)$. From the properties of transformation A in § **92**, given there with reference to the transformation of the points S into the points T, it is easy to see that A may be so determined as to have the properties required here, since besides the coefficients in the transformation which are required to carry $P_0, P_1, \cdots, P_m$ to a base set of points of S_m we have others which enable us to make the value of the determinant equal to unity.

We shall now show that the permutation group induced in the m-spaces of $PG(k, p^n)$ by the group $C_0(k, p^n)$ is primitive. Since the group is doubly transitive when $m = 0$ or $k - 1$, we may confine ourselves to the case in which $0 < m < k - 1$. We assume that the group is imprimitive and show that we are thus led to a contradiction. Since the m-spaces in any given $(m + 1)$-space of $PG(k, p^n)$ are permuted among themselves in a doubly transitive way by the subgroup which leaves this $(m + 1)$-space invariant, it follows that the m-spaces in any given $(m + 1)$-space must all belong to the same set of imprimitivity, for otherwise two of them belonging to one system could be transformed to two of them taken from different systems. Thence it follows that the set of imprimitivity to which any given m-space M belongs must contain all the m-spaces included in the totality of $(m + 1)$-spaces each of which contains M. If $m + 1 < k$, fix attention on all the $(m + 1)$-spaces containing M and lying in one and the same $(m + 2)$-space, and also on all the $(m + 1)$-spaces lying in this $(m + 2)$-space and containing any m-space already obtained by this process of construction. Since every two $(m + 1)$-spaces in this $(m + 2)$-space contain an m-space in common, it follows that the named process brings into consideration all the $(m + 1)$-spaces in the given $(m + 2)$-space. Hence every m-space in the $(m + 2)$-space belongs to the same set of imprimitivity as M itself. If $m + 2 < k$, one can prove in a similar manner that the set of imprimitivity containing M contains also all the m-spaces in a given $(m + 3)$-space containing the given $(m + 2)$-space; and so on. Hence the given set of imprimitivity contains all the m-spaces in $PG(k, p^n)$. Since this is impossible for a set of imprimitivity, we conclude that the permutation group in question is primitive.

Since C_d and $\overline{C}_d$ contain $\overline{C}_0$, it follows that C_d and $\overline{C}_d$ both transform the m-spaces of $PG(k, p^n)$ according to a primitive group.

Therefore we have the following theorem:

V. When $k > 1$ each of the groups $C_d(k, p^n)$ and $\overline{C}_d(k, p^n)$ transforms the m-spaces of $PG(k, p^n)$ $(m < k)$ according to a primitive permutation group; this group is doubly transitive when $m = 0$ or $k - 1$, otherwise it is simply transitive.

From Theorems IV and V and from the groups $C_d(k, p^n)$ of Theorem II we have the following theorem as an obvious corollary:

VI. There is no upper limit K to the possible number of primitive groups (of varying degrees) in a set of primitive groups each group of which is simply isomorphic with each of the others in the set. For every integer L there exist integers s [t] such that the number of doubly transitive [triply transitive] groups of degree s [t] is greater than L.

EXERCISES

1. By aid of Theorem I in § **92** show that $P(k, p^n)$ contains a subgroup which is simply isomorphic with the symmetric group of degree $k + 2$.

2. If G is any finite group and p^n is any prime power, show that an integer k exists such that $P(k, p^n)$ contains a subgroup which is simply isomorphic with G.

3. For every pair of positive integers L and k and for every prime p there exists an integer s of the form $1 + p^n + p^{2n} + \cdots + p^{kn}$ such that a group G_s of degree s exists which is doubly transitive and contains more than L doubly transitive subgroups of different orders and each of degree s.

4. For every integer L and prime p there exists an integer s of the form $1 + p^n$ such that a group G_s exists which is triply transitive of degree s and contains more than L triply transitive subgroups of different orders and each of degree s.

5. Prove that the set of transformations $t' = \alpha t + \beta$, where α runs over the λth powers in the $GF[p^n]$ and β over all the marks of the $GF[p^n]$, constitute a primitive permutation group on the marks of the $GF[p^n]$ if λ is a factor of $p - 1$.

6. Show that the group $C(3, 2)$ of degree 15 has a doubly transitive subgroup of index 8 and of degree 15.

7. Using for the $PG(3, 2)$ the symbols in Ex. 4 on page 336, show that the collineations which leave A, B, C individually fixed, together with the nonlinear transformation

$$x'_0 = x_0 + x_1x_2x_3, \quad x'_1 = x_1, \quad x'_2 = x_2, \quad x'_3 = x_3,$$

generate a group which permutes the 12 points $D, E, F, \cdots, O$ according to the symmetric group of degree 12. What group is generated by the given nonlinear transformation and the whole collineation group in $PG(3, 2)$?

8. Let G be the largest subgroup of the projective group in $PG(2, p^n)$ in which one point P and one line l through P are held fixed. Show that G may be represented as a permutation group of degree p^{2n} on the points of $PG(2, p^n)$ which are not on l, and prove that its order is $p^{3n}(p^n - 1)^2$. Determine the corresponding subgroup of the collineation group in $PG(2, p^n)$. Observe that, when $p^n = 2$, the group so obtained from the projective group is the octic group.

9. Let G be an Abelian group of order p^m and type $(1, 1, \cdots, 1)$, and let $A_1, A_2, \cdots, A_s$ be the totality of subgroups of order p in G, or, more generally, any geometric set of subgroups of G. Let K be any one-to-one correspondence of the groups A to the groups A such that for every pair of subgroups A_i and A_j and corresponding pair A_{k_i} and A_{k_j} it is true that the group $\{A_{k_i}, A_{k_j}\}$ contains the correspondent of every group A contained in $\{A_i, A_j\}$. Prove that there exists an isomorphism of G with itself of such sort as to induce the correspondence K among the groups $A_1, A_2, \cdots, A_s$. How many such isomorphisms are there?

10. Suppose that the transformation T employed in the proof of Theorem II of § 93 is further restricted so that a point ρ on the line $x_0 = 0$ is fixed, where ρ is a primitive mark of the $GF[p^\nu]$ included in the $GF[p^n]$. Then show that the function $\phi(x)$ employed in that proof is of the form $\phi(x) = x^{p^{\nu l}}$.

11. Show that the group I of isomorphisms of an Abelian group G of order $p^{(k+1)n}$ and type $(1, 1, \cdots, 1)$ contains a subgroup which permutes a given geometric set of subgroups of order p^n according to the permutation group $C(k, p^n)$.

12. Apply Ex. 11 to the problem of constructing subgroups of the group I of isomorphisms of the Abelian group of order p^6 and type $(1, 1, \cdots, 1)$.

95. Collineation Groups Leaving an $EG(k, p^n)$ Invariant. The groups described in Theorem III of § **94** obviously contain corresponding subgroups each of which leaves invariant a given $PG(k-1, p^n)$ in $PG(k, p^n)$. The points of $PG(k, p^n)$ which are not in this $PG(k-1, p^n)$ form a Euclidean finite geometry $EG(k, p^n)$ of p^{kn} points; it is denoted by $EG(k, p^n)$. The named subgroups transform among themselves the points of this $EG(k, p^n)$. Without real loss of generality we take the fixed $PG(k-1, p^n)$ to be that defined by the equation $x_0 = 0$ and employ the corresponding $EG(k, p^n)$. Then we have the following theorem, which we shall now prove:

VII. (1) The collineation group $C(k, p^n)$ has a subgroup $EC(k, p^n)$ whose transformations may be represented analytically in the form

$$(A_1) \qquad \begin{aligned} \rho x'_0 &= \beta_\tau x_0^{p^\tau}, & (\beta_\tau \neq 0) \\ \rho x'_i &= \sum_{j=0}^{k} \beta_{ij\tau} x_j^{p^\tau}, & (i = 1, 2, \cdots, k) \end{aligned}$$

where τ runs over the sequence $0, 1, \cdots, n-1$. Its order is n times the order of its subgroup $EP(k, p^n)$, or $EC_0(k, p^n)$, made up of those transformations of (A_1) in each of which $\tau = 0$ and is therefore

$$np^{kn} \prod_{i=0}^{k-1} (p^{kn} - p^{in}).$$

The group EC is generated by EC_0 and the collineation

$$\rho x'_i = x_i^p. \qquad (i = 0, 1, \cdots, k)$$

The last element transforms EC_0 into itself.

(2) If d is any proper divisor of n, then we have a subgroup $EC_d(k, p^n)$ of $EC(k, p^n)$ (with $EC_1 \equiv EC$) generated by EC_0 and the collineation

$$\rho x'_i = x_i^{p^d}, \qquad (i = 0, 1, \cdots, k)$$

and EC_d is of index d in EC. The transformations of EC_d are those of the form (A_1), with the restriction that τ shall be confined to the multiples of d belonging to the sequence $0, 1, 2, \cdots, n-1$.

(3) Those transformations in EC_d whose determinants are $(k+1)$th powers in the $GF[p^n]$ form a subgroup $E\overline{C}_d(k, p^n)$ of EC_d of index μ, where μ is the greatest common divisor of $k+1$ and $p^n - 1$.

(4) The group $EP(k, p^n)$, considered as a permutation group on the p^{kn} points of the $EG(k, p^n)$, is doubly transitive. Moreover, it is triply transitive when $k > 1$ and $p^n = 2$. The same property of transitivity belongs to each of the previously named groups which contains $EP(k, p^n)$ as a subgroup.

(5) Considered as a permutation group on the p^{kn} points of $EG(k, p^n)$, the group $E\overline{C}_d(k, p^n)$ is doubly transitive when $k > 1$ and also when $k = 1$ and $p = 2$; it is singly transitive when $k = 1$ and p is an odd prime. This singly transitive group is primitive.

(6) Finally, in a special case, we have another subgroup of EC defined as follows. Let $k+1$ be a divisor of n and let σ be a fixed divisor of $n/(k+1)$. Moreover, let $k+1$ be a divisor of $p^\sigma - 1$. Any multiple of σ in the set $0, 1, \cdots, n-1$ can be written in just one way in the form $\{(k+1)s + \alpha\}\sigma$, where $0 \leqq \alpha \leqq k$ and s is a non-negative integer. For every

such multiple of σ form the entire set of homogeneous transformations

$$(B_1)\qquad \begin{aligned} \rho x'_0 &= \beta_{s\alpha} x_0{}^{p\{(k+1)s+\alpha\}\sigma} \\ \rho x'_i &= \sum_{j=0}^{k} \beta_{ijs\alpha} x_j{}^{p\{(k+1)s+\alpha\}\sigma}, \qquad (i = 1, 2, \cdots, k) \end{aligned}$$

in which each determinant of a transformation is equal to ω^α times a $(k+1)$th power in the $GF[p^n]$, ω being a primitive mark of the $GF[p^n]$. The totality of these transformations forms a subgroup $EH_\sigma(k, p^n)$ of EC_σ which is of index $k+1$ in EC_σ and of index $(k+1)\sigma$ in EC. The group EH_σ is generated by $E\overline{C}_0$ and the transformations of the form

$$(C_1)\qquad \rho x'_i = \omega^{t_i} x_i{}^{p\{(k+1)s+\alpha\}\sigma}, \qquad (i = 0, 1, \cdots, k)$$

where $t_0 + t_1 + \cdots + t_k \equiv \alpha \bmod (k+1)$. Considered as a permutation group on the p^{kn} points of the $EG(k, p^n)$, the group $EH_\sigma(k, p^n)$ is doubly transitive.

That the transformations named in paragraph (1) of the theorem form a group is easily verified, as is also the fact that it is generated in the way indicated. It is also easily shown that EC_0 is invariant under transformation by the last collineation defined in the paragraph. As regards this first paragraph of the theorem, it remains to be shown that the order given for the group is correct. For this purpose we notice that a necessary and sufficient condition on the coefficients $\beta_{ij\tau}$, for $j > 0$, is that for each τ the determinant $|\beta_{ij\tau}|$ of order k shall be different from zero. The number of choices for these β's and β_τ, satisfying this condition for fixed τ, is known (from Theorem III in § **94**) to be

$$\prod_{i=0}^{k-1} (p^{kn} - p^{in}).$$

The coefficients $\beta_{i0\tau}$ may each be chosen in p^n different ways for each value of τ; and hence the set for each value of τ

may be chosen in p^{kn} different ways. Taking $\tau = 0$, we see that the number of transformations in EC_0 is the number given in the theorem. From this it follows readily that EC has the order stated in the theorem.

The proofs of the statements in paragraphs (2) and (3) of the theorem are similar to the proofs of the corresponding parts of Theorem III in § **94**; they are therefore omitted.

To establish the transitivity properties named in paragraph (4) of the theorem, note first that there is in $P(k, p^n)$ a transformation that carries any ordered set of $k+2$ points of $PG(k, p^n)$, no $k+1$ of which are on the same $(k-1)$-space, into any like ordered set of $k+2$ points, and in each of two such sets two points may be taken at will in $EG(k, p^n)$, while the remaining k points may be chosen from the $(k-1)$-space $x_0 = 0$. This transformation leaves invariant this $(k-1)$-space; hence it belongs to $EP(k, p^n)$. Hence $EP(k, p^n)$, considered as a permutation group on the points of $EG(k, p^n)$, is doubly transitive.

This transitivity property may also be established analytically. Let A and B be any two points of $EG(k, p^n)$. There is obviously a transformation in $EP(k, p^n)$ replacing A by $(1, 0, 0, \cdots, 0)$. Let C be the point by which this transformation replaces B. Then it is sufficient to show that $EP(k, p^n)$ contains a transformation that leaves $(1, 0, 0, \cdots, 0)$ fixed and replaces C by $(1, 1, 0, 0, \cdots, 0)$, or, what is equivalent, that leaves $(1, 0, 0, \cdots, 0)$ fixed and replaces $(1, 1, 0, 0, \cdots, 0)$ by C. The transformations available for the latter are those in which each β_{i00} is zero. Then the point $(1, 1, 0, 0, \cdots, 0)$ is replaced by $(\beta_0, \beta_{110}, \beta_{210}, \cdots, \beta_{k10})$. It is obvious that the β's may be so chosen that this is the point C. Hence the named transitivity property is established analytically.

It remains to treat further the case in which $k > 1$ and $p^n = 2$. For this purpose consider those transformations of $EP(k, 2)$ which leave fixed a given point P of $EG(k, 2)$. This group is obviously simply isomorphic with the projective group in $PG(k-1, 2)$, whence it follows readily that it is doubly transitive on the points of $EG(k, 2)$ exclusive of P. Hence $EP(k, 2)$ is triply transitive on the points of $EG(k, 2)$.

The remaining statement in paragraph (4) of the theorem is now obviously true.

To establish the transitivity properties named in paragraph (5) of the theorem, let us denote any two points C and D of $EG(k, p^n)$ by

$$(\beta_\tau, \beta_{10\tau}, \beta_{20\tau}, \cdots, \beta_{k0\tau})$$

and $(\beta_\tau, \beta_{10\tau} + \beta_{11\tau}, \beta_{20\tau} + \beta_{21\tau}, \cdots, \beta_{k0\tau} + \beta_{k1\tau}).\qquad (\beta_\tau \neq 0)$

Since C and D are distinct (by hypothesis), it follows that at least one $\beta_{\mu 1\tau}$ is different from zero. Let λ be a fixed quantity such that $\beta_{\lambda 1\tau} \neq 0$. Then take $\beta_{\lambda s\tau} = 0$ when $s > 1$. Taking the quantities β, as thus defined, to be the coefficients in the transformation (A_1) which are denoted by the same symbols, we see that the points $(1, 0, 0, \cdots, 0)$ and $(1, 1, 0, 0, \cdots, 0)$ are transformed by (A_1) into C and D respectively. Now if $k > 1$ the remaining coefficients in the transformation can be so determined that the determinant of the transformation shall have any preassigned value. Hence these coefficients and the value of τ may be so chosen that the transformation belongs to $E\overline{C}_d(k, p^n)$. Therefore $E\overline{C}_d(k, p^n)$ is doubly transitive when $k > 1$. It is easy to treat analytically the case when $k = 1$ and to show that $E\overline{C}_d(1, 2^n)$ is doubly transitive, while $E\overline{C}_d(1, p^n)$, for $p > 2$, is only singly transitive. To prove that this singly transitive group is primitive, we observe that its elements may be denoted in nonhomogeneous co-ordinates by the transformations $t' = \alpha t + \beta$, where α runs over the squares in the $GF[p^n]$ and β over all the marks of the $GF[p^n]$. Then it contains the transformation $t' = \omega^2 t$, where ω is a primitive mark of the $GF[p^n]$. The corresponding permutation consists of two cycles each of order $\frac{1}{2}(p^n - 1)$ on nonzero marks of the field. Hence if the group is imprimitive, the set of imprimitivity containing zero must contain more than half the symbols, and this is impossible. Hence the group is primitive.

It may be remarked in passing that the set of transformations $t' = \alpha t + \beta$, where α runs over the λth powers of the $GF[p^n]$ and β over all the marks of the field, λ being a proper factor of $p^n - 1$ greater than unity, form a singly transitive group of order $p^n(p^n - 1)/\lambda$; that this group is primitive when

λ is a factor of $p-1$; and that in other cases it is sometimes primitive and sometimes imprimitive.

It remains to prove the statements in the last paragraph of the theorem.

The fact that the transformations (B_1) form a group may be proved in the same way as the corresponding fact was established in the proof of Theorem III in § **94**. That EH_σ has the named generators is then established in an obvious manner. That EH_σ has the named indexes in the groups mentioned is proved in the same way as that in which the corresponding results in Theorem III of § **94** were established. The transitivity property stated in the conclusion of the theorem may be established by the method employed in establishing the transitivity properties of $E\bar{C}_d(k, p^n)$.

Thus the proof of the theorem is completed.

If the coefficients β_{i00} in (A_1) $(i=1, 2, \cdots, k)$ are zero, then the point $(1, 0, 0, \cdots, 0)$ is left invariant by the transformation (A_1), and conversely. Thus we have an obvious analytical representation of that subgroup of each group in Theorem VII which consists of all the transformations in it which leave $(1, 0, 0, \cdots, 0)$ fixed. The subgroup of $EC_0(k, p^n)$ which leaves $(1, 0, 0, \cdots, 0)$ fixed is obviously equivalent to the general linear homogeneous group on k variables, while EC_0 itself is equivalent to the corresponding general linear nonhomogeneous group on k variables.

It is obvious that the group $EC(k, p^n)$ is multiply isomorphic with the group $C(k-1, p^n)$ in the $PG(k-1, p^n)$ defined by the equation $x_0=0$. By a comparison of the orders of these two groups one finds that the isomorphism is $p^{kn}(p^n-1)$ to 1. In a transformation (A_1) of $EC(k, p^n)$ a variation in the coefficients β_τ, $\beta_{i0\tau}$ for $i=1, 2, \cdots, k$ and τ fixed has no effect on the permutation in the $(k-1)$-space $x_0=0$; and the variation of these coefficients gives $p^{kn}(p^n-1)$ different transformations in $EC(k, p^n)$ corresponding to a given transformation in the subspace. Corresponding to the identity in $C(k-1, p^n)$ we have in $EC(k, p^n)$ the $p^{kn}(p^n-1)$ transformations

$$\rho x'_0=\beta_\tau x_0, \quad \rho x'_i=\beta_{i0\tau}x_0+x_i. \qquad (i=1, 2, \cdots, k)$$

It is obvious that there is a transformation in this set which replaces $(1, 0, 0, \cdots, 0)$ by any previously assigned point in $EG(k, p^n)$, whence this subgroup is transitive on the points of $EG(k, p^n)$. From this it follows that for every subgroup S of $C(k-1, p^n)$ there is a corresponding subgroup T of $EC(k, p^n)$, transitive on the p^{kn} points of $EG(k, p^n)$, the latter subgroup having with the former a $p^{kn}(p^n-1)$ to 1 isomorphism. Moreover, if the former subgroup is transitive the latter is doubly transitive, a fact which may be established as follows. The largest subgroup of T which leaves fixed one point A of $EG(k, p^n)$ contains a transformation carrying any line through A into any other line through A. Hence any given point in $EG(k, p^n)$, other than A, can be carried by a transformation of T into a point B of $EG(k, p^n)$ on any line through A, while A itself remains fixed. Then, holding this line fixed, as well as the point A on it, we can take a transformation in T (namely, one of the form $x'_0 = x_0$, $x'_i = \beta x_i$ ($\beta \neq 0$; $i = 1, 2, \cdots, k$), if A is taken to be $(1, 0, 0, \cdots, 0)$, as it may be without loss of generality) which leaves point-wise invariant the subspace $x_0 = 0$ and carries B to any preassigned point C in $EG(k, p^n)$ and on the line AB. Hence the subgroup of T which leaves A fixed carries any given point of $EG(k, p^n)$ other than A to any such point. Hence T is doubly transitive on the points of $EG(k, p^n)$ when S is transitive on the points in the subspace $x_0 = 0$. When S is intransitive it is easy to show in a similar way that T is only singly transitive.

We have thus demonstrated the following theorem, except for the statement about the primitivity of the singly transitive subgroups of $EC(k, p^n)$; and this is an immediate consequence of the corollary to Theorem XIV in § **46**.

VIII. The group $EC(k, p^n)$ has a $p^{kn}(p^n-1)$ to 1 isomorphism with the group $C(k-1, p^n)$ on the points of the subspace $x_0 = 0$. The subgroup T of $EC(k, p^n)$ having a $p^{kn}(p^n-1)$ to 1 isomorphism with a given subgroup S of $C(k-1, p^n)$ and corresponding to it in the isomorphism just mentioned is a transitive group, when considered as a permutation group on the p^{kn} points of $EG(k, p^n)$. Moreover, when S is transitive, the group T is doubly transitive; otherwise it is singly transitive. When S is intransitive, a necessary and sufficient condition that the singly transitive group T shall be primitive is that it shall be generated by the largest subgroup leaving the point $(1, 0, 0, \cdots, 0)$ fixed and any single transformation whatever of T that does not leave this point fixed.

Every line in the Euclidean k-space $EG(k, p^n)$ has a point in common with the projective $(k-1)$-space $x_0 = 0$ which was excluded from $PG(k, p^n)$ in forming $EG(k, p^n)$. With a line of $EG(k, p^n)$ and a point of it not on this line we may form a Euclidean plane lying in $EG(k, p^n)$; as a plane of $PG(k, p^n)$ it contains a line in the excluded $(k-1)$-space. With such a plane and an additional point of $EG(k, p^n)$ we may form a three-space which is composed of a Euclidean three-space and a plane lying in the excluded $(k-1)$-space. It is clear that this process may be continued and that one may conclude to the existence in $EG(k, p^n)$ of a Euclidean m-space $EG(m, p^n)$ for every value m of the set $1, 2, \cdots, k-1$; and in each case the remainder of the projective space $PG(m, p^n)$ which contains $EG(m, p^n)$ lies in the excluded $(k-1)$-space $x_0 = 0$.

Now any collineation group in $EG(k, p^n)$ obviously permutes among themselves the m-spaces $EG(m, p^n)$ contained in $EG(k, p^n)$. Hence each of the named groups in Theorems VII and VIII, interpreted there as a permutation group on the points of $EG(k, p^n)$, may likewise be interpreted as a permutation group on the lines of $EG(k, p^n)$, or on its planes, or in general on its m-spaces. The several permutation groups arising in this way from one and the same transformation group are obviously simply isomorphic each to each. Hence we have the following theorem:

IX. Any collineation group in $EG(k, p^n)$ may be interpreted as a permutation group on the included

m-spaces $EG(m, p^n)$ for each value m of the set $1, 2, \cdots, k-1$. The several permutation groups obtained by varying the value of m are simply isomorphic each to each.

We shall next prove the following theorem:

X. Let T and S have the same meanings as in Theorem VIII. If S is transitive on the points of the $(k-1)$-space $x_0 = 0$, then the group T is transitive when interpreted as a permutation group on the lines of $EG(k, p^n)$. If S is transitive on the projective l-spaces contained in the projective $(k-1)$-space $x_0 = 0$, l being less than $k-1$, then T is transitive on the $(l+1)$-spaces contained in $EG(k, p^n)$; this group T is imprimitive.

The truth of the statement in the second sentence of the theorem is a consequence of Theorems VIII and IX. To prove the statement in the last sentence, we observe first that T contains a transformation carrying one point of $EG(k, p^n)$ into any other, while at the same time the projective $(k-1)$-space $x_0 = 0$ is left point-wise invariant. Now any Euclidean $(l+1)$-space in $EG(k, p^n)$ may be defined by a projective l-space in the subspace $x_0 = 0$ and a point of $EG(k, p^n)$, it being understood that each point of $EG(k, p^n)$ collinear with the given point and a point of the given l-space is to be a point of the named $(l+1)$-space. Now let A and B be two Euclidean $(l+1)$-spaces so defined, and let P and Q be the points in $EG(k, p^n)$ used in thus defining them. Leaving the subspace $x_0 = 0$ point-wise invariant, take P to Q by means of a transformation belonging to T. Then, holding Q fixed, take the l-space of A which is in the subspace $x_0 = 0$ into the corresponding l-space of B by means of an element of T. These two transformations taken in order carry A into B. Hence T has the stated property of transitivity.

It remains to be shown that the group T is imprimitive on the named $(l+1)$-spaces. For this purpose it is sufficient to observe that all the $(l+1)$-spaces of $EG(k, p^n)$ which are based, in the way indicated, on a given l-space of the subspace $x_0 = 0$ are permuted among themselves when that l-space is left invariant, and that they are transformed into a like set of $(l+1)$-spaces when the given l-space is transformed into another like l-space.

96. Collineation Groups Leaving Other Subspaces Invariant. We shall now prove the following theorem:

XI. The group $C^{(l)}(k, p^n)$, consisting of all transformations of the form

$$(A_2) \qquad \begin{aligned} \rho x'_i &= \sum_{j=0}^{l} \beta_{ij\tau} x_j^{p^\tau}, \qquad (i = 0, 1, \cdots, l) \\ \rho x'_i &= \sum_{j=0}^{k} \beta_{ij\tau} x_j^{p^\tau}, \qquad (i = l+1, l+2, \cdots, k) \end{aligned}$$

where $0 \leqq l < k$, τ runs over the sequence $0, 1, \cdots, n-1$, and the coefficients β are marks of the $GF[p^n]$ such that the determinant of the transformation is different from zero, is a collineation group in $PG(k, p^n)$ which leaves invariant the subspace $PG(k-l-1, p^n)$ defined by the equations $x_i = 0$ $(i = 0, 1, \cdots, l)$. It also leaves invariant the complementary set of

$$p^{(k-l)n} + p^{(k-l+1)n} + \cdots + p^{kn}$$

points in $PG(k, p^n)$. Its order is

$$\frac{np^{(k-l)(l+1)n}}{p^n - 1} \cdot \prod_{i=0}^{l} (p^{(l+1)n} - p^{in}) \cdot \prod_{i=0}^{k-l-1} (p^{(k-l)n} - p^{in}).$$

The group is generated by its subgroup $C_0^{(l)}(k, p^n)$ for which $\tau = 0$ and the collineation

$$(B_2) \qquad \rho x'_i = x_i^p. \qquad (i = 0, 1, \cdots, k)$$

The last element transforms $C_0^{(l)}(k, p^n)$ into itself.

For each proper divisor d of n the group $C^{(l)}(k, p^n)$ has an obvious subgroup $C_d^{(l)}(k, p^n)$ of index d generated by $C_0^{(l)}(k, p^n)$ and the dth power of the collineation (B_2). Moreover, $C_d^{(l)}(k, p^n)$ has an obvious subgroup $\overline{C}_d^{(l)}(k, p^n)$ of index μ consisting of those transformations of $C_d^{(l)}(k, p^n)$ whose determinants are $(k+1)$th powers, μ being the greatest common divisor of $k+1$ and $p^n - 1$.

The group $C_0^{(l)}(k, p^n)$ is transitive when interpreted as a permutation group on the set of $p^{(k-l)n} + \cdots + p^{kn}$ points mentioned in the first paragraph of the theorem.

That the given set of transformations forms a group leaving invariant the named subspace, and hence the complementary set of points, is obvious. To determine the order of the group, we notice first that the determinant of the coefficients $\beta_{ij\tau}$ for i and j running over the set $0, 1, \cdots, l$ must be different from zero; whence it follows (from a comparison with Theorem III of § **94**) that these coefficients can be chosen in

$$\prod_{i=0}^{l} (p^{(l+1)n} - p^{in})$$

different ways, τ remaining fixed. The coefficients $\beta_{ij\tau}$, for i and j running over the set $l+1, l+2, \cdots, k$ and τ remaining fixed, can be chosen independently in any way so that their determinant shall be different from zero, and hence can be chosen in

$$\prod_{i=0}^{k-l-1} (p^{(k-l)n} - p^{in})$$

different ways. Then for τ still fixed each of the remaining $(k-l)(l+1)$ coefficients β can be chosen independently in p^n ways, so that altogether this set of coefficients can be chosen in

$$p^{(k-l)(l+1)n}$$

different ways. Finally, there are n values for τ. Hence the order of the group is the product of n and the three numbers just determined, divided by $p^n - 1$ to allow for the factor of proportionality. This gives the order stated in the theorem.

It is obvious that the group is generated in the way stated. The second paragraph of the theorem is established by the method used in proving the corresponding part of Theorem VII in § **95**.

The truth of the last proposition in the theorem is readily established by means of the following considerations: since any ordered set of $k+2$ points, no $k+1$ of which are on a $(k-1)$-space, can be carried by the projective group into any other such ordered set, it is obvious that an l-space may be held fixed while any point not on it is transformed into any other such point.

The common subgroup of $C^{(l)}(k, p^n)$ and the group $H_\sigma(k, p^n)$ of Theorem III of § **94** may be constructed in an obvious manner.

97. Some Special Cases. Let G be a permutation group of degree ν on the symbols $a_1, a_2, \cdots, a_\nu$; and let $L_1, L_2, \cdots, L_\mu$ $(\mu = \nu(\nu-1)\cdots(\nu-k+1)/(k!))$ be the combinations of these symbols a_i taken k at a time. Let P be any permutation belonging to G. This permutation P on the a's induces a permutation on the symbols L_i. Hence to the totality of permutations of G there corresponds a totality of permutations on the L's, and these constitute a permutation group $\bar{G}$ of degree μ on $L_1, L_2, \cdots, L_\mu$. It is obvious that $\bar{G}$ is simply isomorphic with G.

Now if G is k-ply transitive on its symbols, it contains a permutation replacing any given L_i by any given L_j. Hence the group $\bar{G}$ is transitive on its μ symbols L_i. Moreover, it is only simply transitive when $1 < k < \nu - 1$; for the ordered sets $a_1, a_2, \cdots, a_k$ and $a_1, a_2, \cdots, a_{k-1}, a_{k+1}$ can be carried into two other ordered sets only if these latter two sets have their first $k-1$ symbols alike. This singly transitive group $\bar{G}$ may be either primitive or imprimitive. (See Ex. 3 on page 391.)

The results of the previous two paragraphs may be interpreted (somewhat artificially, it is true) in the finite geometries. If we have a group G in $PG(\nu-2, p^n)$ which permutes among themselves ν points $a_1, a_2, \cdots, a_\nu$ of the geometry, no $\nu-1$

of which are in the same $(\nu - 3)$-space, then the combinations $L_1, L_2, \cdots, L_\mu$ may be interpreted as the $(k-1)$-spaces generated by all subsets of k points each formed from the given ν points. Corresponding to the transformations on the ν points, we have permutations of these $(k-1)$-spaces among themselves, giving rise to the permutation group $\overline{G}$ on the $(k-1)$-spaces.

XII. *For every transitive group G of degree 4 there exists a doubly transitive group of degree 9 having an (18, 1) isomorphism with G.*

The group $C(1, 3)$ is the symmetric group of degree 4. Hence every transitive group G of degree 4 is a subgroup of $C(1, 3)$. From Theorem VIII in § **95** it follows then that there exists in the $EG(2, 3)$ of 9 points a doubly transitive group of degree 9 having an (18, 1) isomorphism with G.

XIII. *For every transitive group G of degree 5 there is a doubly transitive group of degree 16 having a (48, 1) isomorphism with G.*

The group $C(1, 2^2)$ is of degree 5 and order 120; hence it is the symmetric group of degree 5. Then apply Theorem VIII as in the proof of Theorem XII.

We shall now prove the following special theorem, extending in one respect the results in Theorem VIII.

XIV. *For every transitive group G of degree $1 + 2 + 2^2 + \cdots + 2^k$ contained in the group $C(k, 2)$ of this degree there exists a multiply transitive group H of degree 2^{k+1}, contained in $EC(k+1, 2)$ and having a $(2^{k+1}, 1)$ isomorphism with G and having its degree of transitivity greater than that of G by unity.*

This theorem is implied by Theorem VIII, except for the fact relating to the degree of transitivity of H; and this part of the theorem is an immediate consequence of the fact that the largest subgroup of H leaving one point fixed is simply isomorphic with G.

98. Generators of Certain Multiply Transitive Groups of Prime Degree. It is convenient to insert in this section and the next certain theorems concerning multiply transitive groups of prime degree.

Let G be a nonsymmetric multiply transitive group of odd prime degree p different from the metacyclic group of degree p, and let l denote the degree of transitivity of G. Choose the notation so that one permutation in G is P, where

$$P = (x_0x_1x_2 \cdots x_{p-1}).$$

Now G contains a transitive subgroup on the letters $x_{l-1}, x_l, \cdots, x_{p-1}$. On transforming P by suitable elements from this subgroup one proves the existence in G of a set of permutations of the form

$$\begin{aligned} P_l &= (x_0x_1 \cdots x_{l-2}x_l \cdots), \\ P_{l+1} &= (x_0x_1 \cdots x_{l-2}x_{l+1} \cdots), \\ &\cdots\cdots\cdots\cdots \\ P_{p-1} &= (x_0x_1 \cdots x_{l-2}x_{p-1} \cdots), \end{aligned}$$

where the second continuation sign in each parenthesis is used to denote the presence in some order of the x's not otherwise assigned a place in the symbol for the corresponding permutation. We denote by these symbols P any elements in G having the form indicated.

We shall now prove the following theorem:

XV. Any set of elements in G having the form of the elements $P, P_l, P_{l+1}, \cdots, P_{p-1}$ generate a (proper or improper) subgroup H of G which is at least $(l-1)$-ply transitive; moreover, H is certainly l-ply transitive if the elements $P_{l+i}P^{-1}$ $(i = 0, 1, \cdots, p-l-1)$ leave x_{p-1} fixed.

Let us consider the largest subgroup K in

$$\{P, P_l, P_{l+1}, \cdots, P_{p-1}\}$$

each element of which leaves fixed $x_0, x_1, \cdots, x_{l-3}$. It contains the elements $P_{l+i}P^{-1}$ $(i = 0, 1, \cdots, p-l-1)$. The element $P_{l+i}P^{-1}$ replaces x_{l-2} by x_{l+i-1}. Hence K contains permutations changing x_{l-2} respectively into $x_{l-2}, x_{l-1}, \cdots, x_{p-2}$. There are now two cases to be distinguished. If K does not leave x_{p-1} fixed, then it is clear that K is transitive on the symbols $x_{l-2}, x_{l-1}, \cdots, x_{p-1}$; otherwise it is transitive on the symbols $x_{l-2}, x_{l-1}, \cdots, x_{p-2}$. Then $P^{-1}KP$ is a transitive group on $x_{l-1}, x_l, \cdots, x_{p-1}, x_0$ or on all these except x_0 according to the case in consideration. Hence $\{K, P^{-1}KP\}$ is at least doubly transitive on the symbols which it displaces. If these are not all the symbols $x_0, x_1, \cdots, x_{p-1}$, we may adjoin successively the groups $P^{-2}KP^2$, $P^{-3}KP^3$, $\cdots$ and thus establish the result stated in the theorem.

XVI. The same group G contains P and elements of order p and of the form $Q_{l+1}, Q_{l+2}, \cdots, Q_{p-1}$, where each element Q replaces x_0 by x_1, x_1 by x_2, $\cdots$, x_{l-2} by x_{l-1}, while Q_{l+i} replaces x_{l-1} by x_{l+i} for $i = 1, 2, \cdots, p-l-1$. These elements generate an l-ply transitive group contained in G.

The named elements Q_{l+i} are of the form

$$Q_{l+i} = (x_0 x_1 x_2 \cdots x_{l-1} x_{l+i} \cdots). \qquad (i = 1, 2, \cdots, p-l-1)$$

That G contains elements of this form may be shown by the following considerations. Since G contains a transitive subgroup on $x_{l-1}, x_l, \cdots, x_{p-1}$, it contains for each i of the set $1, 2, \cdots, p-l-1$ an element replacing x_{l-1} by x_{l+i-1} and leaving $x_0, x_1, \cdots, x_{l-2}$ fixed. This element followed by P gives an element of the form Q_{l+i}. The largest subgroup L in

$$\{P, Q_{l+1}, Q_{l+2}, \cdots, Q_{p-1}\}$$

which leaves fixed $x_0, x_1, \cdots, x_{l-2}$ contains elements replacing x_{l-1} respectively by the elements $x_l, x_{l+1}, \cdots, x_{p-2}$, as may be shown by the method used in the proof of the preceding theorem. Then L must not leave x_{p-1} fixed, for in that case G would contain a transitive subgroup on $p-l$ symbols, and this is impossible since by hypothesis G is l-ply transitive but not $(l+1)$-ply transitive. Hence L is transitive on the symbols $x_{l-1}, x_l, \cdots, x_{p-1}$. Then by adjoining successively $P^{-1}LP$, $P^{-2}LP^2, \cdots$ we show finally that the group

$$\{P, Q_{l+1}, Q_{l+2}, \cdots, Q_{p-1}\}$$

is l-ply transitive, as asserted in the theorem.

Groups illustrating these theorems are afforded by the collineation groups in $PG(k, p^n)$ when the number of points in the geometry is a prime. Thus for $k=2$ we have examples for groups of degrees 13, 31, 307, etc.

99. Groups of Certain Prime Degrees. We begin with a proof of the following theorem:

XVII. If p and $p-2$ are primes and $p>5$, there exists no triply transitive group of degree p which is not also quadruply transitive.

Let G be a triply (but not quadruply) transitive group of prime degree p ($\geqq 5$), where $p-2$ is also a prime. We shall show that p must then be equal to 5, from which fact the theorem follows. Let G_2 be the group composed of all permutations in G each of which leaves two given letters fixed. Then G_2 is simply transitive and hence (Theorem XVIII of § **60**) is of order $(p-2)\nu$, where ν is a proper factor of $p-3$; in case G_2 has only even permutations, then ν is a factor of $\frac{1}{2}(p-3)$. But the order of G is of the form $(kp+1)p\mu$, where μ is a factor of $p-1$, as one sees from Sylow's theorem and Theorem XVIII of § **60**; in case G has only even permutations, then μ is a factor of $\frac{1}{2}(p-1)$. Therefore

$$(kp+1)p\mu = p(p-1)(p-2)\nu; \text{ or, } (kp+1)\mu = (p-1)(p-2)\nu.$$

Hence $\mu \equiv 2\nu \bmod p$, while μ and ν are both positive numbers less than p. In case G_2 contains only even permutations, then μ and 2ν are both less than p. Therefore in this case $\mu = 2\nu$, while μ and ν are factors of $\frac{1}{2}(p-1)$ and $\frac{1}{2}(p-3)$ respectively, so that the highest common factor of μ and ν is 1. Hence, when G contains only even permutations, we have $\nu = 1$ and $\mu = 2$.

Now suppose that $\nu = 1$, whether or not G consists of even permutations only. Then the order of G is $p(p-1)(p-2)$. The largest subgroup of G leaving one given letter fixed is doubly transitive of degree $p-1$ and order $(p-1)(p-2)$; hence (Theorem V of § **40**) $p-1$ is a power of a prime. Since $p-1$ is even, we must have $p = 2^m + 1$ and $p - 2 = 2^m - 1$. Since $2^m - 1$ is prime, m itself must be a prime; since $2^m + 1$ is prime, m must be a power of 2. Therefore $m = 2$ and $p = 5$. The alternating group of degree 5 is therefore the only group belonging to the case when $\nu = 1$.

There is left for further examination the case in which G contains odd permutations and $\nu > 1$. The subgroup of G consisting of all its even permutations is then of order $\frac{1}{2}\ \mu p(kp+1)$, and this is equal to $\frac{1}{2}\, p(p-1)(p-2)\nu$. Hence this subgroup of G is not contained in the metacyclic group of degree p. It is therefore at least doubly transitive, as one sees from Theorem XVIII of § **60**. But the largest subgroup leaving just two given letters fixed is of order $\frac{1}{2}\ \nu(p-2)$; it is therefore transitive on its $p-2$ symbols, since $p-2$ is a prime. Hence the named subgroup of index 2 in G is triply transitive. Then from the conclusion in the preceding case it follows that we must have $p = 5$. Then G must be the symmetric group of degree 5, contrary to the hypothesis that it is only triply transitive.

From these results the theorem follows as stated.

If $\frac{1}{2}(p-3)$ is a prime q, whence $p = 2\,q + 3$, it follows, from Miller's theorem (Theorem VIII of § **41**) and a separate consideration of transitive groups of degree 7, that a group G of degree p which does not contain the alternating group of degree p cannot be more than triply transitive. Combining this fact with the foregoing theorem and the facts associated with the metacyclic group in Theorem XVIII of § **60**, we have the following theorem:

XVIII. If p is a prime number greater than 5 such that $p-2$ and $\frac{1}{2}(p-3)$ are both primes, then a transitive group G of degree p, which does not contain the alternating group of degree p and is not contained in the metacyclic group of degree p, is itself doubly transitive but not triply transitive.

From this theorem we see that, for all primes p of the sort described in it, the degrees of transitivity of transitive groups of degree p are precisely 1, 2, $p-2$, p. The metacyclic group is doubly transitive; it contains singly transitive subgroups; and the alternating and symmetric groups are respectively $(p-2)$-fold and p-fold transitive. That these groups do not always contain the totality of transitive groups of such prime degree p follows from the example afforded by the case $p = 13$, whence $p - 2 = 11$ and $\frac{1}{2}(p-3) = 5$. The collineation group in the $PG(2, 3)$ permutes the 13 points of the geometry according to a doubly transitive group of degree 13 and order $13 \cdot 12 \cdot 9 \cdot 4$.

EXERCISES

1. The theorem in Ex. 3 on page 372 persists when s is of the form p^{kn}.

2. For every integer L and odd prime p there exists an integer s of the form p^n such that a group G_s exists which is of degree s and is singly transitive and primitive and which contains more than L singly transitive primitive subgroups of different orders and each of degree s.

3. Let the group G of the first three paragraphs of § **97** be of degree 6 and take $k = 2$. Then the group $\bar{G}$ is of degree 15. If G is the alternating or the symmetric group of degree 6 show that $\bar{G}$ is primitive. If G is the triply transitive group $C(1, 5)$ of degree 6, show that $\bar{G}$ is imprimitive.

4. By means of Theorem XII in § **97** show that there are five doubly transitive groups of degree 9 having orders 432, 216, 144, 72, 72 respectively. Then by aid of $EC(2, 3)$ and $C(1, 2^3)$ and their subgroups show how to construct 11 primitive groups of degree 9. (See Ex. 10 on page 162.)

5. By means of Theorem XIII in § **97** show that there are five doubly transitive groups of degree 16 having orders 5760, 2880, 960, 480, 240 respectively.

6. In Ex. 10 on page 162 is found a table of the number of primitive groups of each degree less than 21. Exercises have already been given calling for the construction of the indicated number of primitive groups for certain of these degrees, as follows: For degrees 2, 3, 4, 5, 6, 14, 18, 19, 20 see Ex. 10 on page 162; for degree 7 see Ex. 12 on page 163; for degree 8 see Ex. 16 on page 165; for degrees 11 and 12 see Ex. 17 on page 165; for degree 13 see Ex. 18 on page 165; for degree 15 see Ex. 19 on page 165 and Ex. 4 on page 304; for degree 17 see Ex. 11 on page 305; and for degree 9 see Ex. 4 on page 391. The following are suggestions and exercises for completing the determination of the indicated number of primitive groups of each degree less than 21, alternative methods being given for some of the degrees already listed.

(1) Use Theorem III in § **94** and Ex. 5 on page 373 in constructing ten primitive groups of degree 17 and nine primitive groups of degree 13.

(2) By aid of theorems in this chapter construct seven primitive groups of degree 8 and nine primitive groups of degree 10. (See Ex. 3 on page 162 and Ex. 30 on page 42.)

(3) Construct 22 primitive groups of degree 16, obtaining twenty of them as subgroups of $EP(4, 2)$, utilizing for the latter purpose the fact that $EP(4, 2)$ is $(16, 1)$ isomorphic with $P(3, 2)$ and hence with the alternating group of degree 8 (Ex. 3 on page 304).

7. Let p be a prime of the form $4k + 3$, and let G be the doubly transitive group of degree $p + 1$ and order $\frac{1}{2}(p + 1)p(p - 1)$ on the symbols $\infty, 0, 1, \cdots, p - 1$ which is induced by the linear fractional transformations modulo p of square determinant. Show that G (although it is only doubly transitive) contains an element which displaces any given three of its symbols in some order into any other given three of its symbols.

8. Show that the (singly transitive) subgroup of index 2 in the metacyclic group of prime degree p $(p = 4k + 3)$ contains a permutation which displaces any given pair of its symbols in some order into any other given pair.

9. Show that for every prime p there exist at least twelve multiply transitive groups of degree p^6. Discuss cases in which the number is still larger.

10. For degrees p^4 and p^8 investigate the existence of multiply transitive groups after the manner suggested by Ex. 9.

11. Determine the number of points on the "conic" $x_1^2 - x_0x_2 = 0$ in the $PG(2, p^n)$ when p is odd. Determine the permutation group on the points of the conic induced by the largest subgroup of the $C(2, p^n)$ each element of which transforms this conic into itself.

12. In the $PG(2, p^n)$, where $p > 2$, show that the conic

$$a_{00}x_0^2 + a_{11}x_1^2 + a_{22}x_2^2 + 2\,a_{01}x_0x_1 + 2\,a_{02}x_0x_2 + 2\,a_{12}x_1x_2 = 0$$

breaks up into (distinct or coincident) straight lines if and only if

$$\begin{vmatrix} a_{00} & a_{01} & a_{02} \\ a_{01} & a_{11} & a_{12} \\ a_{02} & a_{12} & a_{22} \end{vmatrix} = 0.$$

MISCELLANEOUS EXERCISES

1. From the array in the margin form the triples

$$\begin{matrix} a & b & c \\ d & e & f \\ g & h & i \end{matrix}$$

abc, def, ghi, adg, beh, cfi, aei, ceg

of elements from rows and columns and diagonals, determine the largest permutation group on these letters which permutes among themselves the eight triples so formed, and construct the group according to which these triples are themselves permuted.

2. Generalize Ex. 1 to the case of an array of n^2 elements.

3. By a magic square is meant a square array of n^2 numbers such that the $2\,n + 2$ sums of elements, namely,

(1) those in each of the n rows,
(2) those in each of the n columns, and
(3) those in each of the 2 diagonals

$$\begin{matrix} 4 & 9 & 2 \\ 3 & 5 & 7 \\ 8 & 1 & 6 \end{matrix}$$

are all equal. An example for $n = 3$ is given in the margin, each of the sums being 15. Determine all the permutations on 1, 2, · · ·, 8 each of which transforms the given magic square into a magic square. Thus the given magic square is said to be transformed into the second one here written by the permutation (24)(37)(68). Do these permutations form a group?

$$\begin{matrix} 2 & 9 & 4 \\ 7 & 5 & 3 \\ 6 & 1 & 8 \end{matrix}$$

4. Treat similarly the following magic squares:

$$\begin{matrix} 15 & 6 & 9 & 4 \\ 10 & 3 & 16 & 5 \\ 8 & 13 & 2 & 11 \\ 1 & 12 & 7 & 14 \end{matrix} \qquad \begin{matrix} 23 & 6 & 19 & 2 & 15 \\ 4 & 12 & 25 & 8 & 16 \\ 10 & 18 & 1 & 14 & 22 \\ 11 & 24 & 7 & 20 & 3 \\ 17 & 5 & 13 & 21 & 9 \end{matrix}$$

5. Show that there are just two distinct ways in which six elements may be arranged into nine pairs in such a manner that each element occurs in just three pairs. In each case determine the permutation group leaving the configuration invariant.

6. Prove that through a given point P in $PG(3, p^n)$ and not on either of two skew lines l and l' in $PG(3, p^n)$ there is one and only one line meeting both the lines l and l'. Translate this into the corresponding theorem about the Abelian group of order p^{4n} and type $(1, 1, \cdots, 1)$. (See § **87**.)

7. Prove that any two lines in $PG(3, p^n)$ each of which meets three given skew lines in $PG(3, p^n)$ are themselves skew to each other. Translate this into a theorem relating to Abelian groups.

8. Generalize the results in Exs. 6 and 7.

9. Show that, if three triangles in $PG(2, p^n)$ are perspective from the same point, then the three axes of perspectivity of the three pairs of triangles are concurrent; and conversely. Translate this into a theorem concerning Abelian groups.

10. Translate into a theorem concerning Abelian groups the following geometric theorem (Veblen and Young, *Projective Geometry*, Vol. I, p. 59): If A, B, C are three points of a line l and A', B', C' are three points of another line l', then A can be projected into A', B into B', and C into C' by means of two centers of perspectivity.

11. In $PG(2, p^n)$ let a triangle ABC and a point A' be given; determine two points B' and C' such that the triangles ABC and $A'B'C'$ are perspective from four different centers. Formulate and solve a corresponding problem in the theory of Abelian groups.

12. By aid of Theorems VII and VIII construct three doubly transitive groups of degree 27 having a (54, 1) isomorphism with transitive groups of degree 13.

CHAPTER XIII

Algebras of Doubly Transitive Groups of Degree p^n and Order $p^n(p^n - 1)$

100. On the Definition of Group. In the definition of group in § 3 certain redundancies appear in the postulates. It is desirable now to restate the postulates in such a way as to avoid these redundancies. They are accordingly presented here in the following form:

I. If a and b are elements of G, whether the same or different, ab is also an element of G.

II. If a, b, c are elements of G, then $(ab)c = a(bc)$.

III. The set G contains an element i such that for every element a of G we have $ai = a$.

IV. If such an element i occurs in G, then for a particular i and for every element a of G there occurs an element a' such that $aa' = i$.

We shall now prove that these postulates imply the other conditions assumed in the postulates as presented in § 3.

For any given i and for any a there exist in G elements a' and a'' such that $aa' = i$ and $a'a'' = i$. Then we have

$$a = ai = a(a'a'') = (aa')a'' = ia'';$$

then

$$a'a = a'(ia'') = (a'i)a'' = a'a'' = i.$$

Hence $a'a = i$. Applying this result for a to the element a', we have $a''a' = i$. Then

$$ia = (ii)a = [i(a''a')]a = (ia'')(a'a) = ai = a.$$

Then for every a we have $ai = a = ia$. Then we call i an identity with respect to the rule of combination of the group. If j is an identity with respect to this rule, then $j = j \cdot i = i$.

Hence there is only one identity. Since the identity i is unique and since $ai = a = ia$ for every element a of G, it follows that the whole of Postulate III as given in § **3** is implied by the postulates here given.

Now we have seen that $aa' = i$ implies that $a'a = i$. Then we call a' an inverse of a. If α is an inverse of a we have

$$\alpha = \alpha i = \alpha(aa') = (\alpha a)a' = ia' = a'.$$

Hence there is just one inverse a' of a given element a, and $aa' = a'a = i$. Hence the postulates of this section imply Postulate IV of § **3**.

Therefore the postulates of this section imply all the propositions stated in the postulates of § **3**.

101. Definition of Algebras $A[s]$. Dickson (Göttingen *Nachrichten*, 1905), generalizing the notion of a Galois field, has defined an important class of finite algebras each of which consists of a finite set of elements or marks (two or more in number) subject to two operations (or rules of combination) called addition and multiplication and symbolized by $+$ and $\times$ respectively, the set of elements of a particular finite algebra satisfying the following system of nine postulates:

I^+. If a and b are elements of the set, then $a + b$ is uniquely determined as an element of the set.

II^+. If a, b, and c are elements of the set, then $(a + b) + c = a + (b + c)$.

III^+. There is in the set an element i_+ such that $a + i_+ = a$ for every element a of the set.

IV^+. If such an element i_+ occurs in the set, then for a particular i_+ and for every element a there occurs an element a' such that $a + a' = i_+$.

$\mathrm{I}^\times$, $\mathrm{II}^\times$, $\mathrm{III}^\times$. Same as I^+, II^+, III^+, with $\times$ throughout instead of $+$.

$\mathrm{IV}^\times$. If such an element $i_\times$ occurs in the set, then for a particular $i_\times$ and for every element a distinct from i_+ there occurs in the set an element a' such that $a \times a' = i_\times$.

V. If a, b, c are elements of the set, then $a \times (b+c) = a \times b + a \times c$.

If s is the number of elements in such an algebra we shall denote the algebra itself by $A[s]$.

We take over at once for the algebras $A[s]$ the terminology of ordinary algebra. We shall also use the symbol ab to denote what is written $a \times b$ in the postulates. Thus the equation in Postulate V will be written $a(b+c) = ab + ac$.

From § **100** it follows that all the s elements of an algebra $A[s]$ form a group whose law of combination is that denoted by $+$ in the postulates. In particular, there is but one element i_+. This additive group of the algebra we denote by H. The identity i_+ in this group has the additive properties of 0; it will often be denoted by this symbol. That i_+ also has the multiplicative properties of 0 may be shown as follows. We have

$$ai_+ = a(i_+ + i_+) = ai_+ + ai_+.$$

Hence $ai_+ = 0$ for every a in the set. We also have

$$i_+c = (i_+i_+)c = i_+(i_+c).$$

If i_+c is not i_+ it has an inverse under multiplication (since all the elements except i_+ form a group under multiplication, as one sees readily from § **100**). From the foregoing equation it follows then that $i_\times = i_+$, since $i_\times$ is the identity element in the multiplicative group of the algebra. Then we should have $a = ai_\times = ai_+ = i_+$ for every a. Since this is impossible, it follows that i_+c does not have an inverse under multiplication. Therefore $i_+c = i_+$ for every c in the algebra. Next, if $ab = i_+$ and $b \neq i_+$ we have

$$i_+ = i_+c = (ab)c = a(bc)$$

for every c in the algebra; taking c so that $bc = i_\times$ we get $i_+ = ai_\times = a$. Therefore, if $ab = i_+$, then either $a = i_+$ or $b = i_+$. *Therefore i_+ has the ordinary properties of zero under both addition and multiplication.*

From these considerations we have the following proposition:

> The s elements of an algebra $A[s]$ form an additive group H whose rule of combination is that of addition in the algebra. The identity i_+ in H plays the role of zero in the algebra. The $s-1$ elements of $A[s]$ other than i_+ form a multiplicative group M whose rule of combination is that of multiplication in the algebra.

102. Construction of Algebras $A[s]$ by Means of Certain Doubly Transitive Groups. From Theorem V of § **40** it follows that a doubly transitive group of degree ρ and order $\rho(\rho-1)$ exists when and only when ρ is a prime power p^n $(n \geqq 1)$, that such a doubly transitive group G contains a single subgroup H of order p^n, that this Sylow subgroup H is Abelian and of type $(1, 1, \cdots, 1)$, that H contains all the elements of G $(p^n-1$ in number) each of which displaces all the symbols permuted by G, that H is self-conjugate in G, and that every element in G and not in H is a regular permutation on just p^n-1 symbols.

Let $a_0, a_1, a_2, \cdots, a_\mu$, where $\mu = p^n - 1$, be the p^n symbols permuted by G. Then H permutes these symbols among themselves according to a regular group, as may readily be shown from the fact that H consists of the identity and p^n-1 elements each of which permutes all the symbols. Then there is one and just one element h_i of H which replaces a_0 by a_i.

Let us denote by M the subgroup of order p^n-1 in G each element of which leaves a_0 fixed. It is a regular group on $a_1, a_2, \cdots, a_\mu$. Hence there is one and just one element m_i of M which replaces a_1 by a_i. It is evident that $m_i^{-1}h_1m_i = h_i$.

By means of these properties of G we shall define an algebra $A[p^n]$. Let the p^n symbols or marks of this algebra be denoted by $u_0, u_1, u_2, \cdots, u_\mu$. We introduce a law of addition for the marks u_i in the following manner: The sum $u_i + u_j$ is the mark u_k $(u_i + u_j = u_k)$, where k is such that $h_ih_j = h_k$ in the group G. Then, in particular, $u_i + u_0 = u_i$ for every mark u_i. With this law of addition the named marks satisfy postulates I^+, II^+, III^+, IV^+ of § **101** with $i_+ = u_0$.

For the purpose of defining a law of multiplication for the marks u_i, exclusive of the zero mark u_0, we employ the elements of the subgroup M of G. We write $u_i u_j = u_l$ $(i > 0, j > 0)$, where l is defined by the relation $m_l^{-1} = m_i^{-1} m_j^{-1}$ or $m_l = m_j m_i$. (At this point it would seem more natural to take $u_i u_j = u_\lambda$, where $m_\lambda = m_i m_j$; but this would give $(b + c)a = ba + ca$ instead of the relation in Postulate V). We define the products $u_i u_0$ and $u_0 u_i$ by the requirement that each shall have the value u_0. When multiplication is so defined, the symbols $u_0, u_1, u_2, \cdots, u_\mu$ satisfy Postulates $I^\times$, $II^\times$, $III^\times$, $IV^\times$ of § **101**.

It remains to be shown that the operations of addition and multiplication, as here defined, are connected by the condition imposed in Postulate V of § **101**. As expressed in terms of the u's, we have to prove the following relation:

$$u_i(u_\rho + u_\sigma) = u_i u_\rho + u_i u_\sigma. \tag{1}$$

This is immediately verified if any one of the subscripts i, ρ, σ is zero. Then for the further argument suppose that each of them is greater than zero. Since (1) involves two operations, it is convenient to reduce the result to be proved to a corresponding relation among the elements of H and M, since they are all subject to the single rule of combination in G. From the definitions of addition and multiplication we have the following propositions:

$$u_\rho + u_\sigma = u_\tau \text{ if } h_\rho h_\sigma = h_\tau, \qquad u_i u_\rho = u_\lambda \text{ if } m_\rho m_i = m_\lambda,$$
$$u_i u_\sigma = u_\nu \text{ if } m_\sigma m_i = m_\nu, \qquad u_i u_\tau = u_\alpha \text{ if } m_\tau m_i = m_\alpha,$$
$$u_\lambda + u_\nu = u_\beta \text{ if } h_\lambda h_\nu = h_\beta.$$

In order to establish the required relation (1) it is necessary and sufficient to show that $\alpha = \beta$. Now we have

$$\begin{aligned} h_\beta = h_\lambda h_\nu &= m_\lambda^{-1} h_1 m_\lambda \cdot m_\nu^{-1} h_1 m_\nu \\ &= (m_\rho m_i)^{-1} h_1 (m_\rho m_i) \cdot (m_\sigma m_i)^{-1} h_1 (m_\sigma m_i) \\ &= m_i^{-1} h_\rho h_\sigma m_i = m_i^{-1} h_\tau m_i \\ &= m_i^{-1} m_\tau^{-1} h_1 m_\tau m_i = (m_\tau m_i)^{-1} h_1 (m_\tau m_i) \\ &= m_\alpha^{-1} h_1 m_\alpha = h_\alpha. \end{aligned}$$

Since $h_\beta = h_\alpha$, it follows that $\alpha = \beta$, and hence that (1) is established.

From the foregoing analysis it follows that every doubly transitive group of prime-power degree p^n ($n \geqq 1$) and order $p^n(p^n - 1)$ may be employed for the definition of an algebra $A[p^n]$. In the next section we consider the converse problem.

103. Linear Transformations on the Marks of an $A[s]$. Let $u_0, u_1, u_2, \cdots, u_{s-1}$ be the elements or marks of any algebra $A[s]$ of s marks, and let u_0 be the zero mark of the algebra and u_1 the identity element in the multiplicative group of the algebra. Then u_1 plays the role of unity in the algebra.

If β is any given mark of the algebra and x is a variable running over the marks of the algebra, then $x + \beta$ is a new variable x' running over the marks of the algebra. Thus we have the transformation $x' = x + \beta$ corresponding to the addition of β on the right to all the marks of the algebra. By varying β we obtain thus a set of s transformations. They form a group.

More generally the set of all transformations of the form

$$x' = \alpha x + \beta, \tag{2}$$

where α and β run independently over all the marks of the algebra except that α is different from u_0, constitutes a group K, as one may verify by aid of the postulates of the algebra. Its order is $s(s-1)$. Each element of K permutes the marks of $A[s]$ among themselves; thus K gives rise to a permutation group K_1 of degree s on the marks $u_0, u_1, \cdots, u_{s-1}$. If a and b are any two distinct marks of $A[s]$, then the marks u_0, u_1, as values of x, are replaced by the marks a, b respectively, as values of x', by the transformation

$$x' = (b - a)x + a.$$

Therefore K_1 is a doubly transitive group of degree s and order $s(s-1)$.

From this it follows that *the number s of marks in an algebra $A[s]$ is of the form $s = p^n$, where p is a prime and n is a positive integer* (Theorem V in § **40**).

Those transformations (2) in which $\alpha = u_1$ correspond to the additive group of the algebra, since they may be written in the form $x' = x + \beta$. From the corresponding property of doubly transitive groups of degree p^n and order $p^n(p^n - 1)$ it follows that the additive group of the algebra is Abelian of order p^n and type $(1, 1, \cdots, 1)$. The transformations (2) in which $\beta = u_0$ may be written in the form $x' = \alpha x$. They correspond to the multiplicative group of the algebra, the element $x' = \alpha x$ corresponding to multiplication on the left by α. This multiplicative group induces on the nonzero marks of the algebra a regular permutation group of order $p^n - 1$.

Let M denote the permutation group on the marks $u_1, u_2, \cdots, u_\mu$ $(\mu = p^n - 1)$ induced by the multiplicative group of the algebra, and denote by m_i the element of M induced by the transformation $x' = u_i x$ $(u_i \neq u_0)$. Let H denote the permutation group on the marks $u_0, u_1, u_2, \cdots, u_\mu$ induced by the additive group of the algebra, and denote by h_i the element of H induced by the transformation $x' = x + u_i$. Let G be the group generated by H and M. Then h_i replaces $x = u_0$ by $x' = u_i$ and m_i replaces $x = u_1$ by $x' = u_i$; whence it follows that $h_i = m_i^{-1} h_1 m_i$. Then $u_i + u_j = u_k$, where k is such that $h_k = h_i h_j$; while $u_i u_j = u_l$, where l is such that $m_l^{-1} = m_i^{-1} m_j^{-1}$.

From these results it follows that the group G to which the algebra leads by use of (2) may in turn be employed, as in § **102**, to recover the algebra itself. Therefore *every possible algebra $A[s]$ is an algebra $A[p^n]$ defined, as in* § **102**, *by means of a doubly transitive group of prime-power degree p^n and order $p^n(p^n - 1)$, while, conversely, such a doubly transitive group is induced by the totality of transformations of the form* (2) *on the marks of such an algebra.*

The problem of constructing all algebras $A[p^n]$ is therefore equivalent to the problem of constructing all doubly transitive groups of degree p^n and order $p^n(p^n - 1)$. We have already seen (§ **77**) that the latter is equivalent to an important problem concerning certain regular subgroups I_1 of the group I of isomorphisms (with itself) of an Abelian group H of order p^n and type $(1, 1, \cdots, 1)$.

From Theorem III of § **77** and from results in this section it follows that the multiplicative group of an algebra $A[p^n]$ is simply isomorphic with a regular subgroup I_1 of degree $p^n - 1$

contained in the group I of isomorphisms (with itself) of an Abelian group H of order p^n and type $(1, 1, \cdots, 1)$ when I is represented in the usual way as a permutation group on the elements of H exclusive of the identity.

From the connection established between the algebras $A[p^n]$ and the doubly transitive groups of degree p^n and order $p^n(p^n-1)$ it follows that many properties of the latter may at once be translated into corresponding properties of the former.

104. Simple Isomorphism of Algebras $A[p^n]$. Two algebras $A_1[p^n]$ and $A_2[p^n]$ will be called simply isomorphic if each element of A_1 may be made to correspond uniquely to an element of A_2 in such a way that each element of A_2 is the correspondent of a single element of A_1 while, moreover, the sum [product] of any two elements in A_1 corresponds to the sum [product] of the corresponding two elements in A_2. It will be said that two simply isomorphic algebras are identical. Any two algebras having p^n elements each are such that their additive groups are simply isomorphic, since each of these is an Abelian group of order p^n and type $(1, 1, \cdots, 1)$. An obvious necessary condition for the algebras to be simply isomorphic is that their multiplicative groups of order p^n-1 shall be simply isomorphic. We shall show that this condition is also sufficient.

If the multiplicative groups of $A_1[p^n]$ and $A_2[p^n]$ are simply isomorphic, then they lead, as in § **103**, to doubly transitive groups of degree p^n and order $p^n(p^n-1)$ which have simply isomorphic regular subgroups of degree p^n-1, as is seen from the named isomorphism of the multiplicative groups of the algebras. Hence the two doubly transitive groups of degree p^n are conjugate (Theorem III in § **77**). Now, on recovering the algebras from these conjugate groups by the method of § **103**, we exhibit the algebras themselves as simply isomorphic.

Therefore we have the following theorem:

> Two algebras $A_1[p^n]$ and $A_2[p^n]$ are simply isomorphic when and only when their multiplicative groups are simply isomorphic.

EXERCISES

1. Show directly from §§ **100** and **101** (that is, without the use of the properties of doubly transitive groups) that the additive group of an algebra $A[s]$ is Abelian of prime-power order p^n and type $(1, 1, \cdots, 1)$ and that its multiplicative group has the property stated near the end of § **103**. (Dickson, Göttingen *Nachrichten*, 1905.)

2. If the multiplicative group of an algebra $A[p^n]$ is Abelian, show that the algebra is the Galois field $GF[p^n]$. [SUGGESTION. Compare the postulates relating to the two cases.]

3. Show that the only algebra $A[p]$, where p is a prime, is the Galois field $GF[p]$.

4. Show that there is just one algebra $A[2^n]$ when $n = 1, 2, 3, 4, 5$, or 7, and determine all the algebras $A[2^6]$.

5. Determine all the algebras $A[s]$ each of which has fewer than 81 marks.

6. If p is an odd prime the multiplicative group M of an algebra $A[p^n]$ contains just one element of order 2.

7. In the multiplicative group M of an algebra $A[p^n]$ the Sylow subgroups of odd order are cyclic and those of even order are either cyclic or of the sole noncyclic type containing a single element of order 2.

8. Give examples of algebras $A[p^n]$ to show that both types (Ex. 7) of Sylow subgroups of M of even order are actually to be found.

9. Show that an algebra $A[p^n]$ whose multiplicative group M contains a noncyclic Sylow subgroup of order 2^α has in a given Sylow subgroup of order 2^α at least three subgroups of each of the orders $2^2, 2^3, \cdots, 2^{\alpha-1}$.

10. The multiplicative group M of an algebra $A[p^n]$ contains an element of order $p - 1$.

11. Prove Theorem IV of § **79** by aid of the foregoing Ex. 2.

12. Show that the $GF[p^n]$ is the only algebra $A[p^n]$ when $p^n = 2^7$, $2^9, 2^{11}, 2^{13}, 2^{17}, 2^{19}, 3^5, 3^7, 3^9, 3^{13}$.

13. Show that there are just two distinct algebras $A[81]$.

14. For every positive integer L there exist a prime p and a positive integer n such that the number of algebras $A[p^n]$ is greater than L. (See Ex. 14 on page 286.)

15. If an algebra $A[p^n]$ has, in addition to satisfying the postulates of § **101**, the property that $(b+c)a = ba + ca$ when a, b, c are marks of the algebra, then this algebra is the $GF[p^n]$. (Dickson, Göttingen *Nachrichten*, 1905.)

105. Integral Elements of an Algebra $A[p^n]$. Let the elements of an algebra $A[p^n]$ be denoted by the symbols $u_0, u_1, u_2, \cdots, u_\mu$ $(\mu = p^n - 1)$; and let u_0 and u_1 denote the zero element and the unit element respectively. Then an element of the form $u_1 + u_1 + \cdots + u_1$ is called an integral element of the algebra, while all other elements are said to be nonintegral. Since the additive group H of the algebra is Abelian of order p^n and type $(1, 1, \cdots, 1)$, it follows that there are just p integral elements in $A[p^n]$. When there is no danger of confusion we shall denote them by $0, 1, 2, \cdots, p-1$, where 0 and 1 denote the elements u_0 and u_1 respectively and where $k = u_1 + u_1 + \cdots$ to k terms, k being a number of the set $2, 3, \cdots, p-1$. Addition and multiplication of these elements in the algebra consist of addition and multiplication of these numbers followed by a reduction modulo p to a number of the set. For the case of addition this result follows at once from the definition of integral elements. For the case of multiplication we have

$$\begin{aligned} ab &= (u_1 + u_1 + \cdots \text{ to } a \text{ terms})(u_1 + u_1 + \cdots \text{ to } b \text{ terms}) \\ &= (u_1 + u_1 + \cdots \text{ to } a \text{ terms})\, u_1 + (u_1 + u_1 + \cdots \text{ to } a \text{ terms}) u_1 \\ &\qquad + \cdots \text{ to } b \text{ terms} \\ &= u_1 + u_1 + \cdots \text{ to } ab \text{ terms.} \end{aligned}$$

Thence it follows that $ab = c$ if c is the number of the set $0, 1, \cdots, p-1$ to which the number ab is congruent modulo p.

From this result it follows that the integral elements of the algebra form the $GF[p]$. In particular, an algebra $A[p]$ consists entirely of integral elements and is the $GF[p]$.

We have seen (§ **65**) that a $GF[p^n]$ contains a subfield $GF[p^k]$ when and only when k is a factor of n. We have seen that every $A[p^n]$ contains an $A[p]$. If an $A[p^n]$ contains an $A[p^k]$, then the multiplicative group of order $p^k - 1$ of the latter must be a subgroup of the multiplicative group of order $p^n - 1$ of the former. Hence $p^k - 1$ must be a factor of $p^n - 1$, whence it follows that k must be a factor of n.

106. Analytical Representations of Algebras $A[p^n]$. Let us write $n = k\nu$, where k and ν are positive integers (either or both of which may be unity). We denote the p^n elements of an algebra $A[p^n]$ by $(a_1, a_2, \cdots, a_k)$, where the a's run independently over the marks of the $GF[p^\nu]$. In view of the properties of the additive group H of the algebra it is evident that we may take for the rule of addition in the algebra that expressed by the formula

$$(a_1, a_2, \cdots, a_k) + (b_1, b_2, \cdots, b_k) = (a_1 + b_1, \cdots, a_k + b_k).$$

Then $(0, 0, \cdots, 0)$ is the zero element of the algebra. The product of the zero element by any other element (in either order) is taken to be the zero element. It remains to define a suitable rule of multiplication for the nonzero elements of the algebra.

The multiplication of the nonzero elements of the algebra is according to a group M which permutes the nonzero elements of the algebra according to a regular group contained in the group of isomorphisms of H with itself. Moreover, the group of linear transformations in the algebra permutes (§ **103**) the marks of the algebra according to a doubly transitive group of degree p^n and order $p^n(p^n - 1)$. From these facts and § **78** it follows that if

$$(a_1, a_2, \cdots, a_k) \cdot (x_1, x_2, \cdots, x_k) = (x'_1, x'_2, \cdots, x'_k),$$

then we have

$$x'_i = \sum_{s=1}^{\nu} \sum_{j=1}^{k} a_{ijs} x_j^{p^{n-s}}, \qquad (i = 1, 2, \cdots, k)$$

where the coefficients a_{ijs} are marks of the $GF[p^\nu]$ which depend on $(a_1, a_2, \cdots, a_k)$ but are independent of $(x_1, x_2, \cdots x_k)$. Consequently the multiplicative group of the algebra may be defined by means of a transformation group whose elements have the foregoing form. A necessary and sufficient condition on these transformations is that they shall permute the nonzero marks of the algebra according to a regular group.

When $\nu = 1$ this transformation group is linear. When $k = 1$ we have the other extreme case of the foregoing transformations. In this case $\nu = n$, and the marks of the algebra are the symbols (a), where a runs over the marks of the Galois field $GF[p^n]$. The rule of addition in the algebra, namely, $(a)+(b) = (a+b)$, coincides with the rule of addition in the $GF[p^n]$. For the product $(a)(x)$ we have $(f(a, x))$, where $f(a, x)$ has the form

$$f(a, x) = \sum_{s=1}^{n} a_s x^{p^{n-s}}.$$

Therefore we may write

$$(\alpha_i)(x) = (f(\alpha_i, x)) = \left(\sum_{s=1}^{n} a_s^{(i)} x^{p^{n-s}}\right), \qquad (i = 0, 1, 2, \cdots, p^n - 2)$$

where the α's are the nonzero marks of the $GF[p^n]$ and the $a_s^{(i)}$ are marks of the $GF[p^n]$ to be suitably determined. We take (1) to be the unit element in the algebra. Then we have

$$a_1^{(i)} + a_2^{(i)} + \cdots + a_n^{(i)} = \alpha_i.$$

We have also $(0)(x) = (f(0, x)) = (0)$.

It thus appears that every algebra $A[p^n]$ may be represented analytically by means of the $GF[p^n]$. The problem of determining all algebras $A[p^n]$ has not been completely solved. (Compare § **77**.) In the following section we shall employ the method just indicated to set forth the analytical representations of each of a large class of algebras $A[p^n]$.

107. The Algebras $A_{\sigma, l}[p^n]$. In Theorem XXX of § **69** and its first corollary we have a means of defining an important class of algebras $A[p^n]$. We denote their elements by (a), where a runs over the marks of the $GF[p^n]$ and (0) and (1) are to be the zero and unit elements of the algebra respectively. Addition is defined by he relation $(a)+(b) = (a+b)$. For the product $(a_i)(x)$ we take the element $(a_i x^{p^{t_i}})$, where the symbols are those of the theorem cited and its first corollary. Such an algebra will be called an algebra $A_{\sigma, l}[p^n]$, where σ and l are defined in connection with Theorem XXX. They do not include all the algebras $A[p^n]$, as is shown from an examination of the three algebras $A[5^2]$. (Compare §§ **80** and **102**.)

Now (Theorem XXX of § **69**) σ is a factor of

$$1 + p^t + p^{2t} + \cdots + p^{(\sigma-1)t} = \frac{p^n - 1}{p^t - 1},$$

and hence it is a factor of the following multiple of the foregoing number:

$$\frac{p^n-1}{p^t-1}\cdot\frac{p^t-1}{p-1}=\frac{p^n-1}{p-1}.$$

Therefore the order of the group $\{S^\sigma\}$ is a multiple of $p-1$, and hence that group contains a cyclic subgroup of order $p-1$ and hence contains all the transformations of the form $x'=\alpha x$, where α is an integral mark of $GF[p^n]$. Therefore in $A_{\sigma,\iota}[p^n]$ we have $(\alpha)(x)=(\alpha x)$, where (x) is any element of the algebra. But $(a_i)(\alpha)=(a_i\alpha)=(\alpha a_i)$, since $\alpha^p=\alpha$. Therefore an integral element of $A_{\sigma,\iota}[p^n]$ is permutable under multiplication with every element of the algebra.

That this property of permutability of integral elements with all elements is not common to all algebras $A[p^n]$ may be seen from the example of the $A[5^2]$ defined by means of the transformations given near the end of § **80**. Transforming the element $x'=\omega^{12}x^5+\omega^{21}x$ by the element $x'=\omega^{16}x$, we have the element $x'=\omega^{20}x^5+\omega^{21}x$. Since $\omega^{20}+\omega^{21}=\omega^8=3$, we have $(3)(\omega)=(\omega^{25}+\omega^{22})=(\omega+\omega^{22})=(\omega^8)$, whereas $(\omega)(3)$ $=(3\,\omega)=(\omega^{19})$.

Let k be any factor of n, and consider the subset (r) of elements in an algebra $A_{\sigma,\iota}[p^n]$, where r runs over the marks of the subfield $GF[p^k]$ contained in $GF[p^n]$. Under addition these elements (r) obviously form a group of order p^k. Moreover, the product of two of these elements (r) is an element of this set. Therefore the p^k elements named form a subalgebra $A[p^k]$. Therefore an algebra $A_{\sigma,\iota}[p^n]$ contains a subalgebra $A[p^k]$ when and only when k is a factor of n, as one sees by aid of the result at the end of § **105**.

108. Analytic Finite Plane Geometries. The algebras $A[p^n]$ afford number systems suitable for use in constructing finite plane geometries. In fact, this is true of the number systems afforded by more general classes of finite algebras, as has been shown by Veblen and Wedderburn (*Trans. Amer. Math. Soc.*, **8** (1907), 379–388). Accordingly we define such a finite algebra to be one consisting of a finite number n $(n>1)$ of elements satisfying the following conditions:

1. The numbers of the algebra form an Abelian group under addition, the identical element of which is denoted by 0.

2. For any two numbers a and b there is a unique number c such that $ab = c$; and if $a \neq 0$ there are unique numbers d and d' such that $da = b$ and $ad' = b$; also $0a = a0 = 0$ for every a.

3. If a, b, c are numbers of the algebra, then $a(b + c) = ab + ac$.

Neither the associative nor the commutative law of multiplication is assumed, nor is there necessarily in the algebra an identical element with respect to multiplication. And no use is made of the other distributive law $(b + c)a = ba + ca$.

A point is defined as one of any one of the systems of three co-ordinates

$$(1)\ (x, y, \phi), \quad (2)\ (x, \phi, 0), \quad (3)\ (\phi, 0, 0\ ,$$

where ϕ is different from zero and is the same for all points. If n is the number of elements in the algebra, the number of points is $n^2 + n + 1$. A *line* is defined as the set of all points which satisfy an equation of one of the forms

$$(1)\ x\psi + yb + zc = 0, \quad (2)\ y\psi + zc = 0, \quad (3)\ z\psi = 0,$$

where ψ is different from zero and is the same for all the lines. There are then $n^2 + n + 1$ lines, and each line contains $n + 1$ points, as may easily be verified. The number of lines through a given point is $n + 1$.

These points and lines will be said to form a *projective finite plane geometry*, since they will be shown to satisfy the following postulates:

I. If A and B are any two points, there is one and only one line containing both A and B.

II. If a and b are any two lines, there is one and only one point contained in both a and b.

III. Each line contains at least three points.

The third postulate is satisfied, since $n > 1$ and each line contains $n + 1$ points.

In order to show that Postulate II is satisfied, we have to treat several cases, as follows:

(a) Two lines of type (1):

$$x\psi + yb + zc = 0, \quad x\psi + yb' + zc' = 0.$$

The co-ordinates of a point of intersection must satisfy the condition

$$y(b - b') + z(c - c') = 0.$$

We cannot have both $b = b'$ and $c = c'$, for then the two lines would be identical. If $c = c'$ and $b \neq b'$, we have $y = 0$ and $z \neq 0$, so that the point is $(\alpha, 0, \phi)$, where $x = \alpha$ is the unique solution of the equation $x\psi = -\phi c$. Similarly, when $b = b'$ and $c \neq c'$, we have the unique point $(\beta, \phi, 0)$, where $x = \beta$ is the unique solution of the equation $x\psi = -\phi b$. If $b \neq b'$ and $c \neq c'$, we have $z = \phi$, and hence the point is uniquely determined as (α, β, ϕ), where $\beta(b - b') = -\phi(c - c')$ and $\beta\psi = -(\alpha b + \phi c)$.

(b) Lines of types (1) and (2):

$$x\psi + yb + zc = 0, \quad y\psi + zc' = 0.$$

Then $z = \phi$. Then y is uniquely determined from the second equation, and then x from the first.

(c) Lines of types (1) and (3). Then $z = 0$ and $y = \phi$ and x is uniquely determined.

(d) Two lines of type (2). We have the unique point $(\phi, 0, 0)$.

(e) Lines of types (2) and (3). The only solution is $(\phi, 0, 0)$.

From these results it follows that Postulate II is satisfied.

By a similar separation into cases one may readily show that Postulate I is satisfied.

Since the algebras $A[p^n]$ satisfy all the conditions here imposed upon the more general classes of algebras, it follows that the former are suitable for use in constructing analytically certain projective finite plane geometries. When $A[p^n]$ is the $GF[p^n]$, then the geometry is a $PG(2, p^n)$ in accordance with the notation of Chapter XI. When $A[p^n]$ is some other algebra of the type denoted by this symbol in the present chapter, the geometry may be different from $PG(2, p^n)$. In each of these geometries we may take $\phi = \psi = 1$. These remarks will be justified by considering a special case.

The case when $p^n = 3^2$ affords the simplest case of an algebra $A[p^n]$ which is not a $GF[p^n]$ — simplest in the sense that the number of elements is a minimum. In this case we have 91 points in the geometry; and they fall into lines in such a way that there are just 10 points on each line. We construct the named geometry.

The polynomial x^2+1 is irreducible modulo 3. We may therefore use it to construct the $GF[3^2]$. If in this $GF[3^2]$ we denote a solution of the equation $x^2+1=0$ by j, then the marks of the field may be denoted by $x+yj$, where x and y are integers to be reduced modulo 3 to numbers of the set 0, 1, 2. We take these same symbols $x+yj$ to denote the marks of the algebra $A[3^2]$. Since it is to be the one which is not identical with $GF[3^2]$, we have for the product $(x_1+y_1j)(x_2+y_2j)$ the mark obtained by multiplying the marks of the field in case x_1+y_1j is a square; but when x_1+y_1j is not a square the corresponding product mark in the algebra is obtained by multiplying x_1+y_1j by the cube of x_2+y_2j in the $GF[3^2]$. Thus we may construct the following multiplication table of the algebra (excluding the zero and the unit mark):

	2	j	$2j$	$1+j$	$1+2j$	$2+j$	$2+2j$
2	1	$2j$	j	$2+2j$	$2+j$	$1+2j$	$1+j$
j	$2j$	2	1	$2+j$	$1+j$	$2+2j$	$1+2j$
$2j$	j	1	2	$1+2j$	$2+2j$	$1+j$	$2+j$
$1+j$	$2+2j$	$1+2j$	$2+j$	2	$2j$	j	1
$1+2j$	$2+j$	$2+2j$	$1+j$	j	2	1	$2j$
$2+j$	$1+2j$	$1+j$	$2+2j$	$2j$	1	2	j
$2+2j$	$1+j$	$2+j$	$1+2j$	1	j	$2j$	2

Now in the $PG(2, 3^2)$ the Desargues theorem is valid (§ **87**). It may be shown readily (see Ex. 1 on page 412) that in the geometry indicated in the foregoing remarks the Desargues theorem is not valid. Hence this new geometry is different from the $PG(2, 3^2)$.

Instead of exhibiting this new geometry explicitly we shall employ the same algebra to construct a non-Desarguesian geometry in another way, the new geometry so constructed being capable of being explicitly exhibited in compact form.

Since the number system is associative and verifies the distributive law $a(b+c)=ab+ac$, the point (x, y, z) may also be represented by (kx, ky, kz), where $k \neq 0$. Then a linear transformation changes points into points; and, if the coefficients are integral, two transformations may be combined in the usual way.

The following transformation is of order 13:

$$A: \qquad x' = 2y, \quad y' = 2x + 2y + 2z, \quad z' = x + y.$$

Let $A_0, B_0, \cdots, G_0$ denote the points $(2, 0, 1)$, $(2+2j, j, 1)$, $(2+j, 2j, 1)$, $(1+2j, 1+j, 1)$, $(j, 2+2j, 1)$, $(1+j, 1+2j, 1)$, $(2j, 2+j, 1)$, respectively; and let $A_k, B_k, \cdots, G_k$ $(k=0, 1, \cdots, 12)$ denote the points into which $A_0, B_0, \cdots, G_0$ are changed by the kth power of A. Then seven of the lines of our geometry are:

$$\begin{aligned}
x+y+z=0&: A_0\ A_1\ A_3\ A_9\ B_0\ C_0\ D_0\ E_0\ F_0\ G_0,\\
x+yj+z=0&: A_0\ B_1\ B_8\ D_3\ D_{11}\ E_2\ E_5\ E_6\ G_7\ G_9,\\
x+y(2j)+z=0&: A_0\ C_1\ C_8\ E_7\ E_9\ F_3\ F_{11}\ G_2\ G_5\ G_6,\\
x+y(1+j)+z=0&: A_0\ B_7\ B_9\ D_1\ D_8\ F_2\ F_5\ F_6\ G_3\ G_{11},\\
x+y(2+2j)+z=0&: A_0\ B_2\ B_5\ B_6\ C_3\ C_{11}\ E_1\ E_8\ F_7\ F_9,\\
x+y(1+2j)+z=0&: A_0\ C_7\ C_9\ D_2\ D_5\ D_6\ E_3\ E_{11}\ F_1\ F_8,\\
x+y(2+j)+z=0&: A_0\ B_3\ B_{11}\ C_2\ C_5\ C_6\ D_7\ D_9\ G_1\ G_8.
\end{aligned}$$

Transforming these seven sets of 10 each by the powers of A, we obtain altogether ninety-one sets of 10 each formed from the 91 points of the geometry. These ninety-one sets constitute the lines of a geometry, as the reader may verify.

It is not difficult to show that this geometry is non-Desarguesian, the method being to exhibit a pair of triangles which are perspective from a point while the intersections of corresponding sides do not lie on a line (see Ex. 2 on page 412).

It is not difficult to construct the largest possible permutation group on its points which has the property of transforming this geometry into itself (Ex. 3 on page 412). It is a problem of interest to determine the collineation group of all geometries derived from particular classes of algebras $A[p^n]$.

The problem seems not to have been solved.

EXERCISES

1. Establish the non-Desarguesian character of the first geometry based on the noncommutative $A[3^2]$ in § **108**.

2. Establish the non-Desarguesian character of the geometry explicitly exhibited in the latter part of § **108**.

3. Determine the collineation group of the geometry explicitly exhibited in the latter part of § **108**.

4. If a and b are elements of the algebra whose multiplication table is given in § **108**, show that $ab = \pm ba$.

5. Prove analytically that the 91 sets of 10 each described in the latter part of § **108** form a projective geometry.

6. Consider all numbers of the form $ae_1 + be_2$ where a and b are integers reduced modulo 2 and where e_1 and e_2 are independent units. Define addition by the formula

$$(ae_1 + be_2) + (ce_1 + de_2) = (a + c)e_1 + (b + d)e_2.$$

Writing e_3 for $e_1 + e_2$, define multiplication by means of either of the following tables:

(1)

	e_1	e_2	e_3
e_1	e_3	e_2	e_1
e_2	e_2	e_1	e_3
e_3	e_1	e_3	e_2

(2)

	e_1	e_2	e_3
e_1	e_1	e_2	e_3
e_2	e_3	e_1	e_2
e_3	e_2	e_3	e_1

Show that multiplication is commutative in case (1). In both systems show that the two-sided distributive law holds.

7. By the method of § **108** construct plane geometries based on the number systems of Ex. 6. Show in each case that the geometry is equivalent to $PG(2, 2^2)$.

8. Show that there is only one projective plane geometry with just 5 points on a line.

9. Show that there is one and just one projective plane geometry with s points on a line when $s = 3, 4, 5, 6$, namely, the corresponding $PG(2, p^n)$ in each case (see Ex. 8).

10. Show that there is no projective plane geometry having just seven points on a line.

11. Determine all the projective plane geometries having just 8 points on a line.

12. Form an algebra whose marks are 0, 1, 2, 3, 4, and let addition be identical with ordinary addition modulo 5. Let $a0 = 0a = 0$ for every a. Otherwise define multiplication by the table

	1	2	3	4
1	1	2	3	4
2	4	3	2	1
3	3	1	4	2
4	2	4	1	3

Use this number system to form a geometry by the method of § **108**, taking $\phi = \psi = 1$. Show that the resulting geometry is $PG(2, 5)$.

MISCELLANEOUS EXERCISES

1. Determine all the algebras $A[p^2]$ by the method employed by Dickson in Göttingen *Nachrichten*, 1905.

2. By aid of Ex. 1 determine all the doubly transitive groups of degree p^2 and order $p^2(p^2 - 1)$.

3. Determine all the algebras $A[p^n]$ each of which has the property that its multiplicative group contains a cyclic subgroup of index 2.

4. Determine all the doubly transitive groups of degree p^n and order $p^n(p^n - 1)$ in each of which the regular subgroup of order $p^n - 1$ contains a cyclic subgroup of index 2.

5. Determine all the triply transitive groups of degree $p^n + 1$ and order $(p^n + 1)p^n(p^n - 1)$ in each of which the regular subgroup of order $p^n - 1$ contains a cyclic subgroup of index 2.

6. Consider the geometry built by the method of § **108** from the $A[p^2]$ defined in § **107** by aid of Theorem XXX of § **69** and its first corollary. Show how to represent the points of this geometry by triples of marks in the $GF[p^2]$, with suitable definition of equivalence of symbols, in such way that the lines of the geometry shall be defined by means of suitable *nonlinear* equations in the $GF[p^2]$. [SUGGESTION. For the solution of this problem employ the function $f(a, x)$ of § **106** associated with the definition of multiplication.]

7. Extend the results of Ex. 6 to the case of algebras $A[p^{2n}]$.

8. For the case $p^n = 3^2$ compare the geometry defined in Ex. 6 with those on the same number of points discussed in § **108**.

9. Let i and j be two independent units such that $i^2 = j$, $ij = ji = b + \beta i$, $j^2 = -\beta^2 - 8bi - 2\beta j$, where b and β are given integers such that the equation $x^3 - \beta x - b = 0$ is irreducible for a given odd prime modulus p. Define an algebra subject to the postulates of § **108** and having for its marks all numbers of the form $a + di + ej$, where a, d, e are marks of the $GF[p^n]$. Extend this to the case when b and β are marks of the $GF[p^n]$.

10. Employ the algebra defined in Ex. 9 in the construction of a finite plane projective geometry after the manner of § **108,** simplifying the theory by aid of the fact that the algebra is commutative. Determine whether a Desargues theorem is valid in this geometry.

11. Discuss the special case of the geometry in Ex. 10 when $p^n = 3$.

12. Determine all finite plane projective geometries having not more than nine points on a line (see Exs. 9, 10, 11 on page 412), and thus determine the smallest possible number of points on a line in a finite plane projective geometry in which the Desargues theorem is not valid.

CHAPTER XIV

Tactical Configurations

109. Immediate Examples. In § 91 we have defined tactical configurations $\Delta_{l,m}^{\lambda,\mu}$ of rank two and have given several classes of examples based on the $PG(k, p^n)$. In this section we give other immediate examples.

In the configurations which we shall usually consider there is a certain symmetry in the role played by the l elements and the m sets. We may consider the m sets themselves as elements. The μ sets which contain a given symbol may be thought of as a combination of sets which give rise to that symbol, *provided* that there is no additional symbol common to these μ sets. From this point of view the configuration becomes a new configuration having the symbol $\Delta_{m,l}^{\mu,\lambda}$. The two configurations $\Delta_{l,m}^{\lambda,\mu}$ and $\Delta_{m,l}^{\mu,\lambda}$ are therefore closely related when they satisfy the restrictive condition just named. They are called *associated* configurations.

With each of the m sets of λ elements we may associate the complementary set of $l-\lambda$ elements, thus forming m sets each of which contains $l-\lambda$ elements; in these sets each element occurs $m-\mu$ times. Thus we have a configuration $\Delta_{l,m}^{l-\lambda,m-\mu}$ which is said to be *complementary* to the configuration $\Delta_{l,m}^{\lambda,\mu}$.

From the tactical configurations afforded by the $PG(k, p^n)$ it is apparent that the configurations $\Delta_{l,m}^{\lambda,\mu}$ are of importance in the theory of groups. They have also been found useful in constructing poristic forms in connection with the study of geometrical configurations similar to and including those associated with the Poncelet polygons which arise in the theory of conic sections. The same tactical problem also appears in the theory of certain irrational invariants. Its importance is therefore clear.

We now proceed to the examples promised.

From a cycle $a_1a_2 \cdots a_n$ of n elements we may select cyclically the set $a_1a_2 \cdots a_k$, $a_2a_3 \cdots a_{k+1}, \cdots, a_ka_1a_2 \cdots a_{k-1}$, thus obtaining a configuration with the symbol $\Delta_{n,n}^{k,k}$.

Let us take two sets of n things each, say $a_1, a_2, \cdots, a_n$ and $\alpha_1, \alpha_2, \cdots, \alpha_n$. Each element in one set may be paired with each element in the other set, giving rise to n^2 pairs of the $2n$ elements. Thus we have a $\Delta_{2n,n^2}^{2,n}$. Again, each element in one of the two sets may be paired with every other element in the same set: thus we have a $\Delta_{2n,n(n-1)}^{2,n-1}$. Again, we may make the pairs from each one of the sets run in cyclical order, thus obtaining a configuration with the symbol $\Delta_{2n,2n}^{2,2}$.

The three configurations of the foregoing paragraph are capable of a ready generalization. Generalizing the first of them we have a configuration with the symbol

$$\Delta_{ln,n^l}^{l,n^{l-1}}$$

obtained from l sets of n elements each by forming all the possible combinations of l elements each gotten by taking one element from each of the l sets. One may similarly generalize the other two configurations in the preceding paragraph. Moreover, various other similar configurations are readily formed.

Now let us take l sets of n things each, l being greater than 2. Let these l sets be arranged in cyclical order. Form pairs by taking each element in one set with each element in the set which follows it in cyclical order. Thus we form ln^2 pairs from the ln elements, using each element $2n$ times. This gives rise to a configuration with the symbol

$$\Delta_{ln,ln^2}^{2,2n}. \qquad (l > 2)$$

This configuration is capable of generalization in the following manner. Let us consider l sets of n things each, where $l > \lambda$, these l sets being arranged in cyclical order; and let us form combinations of λ elements each, such combinations being formed from λ consecutive sets from the l sets in their fixed cyclical order by taking one element from each of the λ sets in all possible ways. Thus we have ln elements formed into sets of λ elements each, the number of sets being ln^λ and each element appearing in $\lambda n^{\lambda-1}$ sets. This gives rise to a configuration with the symbol

$$\Delta_{ln,\, ln^\lambda}^{\lambda,\, \lambda n^{\lambda-1}}. \qquad (l > \lambda)$$

For the case in which $l = n + 1$ and $\lambda = n$, we have

$$\Delta_{n(n+1),\, n^n(n+1)}^{n,\, n^n}.$$

For $n = 2$ this becomes $\Delta_{6,\,12}^{2,\,4}$; and this configuration consists of all the pairs of the six elements involved except the three pairs from which the configuration was formed.

Other configurations may also be readily formed by various modifications of the methods employed in this section.

110. Configurations Associated with Coble's Box Porism. In the 3-space $PG(3, p^n)$ there are $p^n + 1$ points on a line l and $p^n + 1$ planes on the same line. Let us take p^n of these planes and a point P not on any of these p^n planes (and hence on the remaining plane through l). Let Q be any point on l. In addition to the p^n planes already retained, keep also the p^{2n} planes which are not on the line PQ. We thus retain $p^{2n} + p^n$ planes. Retain the p^{3n} points which are not on the plane through P and l; these points form an $EG(3, p^n)$. The points retained on a given one of the p^n planes first selected and the lines in which that plane is cut by the retained planes through P form a configuration

$$\Delta_{p^{2n},\, p^{2n}}^{p^n,\, p^n}.$$

Hence the p^{3n} retained points appear in sets of p^n each on the $p^{2n} + p^n$ retained planes; moreover each of the retained points appears on one of the retained planes through l and on just p^n of the retained planes on P. We are thus led to a configuration having the symbol

$$\Delta_{p^{3n},\, p^{2n}+p^n}^{p^{2n},\, p^n+1}.$$

When $p^n = 2$ we have here a configuration with the symbol $\Delta_{8,\,6}^{4,\,3}$. It is based on the $PG(3, 2)$. It may be shown that this leads to a configuration equivalent to that defined by the following scheme:

DEFG, LMNO, DELM, FGNO, DGLO, EFMN.

If these six quadruples in the order written are numbered 1, 2, $\cdots$, 6, then the eight letters contained in them are determined by triples of digits according to the following correspondence:

135	136	145	146	235	236	245	246
D	*E*	*G*	*F*	*L*	*M*	*O*	*N*

These eight triples of six elements form the configuration $\Delta_{6,8}^{3,4}$ belonging to the box porism of Coble (*Amer. Journ. Math.* **43** (1921),15). The latter is therefore exhibited as belonging to an infinite class of configurations; the class was suggested by this example.

Another infinite class of configurations having the same symbols as the foregoing may be constructed in the following manner. From $PG(3, p^n)$ form the corresponding $EG(3, p^n)$ by omitting a plane with its points. Let P be a point on this plane; then there are $p^{2n} + p^n$ additional planes on P; these are to be retained. The p^{3n} points of the $EG(3, p^n)$ fall on these planes, p^{2n} points on each plane thus considered. Moreover a given one of these points is on each of the planes containing the line joining this point to P, and hence it is on $p^n + 1$ of the retained planes. Thus we are led to another configuration with the symbol

$$\Delta_{p^{3n},\, p^{2n}+p^n}^{p^{2n},\, p^n+1}.$$

111. Certain Additional Configurations. From the $PG(k, p^n)$ $(k > 2)$ let us omit a line of points and also all the lines on each of these points. The number of points remaining is l, where

$$l = p^{2n} + p^{3n} + \cdots + p^{kn}.$$

Now the total number of lines on a point is $1 + p^n + \cdots + p^{(k-1)n}$. Hence the number of omitted lines is

$$(1 + p^n)(p^n + p^{2n} + \cdots + p^{(k-1)n}) + 1.$$

Hence the number m of retained lines is

$$m = \frac{(p^{(k+1)n} - 1)(p^{kn} - 1)}{(p^{2n} - 1)(p^n - 1)} - (1 + p^n)(p^n + p^{2n} + \cdots + p^{(k-1)n}) - 1.$$

The retained points fall λ at a time on the retained lines, where

$$\lambda = 1 + p^n,$$

each point appearing on μ of the lines, where

$$\mu = p^{2n} + p^{3n} + \cdots + p^{(k-1)n}.$$

This gives rise to a $\Delta_{l,m}^{\lambda,\mu}$ where l, m, λ, μ have the values given.

To form another configuration let us omit from $PG(3, p^n)$ the points on two nonintersecting lines and all the lines through these points. This leaves

$$p^n(p^{2n} - 1)(p^n - 1)$$

lines of the $PG(3, p^n)$. Each of these contains $p^n + 1$ points of the $PG(3, p^n)$; and each of these retained points is on $p^{2n} - p^n$ retained lines. Hence the retained points and lines yield a configuration $\Delta_{l,m}^{\lambda,\mu}$ where

$$l = (p^n + 1)(p^{2n} - 1), \quad m = p^n(p^n - 1)(p^{2n} - 1),$$
$$\lambda = p^n + 1, \quad \mu = p^n(p^n - 1).$$

Again, from the $(2k + 1)$-dimensional space $PG(2k + 1, p^n)$ let us omit the points of a k-dimensional subspace S_k and also all the $(2k)$-spaces containing S_k. We thus retain l points and l $(2k)$-spaces, where

$$l = p^{(2k+1)n} + p^{2kn} + \cdots + p^{(k+1)n}.$$

Each of the retained $(2k)$-spaces has λ retained points, where

$$\lambda = p^{2kn} + p^{(2k-1)n} + \cdots + p^{kn},$$

and each of the retained points lies on λ of the retained $(2k)$-spaces. Thus we are led to a configuration $\Delta_{l,l}^{\lambda,\lambda}$ where λ and l have the values just given.

112. Subgeometries and the Complementary Sets. Let ν be any proper factor of n. Then in the $PG(k, p^n)$ there is included (§ **86**) the geometry $PG(k, p^\nu)$, namely, those points of $PG(k, p^n)$

whose co-ordinates may be taken as marks of the $GF[p^\nu]$ included in the $GF[p^n]$. We shall denote by $C(k, p^n, p^\nu)$ the complementary set of points, namely, the points of $PG(k, p^n)$ which are not contained in the included $PG(k, p^\nu)$. The number l of points in $C(k, p^n, p^\nu)$ is

$$l = (p^{kn} - p^{k\nu}) + (p^{(k-1)n} - p^{(k-1)\nu}) + \cdots + (p^n - p^\nu).$$

If a line in $PG(k, p^n)$ contains two points of $PG(k, p^\nu)$, it contains all the points of a line in $PG(k, p^\nu)$. Hence the lines of $PG(k, p^n)$ may be separated into three classes: the first class consists of those lines each of which contains a whole line of the $PG(k, p^\nu)$; the second class consists of those lines each of which contains just one point of the $PG(k, p^\nu)$; the third class consists of those lines containing no point of the $PG(k, p^\nu)$. The numbers of lines in these three classes are readily shown to be, respectively,

$$\frac{(p^{(k+1)\nu} - 1)(p^{k\nu} - 1)}{(p^{2\nu} - 1)(p^\nu - 1)}, \quad \left(\frac{p^{kn} - 1}{p^n - 1} - \frac{p^{k\nu} - 1}{p^\nu - 1}\right) \frac{p^{(k+1)\nu} - 1}{p^\nu - 1},$$

$$\frac{(p^{(k+1)n} - 1)(p^{kn} - 1)}{(p^{2n} - 1)(p^n - 1)} - \frac{p^{(k+1)\nu} - 1}{p^\nu - 1}\left(\frac{p^{kn} - 1}{p^n - 1} - \frac{p^\nu(p^{k\nu} - 1)}{p^{2\nu} - 1}\right).$$

It is not difficult to show that the third class is the null class when and only when $k = 2$ and $n = 2\nu$.

With these classes we readily construct tactical configurations as follows:

Let us consider the second class of lines in the case when $k = 2$ and $n = 2\nu$. Each of the $p^{2\nu} + p^\nu + 1$ lines of the $PG(2, p^\nu)$, when extended to a line of $PG(2, p^{2\nu})$, contains just $p^{2\nu} - p^\nu$ points of $C(2, p^{2\nu}, p^\nu)$; and no point P of $C(2, p^{2\nu}, p^\nu)$ occurs on two such extended lines. Hence each of the $(p^{2\nu} - p^\nu) \cdot (p^{2\nu} + p^\nu + 1)$ points of $C(2, p^{2\nu}, p^\nu)$ occurs on one and just one line which contains a line of $PG(2, p^\nu)$. Hence each point P of $C(2, p^{2\nu}, p^\nu)$ lies on just $p^{2\nu}$ lines of the second class, this being the number of lines joining P to points of $PG(2, p^\nu)$ other than the line of $PG(2, p^\nu)$ on the extension of which P lies. Moreover, each line of the second class contains just $p^{2\nu}$ points of $C(2, p^{2\nu}, p^\nu)$. Hence the $(p^{2\nu} - p^\nu)(p^{2\nu} + p^\nu + 1)$ points of

$C(2, p^{2\nu}, p^\nu)$ lie $p^{2\nu}$ at a time on the $(p^{2\nu} - p^\nu)(p^{2\nu} + p^\nu + 1)$ lines of the second class, and each point is on just $p^{2\nu}$ of these lines. This gives rise to a tactical configuration $\Delta_{l, m}^{\lambda, \mu}$ where

$$\lambda = \mu = p^{2\nu}, \quad l = m = (p^{2\nu} - p^\nu)(p^{2\nu} + p^\nu + 1).$$

In the case when $p^\nu = 2$ this gives a $\Delta_{14, 14}^{4, 4}$.

From the general configuration of the preceding paragraph a certain reduced configuration is readily obtained. Let us omit from $PG(2, p^\nu)$ one of its lines and at the same time omit from $PG(2, p^{2\nu})$ the line L, which has $p^\nu + 1$ points in common with the omitted line of $PG(2, p^\nu)$. This line contains $p^{2\nu} - p^\nu$ points of $C(2, p^{2\nu}, p^\nu)$. The remaining points of $C(2, p^{2\nu}, p^\nu)$ are $(p^{2\nu} - p^\nu)(p^{2\nu} + p^\nu)$ in number. These points fall $p^{2\nu}$ at a time on the lines of the second class other than the lines containing each a point of L which is in the set $C(2, p^{2\nu}, p^\nu)$. These latter lines are $(p^{2\nu} - p^\nu)p^{2\nu}$ in number, since each of the excluded $p^{2\nu} - p^\nu$ points is on just $p^{2\nu}$ lines of the second class and no two of them are on the same line of the second class. Excluding these lines and retaining the others of the second class, we have $p^\nu(p^{2\nu} - 1)$ retained lines. Each of the retained points is on just p^ν of the retained lines. Hence we have a tactical configuration $\Delta_{l, m}^{\lambda, \mu}$ where

$$l = p^{2\nu}(p^{2\nu} - 1), \quad \lambda = p^{2\nu}, \quad \mu = p^\nu, \quad m = p^\nu(p^{2\nu} - 1).$$

For $p^\nu = 2$ this is a $\Delta_{12, 6}^{4, 2}$. The associated configuration $\Delta_{6, 12}^{2, 4}$ has an obvious generalization to a configuration

$$\Delta_{2n, 2n(n-1)}^{2, 2(n-1)}$$

consisting of all the pairs of $2n$ symbols $\alpha_1, \alpha_2, \cdots, \alpha_{2n}$ except the pairs α_1, α_2; α_3, α_4; $\cdots$; $\alpha_{2n-1}, \alpha_{2n}$, each α occurring in $2(n-1)$ pairs. And this in turn is capable of an immediate generalization to the case of kn things taken k at a time except for the omission of n sets of k each, the latter sets involving each symbol once and just once.

Let us consider the second class of lines in the case when $k = 2$ and $n = \rho\nu$ $(\rho > 2)$. The number l of points in $C(2, p^{\rho\nu}, p^\nu)$

and the number m of lines in the second class and the number N of lines in the third class are now, respectively,

$$l = (p^{\rho\nu} - p^{\nu})(p^{\rho\nu} + p^{\nu} + 1),$$
$$m = (p^{\rho\nu} - p^{\nu})(p^{2\nu} + p^{\nu} + 1),$$
$$N = (p^{\rho\nu} - p^{\nu})(p^{\rho\nu} - p^{2\nu}).$$

Moreover, each line of the second class contains just $p^{\rho\nu}$ points of $C(2, p^{\rho\nu}, p^{\nu})$. We may separate the points of $C(2, p^{\rho\nu}, p^{\nu})$ into two subclasses $C_1(2, p^{\rho\nu}, p^{\nu})$ and $C_2(2, p^{\rho\nu}, p^{\nu})$, those of the subclass C_1 being each on a line of $PG(2, p^{\rho\nu})$ which contains $p^{\nu} + 1$ points of the $PG(2, p^{\nu})$, while the subclass C_2 consists of the remaining points of $C(2, p^{\rho\nu}, p^{\nu})$. Now these subclasses C_1 and C_2 contain l_1 and l_2 points respectively, where

$$l_1 = (p^{\rho\nu} - p^{\nu})(p^{2\nu} + p^{\nu} + 1), \quad l_2 = (p^{\rho\nu} - p^{\nu})(p^{\rho\nu} - p^{2\nu}),$$

a result which may be proved as follows. The $PG(2, p^{\nu})$ contains $p^{2\nu} + p^{\nu} + 1$ lines, and each of these lines has $p^{\rho\nu} - p^{\nu}$ points of C_1, while no point of C_1 is on two of these lines, since two such lines have a point of the $PG(2, p^{\nu})$ in common. Hence l_1 has the value given; then l_2 is obtained from the formula $l_2 = l - l_1$.

Each point of C_1 is on just $p^{2\nu}$ lines of the second class, since it is on just one line of the first class and this line contains just $p^{\nu} + 1$ of the $p^{2\nu} + p^{\nu} + 1$ points of the $PG(2, p^{\nu})$; and each point of C_2 is on just $p^{2\nu} + p^{\nu} + 1$ lines of the second class. But just $p^{\rho\nu} + 1$ lines of $PG(2, p^{\rho\nu})$ pass through any given point of this geometry. Hence each point of C_1 is on just $p^{\rho\nu} - p^{2\nu}$ lines of the third class, and each point of C_2 is on just $p^{\rho\nu} - p^{2\nu} - p^{\nu}$ lines of the third class. Every line of the second class contains just as many points of C_1 as there are lines in $PG(2, p^{\nu})$ not containing the point which this line of the second class has in common with the $PG(2, p^{\nu})$, and this number is $p^{2\nu}$; therefore every line of the second class contains just $p^{\rho\nu} - p^{2\nu}$ points of C_2.

Now we have seen that the l_1 points of C_1 fall, in sets of $p^{2\nu}$ each, on the m lines of the second class, each point of C_1

belonging to just $p^{2\nu}$ lines of the second class. Thus we have a $\Delta_{l,m}^{\lambda,\mu}$, with

$$l = m = (p^{\rho\nu} - p^{\nu})(p^{2\nu} + p^{\nu} + 1), \quad \lambda = \mu = p^{2\nu}.$$

For $\rho = 3$ and $p^{\nu} = 2$ we have thus a $\Delta_{42,42}^{4,4}$.

Again, the l_2 points of C_2 fall, in sets of $p^{\rho\nu} - p^{2\nu}$ each, on the m lines of the second class, each point of C_2 belonging to just $p^{2\nu} + p^{\nu} + 1$ lines of the second class. Thus we have a $\Delta_{l,m}^{\lambda,\mu}$ where

$$\lambda = p^{\rho\nu} - p^{2\nu}, \quad \mu = p^{2\nu} + p^{\nu} + 1, \quad l = l_2,$$

and m and l_2 have the values already given.

Each line of the third class contains just $p^{2\nu} + p^{\nu} + 1$ points of C_1, since it contains no point of $PG(2, p^{\nu})$ and has one and just one point in common with each of the $p^{2\nu} + p^{\nu} + 1$ lines each of which contains $p^{\nu} + 1$ points of the $PG(2, p^{\nu})$. Hence each line of the third class contains also $p^{\rho\nu} - p^{2\nu} - p^{\nu}$ points of C_2.

From the foregoing results we see that the l_1 points of C_1 fall, in sets of $p^{2\nu} + p^{\nu} + 1$ each, on the N lines of the third class. This defines a tactical configuration of rank two.

Similarly, we see that the l_2 points of C_2 fall, in sets of $p^{\rho\nu} - p^{2\nu} - p^{\nu}$ each, on the N lines of the third class, each point of C_2 belonging to just $p^{\rho\nu} - p^{2\nu} - p^{\nu}$ lines of the third class. Thus we have a tactical configuration $\Delta_{l,l}^{\lambda,\lambda}$ where

$$\lambda = p^{\rho\nu} - p^{2\nu} - p^{\nu}, \quad l = (p^{\rho\nu} - p^{\nu})(p^{\rho\nu} - p^{2\nu}).$$

It is evident that other configurations may readily be constructed by means of finite geometries of more than two dimensions and the subgeometries contained within them.

EXERCISES

1. Construct the configuration $\Delta_{6,8}^{4,3}$ of the first paragraph of § **110** and determine the group characterized by it.

2. Construct the configuration $\Delta_{6,8}^{4,3}$ of the last paragraph of § **110** and determine the group characterized by it.

3. By means of all but one of the planes on a point P of $PG(3, p^n)$ and the intersecting lines of these planes, the lines being taken as elements and the planes as sets of elements, construct a configuration having the symbol $\Delta_{l,\,m}^{\lambda,\,\mu}$ where

$$l = p^{2n}, \quad m = p^{2n} + p^n, \quad \lambda = p^n, \quad \mu = p^n + 1.$$

4. Construct the configuration $\Delta_{12,\,16}^{3,\,4}$ of the first paragraph of § **111** (for $k = 3$ and $p^n = 2$) and determine the group characterized by it.

5. Construct the configuration $\Delta_{9,\,6}^{3,\,2}$ of the second paragraph of § **111** (for $p^n = 2$) and determine the group characterized by it.

6. Construct the configuration $\Delta_{12,\,12}^{6,\,6}$ of the last paragraph of § **111** (for $k = 1$ and $p^n = 2$) and determine the group characterized by it.

7. Construct from the $PG(2, 2^2)$ the configuration $\Delta_{14,\,14}^{4,\,4}$ mentioned in § **112** and determine the group characterized by it.

8. Construct from the $PG(2, 2^2)$ the configuration $\Delta_{12,\,6}^{4,\,2}$ of § **112** and determine the group characterized by it.

9. Show that the system consisting of the five sets of three pairs each, $\infty 0$, 14, 23; $\infty 1$, 20, 34; $\infty 2$, 31, 40; $\infty 3$, 42, 01; $\infty 4$, 03, 12, is left invariant by each element of the group

$$\{(01234),\ (1243),\ (\infty 0)(14)\}$$

and by no other permutations on its symbols.

10. Show that the system consisting of the seven sets of four pairs each,

$$\infty 0,\ 16,\ 25,\ 43;\ \infty 1,\ 20,\ 36,\ 54;\ \infty 2,\ 31,\ 40,\ 65;\ \infty 3,\ 42,\ 51,\ 06;$$
$$\infty 4,\ 53,\ 62,\ 10;\ \infty 5,\ 64,\ 03,\ 21;\ \infty 6,\ 05,\ 14,\ 32,$$

is left invariant by each element of a doubly transitive group of degree 7 and order $7 \cdot 6$ and by no other permutation on its symbols.

11. Show that the system consisting of the seven sets of four pairs each,

$$\infty 0,\ 13,\ 45,\ 26;\ \infty 1,\ 24,\ 56,\ 30;\ \infty 2,\ 35,\ 60,\ 41;\ \infty 3,\ 46,\ 01,\ 52;$$
$$\infty 4,\ 50,\ 12,\ 63;\ \infty 5,\ 61,\ 23,\ 04;\ \infty 6,\ 02,\ 34,\ 15,$$

is invariant under the triply transitive group of degree 8 and order $8 \cdot 7 \cdot 6 \cdot 4$ on its symbols and under no other permutations on these symbols.

12. Solve the like problem for the four sets of three triples each,

$$123,\ 456,\ 789;\ 147,\ 258,\ 369;\ 159,\ 267,\ 348;\ 186,\ 294,\ 375.$$

Discuss the isomorphism of the resulting group with the symmetric group of degree 4.

13. Noting the way in which Ex. 12 depends on the regular group generated by (123)(456)(789) and (147)(258)(369), construct and solve a similar problem depending on the regular noncyclic permutation group of order 25.

14. Investigate other groups by methods suggested by the results in the foregoing Exs. 9 to 13 inclusive.

113. Triple Systems and Triple Groups.* If n elements $x_1, x_2, \cdots, x_n$ can be arranged in triples so that each pair $x_\alpha x_\beta$ occurs in one and in just one triple, then the arrangement so made is called a *triple system*. The largest permutation group on $x_1, x_2, \cdots, x_n$ each element of which transforms the triple system into itself is said to be a *triple group* and to *belong* to the triple system.

It is easy to determine a necessary condition on the form of n in order that a triple system of n elements may exist. Since there are $\frac{1}{2}n(n-1)$ pairs of n things and since a given triple contains three of these pairs, it follows that the number of triples in a triple system on n elements is $\frac{1}{6}n(n-1)$, so that this last number must be an integer. Moreover, a given letter must occur with each of the others taken in pairs; whence n must be odd. These two conditions require that n shall have one of the forms $6m+1$ and $6m+3$. It has been shown (see Netto's *Lehrbuch*, loc. cit.) that a triple system exists for each n of either one of the given forms, and indeed that at least two inequivalent triple systems exist for each such n greater than 9, while there is just one when $n=3$ or 7 or 9. [Two triple systems are said to be equivalent if there exists a permutation which transforms one of them into the other.] The number of distinct triple systems on a given number of elements has not yet been determined in general.

The finite geometry $PG(k, 2)$ affords an example of a triple system on $2^{k+1}-1$ elements, the lines of the geometry con-

* See Netto, *Math. Annalen* **42** (1893), 143–152. See also Netto, *Lehrbuch der Combinatorik*, second edition, pp. 202–227, 321–334, for a much fuller account of this subject, with numerous references to the literature.

stituting the triples of the system. The corresponding triple group is then the collineation group in the finite geometry. When $k > 1$ the group is doubly transitive and contains cyclic permutations of all its elements. [It is obvious that a triple group of degree greater than 3 cannot be triply transitive.]

The finite geometry $EG(k, 3)$ affords an example of a triple system on 3^k elements, the lines of the geometry constituting the triples of the system. The group belonging to the system is the collineation group in the geometry.

A triple system on n elements leads to one on $2n+1$ elements, in the following manner. To the n elements $x_1, x_2, \cdots, x_n$ of the given system adjoin the $n+1$ additional elements $x'_0, x'_1, \cdots, x'_n$. From each triple $x_\alpha x_\beta x_\gamma$ of the first system form the four triples

$$x_\alpha x_\beta x_\gamma, \quad x'_\alpha x'_\beta x_\gamma, \quad x'_\alpha x_\beta x'_\gamma, \quad x_\alpha x'_\beta x'_\gamma.$$

Then add the remaining triples

$$x'_0 x_1 x'_1, \; x'_0 x_2 x'_2, \; \cdots, \; x'_0 x_n x'_n.$$

No pair of the $2n+1$ elements occurs twice. The number of triples is

$$\frac{4n(n-1)}{6} + n, \quad \text{or} \quad \frac{(2n+1)(2n)}{6},$$

whence it follows that the named set of triples forms a triple system on $2n+1$ elements.

Applying this process to the triple system on three elements, one has a system on 7 elements; from the latter a system on 15 elements is obtained in the same way; and then one on 31 elements; and so on. The systems thus determined constitute the geometries $PG(k, 2)$, as one may readily show, the triples being the lines of the geometry.

Let T_1 and T_2 be triple systems on n_1 and on n_2 elements respectively; and denote them by the symbols

$$(T_1) \;\; abc, ade, bdg, \cdots; \quad (T_2) \;\; \alpha\beta\gamma, \alpha\delta\epsilon, \alpha\zeta\eta, \cdots.$$

Employ the $n_1 n_2$ elements $x_{a\alpha}, x_{a\beta}, \cdots, x_{b\alpha}, x_{b\beta}, \cdots$. Then form triples as follows, of the numbers indicated:

$$n_2 \frac{n_1(n_1-1)}{6} \text{ triples: } x_{\alpha a}x_{\alpha b}x_{\alpha c},\ x_{\alpha a}x_{\alpha d}x_{\alpha e},\ \cdots,\ x_{\beta a}x_{\beta b}x_{\beta c},\ \cdots;$$

$$n_1 \frac{n_2(n_2-1)}{6} \text{ triples: } x_{a\alpha}x_{a\beta}x_{a\gamma},\ x_{a\alpha}x_{a\delta}x_{a\epsilon},\ \cdots,\ x_{b\alpha}x_{b\beta}x_{b\gamma},\ \cdots;$$

$$6\frac{n_1(n_1-1)}{6}\frac{n_2(n_2-1)}{6} \text{ triples: } x_{a\alpha}x_{b\zeta}x_{c\eta},\ x_{a\alpha}x_{b\eta}x_{c\zeta},\ x_{a\zeta}x_{b\alpha}x_{c\eta},$$
$$x_{a\zeta}x_{b\eta}x_{c\alpha},\ x_{a\eta}x_{b\alpha}x_{c\zeta},\ x_{a\eta}x_{b\zeta}x_{c\alpha},$$

and so on for the various pairs of triples from T_1 and T_2 respectively.

No pair of elements occurs in two triples, while the total number of triples has the appropriate value

$$n_2\frac{n_1(n_1-1)}{6}+n_1\frac{n_2(n_2-1)}{6}+6\frac{n_1(n_1-1)}{6}\frac{n_2(n_2-1)}{6}=\frac{n_1n_2(n_1n_2-1)}{6}.$$

Hence the triples formed from the x_{ij} constitute a triple system on n_1n_2 elements.

We shall now form a triple system on p elements, where p is a prime of the form $6m+1$. Let g be a primitive root modulo p, and denote the residues modulo p by $0, g, g^2, \cdots, g^{p-1}$. Form the triples

$$k,\ k+g^{\alpha},\ k+g^{m+\alpha}, \qquad (\alpha=0,1,\cdots,m-1;\ k=0,1,\cdots,6m)$$

the numbers in the triple in each case being reduced modulo p. The number of triples so formed is $m(6m+1)=\frac{1}{6}p(p-1)$. Hence, to show that they form a triple system it is sufficient to prove that no pair occurs in two triples. Since the set of triples is transformed into itself by the transformation $t'\equiv t+1$ mod p, it follows that if any pair occurs in two triples, then there exists a number ρ such that the pair $(0, \rho)$ occurs in two triples, while the zero element is either that for which $k=-g^{\alpha}$ or that for which $k=-g^{m+\alpha}$. Hence we have to examine only the following sets:

$$0,\ g^{m+\alpha}-g^{\alpha},\ -g^{\alpha}; \qquad (\alpha=0,1,\cdots,m-1)$$
$$0,\ -g^{m+\alpha},\ g^{\alpha}-g^{m+\alpha}. \qquad (\alpha=0,1,\cdots,m-1)$$

Now $g^{6m}\equiv 1 \bmod p$, while $g^{3m}\not\equiv 1 \bmod p$, whence $g^{3m}\equiv -1 \bmod p$. But $g^{3m}+1=(g^m+1)(g^{2m}-g^m+1)\equiv 0 \bmod p$, while

$g^m \not\equiv 1 \bmod p$. Hence $g^m - 1 \equiv g^{2m} \bmod p$. Therefore the last-named triples may be written

$$0,\ g^{2m+\alpha},\ g^{3m+\alpha}; \qquad (\alpha = 0, 1, \cdots, m-1)$$
$$0,\ g^{4m+\alpha},\ g^{5m+\alpha}. \qquad (\alpha = 0, 1, \cdots, m-1)$$

No pair $(0, \rho)$ occurs in two of these. Therefore the original set of triples constitutes a triple system.

We shall next construct a triple system on 3μ elements, where μ is an odd number which is not divisible by 3. We denote the 3μ elements by the numbers $1, 2, \cdots, 3\mu$. Then form the pairs (s, t), where

$$s + t \equiv 0 \bmod \mu, \quad s \not\equiv 0 \bmod \mu, \quad t \not\equiv 0 \bmod \mu, \quad s \equiv t \equiv 1 \bmod 3.$$

The numbers which are congruent to 1 modulo 3 and are not congruent to 0 modulo μ fall into $\mu - 1$ classes of residues modulo 3μ. If s is such a number, then there is another such number t, uniquely determined modulo 3μ, such that $s + t \equiv 0 \bmod \mu$. Thus one has $\frac{1}{2}(\mu - 1)$ pairs (s, t) meeting the conditions named for such pairs. Then form the $\frac{1}{2}\mu(3\mu - 1)$ triples

$$r,\ r+s,\ r+t; \qquad (r = 0, 1, \cdots, 3\mu - 1) \qquad [1]$$
$$r,\ r+\mu,\ r+2\mu. \qquad (r = 0, 1, \cdots, \mu - 1) \qquad [2]$$

It may be shown that these form a triple system. For this purpose it is sufficient to show that no pair occurs in two triples. Since the addition of unity to each element in each triple transforms the set of triples into itself, it is sufficient to show that no element ρ exists such that the pair $(0, \rho)$ occurs in two triples; moreover, there is no loss of generality in supposing that the element 0 occurs in either the second or the third place in the triple as written in [1] or in the last place as written in [2]. Then we have to examine only the triples

$$(-s, 0, t-s), \quad (-t, s-t, 0), \quad (-2\mu, -\mu, 0),$$

and to show that no pair $(0, \rho)$ occurs in two of them. It is obvious that the last does not have a nonzero element in common with either the first or the second. The reader may show that no nonzero element occurs in two triples of the first two sets. Thus the proof of the proposition is completed.

114. Quadruple Systems. If n elements $x_1, x_2, \cdots, x_n$ can be arranged in quadruples so that each triple $x_\alpha x_\beta x_\gamma$ of distinct elements occurs in one and just one quadruple, then the arrangement so made is called a *quadruple system.* The number n of elements in a quadruple system must be of one of the forms $6m + 2$ and $6m + 4$, as one may easily prove by showing that each of the numbers

$$\frac{n(n-1)(n-2)}{4 \cdot 3 \cdot 2}, \quad \frac{(n-1)(n-2)}{3 \cdot 2}, \quad \frac{n-2}{2}$$

must be an integer: the first of these numbers is the number of quadruples in the system; the second is the number of quadruples containing a given element; while the third is the number of quadruples containing a given pair of elements. The quadruples containing a given element evidently lead to a triple system on the remaining elements.

From a given quadruple system on the n elements $x_1, x_2, \cdots, x_n$ one may form a quadruple system on the $2n$ elements $x_1, x_2, \cdots, x_n, x'_1, x'_2, \cdots, x'_n$ in the following manner. For each quadruple $x_\alpha x_\beta x_\gamma x_\delta$ of the given set form also the quadruple $x'_\alpha x'_\beta x'_\gamma x'_\delta$ and retain $x_\alpha x_\beta x_\gamma x_\delta$. For each quadruple containing a given pair $x_\alpha x_\beta$, as for instance $x_\alpha x_\beta x_\lambda x_\mu$, form also the quadruple $x'_\alpha x'_\beta x_\lambda x_\mu$. Form also the quadruples $x'_\alpha x'_\beta x_\alpha x_\beta$ for every pair (α, β) of the set $1, 2, \cdots, n$. The total number of quadruples thus formed is

$$\frac{2(n)(n-1)(n-2)}{24} + \frac{n(n-1)}{2}\frac{n-2}{2} + \frac{n(n-1)}{2},$$

or

$$\frac{2n(2n-1)(2n-2)}{24}.$$

This is just the required number of quadruples for a quadruple system on $2n$ elements. Therefore the named quadruples form a quadruple system provided that no triple occurs in two quadruples. That this condition is met is readily shown by considering the triples of each of the forms $x_\rho x_\sigma x_\tau$, $x'_\rho x'_\sigma x'_\tau$, $x_\rho x_\sigma x'_\tau$, $x'_\rho x'_\sigma x_\tau$. Hence, from a given quadruple system on n elements one may construct (in the manner indicated) a quadruple system on $2n$ elements.

Now $x_1x_2x_3x_4$ forms a (trivial) quadruple system. Applying to it the method of the previous paragraph one obtains a quadruple system on 8 elements (see Ex. 4 on page 353). It is easy to show that this is the only quadruple system on 8 elements. From the quadruple system on 8 elements one may form one on 16 elements; from this, one on 32 elements; and so on. Thus one has quadruple systems on 2^k elements for $k = 3, 4, 5, \cdots$. In § **91** the same quadruple systems were constructed by means of the finite geometries (see Ex. 6 on page 436).

Now consider the collineation group $C(1, 3^k)$ of the $PG(1, 3^k)$. It has a subgroup consisting of those transformations

$$x' = \frac{\alpha x + \beta}{\gamma x + \delta}$$

for which α, β, γ, δ belong to the $GF[3]$; this subgroup is of order $4 \cdot 3 \cdot 2$; it permutes among themselves the elements ∞, 0, 1, 2; these elements are left individually fixed by the transformation $x' = x^3$; this transformation and the group of order 24 just mentioned generate a group of order 24 k, each element of which leaves fixed the set ∞, 0, 1, 2. Hence the group $C(1, 3^k)$ transforms this quadruple into $(3^k + 1)3^k(3^k - 1)/24$ quadruples (as does also the projective group $P(1, 3^k)$). Since the group is triply transitive, it follows that every triple of the $3^k + 1$ points of $PG(1, 3^k)$ occurs among these quadruples. The quadruples therefore constitute a quadruple system. When $k = 1$ we have a trivial case. When $k = 2$ we have a quadruple system on 10 elements.

From the three preceding paragraphs it follows that quadruple systems of n elements certainly exist for every number n of the form

$$n = (3^k + 1)2^l. \quad (k = 1, 2, 3, \cdots; \ l = 0, 1, 2, \cdots)$$

The general problem of the existence of quadruple systems of n elements when n is of the form $6m + 2$ or $6m + 4$ appears not to have been solved.

Let us return to the quadruple system on $3^k + 1$ elements already constructed. Those quadruples which contain the element ∞ lead to a triple system on the 3^k elements exclusive of ∞.

It may be shown that this is the same as the triple system afforded by the lines of the $EG(k, 3)$ (see Ex. 8 on page 436). Its group is therefore the projective group $EP(k, 3)$, a doubly transitive group of degree 3^k and order

$$3^k(3^k-1)(3^k-3)(3^k-3^2)\cdots(3^k-3^{k-1}).$$

This triple system may also be constructed (in a manner now obvious) by means of the transformation group $x' = \alpha x + \beta$ in the $GF[3^k]$; and when so constructed it leads at once to the larger doubly transitive group just named — a good example of the way in which configurations may lead from a given multiply transitive group to a larger one containing it.

115. Configurations Associated with the Mathieu Groups. The Mathieu groups of degrees 11, 12, 22, 23, 24 (one of each degree) are remarkable for two things: (*a*) they seem to be the only known simple groups which do not appear among the known infinite classes of simple groups; (*b*) among them are found the only known fourfold and fivefold transitive groups other than the alternating and symmetric groups. Examples which stand apart in such a way possess a peculiar interest on account of their isolation. It therefore seems worth while to present (without any details) a very direct method for constructing these groups by means of configurations and to indicate some of their properties which are made manifest by means of these configurations.

The linear fractional group modulo 11 of order $12 \cdot 11 \cdot 5$ is often represented as a doubly transitive group of degree 12 on the symbols $\infty, 0, 1, 2, \cdots, 10$. From the 12 symbols which this transitive group permutes one may select a set of six, namely $\infty, 1, 3, 4, 5, 9$, such that the set is transformed into itself by just five elements of this group. The whole group therefore permutes this set of six symbols into 132 such sets. If any five symbols are selected from the twelve they appear in one and just one of these sextuples. The 132 sextuples therefore afford an interesting configuration on 12 symbols which may well be called a *sextuple system*, in analogy with the terminology employed in the previous section. The symbol ∞ appears in just 66 of these sextuples, whence it follows readily that these 66 sextuples afford a configuration of 66 quintuples on the set 0, 1, 2, $\cdots$, 10. These may be said to form a *quintuple system*, since each set of four of the symbols appears in one and in just one of the quintuples. Any one of the eleven elements occurs in 30 quintuples from which a quadruple system on ten elements may be formed by omitting that element. From this in turn the triple system on nine elements may be constructed.

If one seeks the largest permutation group G on the twelve symbols, each element of which leaves invariant the named sextuple system, it is found that G is a fivefold transitive group of degree 12 and order $12 \cdot 11 \cdot 10 \cdot 9 \cdot 8$. This is the Mathieu group of degree 12. Its largest subgroup each element of which leaves one given symbol fixed is the Mathieu group of degree 11; it is fourfold transitive of order $11 \cdot 10 \cdot 9 \cdot 8$. Moreover, it is the group belonging to the quintuple system already named.

From the foregoing considerations it follows also that the Mathieu group of degree 12 contains a subgroup of order $10 \cdot 9 \cdot 8$ each element of which leaves fixed a given one of the 132 sextuples. This subgroup is intransitive, having two transitive constituents each of degree 6. It thus sets up a simple isomorphism of the symmetric group of degree 6 with itself; and the isomorphism so established is an outer isomorphism. This outer isomorphism is therefore an essential element in the structure of the Mathieu group of degree 12.

The linear fractional group modulo 23 of order $24 \cdot 23 \cdot 11$ is often represented as a doubly transitive group of degree 24 on the symbols ∞, 0, 1, 2, $\cdots$, 22. This transitive group contains a subgroup of order 8 each element of which transforms into itself the set ∞, 0, 1, 3, 12, 15, 21, 22 of eight elements, while the whole group transforms this set into $3 \cdot 23 \cdot 11$ sets of eight each. This configuration of octuples has the remarkable property that any given set of five of the 24 symbols occurs in one and just one of these octuples. The largest permutation group Γ on the 24 symbols, each element of which leaves this configuration invariant, is a fivefold transitive group of degree 24 and order $24 \cdot 23 \cdot 22 \cdot 21 \cdot 20 \cdot 48$. This is the Mathieu group of degree 24. Its fourfold and threefold transitive subgroups of degrees 23 and 22 are the Mathieu groups of these degrees. With these two subgroups we may associate (in a manner now obvious) configurations on 23 and 22 letters respectively. The former consists of septuples such that any set of four of the 23 elements occurs in one and in just one septuple; the latter consists of sextuples such that any set of three of the 22 elements in it occurs in one and in just one sextuple.

The latter set of sextuples on 22 symbols leads readily to 21 quintuples on 21 symbols; it may be shown that these quintuples constitute the lines of the geometry $PG(2, 2^2)$ of 21 points.

The Mathieu group of degree 24 contains a subgroup of index $3 \cdot 23 \cdot 11$ each element of which leaves invariant a given octuple of the previously named configuration of octuples. This subgroup permutes the eight symbols in this octuple according to the alternating group of degree 8; it permutes the remaining 16 symbols according to a triply transitive group of degree 16 and order $16 \cdot 15 \cdot 14 \cdot 12 \cdot 8$; the latter of these two groups is (16, 1) isomorphic with the former. This isomorphism is essential in the structure of the Mathieu group of degree 24. By means of this isomorphism and the known lists of groups of degree not exceeding 8 it is easy to find all the primitive groups of degree 16 contained in the named triply transitive group of degree 16; it turns out that they are twenty in number: these are all the primitive groups of degree 16 except the alternating and symmetric groups of this degree (see Miller, *Amer. Journ. Math.* **20** (1899), 229–241). By means of the named (16, 1) isomorphism it may also be shown without much difficulty that for every transitive group of degree 5 there exists a doubly transitive group of degree 16 which is (48, 1) isomorphic with the group of degree 5. (See Theorem XIII of § **97**.)

116. Some Generalizations. By a *complete* λ-μ-ν-*configuration* of n elements we shall mean a configuration of n elements taken ν at a time so that each set of μ elements shall occur together in just λ of the sets. (Compare Netto's *Lehrbuch der Combinatorik*, second edition, p. 325.) Then a triple system is a complete 1-2-3-configuration; a quadruple system is a complete 1-3-4-configuration; and so on. A finite two-dimensional geometry $PG(2, p^n)$ is a complete 1-2-$(p^n + 1)$-

configuration. In the previous section we have shown the existence of a complete 1-4-5-configuration on 11 elements, a complete 1-5-6-configuration on 12 elements, a complete 1-5-8-configuration on 24 elements, a complete 1-4-7-configuration on 23 elements, and a complete 1-3-6-configuration on 22 elements. These examples are sufficient to show the importance of complete λ-μ-ν-configurations for $\lambda = 1$.

But little has been done towards a general theory of complete λ-μ-ν-configurations. In the next section we shall treat certain complete 2-2-k-configurations.

An infinite class of complete 2-3-4-configurations may be constructed in the following manner: Let p be any prime of the form $6m+1$ and let ρ be a solution of the congruence $t^2 - t + 1 \equiv 0 \bmod p$. The set ∞, 0, 1, ρ is transformed into itself by the group generated by the transformations

$$x' \equiv \frac{x-1}{x} \bmod p \quad \text{and} \quad x' \equiv \frac{\rho}{x} \bmod p,$$

a group whose order is 12. Thence it follows readily that the set ∞, 0, 1, ρ is transformed into $(p+1)p(p-1)/12$ quadruples by the linear fractional group modulo p, the order of which is $(p+1)p(p-1)$. Since this linear fractional group is triply transitive, it follows that each triple of the $p+1$ elements $\infty, 0, 1, 2, \cdots, p-1$ occurs among the quadruples in the named set of quadruples, and indeed that each triple occurs the same number of times as any other, whence it follows that each of them occurs twice. Thence it follows that these quadruples constitute a complete 2-3-4-configuration. In case m is odd (but not when m is even) this configuration breaks up into two equivalent configurations each of which constitutes a complete 1-3-4-configuration, a fact which one may verify readily by showing that the transformations of square determinants in the named linear fractional group then transform ∞, 0, 1 into every triple of the $p+1$ elements.

117. Certain Complete 2-2-*k*-Configurations. We shall now treat those complete 2-2-k-configurations of n elements which are formed by n sets of k things each such that each two sets have just two elements in common. Since each of the $\frac{1}{2}n(n-1)$

pairs of elements occurs just twice and each of the n sets of k elements contains just $\frac{1}{2}k(k-1)$ pairs, it follows that we must have $\frac{1}{2}k(k-1)n = 2 \cdot \frac{1}{2}n(n-1)$, whence it is necessary that

$$n = \frac{1}{2}k(k-1) + 1.$$

The case $k = 2$ is entirely trivial. When $k = 3$ we have $n = 4$ and the configuration consists of the four triples which may be formed from four things. When $k = 4$ we have $n = 7$; then it may be shown that the configuration is equivalent to that given in Ex. 15 on page 25; the group characterized by the configuration is (Ex. 16 on page 25) the doubly transitive group of degree 7 and order 168; the complementary configuration is the $PG(2, 2)$.

When $k = 5$ we have $n = 11$. The configuration is unique (Ex. 17 on page 25) and is equivalent to that given in Ex. 13 on page 24. The group characterized by the configuration is the doubly transitive group of degree 11 and order 660.

When $k = 6$ we have $n = 16$. In Ex. 30 on page 42 (see also Ex. 17 on page 437) we have given an example of a corresponding complete 2-2-6-configuration; the group characterized by this configuration is the doubly transitive group of degree 16 and order $16 \cdot 15 \cdot 12 \cdot 4$. In this case the configuration is not unique; but the total set of inequivalent configurations of this class seems never to have been determined. (See Exs. 14 and 15 on page 437.) There exists (see Ex. 18 on page 437) a complete 2-2-9-configuration of the class here considered; it involves 37 symbols.

The configurations which we have named are apparently all the known configurations of the class here in consideration; but there seems to be nothing known to show their nonexistence for any value whatever of k greater than unity. In particular, it seems not to be known whether such configurations exist for $k = 7$ or 8.

With every configuration of the class here in consideration one may associate an *adjoint* configuration, in the following manner. Number the sets in the configuration from 1 to n inclusive; let $a_1, a_2, \cdots, a_n$ be the symbols appearing in the configuration. Now form a configuration of the numbers 1, 2,

$\cdots, n$ by taking for the ith set the k numbers which designate the k sets in which a_i appears, doing this for $i = 1, 2, \cdots, n$. Then the n numbers appear in n sets of k numbers each. That they form a complete 2-2-k-configuration of the class in consideration is readily shown, as one sees by observing that if a_i and a_j appear together in the λth and μth sets of the original configuration, then λ and μ appear together in just two sets of the new configuration, namely, in those determined by means of a_i and a_j. If the adjoint configuration is equivalent to the original configuration, then that configuration may be called *self-adjoint*. If the second of two configurations is adjoint to the first, then the first is also adjoint to the second.

EXERCISES

1. Show that there is just one triple system of n elements when $n = 3$ or 7 or 9; determine the group belonging to each of these systems.

2. Determine all the triple systems on 13 elements and the group belonging to each of them.

3. If p is a prime of the form $12k + 7$ and if g is a primitive root modulo p, show that the triple $1, g^{4k+2}, g^{8k+4}$ is transformed into a set of triples forming a triple system by means of the elements of the group generated by the transformations $t' \equiv t + 1 \bmod p$ and $t' \equiv g^2 t \bmod p$.

4. Construct in two ways triple systems (1) on 15 elements, (2) on 21 elements, (3) on 105 elements.

5. Show that there is just one quadruple system on 4 or on 8 elements.

6. Show that the quadruple systems on 2^k elements ($k = 3, 4, 5, \cdots$) constructed in §§ **114** and **91** are equivalent.

7. Construct quadruple systems on 10 and on 20 elements and determine the largest groups leaving them invariant.

8. Show that the triple system on 3^k elements determined in § **114** is the same as the triple system afforded by the lines of the $EG(k, 3)$.

9. Construct a triple system on 3^k elements by the method of § **114** associated with the transformations $x' = \alpha x + \beta$.

10. Construct a complete 1-3-5-configuration on 17 elements.

11. By means of the adjacent scheme form nine sets of four each by taking for each of the nine letters the set consisting of the two letters in line with it and the two in column with it. Construct the group determined by this configuration, showing that it is the singly transitive primitive group of degree 9 and order $9 \cdot 8$.

$$\begin{matrix} A & B & C \\ D & E & F \\ G & H & I \end{matrix}$$

12. Solve the similar problem constructed by means of a square array of 25 letters.

13. Show that there is just one complete 2-$(n-2)$-$(n-1)$-configuration of n things. Construct it and show that it is left invariant by the symmetric group on these n things.

14. Show that the columns of the following array constitute a complete 2-2-6-configuration of 16 symbols of the class treated in § **117**:

A	A	A	B	B	C	B	B	C	C	D	D	A	A	A	F
B	B	C	C	D	D	E	J	E	H	F	G	E	E	I	G
C	D	D	F	E	L	F	K	G	I	M	I	F	G	J	H
H	G	F	G	H	E	N	M	O	K	O	L	K	H	L	J
L	K	J	I	I	M	O	N	J	N	H	N	I	M	M	K
P	O	N	M	J	K	L	P	P	O	P	P	P	N	O	L

By determining the group characterized by this configuration, show that it is not equivalent to the configuration appearing in Ex. 30 on page 42.

15. Construct all the inequivalent complete 2-2-6-configurations on 16 symbols and belonging to the class defined in § **117**.

16. Construct the adjoint of the configuration appearing in Ex. 14 and determine whether that configuration is self-adjoint.

17. Show that

$$\{(ab)(cd)(ef)(gh)(ij)(kl)(mn)(op),\ (boejc)(dpknl)(fhgim)\}$$

is a primitive group of degree 16 and order 80, that it permutes the set $a\ b\ c\ e\ o\ j$ into 16 sextuples, and that these sextuples constitute the complete 2-2-6-configuration appearing in Ex. 30 on page 42.

18. Show that the transformations $t' \equiv t+1 \bmod 37$ and $t' \equiv 16t \bmod 37$ induce on the residues modulo 37 a transitive group of degree 37 and order $37 \cdot 9$ and that this permutation group transforms the set 1, 7, 9, 10, 12, 16, 26, 33, 34 into 37 sets which constitute a complete

2-2-9-configuration of the type treated in § **117**. Determine the group characterized by this configuration.

19. Determine certain necessary conditions on k and n for the existence of configurations $\Delta_{n,n}^{k,k}$ such that every two elements occur together in just three sets. Discuss the cases $k=3$ and $k=4$. Show that the $PG(3, 2)$ affords such a configuration for the case $k=7$.

20. Construct a $\Delta_{11,11}^{6,6}$ belonging to the class defined in Ex. 19 and having for its group the doubly transitive group of degree 11 and order $11 \cdot 10 \cdot 6$. Discuss the properties of this configuration.

MISCELLANEOUS EXERCISES

1. Determine the largest permutation group on its letters each element of which permutes among themselves the rows and the columns of the following array:

$$\begin{matrix} A & B & C & D & E \\ F & G & H & I & J \\ K & L & M & N & O \end{matrix}$$

2. Determine the largest permutation group on its letters each element of which permutes among themselves the rows and the columns of a square array of 25 letters or interchanges the rows and the columns.

3. Generalize Exs. 1 and 2 to the case of general rectangular and square arrays.

4. Let ω be a primitive mark of the $GF[p^n]$ and let μ be any (positive) factor of $p^n - 1$, the complementary factor being k. Form the rectangular array whose element in ith row and jth column is $\omega^{(i-1)k} + \omega^{j-1}$, where i and j run over the sets $1, 2, \cdots, \mu$ and $1, 2, \cdots, p^n$ respectively, thus forming a configuration consisting of p^n sets of μ elements each (one set for each column of the array). Discuss the groups characterized by such configurations both in the general case and for particular values of p^n and μ.

5. Let Σ be the set of elements consisting of ∞ and the (nonzero) square marks of the $GF[p]$, and form a configuration by transforming this set into all the sets into which it is taken by linear fractional transformations of square determinant in the $GF[p]$. Discuss the groups characterized by these configurations both in the general case and for special values of p.

6. Show that the triply transitive group $C(1, 2^5)$ of degree 33 and order $33 \cdot 32 \cdot 31 \cdot 5$ (defined in § **94**) transforms any set of four of its symbols in some order into any other set of four of its symbols.

7. By means of the group $C(1, 2^5)$ construct a configuration A consisting of $31 \cdot 3 \cdot 16$ distinct sets of eleven each formed from 33 elements and having the property that each set of four of these elements occurs in just twelve sets of A while each triple occurs in just 45 sets.

8. By means of the group $C(1, 2^5)$ construct a configuration B consisting of $33 \cdot 8 \cdot 31 \cdot 5$ sets of five elements each such that each four of the 33 elements occurs in just five sets. How often does (1) each triple, (2) each pair, (3) each element occur?

9. From configuration B in Ex. 8 form a configuration of $33 \cdot 8 \cdot 31 \cdot 5$ sets of five, each set of five being formed by taking the five elements occurring with a given quadruple of the elements in B, and show that the configuration so formed is the same as B.

10. By means of the group $C(1, 2^5)$ form a configuration of $33 \cdot 8 \cdot 31 \cdot 4$ sets of five such that each quadruple occurs in just four sets.

11. Show that the group of order $16 \cdot 15$ generated by the elements

$$(ab)(cd)(ef)(gh)(ij)(kl)(mn)(op) \quad \text{and} \quad (bfdjinohpcmlegk)$$

permutes the set a, b, m, n into 20 sets of four letters each and that the largest group leaving the resulting configuration invariant is a doubly transitive group of degree 16 and order $16 \cdot 15 \cdot 12 \cdot 2$. Discuss the properties of this configuration.

12. From the configuration of Ex. 17 on page 437 construct a configuration of 120 sets of six elements each by taking for each pair of sets in the given configuration the six elements which are absent from both of these pairs. Discuss the properties of this new configuration and show that the largest group leaving it invariant is a doubly transitive group of degree 16 and order $16 \cdot 15 \cdot 12 \cdot 4$.

13. Construct a configuration by determining all the triples into which 0, 1, 18 is transformed by the group $\{P, Q\}$, where

$$P = (0, 1, 2, \cdots, 30),$$
$$Q = (3, 4)(6, 30)(7, 20)(8, 22)(10, 29)(12, 28)(17, 27)(23, 26).$$

Discuss its properties and determine the group characterized by it.

14. Construct a configuration of 32 things in sets of four each such that each triple appears in one and just one of the quadruples, and determine the group characterized by it.

15. Construct the configuration formed by all the triples into which the triple 0, 1, 6 is taken by the transformations $t' \equiv a^2t + b \bmod 31$, where a and b are integers; discuss its properties and determine the group characterized by it.

16. Generalize Ex. 15 to all primes of the form $12k + 7$, these primes replacing the case 31 in Ex. 15.

17. The $PG(2, 5)$ consists of 31 sextuples. From each of these sextuples form twenty distinct triples, thus constructing a configuration of $31 \cdot 20$ triples. Discuss the properties of this configuration and determine the group characterized by it.

18. Discuss configurations of n things taken in triples so that each pair occurs in just two triples. In particular, discuss in detail the cases for which $n = 7, 9, 6, 10$, determining in each case the group characterized by the configuration. (Emch, *Trans. Amer. Math. Soc.*, 1929.)

19. In a quadruple system formed from eight elements interpret the elements as eight points in a space S_4 of four dimensions; then every quadruple will be represented by a tetrahedron. Two quadruple systems without a common quadruple can be joined so that each face (triple) of the fourteen tetrahedrons in one system will coincide with the same triple-face of the tetrahedron in the second system in which it occurs. In this manner we obtain a closed hypersurface P_{28} in S_4 bounded by 28 tetrahedral cells. Discuss the properties of P_{28}. (Emch, loc. cit.)

20. Discuss the properties of, and determine the group characterized by, the configuration (Emch, loc. cit.) formed by the columns in the following array:

1	5	9	13	1	3	1	2	7	11	5	9	5	9	10	6	3	3	1	1	1	2	2	4
2	6	10	14	2	4	4	3	8	12	6	10	8	12	11	7	7	4	4	2	5	3	6	8
3	7	11	15	5	7	5	6	11	15	9	13	9	13	14	10	11	15	13	13	9	14	10	12
4	8	12	16	6	8	8	7	12	16	10	14	12	16	15	11	15	16	16	14	13	15	14	16

21. The Abelian group of order 8 and type (1, 1, 1) may be represented as a regular group with the following elements besides the identity:

(12)(34)(56)(78), (13)(24)(57)(68), (14)(23)(58)(67), (15)(26)(37)(48),
(16)(25)(38)(47), (17)(28)(35)(46), (18)(27)(36)(45).

Consider as a single entity σ the seven sets of four pairs each afforded by the cycles in these permutations. Find all the conjugates of this entity under the alternating group on $1, 2, \cdots, 8$; determine the permutation group according to which these conjugates are permuted by the named alternating group; and discuss the relation between the two groups.

22. Show that the triple system formed by the columns in the array

$$\begin{matrix} 1 & 4 & 7 & 1 & 2 & 3 & 1 & 2 & 3 & 1 & 2 & 3 \\ 2 & 5 & 8 & 4 & 5 & 6 & 5 & 6 & 4 & 6 & 4 & 5 \\ 3 & 6 & 9 & 7 & 8 & 9 & 9 & 7 & 8 & 8 & 9 & 7 \end{matrix}$$

is transformed into seven conjugate systems by the powers of the permutation (2345678) and that all the 84 triples of the nine elements appear in these seven systems each just once.

23. Let G be a multiply transitive group of degree n whose degree of transitivity is k; and let G have the property that a set S of m elements exists in G such that when k of the elements S are changed by a permutation of G into k of these elements, then all these m elements are permuted among themselves; moreover, let G have the property P, namely, that the identity is the only element in G which leaves fixed the $n - m$ elements not in S. Then show that G permutes the m elements S into

$$\frac{n(n-1)\cdots(n-k+1)}{m(m-1)\cdots(m-k+1)}$$

sets of m elements each, these sets forming a configuration having the property that any (whatever) set of k elements appears in one and just one of these sets of m elements each. Discuss necessary conditions on m, n, k in order that the foregoing conditions may be realized. Exhibit groups illustrating the theorem.

24. Generalize the investigation demanded in Ex. 23 by giving up the hypothesis that G shall have the named property P.

INDEX

PRINTED IN THE UNITED STATES OF AMERICA